Principia Mathematica Decernendi

Mathematical Principles of Decision Making

Generalization of the Analytic Network Process to Neural Firing and Synthesis

Thomas L. Saaty

Library of Congress Cataloging-in-Publication Data
Saaty, Thomas L.

Principia Mathematica Decernendi: Mathematical Principles of Decision Making

ISBN 1-888603-10-0

1. Priorities 2. Decision Making 3. Analytic Hierarchy Process (AHP) 4. Analytic Network Process (ANP) 5. Decision Making with Dependence and Feedback 6. Feedback and Dependence in Decision Making 7. Economic Priorities 8. Social Priorities 9. Complex Decision Making 10. Resource Allocation 11. Conflict Resolution 12. Stimulus Response 13. The Brain 14. Science 15. Cartesian Coordinates 16. Validation 17. Decisions about Decisions

RWS Publications
4922 Ellsworth Avenue
Pittsburgh, PA 15213 USA
Phone: 412-414-5984
FAX: 412-681-4510

CONTENTS

Dedicated

To Michael

Preface

Survival and satisfaction are at the root of human existence. They both depend on our behavior, both to arrange and alter the physical world successfully and to enhance relationship with other people. The sum of all human experience is to tell a story stored in our memories, books, videos, microchips and libraries of our experience and understanding over a long duration of time.

Making decisions requires judgment. Judgment depends on feelings and thoughts and on the ability to interpret the information from the feelings and thoughts which arise from things happening that are inherently tacit, into attributes with different levels of intensity of preference, of importance, or of likelihood. To speak of intensities one thinks of numbers and to speak of numbers one thinks of arithmetic. At root we need to think of our brains which do their work mostly through the firing and synthesis of electric charges of varying frequencies as mathematical instruments that genetically condition the way we look at the world to form our judgments. These judgments also evolve depending on the learning process of the individual over time. It is essential for us in this book to quantify judgments in order to trade them off and determine the best outcome on different attributes. Thus it appears that to understand how to make good decisions requires that we understand a little about how our brain works.

Our brain is physical, made up of energy and matter that is also a form of energy. Our mind, derived from the workings of the brain with its quest for meaning and control, is a highly organized form of energy. The brain must of necessity obey the laws of chemistry and physics. The operations of the brain involving the firing of neurons share with the physical world electrical vibrations but the synthesis of the firing signals produces properties that are not found in the matter and energy of the brain: our perceptions, thoughts and feelings that constitute the mind. Although the mind has its origins and permanent home in the organic matter and energy of the brain, it not only obeys the laws and mathematical principles of the physical world when it works with cause and effect, but also follows additional principles of value, art and beauty, meaning and humor, and of fulfillment. It is purposive rather than purposeful, unlike what machines are. The mathematical principles of the mind are very different from those of the physics of the brain and hence also of natural physics. The properties of the mind cannot be derived deductively from the physics of the brain just as the properties of water cannot be found in its constituents, hydrogen and oxygen. Fundamental to the workings of our minds are the abilities to identify and brainstorm, relate, structure and prioritize and finally evaluate, act and re-evaluate; this is what our minds do when thinking creatively and in particular when making decisions about actions to be taken.

The most basic concern in our lives is that we make choices all the time and these choices can have a profound effect on our lives and on those of others. This means that we are not only responsible for ourselves but also bear responsibility for others. How can we best make these choices? How can we identify and prioritize all the important factors that affect the possible alternatives for action? Following the old adage "trust your instinct" will often lead us to an undesired outcome. We cannot fully rely on our gut feeling alone, no matter how experienced we are. In a group, conventional debate and discussion consume a lot of time and energy which often leads to making compromises or following the group—just to be agreeable—rather than to ensuring that the group has produced the right decision.

Complex decisions must be considered from different angles, each with its own conclusion about the relative preference among the alternative courses of actions. For example, policy decisions may involve economic, social, political, technological, environmental, ethical, and other kinds of controlling influences. Each influence needs to be considered in ranking the alternatives. In the end, the different rankings are combined to yield a top ranking alternative among all the influences. We believe that rational clarity is desirable whenever possible, but that the most important questions in life are not accessible to reason or science. But even science is not as rational as we have been made to think.

Complex decisions have four different contexts: benefits, opportunities, costs and risks. Each by itself is a consideration that needs separate analysis. Ignoring any of the contexts, as well as arbitrarily combining their results into one overall answer as if they are all equally important, can lead to a controversial and questionable outcome. It is clear that to make the best decision we must examine all the possibilities in a careful and systematic conscious way. Identifying all the possibilities requires creative thinking with an open mental attitude not to reject alternatives which may appear "impossible" too early. Without such a valid and manageable scientific method, one may end up doing number crunching without being conscious of the underlying assumptions behind the operations involved.

Consciousness is a process of sensing the world outside and inside us, connecting its events and discovering their influences, and evaluating the priorities of these influences within a structure of our values and motives and deciding how to act or react to them. The principles of decision making developed through thoughts, feelings and judgments arising from the electric firings and synthesis of signals in the neurons of the brain must at bottom include all the physical laws of nature and behavioral laws of psychology to which we are able to react, in order for our decisions to be effective and meaningful to us. Our judgment, the most important thing we do consciously from moment to moment, provides the link between what we perceive to be taking place and how to act on it in terms of our survival values and mores.

There is no better way to approach a complex problem than to structure all the important key influences affecting every important alternative course of action that we can think of. This way, interdependence among the important influences can be understood and their relative strengths measured. Given a valid and comprehensive structure, the accuracy of measurement is the next critical requirement to ensure that the best decision—given all the considerations—can be identified. There are two fundamental questions to address here. First, how can we measure influences knowing that decision making is inherently subjective and involves many intangibles? There is no objective scale for intangibles. The most accurate way for relative measurement of intangibles is to compare them two at a time using the smaller one as the unit and estimating the larger one as a multiple of that unit. To do it successfully, the elements must be *homogeneous*, or near or closely related with respect to a common property. When they are far apart, clustering methods are used to put them in homogeneous groups connected by a common element from one group to the next. We can use relative measurement to represent the intensity of human judgments. We then need a way to derive priorities from the pairwise comparisons of the many things that are compared. The method needs to consider the fact that the human mind is inherently inconsistent. Inconsistency is not as worrisome about judgments from a knowledgeable person who can provide coherent comparison judgments, but it can be for people who are exploring new possibilities that are not familiar and well understood. Knowing that there is noticeable inconsistency, we need a way to provide successive feedback measures for improving the accuracy of the most inconsistent judgments. Redundant judgments enable one to capture more information to improve the validity of the outcome. While inconsistency indicates inaccuracy between the judgments given and the priorities obtained from them, consistency does not necessarily indicate validity because the judgments of people with mental problems can be very consistent yet also very irrelevant.

The tool we use to provide and synthesize judgments is called the Analytic Hierarchy Process (AHP). It is the thinking man's rational way to combine logic to identify connection among attributes and judgment to derive priorities from causal explanation. Its questions revolve around what dominates what on the average or on the whole and how strongly it is expressed verbally and translated numerically with the use of the absolute fundamental scale.

In this book we underline the basic mathematical foundations of consciousness that respond to the laws of nature. Our approach does not involve many assumptions but draws on how we use judgments to make decisions. It is then elaborated and generalized in a meaningful and basic way to what we are like and what we are able to do to the best of our understanding.

There must also be a valid way to combine individual judgments into a representative group judgment to make it possible for the group to make a cooperative decision based on their mutual knowledge and understanding. Making collective decisions simply using voting does not feel right anymore, even to those who win the vote because how strongly people feel can be more important than just having them on the losing side. Finally, we must determine the stability and sensitivity of the best outcome to changes in the importance of all the factors involved. This can be done using the free software Superdecisions that is available online at www.creativedecisions.net/~saaty (of particular interest are the many projects available in the file ANP Sample Projects.zip). Because so many trade-offs need to be considered, the best choice can scarcely be made instinctively in advance. Making an important decision for a group requires careful consideration by knowledgeable and informed people provided with all the necessary data and other information. This book explains how we can make and justify informed decisions.

Here is an outline of the concepts this book is intended to deal with, and they are listed in a logical order below; however, the book itself does not rigorously follow this outline for reasons of exposition.

Order (from chaos or by sequencing into first, second, third and so on) as stimulus $\rightarrow$ Judgment with Regard to Dominance in Response to a Stimulus $\rightarrow$ Comparisons $\rightarrow$ Continuum of Comparisons $\rightarrow$ Fredholm's

Equation of the Second Kind → Fundamental Functional Equation → Solution in Real Domain → The Solution and its First-order Approximation → Weber-Fechner Law of Stimulus - Response → 1-9 Fundamental Scale of Absolute Numbers of AHP → Numerical Judgments to Measure Intangibles → Homogeneity and Reciprocity → Principal Eigenvalue and Eigenvector → Inconsistency and its Measurement → Synthesis in Hierarchic and Network Structures → Decisions in the AHP/ANP → Validation in the Real World → Fourier Transform of Real Valued Solution → Nearly Inverse Square Laws of Response: Newton's Gravitation; Optics; Coulomb → Fourier Transform of Complex Valued Solution → Dirac Type Neural Firing and Response → Simultaneous Response to many Stimuli → Operator Functional Equation → Its Solutions Characterize the most General Type of Responses.

My profound appreciation goes to my eternal friend and constant companion, my wife Rozann, mathematician, computer scientist, editor, gardener, superb cook and both constructive and negative critic for her role in moderating my work and to my long time friend, colleague and former student Professor Luis G. Vargas for his part time work with me. There are surely many little and sometimes big bugs throughout this book for which I apologize in advance. I am grateful to my children, Linda, Michael and Daniel for their editorial help in reading the first two chapters of the book and suggesting changes and organization. My foremost editor and thoughtful friend is my former student and friend with whom I recently coauthored the book Group Decision Making, Professor Kirti Peniwati.

My thanks go to colleagues and associates with whom I wrote joint papers that I initiated and guided their development. I wrote a paper with Professor Hsu-shih Shih based on my works and examples using the AHP/ANP to structure decisions and is now Chapter 3. With Professors Kirti Peniwati and Jennifer Shang I wrote a paper on resource allocation based on examples developed in my course on decision making that is Chapter 9. As an outgrowth of a number of applications in conflict resolution, and as a result of a workshop organized at the university of Pittsburgh with Palestinian and Israeli or pro-Israeli participation, a major example was developed and published as a paper and now is part of Chapter 10. My thanks also go to Professor Mujgan Sagir (formerly Mujgan Ozdemir) for her patient and steadfast friendship to elicit and write down some of my ideas and feelings of which Chapter 12 about adding the unknown "other" to the structure of a decision is one example. Four people have helped me in the development of my ideas in Chapter 15. The first was my former student Hassan Ait-Kaci at the Wharton School in the 1970's who worked with me to generalize the formulation of the judgment process to the continuous case in an unpublished short chapter. This was then followed in the 1980's and 1990's by work on the solution of the equation with my colleague, best friend and former student Luis G. Vargas. From that work I deduced the functional equation $w(as) = bw(s)$ as a necessary condition for the existence of a solution of Fredholm's equation of the second kind with a reciprocal kernel. I also did with him much of the work in Chapter 17 and continue to coauthor with him other kinds of research work. To obtain a wide class of solutions of this functional equation I turned to my friend Janos Aczel of the University of Waterloo in Canada, who is one of the world's leading experts in functional equations. My generalization of the linear equation $w(as) = bw(s)$ to an equation in operators involving functions rather than variables, was solved later by Nicole Brillouet-Belluot of the École Centrale de Nantes, France and shown here in a table in Chapter 18.

I am also very thankful to my student Wei Chang who did his undergraduate work at Tsinghua University in Beijing for reading the manuscript and carefully editing it and to my long time secretary and friend Sarah Lombardo for her rendering the manuscript in good form for publication.

Foundation

The Analytic Hierarchy Process

The AHP is based on the idea of influence, and what dominates what with respect to different kinds of influences. It assumes that everything, whether real or imagined, has some kind of influence that produces a response, whether physical or mental. In the end, energy, matter and mind are kin in receiving and giving out influence. Physical fact does not produce the mental fact but changes in one corresponds to changes in the other. The AHP is a systematic method of synthesizing influences structurally represented with a hierarchy or a network. Frequently the whole is broken down into parts in order to understand the importance of the parts within the whole. This approach is opposite yet complementary to the process of breaking down a system into its parts in order to analyze its workings and diagnose its problems. In addition, the AHP gives rise to priorities, and all priorities belong to a single dimensional scale that belongs to the interval [0,1]. The AHP does not make use of Cartesian axes representing many variables which extend from $-\infty$ to $+\infty$. The structures of the AHP, a hierarchy or a network, with benefits, opportunities, costs and risks represent the different dimensions and different orders of magnitude and whether they are positive or negative.

The Engine of the Analytic Hierarchy Process (AHP)
How to Measure and Evaluate Intangibles

Consider a person who would like to estimate the relative area of the five geometric shapes given in Figure 1. For the purpose of this illustration we also give the relative area inside each shape obtained from actual measurement by using a ruler and dividing each measurement by the sum of all five measurements. Of course in real life situations the relative areas would not be known to the person. He must estimate the relative sizes of the figures by comparing them in pairs. A pairwise comparison consists of identifying the figure with the smaller area of the two, and estimating numerically how many times larger the area of the larger one is than the area of the smaller one. The smaller figure is then assigned the reciprocal value when compared with the larger one. These comparisons are arranged in a five by five matrix as given in Table 1. By convention we compare the item on the left side of the matrix with that on top. If it is larger, we put the whole number corresponding to the judgment in that cell. If it is smaller, we put the reciprocal value in the cell. Finally, one derives priorities of the relative sizes of the areas from all the judgments. Table 1 also gives the estimated and actual relative areas resulting from this exercise in the last two columns. They are very close.

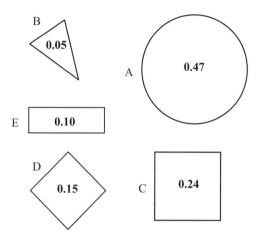

Figure 1 Area Example

    The judgments are entered using the fundamental scale of the AHP: a criterion compared with itself is always assigned the value 1 so the main diagonal entries of the pairwise comparison matrix are all 1. The numbers 3, 5, 7, and 9 correspond to the verbal judgments "moderately more dominant", "strongly more dominant", "very strongly more dominant", and "extremely more dominant" (with 2, 4, 6, and 8 for compromise between the previous values). Reciprocal values are automatically entered in the transpose position. We are permitted to interpolate values between the integers, if desired.

    The next to last priority column can be obtained as an approximation to the priorities given here, by adding the numbers in each column (there are five columns) of the judgment matrix, dividing each number in the column by the total obtained and then averaging the first entries in the five columns (adding them and dividing their sum by 5) and then doing the same for the second entries in the five columns and so on to the fifth entries in the five columns.

Table 1 Pairwise Comparison Judgments of the Different Areas

COMPARING AREAS OF FIVE FIGURES

	A	B	C	D	E	Estimated Relative Areas	Actual Relative Areas
A	1	9	2.5	3.5	5	0.490	0.471
B	1/9	1	1/5	1/2.5	1/2	0.050	0.050
C	1/2.5	5	1	2	2.5	0.235	0.234
D	1/3.5	2.5	1/2	1	1.5	0.131	0.149
E	1/5	2	1/2.5	1/1.5	1	0.094	0.096

The purpose of this example is to show that judgment when carefully quantified according to one's mental approximation can be used to obtain meaningful priorities by someone who is able to judge carefully. This is particularly important when we have no measurement to tell us the relative importance (in this case size) of things.

A Real Life Decision Example

This example demonstrates the usefulness of the AHP to quantify essentially subjective factors in a decision making problem. The methodology is also explained in detail in prior publications in books and papers. My first book on the AHP, "The Analytic Hierarchy Process", was first published by McGraw Hill Book Company 1980 and republished by RWS Publication, Pittsburgh, 1990.

Our example deals with a modern moral dilemma which society faces all too often. In a large city a heart has become available for transplant and three people have the necessary blood and tissue match. All are urgent cases with a prognosis of having only a few days or weeks to live without receiving a transplant. One is a 15 year old girl from a wealthy family, easily capable of affording the entire expense. The second is a poor 30 year old mother of three young children, with no insurance. The third is a married 35 year old scientist with no children, doing research on AIDS with a possible breakthrough, whose insurance covers 50% of the cost. Who should get the heart, remembering that a heart transplant may or may not succeed, and even if it does, the patient may or may not survive for very long? The committee making the decision consists of a social worker, a doctor, a hospital administrator, and a lawyer.

The various elements of this decision problem are organized into a hierarchy of four levels shown in Figure 2. Each level has multiple nodes with respect to which the alternatives on the next level are compared. This figure is a realistic simplification of a larger hierarchy developed with the organ transplant staff at Pittsburgh's Presbyterian Hospital, a prominent transplant center. The *goal* on the first level is to select the "best" recipient for the heart. The second level of the hierarchy includes the *criteria* affecting the decision: Family, Medical History, Social Factors, and Funding. Family has to do with relatives of the patient and how deprived they would be by the patient's death. Medical History has to do with objective biological and hereditary facts favoring success of the transplant. Social Factors have to do with a patient's potential contributions to society. The third level includes subfactors or *subcriteria* which contribute to the complete assessment of each criterion. The subfactor Social Behavior, for instance, takes into account such things as criminal record (which in this case none of the candidates has and therefore all get the full value of the subcriterion). Funding has no subcriteria and connects directly to the fourth level, since funding can be summed up in one comparative step. The fourth, and final, level contains the *alternatives* which are to be prioritized. In this case they are the potential recipients of the heart.

The first step is to compare the elements in each level in pairs. In emotional cases such as this, much thought has to be given to the question whose job is it to decide what the factors of social worth are and how much credit the individuals should get. If no individual feels comfortable about making such decisions, one should form groups to think about them, and even to vote on them. It is important to spell out the decision making process in advance. We will revisit this issue in a later chapter.

The comparisons are made using judgments based on knowledge and experience to interpret data according to their contribution to the parent node in the level immediately above. Once all the pairwise comparisons in a group are completed a scale of relative priorities is derived from them. This process is repeated for all groups on all levels. The final step is a weighting process that uses these priorities to synthesize the overall importance of the criteria, subcriteria and alternatives, and the highest ranking alternative is chosen.

The advantage of this approach is twofold. First, the structure of the problem represented in the hierarchy can be as elaborate as necessary to handle the complexity of the decision. Its design helps the decision makers to visualize the problem and its controlling factors. Second, the judgment process is so simple that they are in command of the problem as they see it.

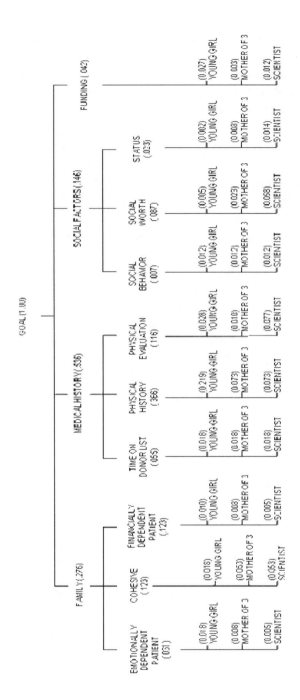

Figure 2 Organ Transplant Hierarchy

The entire process of comparisons is predicated on the use of a unit (of measurement) assigned to the goal. The question asked in making a comparison between a pair of elements has two parts: Dominance: Which of the two elements has the property or meets the criterion more? Intensity: How much more? Dominance stands for importance established through experience, preference perceived in the present, or likelihood projected in the future. As we shall see presently each criterion (subcriterion, alternative) is assigned a weight relative to a node in the next higher level. Since each of these nodes carries only its priority of the unit goal, the derived scale is suitably transformed through multiplication by the weights of the criteria so that each alternative receives its portion of the unit goal.

Let us now turn to how the judgments are recorded and the priorities derived from them. We begin with the judgments for comparing the criteria of the second level with respect to the goal as in Table 2. They can be represented by the matrix below. It is a square matrix with as many rows (and columns) as there are criteria connected to the goal. The numbers in this matrix express the intensity of dominance of the criterion in the column heading over the criterion in the row heading. Inasmuch as we are using the ratio scale, the matrix is reciprocal which means that the numbers, which are symmetric with respect to the diagonal, are inverses of one another, $a_{ij} = 1/a_{ji}$. If one criterion is deemed to be five times more important than another, then the other is 1/5 as important when compared with the first. The numbers in the Priorities column are the components of the eigenvector of the matrix, the inconsistency is a number closely related to the principal eigenvalue of the matrix.

Table 2 Comparisons of Elements in Level 2 with Respect to the Goal

Goal	Family	Medical History	Social Factors	Funding	Priorities
Family	1	1/2	2	7	0.276
Medical History	2	1	5	9	0.536
Social Factors	1/2	1/5	1	5	0.146
Funding	1/7	1/9	1/5	1	0.042

Inconsistency = .034

Of the sixteen entries, four are ones, representing the four self comparisons on the diagonal. Half of the remainder are reciprocals by virtue of the inverted comparison. Thus all we need are six independent comparisons. In general, n(n - 1)/2 comparisons are needed if n is the number of elements being compared in the triangle above the diagonal of ones.

The judgments are entered in the matrix in response to the question: How much more important is one criterion on the left side of the matrix, when compared with another at the top of the matrix, to justify a fair or rational heart transplant decision? When a criterion is compared with itself it is of equal importance and is assigned the value 1. In our example, the value 2 representing "equal to moderate" is assigned to Medical History over Family, and its reciprocal value appears in the first row, second column position. "Equal to moderate" is also assigned to Family over Social Factors. "Very strongly" is selected in favor of Family over Funding. "Strongly" more important is assigned to Medical History over Social Factors. "Extremely" more important is selected for Medical History over Funding. Finally, "strongly" more important is assigned to Social Factors over Funding.

When the number of elements to be compared is reasonably small, between seven and nine, the priorities derived from the comparisons are very stable when small changes, one or two units in either direction, are made. A measure of the coherence of the judgments is the Inconsistency factor displayed at the bottom of the matrix. It offers a clue whether to improve the judgments, by allowing the individual or the group to modify some of their estimates. There is a ceiling above which this factor indicates that the decision is not sound. The judgments in our matrix are slightly inconsistent (0.034).

Now we turn our attention to the Priorities column. Its entries are the components of the principal eigenvector of the matrix. The significance of these numbers is that they represent the conversion of the pairwise comparisons of the criteria into an absolute scale of relative values. Thus, for instance, Medical History is nearly twice as important as Family which, in turn, is nearly twice as important as Social Factors. The eigenvector consolidates the sixteen relative intensity ratios of the matrix into four measures of intensity. This new scale is called the *derived* scale. It is an important property of this scale that the sum of the numbers is always 1.

The importance of this scale becomes apparent if we use the derived scale to form the matrix of the judgment ratios. For instance, instead of giving Social Factors over Family the intensity 2 we use the values in the derived scale to form 0.276/0.146. If we do this for all entries we obtain the matrix of Table 3.

Table 3 Matrix of Ratios of the Priorities in Table 2

Goal	Family	Medical History	Social Factors	Funding	Priorities
Family	1	.276/.536	.276/.146	.276/.042	0.276
Medical History	.536/.276	1	.536/.146	.536/.042	0.536
Social Factors	.146/.276	.146/.536	1	.146/.042	0.146
Funding	.042/.276	.042/.536	.042/.146	1	0.042

Inconsistency = .000

Observe that the Inconsistency is now 0.

Inconsistency is a natural human trait to allow for changing our minds when new facts come to light. For example a person may prefer an apple to an orange, an orange to a banana and still prefer a banana to an apple. This case is an example of the preferences being *intransitive*. Intransitivity is a strong indication of inconsistency. But preferences do not have to be intransitive to be inconsistent. For example one may prefer an apple twice as much as an orange and an orange three times as much as a banana but only prefer the apple five times as much as a banana. This would be inconsistent though an apple is still preferred to a banana. Despite the desirability of consistency, it cannot be forced on people and thereby invalidate their changing feelings.

If a comparison matrix is perfectly consistent, the priorities of the elements can be obtained by adding the numbers in each row and dividing each sum by the total sum of the rows, a process called normalization.

The next step in this example of the AHP is to repeat the procedure above for every criterion. The subcriteria under each criterion are compared as to their importance with respect to that criterion to derive their *local* priorities. To obtain the importance of each subcriterion relative to the overall goal, the local priorities are weighted (multiplied) by the priority of the parent criterion to obtain their *global* priorities with respect to the goal as shown in Figure 2. Finally the three alternatives, the candidates in this case, are compared with respect to each subcriterion, or criterion as in the case of Funding which has no subcriteria, and weighted by the overall priority of the subcriteria. The sum of these products taken for each alternative is the overall priority of that alternative.

In all, this abbreviated illustration would require 6+3×3+3×10=45 judgments, agreed upon through a few hours of discussion. One should then perform sensitivity analysis to determine how much effect a change in judgments would have on the final decision.

The next set of comparison matrices of judgments systematically follows Figure 2 by comparing the subcriteria in Level 3 of the hierarchy with respect to their respective parent criteria in level 2. They are shown in Tables 4.

Tables 4 Comparisons of the Subcriteria with Respect to their Parent Criteria

Family .276	Emotionally Dependent Patient (EDP)	Coehesive (C)	Financially Dependent Patient (FDP)	Priorities	
				Local	Global
EDP	1	1/4	1/4	0.111	0.031
C	4	1	1	0.444	0.123
FDP	4	1	1	0.444	0.123

Inconsistency = .000

Medical History .576	Time on Donor List (ToDL)	Physical History (PH)	Psychological Evaluation (PE)	Priorities	
				Local	Global
ToDL	1	1/7	1/2	0.103	0.055
PH	7	1	3	0.682	0.366
PE	2	1/3	1	0.216	0.116

Inconsistency = .051

Social Factors .146	Social Behavior (SB)	Social Worth (SW)	Status (S)	Priorities	
				Local	Global
SB	1	1/3	2	0.249	0.037
SW	3	1	3	0.594	0.087
S	1/2	1/3	1	0.157	0.023

Inconsistency = .051

Finally, we have the matrices of comparisons of the three candidates with respect to their parent subcriteria or criteria since funding has no subcriteria as in Tables 5.

Tables 5 Ten Comparisons Matrices of the Candidates with Respect to the Subcriteria in Level 3 and the Funding Criterion in Level 2

Emotionally Dependent Patient .031	Young Girl (YG)	Mother of 3 (M)	Scientist (S)	Priorities	
				Local	Global
YG	1	3	3	0.600	0.018
M	1/3	1	1	0.200	0.006
S	1/3	1	1	0.200	0.006

Inconsistency = .000

Cohesive .123	Young Girl (YG)	Mother of 3 (M)	Scientist (S)	Priorities	
				Local	Global
YG	1	1/3	1/3	0.143	0.018
M	3	1	1	0.429	0.053
S	3	1	1	0.429	0.053

Inconsistency = .000

Financially Dependent Patient (FDP) .123	Young Girl (YG)	Mother of 3 (M)	Scientist (S)	Priorities	
				Local	Global
YG	1	1/7	1/3	0.081	0.010
M	7	1	5	0.731	0.090
S	3	1/5	1	0.188	0.023

Inconsistency = .062

Time on Donor List (ToDL) .055	Young Girl (YG)	Mother of 3 (M)	Scientist (S)	Priorities	
				Local	Global
YG	1	1	1	0.333	0.018
M	1	1	1	0.333	0.018
S	1	1	1	0.333	0.018

Inconsistency = .000

Physical History .366	Young Girl (YG)	Mother of 3 (M)	Scientist (S)	Priorities	
				Local	Global
YG	1	3	3	0.600	0.219
M	1/3	1	1	0.200	0.073
S	1/3	1	1	0.200	0.073

Inconsistency = .000

Psychological Evaluation .116	Young Girl (YG)	Mother of 3 (M)	Scientist (S)	Priorities	
				Local	Global
YG	1	3	1/3	0.243	0.028
M	1/3	1	1/7	0.088	0.010
S	3	7	1	0.669	0.077

Inconsistency = .007

Social Behavior .037	Young Girl (YG)	Mother of 3 (M)	Scientist (S)	Priorities	
				Local	Global
YG	1	1/7	1/3	0.333	0.012
M	7	1	5	0.333	0.012
S	3	1/5	1	0.333	0.012

Inconsistency = .000

Social Worth .087	Young Girl (YG)	Mother of 3 (M)	Scientist (S)	Priorities	
				Local	Global
YG	1	1/5	1/9	0.063	0.005
M	5	1	1/3	0.265	0.023
S	9	3	1	0.672	0.058

Inconsistency = .028

Status .023	Young Girl (YG)	Mother of 3 (M)	Scientist (S)	Priorities	
				Local	Global
YG	1	1/5	1/7	0.075	0.002
M	5	1	1/2	0.333	0.008
S	7	2	1	0.592	0.014

Inconsistency = .014

Funding .042	Young Girl (YG)	Mother of 3 (M)	Scientist (S)	Priorities	
				Local	Global
YG	1	7	3	0.649	0.027
M	1/7	1	1/5	0.072	0.003
S	1/3	5	1	0.279	0.012

Inconsistency = .062

It is instructive to study these matrices in some detail because they demonstrate how this process tempers potentially emotional decisions. For instance, the Scientist scores high in the Psychological Evaluation, in Status and in Social Worth. But since these criteria have relatively low priorities he may not receive the highest overall priority. On the other hand, the Young Girl's high rating in Physical History may be of consequence because this criterion has a high overall priority.

In Table 6 we give the local priority of the three candidates for each of the corresponding subcriteria and for Funding. We then weight each row by the priority of the subcriterion and of Funding above it and sum to obtain the overall priorities on the right. In this case the young girl would be selected. This way of obtaining the overall outcome by weighting and adding is known as the distributive mode.

Table 6 Distributive Mode Synthesis of Priorities

	EDP .031	C .123	FDP .123	ToDL .055	PH .366	PE .116	SB .037	SW .087	S .023	F .042	Overall Rank
YG	0.600	0.143	0.081	0.333	0.600	0.243	0.333	0.063	0.075	0.649	0.358
M	0.200	0.429	0.731	0.333	0.200	0.088	0.333	0.265	0.333	0.072	0.296
S	0.200	0.429	0.188	0.333	0.200	0.669	0.333	0.672	0.592	0.279	0.346

Structural and Functional Dependence

In relative measurement elements are compared with each other to derive values for them that are meaningful on a ratio scale. The approach itself makes these elements dependent on each other in measurement. We call this kind of dependence *structural dependence*. Another kind of dependence is *functional dependence*, where the elements depend on each other according to their functions or properties. Structural dependence highlights the presence of a criterion which is not usually considered important in measurement on scales with a unit. That criterion is the number of alternatives. It is of concern, for instance, in problems involving the allocation of limited resources. The more alternatives there are the less of the resource each receives. Even though the elements are functionally independent, each depends on how many others there are, but not on any single one of them. In the heart transplant problem above we may think that the problem as stated here is solved as above. However, if there were additionally several candidates exactly like the young girl, should the non-uniqueness of the girl water down her priority and give the heart to the next runner-up? The answer is no, and in that situation the number of alternatives should not affect the choice. On the other hand, if the choice were to be made between two hats, a hat preferred on style to another may not be chosen if there were other copies of it depriving it of uniqueness. In this case the number of alternatives affects the decision. If it is desired to make a choice independent of the number of alternatives, instead of normalization (dividing by the sum) as in the distributive mode, one divides the local priorities of the candidates by the priority of the top ranking "ideal" candidate and then weights the results. This produces the following Table 7. For this example the ranks (but not the values) are as before.

Table 7 Ideal Mode Synthesis of Priorities

	EDP .031	C .123	FDP .123	ToDL .055	PH .366	PE .116	SB .037	SW .087	S .023	F .042	Overall Rank
YG	1.000	0.333	0.111	1.000	1.000	0.363	1.000	0.094	0.127	1.000	0.639
M	0.333	1.000	1.000	1.000	0.333	0.132	1.000	0.394	0.563	0.111	0.537
S	0.333	1.000	0.257	1.000	0.333	1.000	1.000	1.000	1.000	0.430	0.623

Each new alternative is now pairwise compared with the ideal one and assigned its proportionate rank in the set. A well qualified new applicant may become the most preferred. No un-preferred one on all the criteria can affect the other's ranks.

This example illustrates how a systematic procedure for prioritization can be used to make any decision. What is needed is good knowledge to structure the problem by including all the important factors according to which the alternatives are evaluated using the judgments of experienced people. These judgments can then be combined to satisfy the basic property of reciprocal comparisons which amounts to using the geometric mean. Priorities are derived from the judgments and then synthesized to obtain a ranking of the alternatives based on which action is taken.

Remark: In radar and sonar waveform propagation, information is preserved in phase which is unaffected by normalization of magnitude (as in the distributive mode.) In signal processing, to make noise effect more distinguishable on each trace, one divides all signal values by a constant, the largest value (as in the Ideal Mode). If the signals begin with the same amount of noise, the largest one will have the smallest noise.

Part I

Discrete Judgments
How We Develop Them

The most incomprehensible thing about the universe is that it is comprehensible.
-Albert Einstein

General Observations

The brain and nervous system is a mathematical device endowed with great sensing power, interpretation and meaning. To the human mind all physical things reveal themselves as properties and interaction of properties. Influence is change in property. Every physical object has a collection of properties that can be understood in terms of their intensity as stimuli for the brain or in terms relative to the same property possessed by other similar objects. Which object dominates another with regard to that property and how much does it dominate it? We need a way to measure them in particular instances when we must learn about their individual and collective influences and track these influences over time. Our judgment is always critical in this process. Even when we have measurements we need to interpret the meaning of the numbers. The peculiar way we choose a unit for the measurement and apply it uniformly over the entire range of the property is a concern. When we have no measurements to interpret, we must use our experience and understanding to form judgments from which we then derive measurements in the form of priorities.

To make a decision we need to make tradeoffs among many factors. In order to make tradeoffs more precise so the resulting decision is accurately derived from the different possible actions available, we need measurements and numbers. These measurements must belong to a single scale so they can be combined to produce a single number for each possible outcome in order to rank the outcomes and choose the best one. Doing that is only possible if we have a unit-less measure. To do that we need to be able to measure tangibles and intangibles side by side and combine their measurements. Intangibles are usually more volatile than tangibles in that they do not have a single measurement to be used for all time. Their measurement depends on how we feel about them, on the circumstances where we find them, on the experiences we previously had with them, and also on how we plan to use them. Thus the measurement of intangibles largely depends on our judgment about them. This is also true of the measurement of tangibles because the numbers one has can have different significance in different situations. To a rich person money has different values depending on what it is used for, much more so than to a poor person where it is strongly needed just to survive.

Judgment is often made about rating an element with respect to the ideal standards one has acquired in memory. But what is ideal depends on experience and thus rating things one at a time by assigning each a number can be much more questionable than comparing them with each other. Consequently, to measure intangibles in a credible and reliable way, we need to compare them with each other. More specifically, judgment always compares things with each other with respect to a common property they have according to their relative importance, preference or their likelihood with respect to that property. Unlike the measurement of tangibles on a known scale whereby each element receives a value that is independent of the value of any other element, measuring intangibles by comparing them out of necessity makes them dependent on one another in their values. Adding or deleting elements on different criteria and combining their values with respect to these criteria can cause the rank of elements to change among themselves when new elements are added or old ones deleted. Because of this and of the necessity of comparing elements among themselves and not with respect to a capricious ideal, we see that rank preservation—convenient as it is in some cases in society—is a logical chimera that retards progress by dropping things we previously revered for the new things that are the result of change in our ordering of things.

With metric properties we ask how large or small a measurement is with zero as an origin and an arbitrary unit chosen for convenience; multiples and fractions of which are used to obtain numbers for other things. When we order a finite number of elements, we ask: what is the relative order of that element and how dominant is it with respect to a certain attribute? Order works with regard to this kind of dominance. We create scales of measurement that do not have a single unit for measuring everything and they do not need a zero for origin. We can use these measurements to make comparisons and to make comparisons we need judgment.

In science, measurements of factors with different ratio scales are combined by means of formulas. The formulas apply within structures and involve variables and their relations. Each scale has a zero as an origin and an arbitrary unit applied uniformly in all measurements on that scale but the meaning of the unit remains elusive and only becomes well understood through much practice. The meaning and use of the outcome of any measurement on a ratio scale must in the end be interpreted according to the judgment of an expert. They decide how well it meets understanding and experience for the situation in which it is being applied or how well it satisfies laws of nature that are always there. Science derives results using numbers objectively, that is, everyone gets the same numbers, but it interprets their significance subjectively, that is, how well they serve individual or group goals and understanding.

In decision making, however, because of the diversity of influences with which it is concerned, and the many decisions that may arise, there are no set laws that characterize commonly encountered structures in fine detail as there are in science. Understanding and familiarity with the situation is needed to structure a problem; and judgments are needed to capture importance, preference or likelihood. In the Analytic Hierarchy Process (AHP) these judgments are expressed quantitatively on an absolute scale that denotes dominance of one element over another so that a best outcome can be derived by combining and trading off different factors or attributes. In the end, after applying the AHP rules of composition, a multidimensional scaling problem is reduced to a one-dimensional scale of priorities comprised of relative sets of numbers which belong to an absolute scale. So in the AHP, significance is interpreted subjectively at the beginning of the process through judgments and priority numbers are derived from them objectively. Everyone would derive the same results from those judgments.

Priority scales are similar to probabilities; they are not the same as the ratio scales used in science. Ratio scales are like yardsticks. They have a starting point (a zero) and a unit. Priority scales do not. By the term "relative" we mean a priority scale is specially derived for a situation with its factors and alternatives and it is applicable only to that situation. It is not good for all situations all the time; when the situation changes, the priorities may change. The ratios of AHP priorities are meaningful: for example, a priority of .50 is twice a priority of .25.

In decision making the priority scales are derived objectively after a set of subjective judgments are made to ensure validity and accuracy, and they reflect the importance of the influences we considered. The process is the opposite of what we do in science when the subjectivity of interpreting what the number means comes at the end. Of course there has to be validation of the decision process through many examples that show it works to make it a science based on reason, quantity and mathematics. The AHP has been effective in deciding which policy is the best to implement, in determining a company's share of the market, in selecting a location to build a stadium, and many other ways.

Chapter 1

Influence and Order

Had I been present at the creation, I would have given some useful hints for the better ordering of the universe.

Alfonso X, King of Spain, 13th Century

The mathematics is not there till we put it there.

Sir Arthur Eddington, *The Philosophy of Physical Science* [1]

All the mathematical sciences are founded on relations between physical laws and laws of numbers, so that the aim of exact science is to reduce the problems of nature to the determination of quantities by operations with numbers.

James Clerk Maxwell, *On Faraday's Lines of Force* [2]

This chapter deals with the following ideas:
- Influence as the fundamental way to track everything that happens
- Stimuli are forms of influence. From the human point of view influences are stimuli that cause detector neurons in our brains to fire and the synthesis of the firing of the neurons produces sensations and perceptions which often translate into thoughts and action

Introduction

Every living thing makes decisions thoughtfully, instinctively or randomly. Soren Kierkegaard wrote that "Life ever leads to crossroads and demands decisions that need be made abruptly, by fits or jumps in attitude to tide us between the rational and the irrational." The most distinctive characteristic of human beings, in contrast to all other living things, is that we are preoccupied with attention to the influences of stimuli and respond to them according to their context in seemingly appropriate ways. The second most distinctive characteristic of our species is our ability to abstract the essentials of a situation. It enables us to generalize our understanding and turn it into a class of situations rather than just responding to situations one at a time. It allows us to react in far more efficient and imaginative ways. The third distinctive characteristic of our race is that we care about understanding things and sharing that understanding.

Ultimately we wish to know what we physically, mentally and emotionally want and how to get what we want. Our conscious decision making is only an approximation of our potential to respond to all influences in the world. Thinking about how we make decisions is one step removed in abstraction from thinking about nature. We learn things about how we sense, think and respond to nature from the ideas and theories that we develop about decision making. In order to get what we want we must prioritize our needs, wants, values and abilities to act. It takes determination and commitment. In the end, knowledge about ourselves is far more likely to help us get what we want than knowledge about the world and its unlimited diversity. But knowing about the world is also important, because we then know what is easy and accessible to fulfill our needs and desires, and what is difficult and beyond our reach. So far, science has focused more on learning about what is outside us than what is inside us. Now we need to bring our wants and values into our scientific thinking about who, why, what, when, where and how. We now have new methods from the behavioral sciences that point us in another direction. They combine our knowledge of the natural sciences with who we are, what kind of brains we have and how these brains work.

There has long been an implicit belief in science that our instruments for detecting, gathering and measuring information are innately objective, that they are independent of how our minds and senses work to gather and interpret information. However, take a microscope for example, we did not discover it, but invented it to suit our needs and to extend our vision. In other words, we invented it to extend our senses. We invent things to broaden our reach through the senses, but the final judge and arbiter is our mind which derives from our biological brain. Our instruments are simply a convenient way to help us observe and perceive what our minds are focused on. There is no more objectivity in information collected with instruments than there is in the brains that invented them. It is naive to think that our brains and nervous system have an independent objective origin from our values that can unravel the real mystery of whatever may be out there.

Our scientific method is thought to be objective: if different people use it, each should arrive at more or less the same conclusions as the others. But the scientific method, as a method of inquiry, is not free from human bias. It depends on our senses, on the structure of our brains and how they think, and on the values and objectives that guide the questions that we ask, driven by our collective priorities. Similarly decisions made by individuals about a shared matter have to be integrated into a group decision. Diverse groups of people must collaborate to make decisions and execute them successfully, thus endowing them with the semblance of objectivity. The need to involve people and obtain their agreement on priorities is at the core of decision making, and we need to look at the core to determine how to structure problems and make judgments.

Usually in science one focuses on modeling measurable qualities of objects and on the behavior of the objects as described by such tangible measurements and represented with coordinate axes. In ordering objects and criteria in terms of which the order is derived one is not concerned with which properties have measurement and which do not. Rather one is concerned with properties that are judged as important enough to develop measurements for. Structure comes first and computations come only after.

There is a duality between structure and measurement. In mathematics and science representation is constructed with the use of numbers. In ordering things a number is based on a representation, or we might say, a number is derived with the use of a representation.

Representation of structures of influence as hierarchies and networks is substantially different from the classical use of coordinate axes for the representation of curves and surfaces. To deal with values and their importance, scales need to be derived from measurements rather than measurements from scales. In hierarchies for example, we decompose a problem from its top element, the goal, or alternatively we compose a structure from the bottom up. Decomposition to order things requires using first concepts in an organized way and second introducing measurements. In science, measurements and the use of geometry come first and then theories are built around them. In general, what cannot be measured is not included in a scientific theory.

The difference between science and decision making is that in science the use of axes and scales makes it possible to create a numerical framework to model reality, and meaning is derived afterwards, whereas the use of hierarchies and networks makes it possible to first structure reality qualitatively using meaning and relations and then derive a quantitative framework in the form of priorities for it.

Reality to a human being is about: influences, people and their minds; other forms of life and even inanimate things that respond to, interpret and synthesize these influences; and controlling bones and muscles to act to control influences to fulfill needs. How we capture, interpret, and prioritize these influences is our primary concern in this book.

There is a longstanding historical debate between two schools of thought about knowledge, science, logic and mathematics and why we interpret them the way we do. The Sophist view is that they are all concoctions of the brain of man, where man is one kind of animal existence, and our brain is the measure of all things. The Platonist view is that they are independent mental abstractions grasped by an analytical brain able to sense, interpret and perform intelligible logical thinking about absolute truths. These two adversaries have been debating their subject for more than 2,000 years. In the end these two views are the same depending on our vantage point. We exist in a dynamic environment. Along with other forms of existence, we are brought about and have evolved in special ways in response to natural laws which themselves may evolve and change with the big bang. Our thoughts and abstractions can scarcely be fixed for all time. The big bang was not an explosion from a point of singularity. According to Alan Guth of MIT, the original cosmos ballooned from one billionth of a trillionth of a hydrogen atom's diameter to that of a soccer ball within 10^{-35} seconds creating space and time. There was nothing before. It is one of several possible models to explain the available observations.

We have the suspicion from our analysis later of judgment and of stimulus response that all things living and nonliving obey, that mind as judgment in response to stimuli and itself becoming an influential stimulus for other things is involved in the formation of the universe in a way that our physics has not been able to factor in as an influence, but use of hierarchies and networks that include purpose and also both the tangibles of physics and the intangibles of mind and behavior very likely can. This observation is in conformity with what many scientists and known people have written [3]. The physicist David Bohm wrote: "The question is whether matter is crude and mechanical or whether it gets more and more subtle and becomes indistinguishable from what people have called mind." Again Arthur Eddington writes, "To put the conclusion crudely - the stuff of the world is mind-stuff." According to Charles Reich, "The great and urgent need of these times is transcendence. The last two hundred years have fundamentally and irrevocably altered the terms of man's existence. The price of survival is an appropriate consciousness and social order to go along with the revolution of science and technology that has already occurred. The chaos we are now experiencing is the predictable and inevitable consequence of our failure to rise to this necessity...what is called for is a higher logic and a higher reason.

The creation of a new consciousness is the most urgent of (our) real needs." Swami Muktananda wrote, "To have the awareness that everything is made of one conscious energy is not only the highest science but the highest religion. No matter what we accomplish in the world, if we do not achieve this awareness of equality, none of it will be of any use."

The dynamic world and its influences have no meaning in themselves. It is we who must experience and interpret them. The order in which we discover is suited to how our own mind's work. The more we experience, analyze and synthesize the world around us, the more we learn and the more we impose mental order on the chaos that surrounds us. It is the mind, with its limited analytical methods, that can grasp all the essential details and their influences. Feelings and emotions are not less important than thinking; they are an important factor in this dynamic world. Our methods of thinking and modeling need to include human sensing, feeling and thinking to represent influences more completely. In fact, the use of words and verbal language alone does not always help us capture and accurately synthesize the intensity of the flow of influence. We need a way to quantify feelings and intensities of feelings. The ability to do that (something thought to be impossible by most people) allows us to measure a crucial factor in decision making; and we show how to quantify feelings in this book.

Our universe is not a homogeneous grouping of things, but a heterogeneous arrangement of elements of varying sizes and properties that influence each other differently at different levels. They cannot be known all at once because of gradual and varied linkages. For example, the roots of a tree work to absorb nutrients from the soil in a way that is different than its branches which use material already prepared for them to make the leaves and the fruits. The two ways are related, but comprehending how they are related requires detailed understanding. Knowing about either one alone does not make it any easier to understand the other. The universe appears to be structured into parts of different sizes and properties, and our level of understanding of influence does not automatically make it possible to understand all influences at all levels. The basic ingredients of the universe as we know it can be summarized as follows: space-time; movement; energy (quanta); matter, which in ultimate form is itself a form of energy made up of elementary particles (electrons, and protons and neutrons made up of quarks—swirls of dynamic energy—bound together by a force of gluons and quarks; antiprotons; particles produced by radiation and scattering, such as photons, muons, and neutrinos; leptons, w and z particles; fermions, bosons wide range exotic particles and so on); gravity; electromagnetic force; strong force to hold together the nucleus of an atom; a weak force that controls radioactive decay. Then we have biology—plants and animals, emotions, feelings, thoughts and behavior. A collective subconscious is assumed by some notable people to be there, but has not yet been adequately explored. These things act and interact according to their "size" and empowerment. Sometimes we think that what we consider the laws of nature operate similarly at all levels, but it does not seem likely that these laws operate in the same way on smaller things as they do on larger ones. We intend here to draw distinctions between the finely-tuned hierarchic thinking that relates things gradually in small steps, and today's popular way of studying the world with the "scientific method" wholesale. We believe that if the human race is to last a long time, many of our ways of understanding will inevitably have to change, and what we hold sacred today may seem inadequate tomorrow.

Whether mind is of the same stuff as matter or is transcendental and beyond the physical is important to know, mostly for our intellectual satisfaction. We are proud of the immense progress the human race has made in science and engineering in only a few hundred years, a blink of an eye in the 4.5 billion year existence of the earth. Look at all the innovations we have made since the 20th century: lighting houses with electricity, the refrigerator and air conditioner, the car, airplane, and spacecraft, the highway and airport, pumping water and distributing it to homes and factories, household appliances, electronics with the radio, the television, the computer and the internet, the telephone, mechanized agriculture, health technology, petroleum and petrochemical technologies, the lasers and fiber optics, nuclear technologies, and high performance materials, among others.

In this book, we provide a theory for how to measure intangibles and tangibles which enable us to quantify the importance and priority of the influences we sense and interpret. By using the appropriate structures, we want to show how influences are perceived and synthesized cognitively through our *judgment process*. We can use judgment to consolidate how we feel, in order to determine how to act, by including the impact of all the influences that we experience. Influences both inside and outside us shape our environment, our bodies and our minds. These influences are constantly changing through interaction with other influences. One outcome or consequence of influences is our response to other influences. This response can be physical, biological or mental. Our judgment is an interpretation by our minds that is further conditioned by our memories and feelings. Our purpose is to provide a unifying representation of our response to the diversity of influences we encounter. We will demonstrate how judgment is a conscious expression of the importance, preference and likelihood of happenings. By using judgments to compare influences, we are able to represent the dominance of one influence over another and determine the most likely or most preferred outcome.

The Mind Relates itself to External Reality through the Identification and Measurement of Influences

In the old view of evolution all the influence flows in one direction, from nature to mind. The idea was that things happen at random through natural selection, and that the mind is one of the consequences of evolution with its trial and error varied combinatorial approach. The interactions of chemistry, electricity and matter made the brain. The mind was viewed as being consequential only in that it helps its owner to survive by controlling the body and assisting in the search for food. Its abstractions were only ways to look for order and to try to anticipate the future in order to survive its hazards by organizing and classifying possible scenarios to design strategies that enhance survival. The mind was believed to have no intrinsic influence on nature to change its laws. Nevertheless, today we see that the mind itself is part of nature. It creates meanings and abstractions that are organized and fall in the domain of the laws of nature. The older and different view was that a single intelligent being brought about the natural world and its matter and energy along with all the cosmic influences and interactions. The current evolutionary interpretation of what happens in the real world is that matter and energy from uncertain origins and with unknown structures bring about the mind, and become a growing contender for influence. We can at best say today that it is a form of energy signals with contents and synthesis we can explain with mathematics. It is the third contender in an energy, matter and mind complex system. There are numerous manifestations of the mind in our current scientific understanding of other forms of existence, like orbital atoms, simple forms of life and complex forms of life exhibited in plant and animal forms.

It appears that in its evolution, the universe is arranged to have its story recorded and told through the memory of the mind, and that it has its way of communicating its substance and behavior to the mind through the senses and other influences. These in turn enable the mind to grasp and improve its sensitivity to tell a richer and yet richer story. In a sense, the universe is an actor on the stage of the mind. Consequently, how the mind grasps and tells the story is known through the mind itself that must continuously change to take in the whole story. It is an unspoken intuitive dialogue between mind and the universe that is as real as anything else we can use to account for our zest for knowledge and dedication to learning, particularly in the realm of physics, biology, astronomy, and psychology and neurology.

A major question we have about physics is that it does not allow for intangibles in its considerations or for feedback. Feedback may be the action-reaction stimulus response process in which the reaction does not affect the action in a mathematically concise way.

We ourselves are ordered pieces of chaos that over time understand and obey laws and even make laws of order. Order and chaos are intertwined and moderate one another as part of constant change. Neither is ordained to dominate because it then becomes stable and that violates change.

Julian Huxley, in *Man in the Modern World* [4], observes that something like the human mind might exist even in lifeless matter. To draw a parallel for this curious proposal, he notes that before its harnessing two hundred years ago, the only known forms of electricity were found in lightning and in a few fish. Electrical activity appeared to be a rare phenomenon that was of no particular importance in nature; but following man's comprehension and systematic study of electrical activity, it was discovered to be central to all nerve function, from conscious thought to the fertilization of an egg. Huxley suggests that all natural occurrences involve mental activity, although the mental happenings are at such a low level of intensity that they cannot be detected. In higher animals, mental activity is reinforced through an organized system like the brain to reach a high level of intensity; therefore we become aware of it. According to Huxley, all nature has a degree of awareness and solves problems.

Carl Jung, the famous psychologist conceptualizes the "collective unconscious," which is like a body that connects the lives of all creatures (the amoebas, worms, and man alike), suggesting that there are no isolated psychic processes, just as there are no isolated life processes [5]. One is in all, and all in one. He imagines the collective subconscious as a kaleidoscope of instincts, each holding delicately in place all the others and each shifting and changing with every "twist" of consciousness. Some have interpreted this proposed connection among all living things as a source of inspiration to be tapped for solving problems. Without being specific, we might propose its link to the creative subconscious.

It is not unreasonable to assume that in the long run there is feedback among these forces: the mind with the forces that brought it about, subject to probability and chance happenings. Chance also leads to the formation of natural laws that we use to explain occurrences that then seem less like a result of chance, like the earth moving around the sun in a fairly stable and predictable way. We may say it is all due to chance, everything that we know. A byproduct of chance and awareness is increased knowledge that we can use to explain the influences that make things happen according to chance. That is the way to deal with the interrelationships of all happenings as our minds individually, and more significantly, collectively, work to explain what happens to us personally and around us physically, and how we can best deal with influences. We need our memories to divine with our judgment what, on the average, is the result of an influence that changes from one instant to the next. What interests us is the process of aggregation and synthesis of influences from the simple to the complex, rather than decomposition and analysis from the complex to the simple. The real situation is like stellar dust forming galaxies, or like protons and neutrons forming atoms--it is a process that is directed from the minute and small to the large and then to the still larger.

The Force of Influence

Influence is the power or capacity to produce an effect or a consequence. Effect is a relative change in state. The most general law of nature that also applies to humans is the Law of Influence expressed through some kind of energy that causes a change in state. All other laws, including the laws of physics and the laws of crime and punishment, are special cases of that law. The Law of Influence says that everything has an influence, great or small, on something--including itself. Influences are eternal. The opposite of influence is nonexistence.

Influence is the process of producing an effect as a change of state, sometimes without perceptible exertion of a deliberate effort or intent to use a tangible force. It produces physical effects on physical things and nonphysical effects on conduct, thought or character. Influence is created by all kinds of energy and is the ultimate agent through which anything that exists can continue to exist or cease to exist. How do we sense and experience influence? We do it through our awareness of change leading to a judgment about the change.

Everything that exists has a small or large influence on everything else. Influence takes place both inside and outside the human mind. It can be *physical, biological* (as in chromosomes and genes), or *mental* (which includes psychological and sociological). Consciousness is the process of becoming aware of the presence of influence. To understand influence we need to think of it not just in terms of cause and effect but also in terms of four fundamental attributes. They are: the *purpose* of the influence as a criterion with respect to which the influence takes place, how it performs its *function* by influencing other things, how it carries out its function over time or its *flow*, and what *structure* the flow of influence is confined to. To design a system with influence, one proceeds from the most general purpose to the particular functions of the parts, the flows necessary to perform the functions and the structures that constrains and directs the flows. This framework also makes it possible to differentiate and categorize the kinds and sources of influences. We are perhaps a non-unique but ultimate kind of life form because we are concerned with the outcome of influences; how they are ordered and arranged according to intensity, proportionality, symmetry and other kinds of order; and with change of influence. We may not deal with influence to the degree of refinement and knowledge that are needed, but we are high on the ladder of evolution of beings that seek to influence and to understand the consequences of influence. Speaking of proportion, proportionate response is difficult to achieve when the stimulus is exceedingly strong or exceedingly weak. In particular logarithmic response applies fairly well in the case of responses to strong stimuli.

Relativity theory relates matter and energy with the formula $E = mc^2$ (energy equals mass times the speed of light squared). Energy and matter are essentially one. The equation says that energy and mass (matter) are interchangeable. We can determine how much energy is locked up in the material of the tiniest piece of matter. That energy is in the form of electromagnetic radiation that moves with the speed of light. It is squared because energy involves the square power of speed. According to Einstein, time and space and gravitation have no separate existence from matter. Much more profound is what Leibniz wrote: reality cannot be found except in one single source, because of the interconnections of all things with one another [6]. We may add that their influences can be combined to bring the fragments into a single story.

We have not had a similar formula that relates the mind quantitatively to energy. That is because we have no way to measure the importance of ideas, quanta of energy and particles of matter to introduce purpose into our considerations in a meaningful way. Energy is oscillatory vibration and neural firings are also oscillations, so perhaps the two are related. The question is how to relate meaning and the relative value or priority of the content of ideas to oscillations. Perhaps one way to do it is to use large hierarchic or network structures and only in relative form. It is true that we are a subset of nature that must obey all the laws that everything in nature obeys, but we are endowed with additional properties. We have ideas and feelings that most non-human things don't have – and we can express them and change other things in nature according to them. Does the power of our ideas link us to nature only through our arms and hands and those of robots we control, or is there something that our thoughts and values have in common with those of nature, so that we can make nature work for us directly on command with minimal physical effort by us and without violating its conservation laws?

We have inherent sensing and thinking abilities to grasp influences. In fact, influences of a wide variety of forces define who we are. Everything we think about, say, teach, or write about says something about influences small or large and perhaps less distinctly about sources of influence, which themselves are in turn outcomes of other influences. At the biological level, our brains are mathematical instruments that use electrical firings and their syntheses to process all the information and feelings that we experience through those neural sensors. The frequency of the firings and syntheses that take place in different types of neurons, like a symphony with sounds from different kinds of musical instruments, form our overall feeling and understanding. We are mathematicians biologically, even though we may not understand how our brains use mathematics to work. It is no wonder that quantity and number are basic and familiar concepts to us. It is also no wonder that we can expect mathematics to be effective in helping us describe and understand the world of physics as well as the world of behavior if we know how to represent them in quantitative terms. Given that our brains operate in this way, it would seem to be the most effective way to deal with the realities outside and inside us. We talk to each other and to ourselves with words produced for us by mathematical combinations of neuronal signals, and these words convey meaning associated with feeling and satisfaction about our understanding. The conscious mind uses words that are formed from electrical vibrations of a certain kind, combined in various ways that evoke a variety of feelings. Even though they are ordinal, diffuse and imprecise, they are adequate to create the feelings needed to create the meaning we wish to convey.

The laws of physics are influences on all material bodies in nature, including our own. All these bodies react in accordance with the laws that govern them. Further, the laws of thought are influences on our minds of far greater behavioral, ethical, and metaphysical diversity than physical laws. Physiologists, psychologists and philosophers write about all kinds of influences that are essentially intractable because when they act in combinations, the varying degrees of intensity of response they exhibit and the multitude of possible combinations create unknowable effects. In order to determine the most likely or most desirable outcomes that would be their effects, we need to measure the strengths of the influences and then synthesize them according to special rules. We show here how to organize influences and how to perform measurements that lead us to these outcomes.

Traditionally we think of any kind of creation as an intentional act of making things happen. Responding to influences or stimuli is a dual way of thinking of creation. The Platonist perspective is the *stimulus* and the Sophist perspective is the *response* and neither can have a recognizable meaning without the other. Creation is a decision making process that is usually carried out in small steps through construction by iterating between successive stimuli and reified responses to them. Responses involve decision making. Decision making involves judgments. For a system with a brain (a human or an animal) a decision making process is a synthesis of many judgments. Judgments are spontaneous responses to cognitive processes involving knowledge and experience residing in memory. Synthesizing judgments is best done within a structure that captures the prevailing influences within a system of values that include benefits, opportunities, costs and risks. Synthesis of these responses in nature leads to the formation of the complex physical and biological forms around us with their different capacities for decision and control.

Measuring Responses to Influence: Tangible and Intangible

All stimuli are influences even when their effects are imperceptible. When an influence flows from an origin to a destination, the destination is said to respond to the influence from the origin. We register them strongly when they are large and extremely powerful at their destination. It is possible to measure the dominance and relative amount of influences from various origins to various destinations.

There are myriad kinds of influences. Each influence can vary in strength of magnitude from place to place and moment to moment. No matter how small and simple, weak or strong, everything that exists has influence by the sheer fact that it physically or mentally exists somewhere.

There is a distinction to be made between the nature of influences and how we perceive them. They are objective, but how we perceive them is subjective and depends on our physical bodies and on our prior knowledge and conditioning. Science works with the assumption that we can know reality as it is. But the question is how accurate and how close to the truth is our perception of reality? Our brain is an instrument with a fairly broad, but in the end, established mode of operation. It uses its ways to comprehend the outside world. No matter how imaginative and diverse these ways are, they cannot be separated from the fact that we are one intelligent form of life that is specialized with its genetic code, and is necessarily subjective in its outlook.

There are two kinds of responses to influence. The first kind are the physical responses in which the stronger the impact of the stimulus, the stronger the response. The second are the mental responses whose intensity is caused by their perceived meaning. The outcome of all influences is regular or irregular, short and long term oscillation in nature or certainly in the neurons of the brain. It is the intensity of our responses that become new stimuli that make us take action to change the world to satisfy our needs. Our responses make it possible to organize our world according to the importance of the stimuli and the thoughts that are sparked by them. The laws of physics, for example, are a formulation of our own response to all the physical stimuli that we experience, or else they are the formulation of our perception of the responses of other things to forces in nature. We formulate the laws of physics to describe what we experience. These laws help us to predict outcomes when we know the input influences as forces that make things happen. These forces may in turn be responses of nature to higher order forces that operate or exert influence in more general ways, or they are the result of the interaction of many forces that depend on each other and of which they are a part.

"Cause and effect" is a term generally applied to natural forces, including human actions that cause things to change. It applies less distinctly to ideas as causes. Ideas can be thought of as influences or effects of influences which themselves can serve as new influences on other ideas or on occurrences. The study of influences and their consequence includes the study of forces as causes that produce certain effects.

Dynamics of Influence

Time is the route that change follows. A diversity of forces that influence each other brings about change from moment to moment. Were there no change, there would be nothing happening, no contrasts due to change. Consciousness at a single instant would be meaningless. It appears that it is change that makes consciousness possible. Consciousness is what makes it possible to identify influence in all that happens in the world from the physical to the biological, psychological, social and political forces of living forms. What is fascinating in this process is that more and more complex living forms are created that are able to observe and experience the change of influence, describe and control it. It is as if the physical world through random occurrences acts to reorder and reconstitute existence.

We have developed all our ideas about this world, its physics, biology and psychology from how and what we think about what it may be like. It is as if we are the main influence, the thinking mind that makes the ultimate interpretation. But there is another way to look at the world. Our environment, our bodies and our minds are the outcome of influences both inside and outside us that constantly change through interaction. Can we describe what we should be like as a consequence of or better a response to all the influences that give rise to us and to all other things in the universe? For example, since we survive by controlling and changing the environment around us, what mental attributes must we have in response to all the influences that made us? How is it that we have the ability for such control?

While the critical role of influence in almost all analyses is paramount, there is always the question of how to identify, classify and measure it in a way that humans can comprehend. The challenge is to determine what influences there are, what their effects would be, and how best to act on them when our short and long-term interests are at stake.

Structuring Influence

To better understand influence relationships, we can create structures of the factors and their connections that represent the flow of influence. These structures can take the form of a hierarchy, or a network as in Figures 1 and 2.

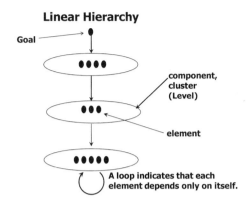

Figure 1 The General Form of a Hierarchy

In a hierarchy, influence flows down from the top of the structure. There can be no feedback in a hierarchy, because feedback needs to go from lower to higher levels, meaning the weight of the top level criteria is not affected by the weight of the lower level criteria.

A network defined by clusters or components whose elements interact among themselves or with elements in the other clusters has the following kind of connections:

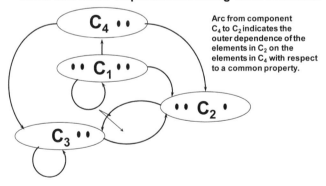

Figure 2 The General Form of a Network

These figures will be expanded and explained in greater detail in chapter 3.

Model as the Means to Understand Structure and Influences

There are three concepts that are critical in creating the structure of a model. They are form, influence, and order. A *form* is the underlying shape or appearance of a structure to the mind, through the eyes, ears and other senses or through inner thought. A tree has a form, the Gulf Stream as it flows in the Atlantic has a form, a cloud has a form, a magnetic field has a form, an idea has a form and a feeling has a form, although less definite. In a form there are smaller parts that have a form. A form can have a boundary although it can also be fuzzy. *Influence* is a unifying concept across all fields of existence. Influence can be weak or strong. Influences are combined to produce one or more new influences. How to identify and arrange all the influences in the universe depends on what purposes we have in mind. *Order* is the outcome of influences as it involves transforming forms in a way that can be understood and related to human purpose. Human purpose seeks to understand order, which is a stable outcome of influences. It is the theme around which all influences are analyzed and synthesized. While human goals are limited in scope from the very significant to the trivial along a certain line of categorization, influences and combinations of influences can be infinite in variety and scope.

Different forms interact and influence each other according to different laws. A form not only influences other forms but also has a field of influence in the environment where it is found and is in turn influenced by that environment. We often speak of the form of a structure and also of the structure of a form, where a form that is still tentative gradually acquires a concrete physical, biological, social or mental structure for its realization. We need a conceptual structure to study a form in detail. Thus a structure relates a form to other forms. The forms are the substructures of the structure. The parts are related among themselves and to the whole according to a rule that has sub-rules, and more sub-rules, of better and more universal laws and sub-laws. All of them are simple to understand as they replicate one rule at different levels. Those who know about fractals will understand this idea in its simplest form. The whole replicates itself in the smaller parts and these in turn in the smaller ones and so on. But the relation need not be precise and systematic because the boundaries can be fuzzy and merge with those of the environment. The whole becomes more difficult to differentiate from its complement.

Quantifying Influence through Subjective Judgment and Prioritization

Our intention now is to describe the steps that lead us to a theory for the measurement and synthesis of influences. The theory not only deals with how we personally perceive influences, but also how we can surmise their likely outcomes from the knowledge we have and how sensitive these outcomes are to changes in the judgments we use to represent the relative strengths of the influences.

At the conscious level, decision-making gives us an excellent idea about numbers and ratios of numbers that arise in the working brain. We all make comparison judgments and from these we create scales of relative values of the qualities we experience. Because there is no single scale built into the brain to measure things, we need to derive scales by making comparisons in relative terms so that all the information can be accurately integrated on a single scale of priorities whose ratios are important to us.

Many people think that measurement needs a physical scale with a zero and a unit to apply to objects or phenomena. That is not true. Surprisingly enough, we can also derive accurate and reliable relative scales that do not have a zero or a unit by using our understanding and judgments that are, after all, the most fundamental determinants of why we want to measure something. In reality we do that all the time and we do it subconsciously without thinking about it. Physical scales help us understand and use things that we know how to measure. But after we obtain readings from a physical scale, they still need to be interpreted according to what they mean and how adequate or inadequate they are to satisfy some need we have. But the number of things we don't know how to measure is infinitely larger than the things we know how to measure, and it is highly unlikely that we will ever find ways to measure everything on a physical scale with a unit. Scales of measurement are inventions of the technological mind. However, we have always had our minds and ways of understanding, and will always have them. We can apply our minds and understanding to make comparisons; and these comparisons, as will be explained below, can be made on a meaningful scale. Each set of comparisons among criteria can be synthesized together just as the criteria form a network which when synthesized together represent the decision being considered. The synthesized network of comparisons provides a solution to the decision.

Decision Making is the End Product of a Process of Comparisons

Making comparisons is fundamental and intrinsic in us. Comparisons are not an intellectual invention nor are they something that can be ignored. The brain is an electrical device of neurons whose firings and synthesis must perform measurement with great accuracy to give us all the meaning and understanding that we have. It enables us to survive and reach out to control a complex world. Can we rely on our minds to be accurate guides with their judgments? The answer depends on how well we know the phenomena to which we are applying measurement and how well our judgments represent our understanding. In our own personal affairs we are the best judges of what may be good for us. In situations involving many people, we need judgments from all the participants. Sometimes there are people who are more expert than others in some areas and their judgments should then have precedence over the judgments of those who know less, as is often the case in practice.

Judgments are embedded in the operations of our brains and that of animals, and one might even say of plants since, for example, many plants emit chemicals that inhibit the growth of nearby competitors. We all make decisions every moment, consciously or unconsciously, today and tomorrow, now and forever, it seems. Decision-making is a fundamental process that is integral in everything we do. How do we do it?

The great mathematician Henri Lebesgue [7], who dealt with the ideas of measure and integration, says:

"It would seem that the principle of economy would always require that we evaluate ratios directly and not as ratios of measurements. However, in practice, all lengths are measured in meters, all angles in degrees, etc.; that is we employ auxiliary units and, as it seems, with only the disadvantage of having two measurements to make instead of one. Sometimes, this is because of experimental difficulties or impossibilities that prevent the direct comparison of lengths or angles. But there is also another reason.

In geometrical problems, one needs to compare two lengths, for example, and only those two. It is quite different in practice when one encounters a hundred lengths and may expect to have to compare these lengths two at a time in all possible manners. Thus it is desirable and economical procedure to measure each new length. One single measurement for each length, made as precisely as possible, gives the ratio of the length in question to each other length. This explains the fact that in practice comparisons are never, or almost never, made directly but through comparisons with a standard scale."

Lebesgue did not go far enough in examining why we have to compare, despite his discussion of measurements. Let us see why not.

The Harvard psychologist Arthur Blumenthal tells us in his book, The Process of Cognition [8], that there are two types of judgment: "*comparative judgment* which is the identification of some relation between two stimuli both present to the observer, and *absolute judgment* which involves the relation between a single stimulus and some information held in short term memory about some former comparison stimuli or about some previously experienced measurement scale using which the observer rates the single stimulus." We call the first *relative measurement* and the second *absolute measurement*. In relative measurement we compare each alternative with many other alternatives. In absolute measurement we compare each alternative with one ideal alternative we know of or can imagine, a process we call *rating alternatives*. The first is descriptive and is conditioned by our observational ability and experience and the second is normative, conditioned by what we know is best, which of course is relative. Comparisons must precede ratings because ideals can only be created through experience using comparisons to arrive at what seems best. It is interesting to rate alternatives with respect to an ideal, the ideal must first be created. The ideal or standard is not independent from the alternatives and can only be created after making comparisons that involve dependence.

When we think about it, both of these processes involve making comparisons. Comparisons imply that all things we know are understood in relative terms to other things. It does not seem possible to know an absolute in itself independently of something else that influences it or that it influences. The question then is how do we make comparisons in a scientific way and derive from these comparisons scales of relative measurement? When we have many scales with respect to a diversity of criteria and subcriteria, how do we synthesize these scales to obtain an overall relative scale? Can we validate this process so that we can trust its reliability? What can we say about other ways people have proposed to deal with judgment and measurement, how do they relate to this fundamental idea of comparisons, and can they be relied on for validity? These are all questions we need to consider in making a decision.

It is useful to remember that there are many people in the world who only know their feelings and may know nothing about numbers and can still make good decisions. How do they do it? It is unlikely that guessing at numbers and assigning them directly to the alternatives to indicate order under a criterion will yield meaningful priorities, because the numbers are arbitrary. Even if they are taken from a scale for a particular criterion, how would we combine them across the criteria since they would likely be from different scales? Our answer to this conundrum is to derive a relative scale for the criteria with respect to the goal and to derive relative scales for the alternatives with respect to each of the criteria, and use a weighting and adding process that will make these scales alike. The scale we derive under each criterion is the same priority scale that measures the preference we have for the alternatives with respect to each criterion, and the importance we attribute to the criteria in terms of the goal. As we shall see below, the judgments made use absolute numbers and the priorities derived from them are also absolute numbers that represent relative dominance. The Analytic Hierarchy Process (AHP) comparisons use such a scale. Among the many applications made by companies and governments, now perhaps numbering in the thousands, the Analytic Hierarchy Process was used by IBM as part of its quality improvement strategy to design its AS/400 computer and win the prestigious Malcolm Baldrige National Quality Award [9].

Unlike measurement on traditional scales, relative scale values exist only after one has the objects or criteria to compare. The values derived for each element are relative to what other elements it is compared with, and thus each time a new element is added it affects the overall relative values of all the elements with which it is compared. The values derived are conditional. Derived relative scales need not have a unit, but by dividing by the value of one of them after they are derived, they can have a unit if desired. In addition, it is possible to create a unity or ideal after a first set is chosen and compare every element that is added thereafter with respect to the standard (unit), and allow it to become larger or smaller than that unit as needed. Relative scales of measurement derived from a fundamental scale of paired comparisons with values that belong to an absolute scale (invariant under the identity transformation) themselves belong to an absolute scale. One can see from the literature of scales that scales derived as in the AHP are a new paradigm in measurement that many people do not understand well, even after a degree of exposure. But numerous examples show that it has useful characteristics not available in existing measurement scales particularly with regard to the measurement of intangibles, and with using judgment and understanding within a sizeable structure to examine possible future happenings. Because comparisons are our biological inheritance, and also because experience and judgment are what distinguishes the expert from the non-expert, it appears that we need but to formalize our understanding within a transparent and justifiable scientific framework like the AHP to make it more reliable and usable.

Suppose we are given a set of objects that are all sufficiently light and can be lifted by hand. We wish to estimate their relative weights. One way would be to directly guess the weight of each object in pounds for example, by lifting it (perhaps using the lightest one as the standard), comparing the whole class, and then dividing the weight of each by the total to get its relative weight. The danger here is that we have no good idea about how much a pound weighs and make poor and arbitrary estimates. Another method, which utilizes more of the available information in the experiment, is to compare the objects in pairs, such as lifting one and then lifting another and then back to the first and then again the second and so on until we have formulated a judgment as to the relative weight (ratio) of each pair of objects. The problem then is to determine the relative values of these objects. The second process has the advantage of focusing on two objects at a time and on how they relate to each other. It also uses redundant information since each object is methodically compared with every other. Unlike estimating weights one at a time using pounds for measurement, paired comparisons is a process of using judgments first in order to derive priority measurements from them.

It may be useful to reinterpret what we just said. To make *tradeoffs* among the many objectives and criteria of a decision, which cannot be made simply by using words and logic, the judgments that are usually made in qualitative terms must be expressed numerically. To do this, one must make pairwise comparisons in a carefully designed scientific way rather than simply assign a seemingly arbitrary score out of a person's memory that appears reasonable. In paired comparisons the smaller or lesser element is used as the unit, and the larger or greater element is estimated as a multiple of that unit with respect to the common property or criterion for which the comparisons are made. The unit element then has the reciprocal value when compared with the larger element. In this sense measurement with judgments is more scientific than assigning numbers more or less arbitrarily. (A word on intuition: although we have been led to believe that intuition is unreliable because single hunches are usually inaccurate, it turns out that intuition is very reliable when a knowledgeable person provides judgments that are many and well-integrated within an organized structure).

In decision making, pairwise comparisons as to dominance of one element over another with regard to an attribute, property or criterion they share, generally occur in three basic ways: *importance, preference* and *likelihood.* Comparisons of importance and preference are straightforward; likelihood means that probabilities can be estimated as priorities obtained from a pairwise comparison process.

From all the paired comparisons, one derives a scale of relative values for the priorities. As we shall see in this book, due to the inevitable inconsistency among the judgments, it is mathematically *necessary* to derive the priorities using the principal eigenvector of a matrix of paired comparisons.

We learn from making paired comparisons in the AHP that if A is 5 times larger than B and B is 3 times larger than C, then A is 15 times larger than C and A dominates C 15 times. Thus, in decision making, dominance rather than closeness is the essential property, and we need the topology of order and not the usual metric topology that is prevalent in the physical sciences. In accordance with metric topology, if A has 5 dollars more than B and B has 3 dollars more than C then A has 8 dollars more than C. Order measurement says 15 times more, whereas metric measurement says 8 dollars more. The first is dimensionless while the second requires a unit of measurement. One attaches measurement to an object, the other attaches dominance between a pair of objects.

Paired comparisons are an essential mode of operation of the mind. As a minimum we will always need them to compare criteria because there are no abstract scales for rating criteria with respect to higher form criteria. The AHP allows us to use our natural ability to make comparisons on a scale that measures and compares our qualitative and quantitative knowledge to make informed decisions.

A Continual Process to Improve Decision Outcomes

The drive for betterment necessitates change, and change creates problems. Decisions made and actions taken to solve current problems do not always produce anticipated effects, resulting in new or unforeseen dilemmas. Also, conditions under which old solutions worked may change, and new solutions to old problems must be found. Fortunately, to develop vital problem solving skills we need not begin as helpless novices. Useful lessons can be learned from wise and experienced problem solvers concerning how to recognize and formulate problems, develop solutions, and evaluate their impact.

In considering the effect on the future of the socialization of mankind and the development of technology, we must place technology first. Socialization tends to resist progress in the name of the interests of many people that are uninvolved in the technologically creative process, but technology expands our human nature in the direction of our growing minds. The result is that our society gradually changes and adapts to our extended consciousness. We will recreate ourselves with new materials and what we are today will become outdated. We can determine our destiny with our knowledge, as we are doing now. In the process of experimentation we will make many mistakes and will seem to be way off our desired target, but in the end that is how we learn to improve. What we think and believe today will seem ancient and archaic to what we will become. The computer revolution and the spread of ideas and knowledge to all corners of the world are small examples of explosive happenings in a very short period of time. In the future, they will seem rudimentary. We cannot fix our destiny by the will to remain the same. That is the nature of our inventive minds.

There are two responders to stimuli of influences studied here. One is the human brain or any consciously responding agent that uses judgment to respond; the second is other kinds of animal and plant life that are appropriately conditioned to respond, and also inanimate objects that may or may not respond depending on the intensity of the stimulus.

The difference between the two types of responders is that people make judgments and when there is age and experience, judgment is scientific and reliable, as we show in the book. Studying how judgment based on comparisons works reveals some of the deepest laws of nature that affect our movement in the physical world. Inanimate objects are induced to behave in certain well-defined ways exerted and maintained by the prevailing influences. In the remaining chapters we deal with these two types of response and from the solution attempt to characterize the responder as an act of creation.

References

1. Eddington, A. (1958), *The Philosophy of Physical Science*, University of Michigan Press; 4th prtg. edition
2. Maxwell, J.C. (1890), *On Faraday's Lines of Force*, in Scientific Papers of James Clerk Maxwell, Part 1, edited by W.D. Niven, pp. 155–229, Dover Publications, New York

3. Gluck, J. (1995-96), *Spirituality and Technology* - Cyberspirit Century Twenty-One - Spiritech U.K., Internet

4. Huxley, J. (1944), *Man in the Modern World*, New American Library, New York

5. Jung, C.G. (1979), *The Collected Works of C.G. Jung*, Princeton University Press

6. Leibniz, G.W. (1988), *Theodicy: Essays on the Goodness of God the Freedom of Man and the Origin of Evil*, Open Court Publishing Company

7. Lebesgue, H. (1928), *Leconis sur l'integration*, 2nd ed., Gauthier-Villars, Paris

8. Blumenthal, A. (1977), *The Process of Cognition*, Prentice-Hall, Inc., Englewood Cliffs, New Jersey

9. Bauer, R.A., E. Collar, and V. Tang (1992), *The Silverlake Project, Transformation at IBM*, Oxford University Press

Chapter 2

The World as We Think It Is

"The whole mass of the electron was found to be due to its electric charge. The notion of substance had to be replaced with the notion of behavior. ..Substance is associated with muscular behavior ... akin scientifically to the quality of inertia... it will not move from rest unless acted upon by a force."

J.W.N. Sullivan, *Limitations of Science* [1]

This chapter deals with the following ideas:

- The brain is the instrument we use to learn about influences and help us understand, control and put together a story about what goes on. Our memory enables us to record and connect things that happen, allowing us to learn from experience and avoid having to constantly respond to each thing as if it were happening for the first time.

- The brain works mathematically and has the properties it needs to capture order through proportionality and symmetry.

- The brain is characterized as a continuous response mechanism that operates through the electrical firings of neurons.

- Inborn precision enables us to deal with the material world in order to control it successfully to meet our goals.

- Neurons fire in response to many different sensory inputs that must be synthesized.

- The synthesis process depends on the use of judgment to make sense of the stream of information.

- The synthesis process also depends on what kind of structure we use and how accurate it is.

- Perceptions, information and knowledge are produced in our brain as it responds to stimuli. Our perceptions are the only reality we can know about either the physical world or the world of ideas.

- When attempting to be practical to control the physical world, our brain perceives things we experience in the real world in miniature, but in proportion to the size that they actually are, and only after adequate experience that is also shared corrected and instilled in us by others. Otherwise the brain can have its own preconceptions and misconceptions about the world.

- Response to stimuli is obtained from an operator functional equation arrived at by generalizing pairwise comparisons judgments from a finite to an infinite number of elements compared.
- A functional equation can be used to describe how the brain responds to the stimuli it receives in a proportionate way relating what happens within to what happens without. Solution of this equation in the complex domain leads to a general inverse square law that is familiar in several forms in physics, such as gravitation and optics. This defines the way we and all other things respond to physical influences.
- Some quantitative forms of symmetry produce multi-dimensional proportionality. The importance of symmetry in describing physics laws and influences further highlights the significance of proportionality in the natural world.

The Brain: Our Mathematical Instrument for Detecting and Acting on Influence

We look at the world, so much bigger than our brains are even able to comprehend, much less able to tell us what to do, and wonder how in the world we can do anything to make a difference. Our ideas and the mental models in our brains are miniscule, yet they are linked to our bodies in a way that enables us to act on the giant world using our miniaturized go-at-it brains, as if what is in our heads were the same as what is out there.

Our nervous system, with its many neurons, takes in and filters all that is out there. To us, the world is mostly what we can sense, measure and interpret. There is also information that we are not equipped to sense, like those who are born blind and are unable to experience light and dark. To us, what does not filter through to our awareness does not exist. Our senses are limited in their ranges of operation. What we can sense of the world around us is limited by a very narrow band of what it is possible to perceive. Because of this, our reality is biased by these limitations of what we can sense. We often forget that there is much that is inaccessible to our minds. Researchers have long suspected that animals have an uncanny ability to sense things that we can't, like impending natural disasters. Sri Lankan wildlife officials said that although the tsunami of 2004 killed over 24,000 people, no dead animals were found. They had retreated inland, away from the coast, before the disaster struck. Many animals have a sixth sense that most of us don't have. Bird migration demonstrates their magnetic sense of direction. Dogs can sense earthquakes long before they happen. Schools of fish move in unison in ways that we do not understand. Thus no matter how much and how strongly we assert our certainty about knowledge, there is much we are missing. Our picture of the world is relative and incomplete and that is likely to always be the way.

The human nervous system has its own ways of operation. It feels, thinks and responds through chemistry and electricity. Response is brought about through stimuli, both external and internal. The external influences that stimulate it can cause it to react only in a way that it is capable of reacting. It cannot function in a way alien to its mode of operation. Heaven and hell and life in other places, whatever they are, all mean something to it, but they have to be translated in terms familiar to how it works. With their electric circuits, our minds are capable of thinking about and imagining things that do not exist in our physical world. This is true even when we want only facts, whatever those facts may appear to be to our neurons. What goes on in each of our minds is a universe of its own.

Most regions of the cortex have two-way connections to the claustrum (a thin sheet of grey matter that lies beneath the outer covering of the brain and carries out computations involved in seeing, hearing and language). When holding a rose we smell its fragrance and see its red petals while feeling its textured stem with the fingers. Smelling, seeing and feeling are processes that take place in different parts of the cortex, but are bound together (synthesized) into a cohesive conscious experience by the claustrum. This was discussed by Francis Crick and Christof Koch [2]. Their work is an example of the location where synthesis happens in the brain. We know that it happens. But with our current logic, we cannot explain exactly how it happens.

There are standard modes of operation of the mind that we use to deal with the world. We learn to act according to the proportionality between what we perceive and what is out there tempered logarithmically when the stimulus is very strong. We act based on our perception, and our perception is often inadequately or wrongly constrained by our mental past experience. In cognitive psychology it is believed that we create a model of how the world works by moving around and learning about how it appears to us. We sense the "objective world," but our sensations depend on the data and all the surrounding conditions outside and inside us. Proportionality governs all this information. Perception is the process of receiving, interpreting, selecting and organizing sensory information. Our mental model sometimes wrongly rejects reality that does not fit. We learn how to deal with higher kinds of control of complexity through thinking that follows perception. There is a partnership between nature that gave rise to us and we who can control it to our benefit. By and large, what we consider to be orderly is that which is in harmony with the proportionality between what we sense and perceive and what is out there in order to grasp its meaning. What is considered chaotic may be what we have not yet learned to characterize in terms of proportionality that corresponds to the natural way we perceive and respond to stimuli. Our methods of predicting order have increased and grown in accuracy. Not too long ago it was thought that there was magic that made things happen. Now we think we know so much that it will never be possible for us to find still more accurate ways to explain how things happen. It is certain that the logic we use to explain the world is not the ultimate tool we have to deal with the unknown. The material of this book provides a fairly general way to study things by using structures and judgments that include the use of the two valued logic we use today, of probability and likelihood and of relevance to our values and meaning and significance or priority of these values and meanings. The AHP with its stability to certain levels of perturbation makes it suitable in predicting an otherwise unpredictable situation that is not too chaotic. This leads to the obvious conclusion that the less chaotic things appear to our minds, the better we are able to survive. The disintegration of our bodies may be merely an example of a chaotic principle in nature that we are not yet able to understand and control to our satisfaction. However, we have made remarkable, if slow, strides in that direction through random experiments on changing body--but not on the mind that runs the body.

From all the perspectives of knowledge that we have: sensory, thought and feeling, everything that happens is a composition of repeated nervous pulsations of declining intensity. Each of these pulsations is eventually a composite of the smallest elementary pulses that are irreducible. It is similar to how strings vibrate. When a string vibrates, the shape of that vibration is a combination of many simple vibrations. Each one of these vibrations corresponds to an overtone or harmonic. All pulsations interact and have feedback. Characteristic of pulsations at any instant is that they repeat with slight changes due to feedback. The universe is made up of an infinite number of pulses. Human thoughts are themselves pulsations of the brain. It seems likely that meaning is the recognition of patterns of pulsations. Pulses lead to pulsations; pulsations lead to feelings; feelings lead to meaning and meaning leads to awareness and consciousness and to further consciousness and thought and to synthesized thoughts of higher order. In the end, all interpretation and thought are manifestations of feelings that are themselves electric oscillations that pass through the nervous system. Consciousness derives from all responses we make with our feelings, from perceptions that are intermediary to thoughts, or from thoughts that are responses to other thoughts that precede them. How we know things depends on our response to information in the form of stimuli. We can never know things as they really are. Truth is the knowledge of things as they are, were and will be. This is true even when we conduct experiments to test our ideas. We obtain results that lead to new responses and to a modification of our thinking, and then to new experiments, and so on. Our purpose here is to quantify all responses mathematically in terms of stimuli. If there is no response, there is no new information gained. We are locked into the nervous system, its very large and intricate structure, its connections and synapses, and how it is programmed to generate its electricity, transmit, synthesize and create the feeling and meaning produced by its signals. Basically whatever we do is reflected by excitement, depression or stability of our nerves, even when we discover the profoundest truths, listen to music, enjoy a painting, sit through a show or enjoy a great meal followed by a rest and a nap. The essence of meaning is created by the up and down vibrations of our nerves.

The story of the universe is that of the history, proliferation, repetition, organization, interaction, decline and renewal of pulses. Human awareness of all this turbulence is expressed through judgments about the feelings we have in response to what we sense and observe. Judgment itself is a pulsation of varying intensity of feeling whose composite pulses tells a story. This story itself can only be told with complex pulsations synthesized from diverse pulsations of varying intensities, like the overall sound we hear from an orchestra playing a symphony with many different instruments. Declining and damped periodicity is the fundamental characteristic of all occurrences.

The firings of neurons and their syntheses are precise in a sense that is inescapably mathematical. We need to simplify the interpretation so we can all become aware of what is happening within us both consciously and subliminally. We need a new way to look at the world that is better and more unified than what we have now in innumerable pieces.

Mathematical forms and representations that are solutions of general functional equations can serve to develop a unifying approach to modeling and solving complex physical and behavioral problems.

It appears that our creative mind is profound as it relates life to a transcendental world that shapes life. It is our way to reach out, or in, to bring about new ideas and forms that are not yet known to us. It is our bridge between the ideal and the real worlds.

The human brain is our means to obtain knowledge so we can interpret experience with all the surrounding noise. Judgment that determines priorities is important, as it enables us to better understand what is important and what is not. In fact judgment about significance is essential to proceed from one thought or sentence to the next one, and decide which idea, among many, best connects to what went before. Judgment about importance, preference and likelihood and how to represent the dominance of one thing over another is fundamental to our existence.

To speak of proportionality we need to learn to measure things with respect to different kinds of properties or attributes to discover their proportionality on these attributes. But measurement now is mostly confined to those attributes for which we have discovered a physical scale to measure, known as tangibles. A few have a mental scale of measurement. Our concern with proportionality, as it was with the Pythagoreans, is universal and applies to all attributes and combinations of attributes. The question is: How do we measure things on attributes that do not yet have a scale of measurement? To do that we need a universal way for measuring things that is easy to use and produces meaningful measurements.

There are two universes that we have to live in and for us they depend on each other. There is the outside four dimensional natural world of matter in which humans, animals and plants, exercise control to ensure survival of their bodies. There is also the inside electrical universe of our brains with its diverse networks, connections within and between the networks and synthesis of responses to stimuli and of ideas that bring forth creativity and imagination for the survival of the workings of the brain. Ontologically, the brain depends on the physical world for its existence and well being, but at this point of its existence, the physical universe does not depend much on what our brains do to it and within it. The universe is an extremely durable wild force that overpowers our bodies and toys with our brains like rag dolls.

We are likely to believe that because our bodies and brains are organically generated from the physical universe that they are a part of its intrinsic organization and operation. However, that is not true. What our brains are made of and the purpose and meaning they create are very different. One is material and the other is intangible and abstract, supernatural and transcendental. Even if we were to say that the ideas generated by the brain are often extrapolations learned in part from nature, our feelings and emotions, our sense of beauty and order, our hopes, aspirations and ambitions are far removed from nature.

There is a chance that the brain and its surrogates like the computer will survive and learn to control the laws of nature and become the dominant influence. At that time it would be believed that the brain came about in detailed and subtle ways that have the appearance to our limited mind today of being random because we cannot account for the details of how it came about in a step by step way with our linear and logical style of causal thinking. But we may be able to do that with nonlinear interdependent accounting of the influences that take place within nature and between the mind and nature.

While we have some knowledge about the outside universe and its laws of gravity, electromagnetism, strong and weak forces that objects within it must obey, we have no such vast knowledge of the laws of our brain operation. Nevertheless the brain is tractable in its stimulus response activities and in its decision making operations. Comparisons to stimuli and in particular pairwise comparisons are being constantly made in response to both. It turns out that there is a law of firing and synthesis of signals in the brain that we can derive from generalizing our representation of the process of creating priorities from pairwise judgments in decision making.

The origins of our minds lie in the brain which depends on matter and energy for its existence. But the mind itself is more orderly and purposeful than its physical origins. Our destiny, or at least our challenge, is to alter our minds in such a way as to make them less dependent on matter and to exercise power over matter so that it does not have the hold on the existence of the mind that it now has by eventually smothering and destroying it through sickness and death. To that end we need to understand better how our minds operate. First in regard to nature and its stimuli, we must learn what powers the mind has over matter through that basic mode of operation as all forms of life do to a greater or lesser extent. Then we must learn how the mind does its own thinking, calculation and original creation so the mind may act autonomously without being constrained by the external matter and energy that stimulate it and give rise to it. Here we can only deal with formulating and solving the response question to stimuli.

How the Brain Responds to Influence

How can we learn to be aware of influences and consciously direct our responses? We need to accept the following observations:

The most pervasive thing all living beings share is that of making choices for action in the face of different kinds of influence. Actions are our way of controlling and responding to influences according to our purpose. Sometimes biology and chemistry have unique built-in choices. Most of the time, because of the long successful evolution of a given response, a built-in choice may be the right one. At other times it might be unfavorable in the circumstances. Usually there are opportunities to try different choices. The most important case is when there are several choices and we have to choose the one that will be best according to some criteria. As humans, we have more freedom of choice than other living beings. Our ability to consciously control our survival and destiny shows that we are an advanced form of existence. Our nervous system is equipped with senses, muscle and bone that enable us to control the environment; but the nervous system also develops judgments about what to do. Still we are limited in what we can sense and perceive and thus our choices are conditioned by our body form, by our senses and by the environment in which we live. Next to chemistry, physics and electricity that create form and function, the decision-making that arises from them is the most important function to further the future of life. The essence of our survival depends on the quality and kind of decisions we make and how much we factor into them influences that may not even be here today, influences that could appear tomorrow and change what happens in the future in a negative way. Global warming is an example of innocent productivity using raw materials and energy from which there are by products that are imperceptible at first, but which build up to a substantial threat to our survival.

Our senses and feelings and our analytical minds are our means to study influence. Influence may be said to be a local change in the status quo. Feelings and judgment determine the kind of influence we react to. Thinking involves risks that are guided and tempered by feelings, good judgment, common sense and proportionality. Proportionality involves relative magnitudes, and relative magnitudes involve intensity of feeling and response. We need proportionality to help us create the appropriate response. Proportionality does not mean the same constant value throughout but could vary according to different ranges of the stimulus.

Pythagoreans believed that the body is strung like an instrument to a certain pitch, hot and cold or wet and dry taking the place of high and low in music. It was natural for Pythagoras to look for similar analogies in the world at large. Briefly stated, the doctrine of Pythagoras was that all things could be represented with numbers. In certain fundamental cases, the early Pythagoreans pictured numbers and explained their properties by means of dots arranged in certain "figures" or patterns. The Pythagorean School of philosophy reduced all meaning to numerical relationships and proposed that all existing objects are not of material substance, but rather are fundamentally composed only of form describable with numbers. Pythagoras discovered the numerical ratios that determine the concordant intervals of the musical scale. In medicine it was the business of the physician to produce a proper "blend" of opposites in the body, such as the hot and the cold, the wet and the dry. So proportion, from the time of the Greeks, is embedded in our framework for seeing the world.

The most fundamental aspect of consciousness is intensity. Every aspect of our consciousness identifies properties and the intensity of their presence. Intensity can be thought of in terms of proportion between different states of existence. Pythagoras believed that all things can be expressed in numbers that correspond to universals, and that the entire universe is composed of mathematical patterns. The Pythagorean School of philosophy reduced all meaning to numerical relationships among intensities of properties.

Similar to the way in which a single neuron behaves as a resonator and in harmony with other neurons, human beings behave as resonators of different modes at the same time. Their interaction with other human beings requires a synthesis of proportionate scales along different modes. The outcome of this synthesis is a higher order of coherence of the modes that represent aspects of the consciousness that people think about.

We can understand the order of the universe by representing it with mathematics. The firing in our brains is conditioned by intensity and frequency which are numerical kinds of expressions. Therefore all that we experience and think is traceable to numerical expressions involving magnitudes and proportions. Whatever the universe may be, our understanding of it is in terms of electrical firings of neurons and its mathematics of firing and synthesis and therefore we tend to identify everything in terms of such mathematics impulse-decay vibration. Much of the diversity of information that we receive from the world is of such abstract nature that it is beyond the synthesis that takes place in our nervous system and thus we have used abstraction to put the pieces together, real or unreal as they may be. Thus understanding the world as a whole is a purely human activity that borders on being a myth. It is natural then that we should fundamentally interpret the world in numerical terms using mathematics. It seems that even art and language or expressions of an electrically working mathematical brain that generates and synthesizes signals.

We refine our understanding by examining the facts and establishing causal relationships among them. The intensity of an influence plays a significant role in estimating the strengths and consequences of interaction among influences. We seek to determine the duration, strength and stability of influence and how it affects our objectives, either in positive or in negative ways.

Our Involvement in Responding to Influence

We are made of two different components, the affective (feeling) and the cognitive (thinking). By feeling, we don't mean tactile sensations, but rather the general feeling of pleasantness or unpleasantness, tension-relaxation, and excitement-calm. In our evolution, as we note from the animals and from our slow evolutionary development, feelings came first with a reptilian brain, and then gradually as the size of our cortex grew, we became more successful in thinking, imagining, and coping with an unpredictable environment. We do our thinking with the brain, particularly the cortex. Emotions range from anger, crying, rage, and grief to laughter and feeling good (in Latin, *emovere* means to stir up, agitate or excite). These emotions are accompanied by changes in physiology such as increased pulse and breathing rates. It is known that in part, emotions are in the thalamus, amygdala and the prefrontal lobes that moderate the strong reactions of the amygdala. According to one theory, emotions are judgmental interpretations of physiological reaction. Another theory says that emotion is a reaction to judgment, appraising a situation as pleasant or unpleasant. However, our feelings of pleasantness, unpleasantness, excitement and depression are also known to reside in the brain and in the autonomic system of sympathetic and parasympathetic nerves outside the brain that act with some independence from the brain. According to Antonio Damasio [3], feelings are indispensable for rational decisions because they point us in the right direction, helping logic to be at its best. We have two minds, a logical one and an emotional one.

The ability of living things to maintain dynamic equilibrium in the face of changing environments is essential to their survival. Equilibrium is a state of overall satisfaction, going along with what is happening as required by the circumstances. In addition there is a higher level of analysis that we use to judge various degrees of satisfaction and their duration. These in turn may eventually become unstable, perhaps due to boredom and lack of stimulation because of ongoing satisfaction. Perhaps satisfaction must itself be adaptive and changeable so that the organism can change its ways and learn to be satisfied under new conditions. This involves maintaining equilibrium in small increments so that change would not have severe consequences.

We can think of life in terms of a fast moving story. We see people rushing through life. Every act is a quick event full of commotion. At the end, the people are gone. In the process, people deal with others quickly, help or hurt them and then move on. Speed up evolution and see it creating species that run through certain durations and become extinct. There is no clear end in sight for any species. Our thought processes, which project backwards and forwards, tell us that— not our feelings.

How the Brain Makes Order from Influences

The human mind can conceive of ideas that are in the realm of imagination and fantasy, driven by inner influences rather than real and concrete occurrences. Our minds are capable of orderly and logical abstractions and do not depend on concrete physical influences outside us. Our mathematics is one example of a creation of the human mind that has ideas and representations which do not necessarily match the physical world. It is possible to write equations that represent logical and consistent ideas and interpretations of an unreal world. People with psychoses are an example of how the mind is capable of forming ideas that are independent of external reality. But it is astounding and far-reaching to think that the physical and material world is the clay that we can adapt to our thinking. We do not simply seek to understand it, but we also mold it according to our images and how we like to think. We impose our thinking on it. Ordering is one way we impose our thinking on the world. There are many definitions of order. The one that turns out to be a consequence of making comparison judgment has to do with ratio and proportion between the parts and within the whole. The question remains as to whether the connections of our brain permit it to perceive all possible forms of order in the physical world, or whether we are strictly limited to certain kinds of ideas and visions as by-products of a limited form of network. People brought up in restricted cultures think in characteristic ways, sometimes too narrowly to understand norms, behaviors and ideas developed in other cultures. Thus we might say that our brain has not have evolved to the point where all possible forms of order can be grasped by it.

Order is related to complexity. How we understand order and degrees of order and chaos depends on our ability to describe complexity. Our universe contains galaxies and stars, atoms, molecules and quanta, apples, oranges, a near infinity of things and their associated phenomena. We are sensory, thoughtful, action-oriented beings. Our scope and breadth depends on what is out there to give us experiences about the properties of objects around us. We create ideas that have a diversity of flavors arising from their content, meaning and intention. How can we, how do we, how should we order the universe?

Order in nature is more than what is first and what is last. There is an ordering of events in time: How do we represent events so they link together over time? In the current representation event A must occur first and exert its influence on B before B can exert its influence. Thus A comes first and then B. This means that commutativity is not allowed because it contradicts time order. Order also can mean that event A can be associated with event B but not with C or D, a property known as non-associativity.

More generally, order is a relation among parts and functions of a system that enables it to operate smoothly. For example, an artery that suddenly emptied into a very narrow blood vessel couldn't function and the flow of blood would be blocked. Functions in a system cannot be performed if the parts are disproportionately connected. To display order, a system must be related both according to its structure and according to its function. The solar system shows order. Its structure is one of spherical objects of varying sizes. We may view them as being functionally related by revolving around the sun and to a lesser extent influencing each other; or we may pick one of the planets, as people once did, using the earth as the center of the universe and making it the fixed point describing the paths of the other objects, including the sun, relative to it.

We can think of a system in terms of purpose, function, structure and flows. Flows within the structure serve certain functions designed to fulfill certain goals. Ratio and proportionality for order hold within each of these four constructs and among them.

An orderly structured system like the human body satisfies (roughly) the following requirements:

(1) Homogeneity within the parts. Essential for proportionality, this means similar things in size and function work together.

(2) Homogeneity between the parts means gradual increase in the size of clusters or parts from the small to the large. The parts must hang together in some orderly way to create a higher order system. An example is the way in which the different organs of the body, with their different functions are kept together by flesh and bones and are linked through the vascular and nervous systems. The overall function is orderly but the way the subsystems are put in their places may not seem so orderly.

(3) Order in how the parts function. In the human body, the smallest parts (like the hormones and blood corpuscles) work at the most basic level throughout. These are followed by the microscopic components of the cells, which together form the cells themselves, which in turn form the skin and the muscles, and so on.

(4) Continuity, uniformity and a degree of smoothness in combining the smaller parts of a system into larger ones and these in turn to still larger ones. This is essential for creating an orderly system.

A structurally disconnected system in terms of physical connections can be functionally ordered like the planets around the sun. If there is no functional law for them to satisfy, then they appear to us as if they exist with no general purpose that binds them together, and hence are interpreted as a less orderly group. Our purpose here is to find ways to connect everything to everything else in our thinking, along some path of influence.

When everything is stable, each part is located appropriately according to its size, and its function contributes a certain amount to the function of the whole. In general, to preserve proportionality, each part contributes a certain fractional amount, and the synergistic combination of these contributions makes up the function of the whole.

For the human mind to understand relations between things, a uniform standard is necessary in order to make linear or introduce linear comparisons. To understand what we mean when we say something is nonlinear, we need something which changes linearly so we can judge what kind of non-linearity we are dealing with.

How to create order? We make the following observations:

- There is a degree of universality that works in living things, plants and animals which forms their bodies and drives them to survive according to certain adaptive forms of behavior.
- The human brain is gradually able to deal with any thought. The human brain is a special case of a very general brain with unlimited increase in connections, and also size, when needed. Human thought perceives and defines order.
- It seems likely that electric synthesis makes perception and generates understanding, at least in genetically determined beings.
- Gravity creates objects out of stellar dust. Electricity creates images and thoughts. Both do clumping and synthesis.
- Influence is a force of interaction. It is more general than cause and effect, which is linear. When an effect is also a cause and a cause is an effect, we can no longer distinguish between them. Composite influence can be deconstructed into its controlling factors. We interpret influence according to our strategic needs.
- Order is a synthesis of physical, psychological or social influences. It is defined by proportionality, repetition and symmetry.
- Stability, instability and evolution of order are the essential concepts. Evolution of order is the single highest form of synthesis that any system can undergo.

To make order, the parts fit together harmoniously in proportion according to size. The contribution of a very small part to the whole is practically unrecognizable. However, the contribution of that part to another part that is equal to it in size or property can be significant. Thus the contribution of parts to larger and larger parts takes place in organized and increasing degrees from the smallest to the larger, by one order of magnitude, and these to the still larger by one order of magnitude and so on. A whole is constructed of parts in gradual degrees of proportionality. The fundamental equation describing proportion is $f(ax)=bf(x)$. However, the variable x here is not an ordinary variable assigned to quantities but is a function of a variable. The equation is better written as $g[af(x)]=bg[f(x)]$. What does this equation say? It says that in the construction of a whole from its parts, the contribution $af(x)$ of the part whose function is defined by $f(x)$ as it functions in the whole is proportional to its contribution as a part of the whole because the function of the whole is made up of the functions of all its parts.

Order, along with proportion and symmetry has great elegance. It can satisfy our feelings. Proportionality is a local attribute between a whole and other wholes or parts to a whole. Symmetry is a global attribute related to movements of the whole with its parts without deformation that has geometric significance in characterizing the whole.

The Importance of Proportion in Forming and Communicating Ideas

Proportionality of perception by the human brain means a little increase in the outside world corresponds to a little increase in the intensity of our perceptions and consequently in the effort we apply to change the world. Judgment is the means we have to capture the proportionality of what we are sensing out there. Barely-noticeable differences are our means to escalate our effort, in little spurts, to apply our ideas in a systematic way. Our brains have to be quantitative so we can judge correctly and act proportionately.

This book advances the proposition that proportion is the main building block in the creation of order. Proportionality is a balancing of the parts within the whole according to their influence—even if it is just a small part, even if it is just a point. Proportionality can be extended principles of symmetry that apply to the making of order, physical and mental, concrete or abstract. It is also applicable in fields of force.

Any objective observation we make must include a discussion of proportion. It is the rule of proportion in the examination of nature that causes us to observe opposing concepts: an organized universe and a universe in chaos, rational and irrational numbers, harmony and discord, truth and falsity. These descriptions are merely proportional balancing effects of the opposition of influences that is inherent in all things.

Proportionality may be local or it may be global and there may not be a proportional transition from one to the other. Complete order requires proportionate transition from the small to the large and still larger. Our way of thinking is to reach out to things that we can detect with our senses, seeking confirmation that what we see is real to us. But that is precisely what a plant does in its own way to deal with its environment. If a plant tried to do an experiment to check that we were thinking beings, it would not be successful because it is not able to understand human thinking. Similarly, we may be unable to understand the methods of someone superior to us. Perhaps if we silence our inner thoughts we would be similar to other forms of life when they do not struggle with anything. We can only know the universe according to ourselves, our senses, our ability to synthesize, but we cannot know the universe according to itself or as it may be known by other forms of life. Ours is a humanly relative universe.

We see harmony in the emotions, feelings, and characteristics present within ourselves. Proportion corresponds to some neural vibrations within us that dictate our sense of pleasure and pain, beauty and ugliness, love and hate. The result is we are captives of the memories fixed in both body and mind. If we were to view nature from an altered state of consciousness, our sense of proportion would also be altered.

Humankind has been finding and embracing our proportionate sense for a long time. Think of chanting around the primitive campfire or the construction of iambic pentameter rhymes in poetry. One early representation of proportion is the idea of Divine Proportion, seen in the beauty and organization within the cosmos. It is the harmony and glue that holds the unity of the universe. This harmony in nature is viewed as Divine Proportion. Divine Proportion has been expressed as, "For of three magnitudes, if the greatest (AB) is to the mean (CB) as the mean (CB) is to the least (AC), they therefore all shall be one. $AB/CB = CB/AC = 1.618...$"

Symmetry - A Generalization of Proportion

Symmetry is proportionality with the interchangeability of order among the parts. It is defined in the Oxford American Dictionary as pleasing proportion within parts of a whole and a degree of repetition. It is a fundamental property needed to characterize different levels of order. To see why symmetry is so essential in our thinking about order, all we have to do is to look at the perfect order of a circle or a sphere. Both have a perfect symmetry of rotation. The less perfect the order, the less the symmetry. Herman Weyl defined symmetry as "that form of concordance of several parts by means of which they form a whole". Andreas Speiser defined it as "harmony of different parts of a whole". According to the Encyclopedia Americana, in ordinary usage symmetry means *balanced proportions*. The use of the word "proportion" interests us here because it is the focus of our concern. As an indication of the profundity of symmetry in science, it is known that in the physical world a conservation law is about a measurable property of an isolated physical system that does not change (such as energy remaining a constant in an isolated system) as the system evolves. Each conservation law is mathematically identical to certain symmetry of a physical system.

Unity - Synthesis of the Parts into the Whole

Our mind needs unity and coherence to make sense of the many things of which it is aware, both observed in the present and registered in the brain's memory. Coherence is a feeling of *understanding, satisfaction, conformity* with other knowledge and *security* that all add up to pursuing a cause to which we subscribe, past, present and future. The pursuit is served best when we assess our understanding in terms of a system in which the whole has meaning beyond the meanings of its parts, and the ultimate meaning has to do with our own goals and purposes that form the basis for what we perceive and what satisfies us. There are two ways to gain this kind of understanding. One is by proceeding from the most general to the specific or vice versa. We start with a goal and descend hierarchically in gradual steps to the objectives for meeting the goal, criteria for meeting each objective and so on down to alternative outcomes that may be policies or courses of action. In this scheme lower levels of the hierarchy contribute to the fulfillment of the functions of the upper more important levels. When upper level elements depend on lower level elements or when elements in a level are interdependent, we need a network to conceptualize the flow of influences, their interactions and feedback. A feedback network more realistically represents how factors can mutually depend on each other according to influence singly or as a group with synergy. New influences can be created through the synergy of other influences. Thus not all influences exist at all times. New influences appear and disappear. We study these influences and what kind of results or responses they yield. These responses vary from the simplest that pass unobserved, to simple observable changes, to fluctuating changes in state like a stone warmed by the sun, to dramatic changes like the winds and the hurricanes, to behavioral changes in living organisms, to the most complex physical and biological creative outcomes like the laws and materials of physics and astronomy and like genetics, biology and physiology and at a higher level consciousness, feelings, mind, and analytical thought.

We are not likely ever to understand reality as we might imagine because our genetics are tied to all the environmental influences. Many of these influences are strictly random from today's vantage point; our increasing control changes some important influences. Such influences ultimately change our genetics then, in turn, our goals and purposes, which change our interpretations of influence, and then our control and action. The process continues in a never-ending cycle. The only way for us to eventually and collectively learn to control everything perfectly is to be of one mind, something that is impossible. Unity is most probably an unattainable destiny.

Influences and the corresponding events that happen in this world may be stable, unstable or chaotic. For the excitement and curiosity of consciousness, permanent stability is as undesirable as constant change is. Some sort of balance between stability and change is the most desirable. The best compromise is transition from stability to change, cycling back to stability. Permanent stability is too orderly, boring and deadly and involves no stimuli. Permanent instability and change are unsettling and lack the cohesiveness of order. Chaos is aimless, unpredictable and purposeless. It has built in it inconsistency that does not conform to any single set of laws and principles. Chaos is inevitable when several different laws can influence the outcome of an event that is undergoing dynamic change.

Unity and Coherence of Total Order Require the Translation of Consciousness into Memory

Through consciousness our minds seek unity and coherence, which is derived from our previous responses. Consciousness means awareness of the environment and of things, of other forms of life, of other people, of ideas and feelings and events, and of influences they all have that in turn cause changes in them and among them. Influence makes the things happen that register in our minds.

Eventually what matters for us is how we feel as we sense and perceive influence and as we think it through. Our feelings are the major determinant of how we represent what we are aware of as satisfactory or unsatisfactory to different degrees and how good or bad, true or false we feel it is. Awareness at a certain instant is static, but the instant after that things change both within us as our hearts pump new blood to our brains to keep us alive with our neurons actively firing, and outside us as things change slowly or fast. We then tire of the occurrences and want to see change slowing down and coming to rest. We want to see the influences reach a stable outcome. We sleep to give our minds some rest and this creates stability until we wake up. The cycle repeats as new stimulation from influences around us again causes us to respond, followed by a period of rest, ad infinitum. Influences and their outcomes keep our consciousness occupied and how we feel about the outcome is the ultimate for us. How we feel is determined by our knowledge and chemistry, by our past and present behavior and the behavior of others, and how we are influenced physically and mentally by what we sense and observe. We can also control and direct influence to some desired end. The pillars of our existence are influence (a stimulus) and the stability or instability of its outcome through the passage of time, behavior (ours and that of others), response (with feeling, and action), and feelings of satisfaction or dissatisfaction. We need a way of understanding that can bring all these elements into a single framework. We have such a framework but it needs further refinements and understanding. This book aims at deepening that understanding and increasing the refinements. That is how we characterize our kind of world. It is what both matter and mind are about, creating stimuli of different intensities of magnitude as influences to bring about effects of different intensities of magnitude. It is a process that needs order and integration to tell a coherent story, even though it may not be entirely consistent. That story is the history of the world. It is a process that creates and organizes memory. It tells our story on a very small scale.

Consciousness can be thought of as a new field in nature arising out of biology. Conservation of consciousness is about conserving all the awareness, feelings and thoughts that a conscious being has. One theory of consciousness survival advocates that all souls are emanations from a single universal consciousness that return to it after death. Similar to the matter-energy relationship, consciousness may survive after death as matter is transformed to energy. In the metaphysical world accepted by faith rather than through scientific observation, consciousness, as energy, is eternal in the form of souls that take on a physical form in this world. Two versions are that the soul is either there forever, or is formed at birth but after a physical life any of a variety of things happen to it: it either survives for ever or is destroyed, never to be recovered, or is tortured until it is changed to something recoverable. At odds with this transcendental interpretation is advocacy in modern science that consciousness is a product of organic matter and its electrical energy interconnections.

Some people in the field of artificial intelligence have written that consciousness is like software that requires a computer (matter) and electrical impulses (energy) to be made concrete, but that still exists as an independent entity. Some believe that in the long run, our technology may even be able to transfer our consciousness into purposefully designed artificial entities. It will be interesting to see how close computer technology will come to emulating the functions of a human being's nervous system.

Unity and Coherence also Require a Sense of Order

There are numerous forces and influences that shape living forms that then respond to them in certain ways in order to survive. These forces and influences are themselves subject to higher laws to which they must respond successfully. The higher laws are themselves subject to some overall law or purpose from which they derive and to which they respond in some meaningful and consistent way. We can understand the abstract version better by proceeding in steps from the particulars that we know. There are two versions. The first is that there is a finite and discrete framework of conscious thinking and judgments, and the second is that there is a continuous version associated with the senses like vision and hearing that leads to two forms of relations.

There are two general laws of order that govern our feeling, responding, thinking and understanding. The first is the law of *proportionality* derived from our ability and that of all living forms to judge and control. The second is the law of *creative memory*, derived from the workings of our network of neurons which is based on proportionality. With proportionality we can deal with nature that is both the environment outside us and within us, and with creative memory we can hypothesize and reason about experience and the meaning of that experience. While it is true that proportionality is not guaranteed in all interactions, if two systems interact in a mutually responsive way with feedback, a proportional response between them must exist, to maintain and control their mutual influences. The greater force has proportionately a greater influence than the weaker one.

Understanding Complexity Requires a Mix of Approaches

According to Leibniz [4] there are two kinds of truths, those of reasoning and those of fact. Truths of reasoning are necessary in that they are a consequence of the assumptions, and their falseness is impossible. Truths of fact are contingent, and their opposite is possible because we can interpret the outcomes of the facts differently as lawyers do in a court. When a truth is necessary, its reason can be found by analysis, resolving it into more simple ideas and truths until we come to those which are primary.

Our inheritance from the scientific age is the belief that there is only one way to think about happenings and that is through causal explanations. The quantitative approach to reality is a culture to which many of us are introduced at an early age. We tend to take it for granted as an innate way of thinking, rather than as a powerful tool which, through painstaking effort, we learned to use over a long period of time.

The social scientist does not have the illusion that the complex problems he encounters can necessarily be subjected to this method of analysis. He regards other approaches as more powerful and more natural ways to deal with his problems, especially problems that are less rigidly structured and more amorphous than we are accustomed to. There are many different metaphors of reality and the versatile problem solver tries to learn to use them all where appropriate. Two thinkers can differ substantially on which of two dramatically different models serves best to represent a given problem. Anthropologists, psychologists, musicians and poets have their own way of constructing metaphors. They look at the causal thinkers in the same humoring way they are looked at in return by the scientists, questioning who knows more about the real reality. In the book by the psychologist LeShan and the physicist Margenau, *Einstein's Space and Van Gogh's Sky: Physical Reality and Beyond* [5], the way that a scientist sees, touches, senses and measures is compared and contrasted with three other recognized ways of looking at the world. A basic limiting principle of the scientist's way is the assumption that all phenomena are sequentially continuous in space and time, and are related by linear cause and effect. Despite disproof of this principle in quantum mechanics, "it has not been clearly understood that its abandonment means the complete collapse of the system of one rationality ruling the entire universe. A completely consistent cosmos cannot be inconsistent in one area: one exception collapses it all."

Causation, a basic tenet of science, works only for isolated systems such as we are able to bring about in the physical world. It does not work in the domain of consciousness, where isolation (such as sensory deprivation) can damage the mind and then break it down. Consciousness constantly reaches to past and future, and to places and possibilities of places. Only a non-causal perspective of numerous alternative realities allows us to understand this domain. The coming intelligent computers will operate more like this kind of many-dimensional consciousness than like linear causality. The challenge is to develop scientific methods to study the other modes of reality that are as effective as the ones used in the sensory mode. Le Shan and Margenau [5] suggest ways to do this in art, ethics, parapsychology and human consciousness. Their four modes of reality are: 1) Sensory 2) Clairvoyant; 3) Transpsychic; 4) Mythic. In the first, the sensory or see/touch way, individuals construct reality as if they are detached observers of a larger whole. It is the way of science that has, in addition to the usual human level of detail, the micro quantum level that is not causal and is studied statistically; the macro astronomical level; the behavior of living things; and the inner experience level. In the behavioral mode, individuals construct reality as if they are extensions of the whole without a sense of separation, as in dancing, music, and meditation. In the inner experience mode, they construct reality as if they are reciprocals to the whole, urging their wishes and desires on the forces of nature, as people do in prayer. In the mythic mode, they construct reality as if they are identical to the whole as it exists in dreaming and play and keeps us fresh and alive, curious and creative.

One sometimes hears people trained in physics ask why the formulas of the AHP/ANP are not like the formulas of physics. We all know that physics is studied by relating natural forces to other more simply defined natural concepts of length, mass, time and other dimensions assumed to be independent of one another. Formulas are derived from principles that apply to all physical happenings. Because nature changes very slowly over very long periods of time one is not concerned that the first principles and the resulting formulas change from application to application. Of course what physics lacks is to determine how such formulas are structured by our neuronal brains and if they are completely objective or are they the result of our own special ability to think. Using the mathematics of the AHP we can shed light on this subject.

Usually we use a prioritized mix of these ways to confront complexity that involves behavior. Hierarchies with goals and criteria and networks with dependence and feedback play an important role in constructing these explanations. They provide the unity we need as we seek to combine these different ways. Rather than black and white, that unity involves different shades of grey. It is in constructing these different shades that we can express our free will to determine what is important and what is not to us as individuals and as groups of people.

The great creative French thinker, paleontologist-philosopher, and Catholic Priest, Pierre Teilhard de Chardin (1881-1955) reflected on the future in profound ways that inspired and influenced many people's thinking about the future [6]. He defined three very broad ways of order in the evolution of the universe: geogenesis, evolution of the physical universe of matter and energy; biogenesis, evolution of life forms of organic matter; and noogenesis, evolution of consciousness of thoughts and feelings created chemically and electrically. In order to survive, life forms need an electrochemical ability to respond to the environment in which they live. In humans (and most advanced forms of life), the ability to respond in this way has given rise to a brain with the neural capability of firing. These firings must be in such a form that they can connect with the firing produced by sensations such as sights and sounds. Feelings and ideas in the brain have their own firings which must link with firings that spring from the senses.

All experience is represented through the formation, transmission and synthesis of chemical and associated electric signals in the nervous system, or some other system in simpler forms of life (and perhaps even in all forms of matter and energy). From the signals and their syntheses we create meaning according to what we already know and remember and, according to how our cumulative feelings, lead us to interpret our experience. All feelings depend on the structure of the brain and on its conditioning. It is a feedback system. The outlets of this system are our judgments about what we feel and think about the different causes of what is happening and the influences that shape the outcome. Because we depend on our nervous system with its underlying signal transmission structure to determine how we feel, we are functions of our physical bodies. People who have defective adrenals or other glands, or even faulty parts in their nervous systems, react differently to things. The feelings we have are electrical syntheses in our imperfect and ever-evolving neural network. Physical reality is transient and changing.

How lasting are effects of the electricity that forms our feelings and their syntheses? Not long because everything changes. There may be a universal field of synthesized feelings or kinds of response that people have adapted to. All that we can affirm is that the reality of existence is in the process of becoming. Its ultimate aim or mathematical limit is either a stable outcome, or it cycles and is therefore not fixed. As we increase our own connectivity we contribute to making the limit a fixed one. Our calling is to connect by increasing our knowledge and agreement on the interpretation of the outcome of all the influences. Our contributions to the universal field, if there is one, may help bring some semblance of order among its diversity.

Because physical influence is a special case of general influence, and because humans have physical bodies but can exert non-physical kinds of influences, not all aspects of influence can be adequately described within the space-time coordinates of physics. The physical four dimensions are part, and only part, of the higher dimensional space of all influences. In addition, the human mind that is capable of detecting influence exists in a larger universe than the physical one. To project ahead, a new concept of sequencing and ordering that includes physical time and psychological time is essential. We call it general time. All influences have duration and can be measured on the general time dimension.

A thing or system as a whole has parts into which it can be decomposed (except perhaps some aspects of physics with its indecomposable particles and quanta). The character of the system is more than the sum of the characters of the parts. The parts have relations among themselves and also to the whole and more abstractly to the criteria that control the operation of that system. The system in turn may be part of a larger system. Relations among the parts of a system must involve proportionality both in the structure of the system and in its function. The proportionality applies among the parts or subsystems and then other proportionalities apply to the subparts and so on, descending gradually in homogeneous steps. The whole itself may have stabilities or instabilities. The physical shapes and functions of the parts usually have similarities that are replicated or recursively constructed in homogeneous but larger and larger phases to the whole system. The system is then seen to be a composite of smaller parts combining into larger parts that are nearly identical in shape, and these again combine into still-larger parts with nearly the same shape, and so on, upwards and downwards in scale. Such repeating patterns of the same shape into larger and larger (or smaller and smaller) sizes are called fractals. Proportionality, symmetry and fractality are three fundamental properties in the analysis of order, stability and replication in the shapes and functions of a system.

The neurologist Richard E. Cytowic [7] writes that the final arbiter within us is none other than the limbic system. Buried deep within the temporal lobe, it creates emotions, motivations and emotional associations with memory. It is *emotion* much more than reason that makes us human. The brain's largest and latest development, the cortex, has more inputs from the limbic system than the limbic system has from the cortex. The number and nature of recursive feedback circuits ensures that the influence of the limbic system is greater. Thus the emotional brain is physiologically able to overwhelm the rationality of the cortex. It turns out that every single division of the nervous system, from the frontal lobes to the spinal cord, contains some component of the limbic system. In other words, the limbic system forms the core, an emotional one, of the human nervous system.

Emotional calculations, not logical ones, animate us. An examination of the mammalian brain shows us why. The human emotional system is more powerful than that of other animals, and the processing of emotional information is qualitatively different from the processing of other information. In evolution, the limbic pathways did not get left behind as the cortex expanded. The two co-evolved. In fact, the number of limbic fiber tracks is greater, both in relative size and in absolute number, than the other fiber systems. It is not the rational content of the truth itself but how strongly we *feel* about it that has the greatest influence on what we do next.

Most people even today do not believe that we can quantify feelings. A.F. MacKay in his article, Arrow's Theorem: The Paradox of Social Choice - A Case Study in the philosophy of Economics [8], writes that pursuing the cardinal approaches is like chasing what cannot be caught.

LeShan and Margenau also write [5]:

"We cannot as we have indicated before, quantify the observables in the domain of consciousness. There are no rules of correspondence possible that would enable us to quantify our feelings. We can make statements of the relative intensity of feelings, but we cannot go beyond this. I can say, "I feel angrier at him today than I did yesterday "We cannot, however, make meaningful statements such as, I feel three and one half times angrier than I did yesterday." The physicists' schema, so faithfully emulated by generations of psychologists, epistemologists and aestheticians, is probably blocking their progress, defeating possible insights by its prejudicial force. The schema is not false—it is perfectly reasonable—but it is bootless for the study of mental phenomena."

We have mathematical theory about perturbation of judgments to assure us that if we did not use the precise value of a number like three and a half but are close to whatever the underlying value may be, the priorities that are derived from judgments would also be close to the true value.

Whether we are here by intelligent design or by random evolutionary mutations, our survival depends on our ability to satisfy our needs through the natural world in which we live. What makes a considerable difference is that human beings are neither like parasites fixed on a victim on whom they conveniently feed, nor are they like cows that move around grazing grass, or like predators hunting for a warm, living and breathing meal. Humans can control and change their environment through their ability to reason, decide and apply their decisions. They use their creativity to invent elaborate and ingenious tools to extend their senses and both their physical and mental abilities to deal with the world and to take care of themselves. The most significant ability of humans is to identify influences and calculate what the most likely outcome of these influences would be. They realize that when decisions are made that involve many interests, they are just one small part of those interests. Although our hopes and desires are important, they are only a small part of what we need to know. It is far more important to describe how the world actually is. That knowledge will help us to transform the world as much as we can from where it is now to where we want it to be. That is the means by which the hopes and desires can become the reality of the future.

The external environment is so varied in its materials and forms that we are at a loss to know how best to organize it in our minds in order to cope with its variety and with variations in that variety. To do that, we resort to introducing principles about form and influences that change that form, so we can track it in our minds with a certain degree of understanding and predictability. In addition, in order to control certain aspects of the environment we need other principles that establish correspondence between what we think and how things actually are, according to size, form and change in the position and shape of that form. Thus it is these two main principles that help our minds retain the shape of things and how we can alter them without using external tools assisted by our cognitive minds. The two subjects that interest us here are symmetry and proportionality. Both are abstract concepts that help us understand reality. Symmetry has to do with form and its invariance and is fundamentally geometric in nature. Proportionality has to do with control and its effectiveness in satisfying our objectives, and is much more arithmetic in its conception and development. Both symmetry and proportionality derive from our ability to compare things. Comparisons, especially pairwise comparisons, are the most basic operations of the conscious working of our minds. First, we identify or perceive things and then we compare them according to different properties that they might have in common. In turn we compare properties, prioritizing them according to how important they are to our objectives in life, and still further, we compare and prioritize objectives according to how important they are to our survival. Prioritization changes often, and enables us to cope with a dynamic environment.

In fact, in order to satisfy our needs and survive we must be able to understand and control physical nature that is transcended by our minds which impose meaning and value on nature that is not there without the mind. To control nature, there has to be a certain correspondence between what we feel and think and what is out there in nature that we need and want. This correspondence requires that there be some kind of proportionality between what happens in our brain and what is out there, so we can approach the natural world in a controlled orderly way. What talent do we need in our biology to enable us to deal with proportionality in a way that enables us to survive? The same concern applies to all animal forms, and to a smaller extent to plants, and still to objects that maintain their identity by conforming to natural law and surviving as they are.

There is no way for us to think anything, imagine anything or feel anything without the firing of neurons. All our experience is electrically recorded. The complex electrical workings of our brain and their synthesis are quantitative in nature and must be interpreted to make sense of how we finally make meaning out of what they do. Our thinking about the environment must deal with angles and direction alongside lengths and heights.

The complex network of the brain has tens of billions of specialized neurons and groups of neurons with varied structures that produce rich combinations of electric firings. These firings enable us to extend our awareness and thinking from simply existing as biological entities that subsist in a physical world to becoming thoughtful and imaginative beings whose conceptions go far beyond what they experience and sense in the environment. We are able not only to describe what we take into our minds from outside about concrete reality, but can also imagine things that are ethereal and that cannot take on a physical existence because they defy the familiar laws of nature. The principles that govern the electrical workings of our minds are far more complex than the laws of physics, especially because the ideas that are generated through electricity transcend the electricity that gives rise to them and the electronics of which it is a part. In that sense one is encouraged to say that our ideas and feelings are transcendental. The most remarkable thing about them is that they get compounded and mixed in well-organized ways to create more complex meanings. It is like the many instruments in a symphony, whose varied sounds create rich and complex music. To us the ultimate reality is the compounding of our thoughts and feelings. They are our essence. Thoughts and feelings are as real as the physical parts. The aim of the survival of our bodies seems not simply to just be, but also to create feelings and ideas and derive from them meaning for our existence.

The nonlinearity and size of our neural network make possible an unlimited number of ideas, feelings and emotions. Firings are associated with intensities and frequencies of electric signal that are quantitative in nature, requiring the use of numbers. The firings of specialized individual neurons must be aggregated and synthesized into more complicated intensities that reflect more complex feelings about a mix of things we experience at the same time. To combine the parts into a meaningful whole requires great precision. Electricity is characterized by phase and amplitude. Therefore the mathematics that is involved in the firing of neurons requires the use of complex numbers of which the real numbers that we use in counting and in measurement are a special case. There is no way for us to avoid the use of complex numbers in all our considerations of proportionality. For example, we cannot recognize shapes, forms and order without proportionality. In our small brain what we think networks with what is out there in nature. Mathematics underlies all the reality we experience with our brains.

Numbers are us. They are in our instincts and behavior. We are made to distinguish between things and to distinguish the difference between the few and the many. We not only compare pairs, but also whole sets of objects, aggregating them in different ways. This requires numbers.

This is contrary to the traditional way of thinking about numbers. Did we discover numbers or did we invent them? The question is moot: whatever the source, we were using them in our thinking, both consciously and subconsciously. Fourier analysis tells us that even our language involves vibrations with amplitude and angle that can be represented by complex numbers with real and imaginary parts.

To summarize, a central theme of existence is concern about the fundamental characteristics of beings that enable them to control their environment. The assumption we make is that in order to cope with the environment, beings must be able to perceive and synthesize information proportionately to the dimensions of natural occurrences that are out there, so they can use what they learn to modify and control the environment.

What It Is All About

One may ask: what is all this concern with the world and its influences and where are we going with it? One way to see the need for our kind of generalization is to answer the question "which time of life and experience is most characteristic of me?" The answer is "all of life," but there are different degrees of impact on the mind. It involves prioritization and synthesis, and the overall personality is shaped accordingly.

Quantifying the intensity of our response to discrete stimuli by making comparisons and deriving priorities from them is our main objective in this book. This is then generalized to the continuous case in which our senses are automatically involved in the comparisons. There are important consequences of our conscious way to respond linearly to stimuli to make proportionality between stimulus and response possible. It turns out that we have a natural built in way to respond in the form of a nearly inverse square law to all phenomena. In addition, our response needs to be expressed in the form of firing functions which in fact coincides with how our brains operate.

Human beings sense and react to the world outside and inside the body and mind and form impressions from these sensations. They also think and reason, to understand and explain the essence of the influences that they experience. In the end it is how they feel about things, satisfied or dissatisfied, good or bad, right and or wrong, that matters. The process is repeated throughout their lives. In the book of Genesis of the bible 1:4 it says "and God saw the light that it was *good*: and God divided the light from darkness." Again Genesis 2:2 says "and he *rested* on the seventh day from all *his work* which he had made." In the end God was pleased with the order He created and set in motion.

References

1. J.W.N. Sullivan, (1933) *The Limitations of Science*, Viking Press Inc.
2. Crick, F.C; Koch, C. (2005) Review. "What is the Function of the Claustrum?" *Phil. Trans. R. Soc. B.* **360**:1271–1279
3. Damasio, A.R., (1988) "Investigating the Biology of Consciousness." *Transactions of the Royal Society* (London) 353:1879-1882
4. Leibniz, G.W., (1988) *Theodicy: Essays on the Goodness of God the Freedom of Man and the Origin of Evil*, Open Court Publishing Company
5. Leshan, L. and Margenau, H, (1983) *Einstein's Space and Van Gogh's Sky: Physical Reality and Beyond*, Macmillan 1st Collier Books
6. Teilhard de Chardin, P., (1961) *The Phenomenon of Man*, Harper & Row
7. Cytowic, R.E., (1993) *The Man who Tasted Shapes*, A Bradford Book, The MIT Press, Cambridge, Mass.
8. MacKay, A.F., (1980) *Arrow's Theorem: The Paradox of Social Choice - A Case Study in the philosophy of Economics*, New Haven and London: Yale University Press

Part II

In the next chapter we deal with the structures of decisions and the general forms in which they arise: as hierarchies with top down dependence and as networks with interdependence and feedback as desired. To make a complete science out of decision making, we need first to make a science out of decision structures. We have made a good start on that subject in several published articles and books and will sketch the ideas below. In the next chapter we deal with the structures of decisions and the general forms in which they arise: as hierarchies with top down dependence and as networks with interdependence and feedback as desired.

Chapter 3

Structures in Decision Making: On the Subjective Geometry of Hierarchies and Networks

This chapter deals with the following ideas:
- The structure of decisions as hierarchies with the dependence of the elements in a lower level on those in the level immediately above.
- Illustrations of many different forms of hierarchies applied in planning and decision making.
- Networks with dependence and feedback with examples.
- The process of structuring problems as a hierarchy or a network and how to validate that a structure meaningfully.

Introduction - Concept Construction [1]

We rely on chance to remember things when we think and talk. We are rarely certain that we are thinking of everything necessary to draw our conclusions. We need to document the important things in our decisions by structuring them to show how those things relate to each other as a unity. How to prioritize?

In the field of decision making, creating a structure is the first step in organizing, representing and solving a problem. A structure is a model, an abstraction of a problem. It helps us visualize and understand the relevant elements within it that we know from the real world and then use our understanding to solve the problem represented in the structure with greater confidence. In general, there are two kinds of structures used to represent problems: hierarchies and networks. Both rely to a varying degree on the interactions of the elements within the structure. Some examples are given followed by a discussion about how to structure the problem. At a minimum, a structure must satisfy two requirements: it must be logical in identifying and grouping similar things together, and it must relate the items accurately according to the flow of influence among them. It must be complete, accounting for whatever has an important influence. The structure is then tested as to whether it helps solve the problem to one's *satisfaction*.

Geometry is a strange dimension that constantly haunts our thinking processes. The word geometry conjures up images of triangles and circles, of similarities and congruencies of lengths and areas, and of higher dimensions and of linearity and curvature which exist in the real world. But that is not the only kind of geometry. There is also a geometry that is associated with our subjective thought processes, the geometry of vertices and edges that connect our subjective thoughts with paths and cycles.

When thinking, our brain identifies objects and ideas and deals with them in terms of their properties. We group elements that have the same property together, and they are further related according to their influence on our goals. We attempt to assign importance to the influences and focus on the most important ones. It might be said that we all associate something like vertices to the things we think about and lines and paths to the perceived influence connections among them.

The outcome of identifying our purposes and relating them to goals in light of the influences is a structure of nodes that depict the elements and lines with arrows that depict the connections. We always have some underlying understanding about the flow of influence among elements with respect to other elements which represent our objectives and goals. The question is: What kinds of generic structures are there to represent this understanding and how do we characterize them?

We need geometric structures to represent our abstract understanding of influences among elements in the real world and their connections and interactions [2]. The human mind, a decision maker, is a collection of cognitive processes involving perception, interpretation, imagination, memory, reasoning, and language, which are unique when compared with other animals. A fundamental process of the human brain is thinking; we use it to understand and solve problems, and deal with them to further our goals and purposes. Thinking involves mental manipulation of information to form concepts, reason, solve problems, and make decisions.

It is worth our while to clarify the relation between thinking and decision making. Not all activities that require decision making involve thinking because many of our decisions are automatic reflexes or are done intuitively [3]. In fact most of us rely more on our intuition to make decisions than on explicit and detailed reasoning. But when we think through a decision, we have to structure it, make judgments, choose, and then act accordingly. We need to systematize and make a science out of the thinking involved in making considered decisions.

Structuring a decision is the first step a thinking mind takes to organize and to represent any problem and in particular a decision problem that needs action. Problem solving usually begins with a feeling of dissatisfaction with an existing situation that may border on unhappiness. Our minds are conditioned and guided by feelings of satisfaction or dissatisfaction that are fulfilled to different degrees as Maslow showed in his hierarchy of needs [4]. To deal with a problem, one attempts to identify the elements that relate to it, their connections and interactions, the cause(s) that give rise to the problem, and possible ways of solution. To identify the elements we have to structure the problem. Although judgment is needed to guide us from one step to another later during the analysis, in this chapter we will only focus on the structuring process and the kinds of structures that are helpful. Thus, we identify all the elements of a problem that we think of by brainstorming the goal which they affect [5], the criteria that serve the fulfillment of that goal, the influences, the actors involved and the actions to be taken. Then we group those elements systematically into components of similar elements and have the choice to arrange them in levels of a hierarchy or as clusters in a network.

Hierarchies and networks deal with the mind and its purpose. Purpose is essential in most of its considerations. In addition, purpose is contextual, different from decision to decision and cannot be treated as a general law. In physics, natural law serves as the purpose and is assumed to hold uniformly for all natural occurrences. The consequences of behavior under natural law are described by formulas involving functions of primary variables such as mass, length and time. Cartesian axes are used as a system of coordinates to describe these functions from zero to infinity by using an arbitrary unit for the measurement of each variable. This unit is applied equally for small and for large magnitudes of measurement of the variable. In contrast with a system of coordinates, a hierarchy is used to derive measurements in the form of priorities in each specific instance because there is nothing like natural law that enables one to derive functions for all instances. There is no unit in deriving priorities. The outcome of the measurements in a hierarchy is described by a vector of numbers and not variables or functions. In the end, the outcome of a hierarchy is a multilinear form and multilinear forms have found their applications in physics as well as in decision making. Perhaps it is there that one should investigate commonalities between the two fields of science and of decision making.

In passing we note that there is at least one other general way for representing influences that are better represented not as being tracked from one point to another point but along a manifold. For example the influence of the sun spreads out in all directions but cannot be always thought of as being transmitted from a source point to a sink point. Similarly winds and hurricanes have a widespread influence and so does the flow of water when not confined in a pipe, electromagnetic fields in which radio and TV signals are transmitted and other similar things like the dissemination of ideas in communication. To analyze such influences requires that we deal with a continuum number of points for their representation. Human thinking is better able to relate elements represented by points to other elements also represented by points. When the number is very large we have difficulty capturing what it is that we should have in mind. The mathematics of this subject has already been explored in the literature in decision making [6].

Hierarchic Structures

A hierarchy is a powerful method of classification used by the mind to order information gained from experience or from our own thinking. It allows us to understand the complexity of the world around us according to the order and distribution of influences that make certain outcomes happen. Decisions do not occur in isolation – there are all sorts of influences that affect the potential outcome of a decision. It can all be regarded as a network of influences of which hierarchies are a special case. In this section we focus on hierarchies. One needs to consider who or what is most influential when important decisions are made in an organization, who gets to make these decisions, and who should be involved because of the special knowledge and understanding they have: internal people, external experts, managers and their subordinates, managers only, and so forth. One also needs to include those people and things affected by the decision and how taking that decision serves their interests. Any influence or interaction between elements would be connected by a link. Only after a problem is represented well by their key elements and their interactions in a hierarchy, can an effective structure be considered to be adequately formulated. The structure of a hierarchy further depends on who interprets it and how they interpret it. Structures can vary for different types of problems, from one person to another having the same problem; or even at different times by the same person with the same problem because that person's perspective may be different. To diminish the effect of current perspective, the problem can be embedded in a very broad setting that includes social, political, economic, environmental and other "control" perspectives.

A hierarchy can be defined formally in mathematical terms [7]. It is a stratified system for organizing people, ideas or things, whereby each element of the system, except for the top element which is the goal of the hierarchy, falls in a level and is subordinate to other elements in the level above. We can identify the world from galaxies to small living organisms in different ways within hierarchical structures. The influences in a hierarchy can be expanded to include metaphysical intangibles, such as ideas and beliefs and is generalized so we can understand the world more fully.

As the examples and graphical representations of hierarchies that we will give, suggest, we may consider a hierarchy a special type of ordered set, or a particular case of a graph. We have chosen the first interpretation as the basis of our formal definition, and the second as an illustration. No doubt, the roles could be reversed.

It is the very definition of a hierarchy in the abstract that entails the idea of levels in that hierarchy. The nature or kind of elements of a particular decision determines the number of levels. Depending on their potential interactions, the homogeneous elements in levels are connected by links to some or all of the elements in the level immediately above and immediately below. There would be different types of elements involved in the levels such as scenarios, environmental factors, actors and their objectives and their policies, people and other things influenced by the policies and actions of the actors, the objectives of these people and how they are served by certain actions to be taken by someone. Scenarios are descriptions of syntheses of possible conditions that can prevail in the environment, so certain actions judged under that set of conditions are more plausible than under other conditions. The likelihoods of the scenarios then enable one to focus on the best mixed strategy to follow.

The environment consists of the external conditions: the resources and stimuli with which the system in which the decision is being made interacts. There are two kinds of factors in the environment, controllable and uncontrollable. Uncontrollable factors are restricted by the physical limitations of the people and other factors involved in the system. Controllable factors are amenable to actions and can be influenced by the people involved. Actors are the active players who control the influences that restrict the actions to be taken which influence people who are affected by the influences according to their importance. Actions are needed to satisfy needs. If the actions work as expected, the result would be a feeling of satisfaction. To understand the effectiveness of the actions taken, one examines the effect to change the environment of the problem. One can study the influences from a top-down or from a bottom-up point of view. The first attempts to emphasize what one thinks is more important to drive the outcome, the second emphasizes the virtue of the actions to be taken as they are influenced by the factors above them. The bottom-up approach has a greater flavor of practicality than the idealism or legalism of the top-down approach. It provides the support to what is thought to be necessary above. In the top-down approach it is thought that the lower levels are parts or decompositions of what is above and are therefore only smaller parts of a larger whole.

For example, deciding whether the level of water in a dam should be kept full or half-full is considered as a single hierarchy [8]. Seven levels, from focus, decision criteria, decision makers, factors, group affected, objectives, to the alternatives, are used to represent all the elements involved and their interactions. One specific feature of this conceptually very useful hierarchy is the different actors included. One group of actors is the decision makers located in the third level of the hierarchy because of their different concerns that affect the outcome of a decision. The other actors are groups that are affected by the decision located in fifth level of the structure. The details are shown in Figure 1.

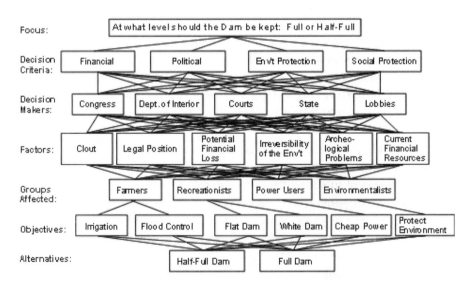

Figure 1 Hierarchy for Level of a Dam: Full or Half-Full

Although all the elements of a hierarchy are arranged in a suitable position in a graph with links in the structure, the actual performance of the elements cannot be illustrated graphically. We need to think about their performance and influence and their importance in our own minds to make the judgments we use to develop performance measures or priorities. Sometimes control hierarchies are used that depict specific kinds of homogeneous influence like economic or political or environmental influences and only that influence is to be considered when making judgments. Our job would be to combine these influences into a single overall appropriately mixed influence according to priority. Every element of a hierarchy must ultimately be related to some or all the alternative actions or outcomes either directly or through a path. No element should be isolated from the alternatives.

Hundreds of examples of decision hierarchies, many of which are commonly encountered in decision situations are illustrated in The Hierarchon [9]. There are some common structures consisting of hierarchies: a single hierarchy; two hierarchies, one that deals only with benefits and another that deals only with costs and pains; four hierarchies, one each for benefits (B), opportunities (O), costs (C), and risks (R) collectively referred to as BOCR. In fact a decision may involve many hierarchies depending on the number and structure of the control criteria used to track influences. That is, economic influence may have its own hierarchy, social influence another hierarchy, and political influences yet another and so on. This entire approach is repeated for each of the four BOCR merits. Because of space limitation in this chapter, we illustrate with the first two kinds of hierarchies, leaving the third kind to another chapter.

1) A Single Hierarchy

This is a common decision structure, though perhaps it is shortsighted except in such simple decisions as purchasing a car or a house where it is cost or some other negative criterion which by proper phrasing can be turned into a positive one (e.g. low cost) and considered a benefit. The decision problem is represented with a single hierarchy in which all the elements are organized into levels in a top-down scheme. Nodes represent the elements, and links connect them to indicate their connections. The elements in two adjacent levels can be fully connected (a complete hierarchy) or only partly connected (an incomplete hierarchy) and used to represent any decision with linear top-down connections.

2) Two Hierarchies

In the two hierarchy case, the considerations of a decision are separated into two hierarchies, one for benefits and another for costs. The costs hierarchy includes all kinds of costs and pains. Both hierarchies have tangibles and intangibles. Thus we need to look at the alternatives in terms of what purposes they fulfill and how strongly and also in terms of what it would cost to bring them about. The resulting priorities of the alternatives can be combined into a single outcome using the benefit/cost ratio in some form to obtain a marginal outcome. More generally, one obtains the final (total) outcome of prioritization by selecting the single top alternative for the benefits and also that for the costs. One then uses the ratings approach of the AHP to consider the performance of each of the two with respect to predetermined intensities assigned to strategic criteria used to evaluate the contributions of the benefits and the costs. After appropriately prioritizing the strategic criteria themselves one uses the process of weighting and adding the priorities of the intensities assigned to the top alternative under benefits and adds to obtain the overall weight of the benefits. One does the same for the top alternative for the costs obtaining the overall weight for the costs. These overall priorities for benefits and costs are normalized and the resulting weights used to combine their respective alternative priorities. Finally one subtracts the outcome for the costs of each alternative from that of its benefits to obtain the final ranking. The outcome may have a negative value

An example of choosing a way for crossing a river is constructed of two hierarchies dealing with benefits and costs [7], each containing four levels: a goal at the top, factors, criteria, and alternatives (the bottom). The factors fall into three categories in each hierarchy: economic, social, and environmental. The details are represented in Figure 2.

Network Structures

A network involves a grouping of elements (scenarios, environmental factors, actors, objectives, actions) into clusters that are not organized in any particular way, unlike the levels of a hierarchy. Its clusters are not grouped in levels. The concept of dependence is central in defining a network. To develop it at length here would take us far afield from the scope of this paper. Suffice it to say that when elements are dependent they can influence one another in the appropriate direction of dependence. For most purposes in practice, influence can be thought of as a primitive notion: a cause that can change the state of a system.

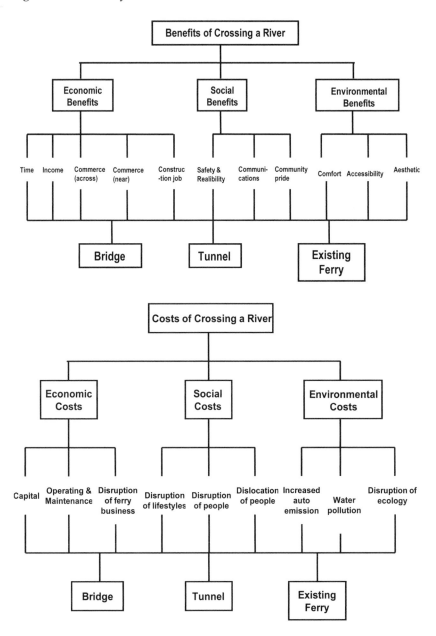

Figure 2 Two Hierarchies for Crossing a River

Definition: Let $\mathfrak{S}$ be a family of nonempty sets (clusters) $\mathfrak{S}_1$, $\mathfrak{S}_2$, ..., $\mathfrak{S}_n$ where $\mathfrak{S}_i$ consists of the elements $\{e_{ij}, j = 1,..., m_i\}$, $i = 1,2,...,n$. $\mathfrak{S}$ is a network if it is a graph with directed arcs whose vertices are $\mathfrak{S}_i$ and whose arcs are defined through the concept of dependence; thus, given two components $\mathfrak{S}_i$ and $\mathfrak{S}_j \in \mathfrak{S}$, there is an arc from $\mathfrak{S}_i$ to $\mathfrak{S}_j$ if some or elements in $\mathfrak{S}_j$ are dependent on some or all the elements in $\mathfrak{S}_i$.

Let $\mathfrak{S}$ be a network consisting of the clusters C_1, C_2 ... C_n. For each C_i there is some C_j so that either C_i depends on C_j or C_j depends on C_i, or both.

It is easy to see that a hierarchy is a special case of a network in which the subsets are arranged linearly in an ascending or a descending order.

A network can refer to any interconnected group, cluster, or system, which consists of nodes or elements that are connected by links. Nodes may be joined by more than one link, but no node is isolated.

The concept of a network is useful in helping us to portray the complex relations of real-world problems. There are many examples of networks in transportation, computer science, neurology, operations research, flow problems, business, marketing and in human society. When a network is used to show connections from points to points without regard to direction, it involves the use of chains for linear connections along a sequence of points, starting from a first point and ending with a last point. It uses circuits to represent closed chains that return to their starting point. When direction is important, arrows are used to represent links and the chains are referred as paths and circuits as cycles. Detailed examples and applications of networks in decision making are abundantly illustrated in The Encyclicon [10] and The Encyclicon, Volume 2 [11].

Networks also deal with control structures. What is a control network? We said before about hierarchies that it is a structure used to study a particular kind of influence such as economic influence, social influence and political influence. The analysis is made by such a decomposition of influences in separate structures whose results are then appropriately combined into an overall result.

As with hierarchies, although there are many types of networks, generally a real-world problem cannot be represented by a single network, only several. There are two typical structures for networks used to represent decisions: a single network with both inner and outer dependence or multiple networks of benefits, opportunities, costs and risks (BOCR).

1) A Single Network

An example of a network in decision making is a model to estimate market-share of 3 competitors in the hamburger industry – that is to determine their relative dollar income [12]. There are eight clusters: direct competitors, indirect competitors, customer group, marketing mix, contemporary issues, public health, traits, and time horizon, fully connected in a single network with both inner (indicated by loops) and outer dependence as depicted in Figure 3.

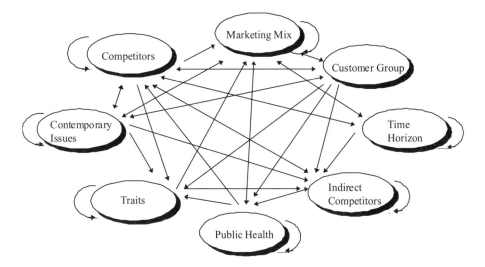

Figure 3 A Single Network to Estimate Relative Market Share Problem in the Hamburger Industry

2) BOCR Decision Framework with Many Sub-Networks

In a more complex problem, one can examine the elements and their influences from three points of view: benefits, opportunities, costs, and risks (BOCR). Here is an example [13]. There has been an ongoing debate in the US since the Report of the National Energy Policy Development Group was submitted for consideration by the government on May 16, 2001. The statements and recommendations of the report have been so controversial that Senate and House committee meetings have been held along with requests that the Vice President come before Congress to explain closed door discussions.

The Vice President's report, as well as many other papers, studies, and presentations, state that the US and the world will soon be in an energy crisis. The energy consumption of the US is currently and will continue to outpace domestic energy production significantly as forecasted for the next 20 years. This effect has already been felt at the gasoline pump, in heating and cooling bills, and in jobs lost due to companies outsourcing to foreign manufacturers as a result of rising domestic fuel costs.

The importance of energy in our society is undeniable. As long as humanity is driven to materialistic consumption and develops technologies that are powered by and depend on energy, something must be done to counteract the energy crisis. Also, with national security always a concern due to the War on Terror, there is an increasing need to determine what direction the US should take with regard to its energy policy. This model attempts to determine which path could effectively circumvent the looming energy crisis.

The US has alternatives ranging from a comparative advantage approach to complete energy independence:

- *Status quo approach.* Fossil fuel imports have reached an all-time high of 60%. The status quo keeps the 60/40 import-to-domestic ratio.
- *Energy independence emphasis.* This is the direct reciprocal of the status quo approach. The US would have a 40/60 ratio of imports to domestic fuel.
- *Complete energy independence.* The US would rely 100% on domestic fuel sources. This is one risky extreme that could lead to isolationism in the world fuel market.
- *Comparative advantage approach.* This is the opposite approach of complete independence. The US would only use domestic sources of fuel if economical, but would mainly rely on the outside market.

The decision networks for this problem were very complex. The following figures show each BOCR network's control criteria and clusters.

Benefits

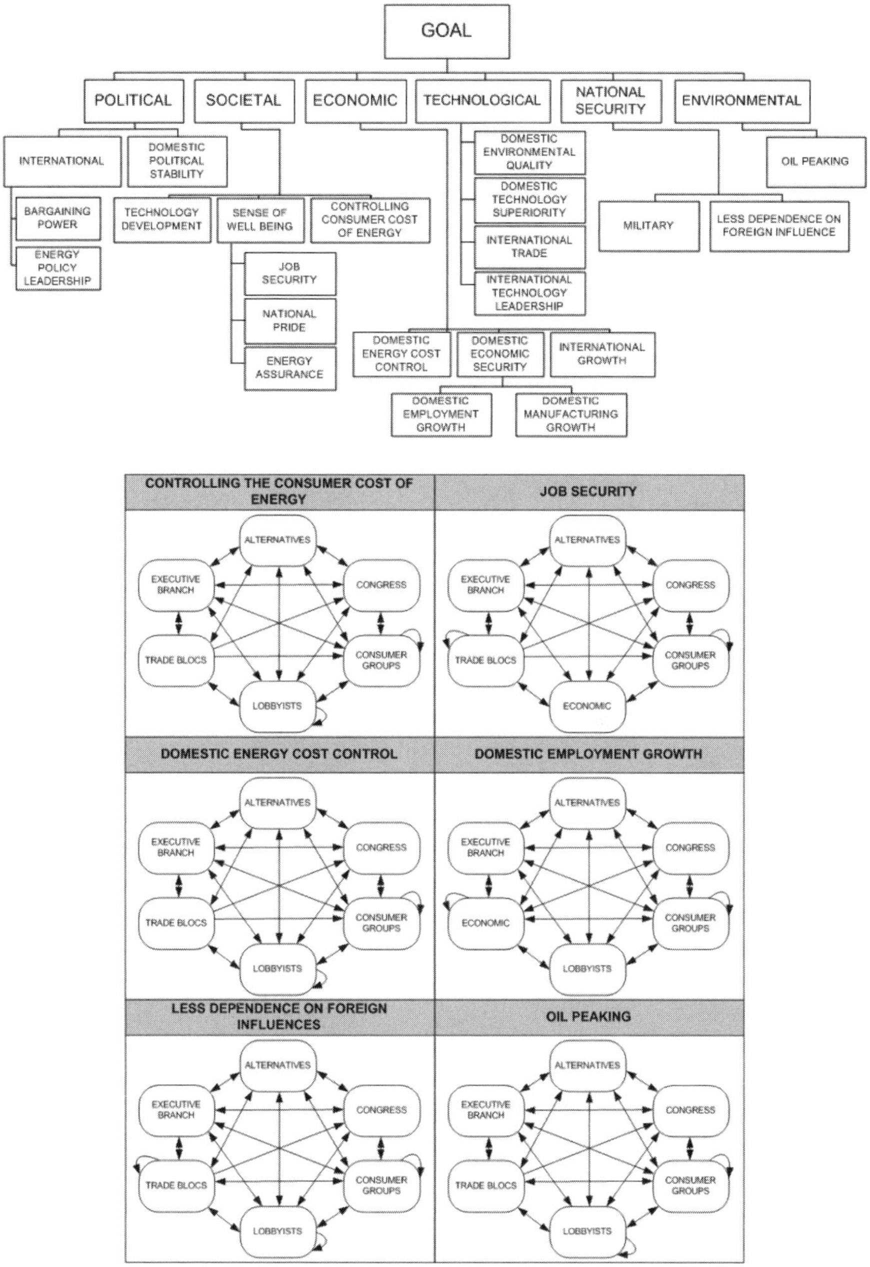

Figure 4 Control Criteria and Decision Network for Benefits

Opportunities

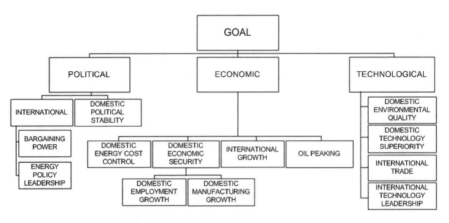

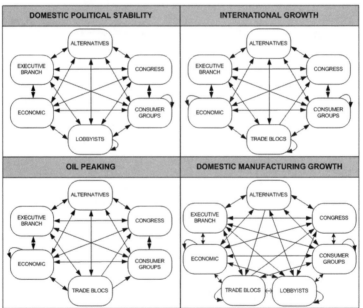

Figure 5 Control Criteria and Decision Network for Opportunities

Costs

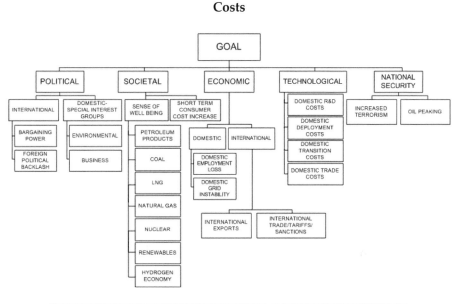

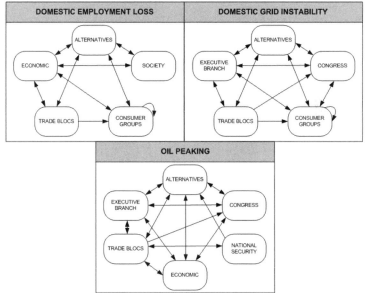

Figure 6 Control Criteria and Decision Network for Costs

Risks

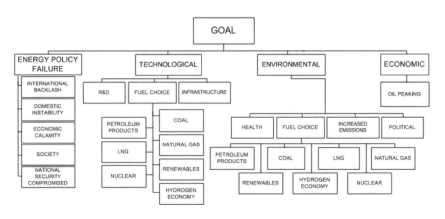

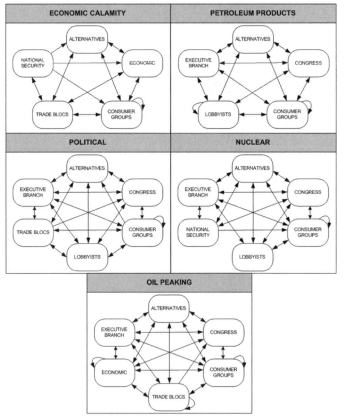

Figure 7 Control Criteria and Decision Network for Risks

How to Structure a Problem

Hierarchic and network structures are forms that help us to think about what a problem is, and offer conceptual guides to solve that problem. A hierarchy or a network is our logical conceptualization of a problem that pares it down to its essentials. In general, if the elements and their connections are easily located in levels of dominance with connections that transmit influence downwards, a hierarchic structure fits the decision best. On the other hand, if the elements and their connections are complicated and can only be grouped in clusters that do not fit well in defined levels, a network structure is more appropriate. There is no better way to determine which to use than the ability to abbreviate and summarize how influences work and reach the level of alternatives without undue need to represent interdependence among the elements in the levels or feedback from lower to upper levels. However, other than an urgent need to obtain a quick answer, it is risky to use a hierarchy in a complex decision because many influences can be lost by not representing them with the needed connections. It is safe to say that the more important and complex a decision is, the more likely that it needs a network for its structure in the BOCR form.

How to structure a problem is an essential concern of problem solving. If the problem can be structured in a systematic way, what one has to do with it would be much like a computational process. No matter how complex the structure may be, the computational process tends to be algorithmic and so that it can be executed on a computer and does not need much human effort. In this situation the problem has become a well-defined structured problem.

But often it is more difficult to deal with how to structure the problem since it involves a considerably greater degree of abstraction than does solving that problem. A substantial amount of human thinking and imagination are needed to create a structure for a complex problem. These two processes or human capabilities are the most valuable human qualities that cannot be replaced by computers. They are related to our goals of enhancing our survival.

In the real world, we always face many problems to be solved. Most existing techniques show us what to solve but not always how to solve. However, we need a way of inventive ideation [14] to structure of a problem. An approach that relies not on psychology but on technology, the inventive problem solving method known widely by the name of TRIZ (Theory of Solving Inventive Problems) is widely taught and widely used to help us explore for solutions in fields other than our own. It provides some guidelines for overcoming our "psychological inertia".

In general, a problem begins with some dissatisfaction with an ongoing situation, or as G.S. Altshuller [15], the creator of TRIZ put it, a problem is a contradiction in the mind. We think of taking action to rid ourselves of the situation. To do that, we identify the relevant elements in the environment and organize them by using our understanding and our memory of past situations of similar problems; if we are successful a pattern emerges that describes our problem. This type of thinking is a complex mental process involving cognition, pattern matching, associative memory and knowledge, judgment, comparisons, and imagination. To find a good structure and to identify a new alternative which is a possible way to act, imagination, one of our most treasured attributes, can be extremely helpful. We really do not know if a good structure will emerge and what it might be like. It could pop out with a rough structure that can be revised to better fit our problem. We generally use a combination of our habitual ways of perceiving, thinking, responding, and acting, together with their formation, dynamics, and basis in experience and knowledge, or what is called our habitual domain [16]. If our habitual domain sufficiently rich, a creative structure for a problem might be generated.

There are two kinds of problem people face: those with generally known solutions and those with unknown solutions. Those with known solutions can usually be solved using information found in books, technical journals, or with the help of experts in the field. Such solutions follow the general pattern of problem solving, and the steps followed are analogous to those we use to solve other problems.

On the other hand, if a problem is one with no known solution, it can be considered to be an inventive problem and such problems often contain contradictory requirements. Solving it may be helped by notions from the field of psychology where the links between the brain and insight and innovation are studied. Methods such as brainstorming and trial-and-error are commonly used.

Altshuller was led to seek ways to standardize the methods of problem solving. At a minimum, he felt that such a method should satisfy the following conditions:

1. be a systematic, step-by-step procedure
2. be a guide through a broad solution space directed toward an ideal solution
3. be repeatable and reliable and not dependent on psychological tools

4. be able to access the body of inventive knowledge
5. be able to add to the body of inventive knowledge
6. be familiar enough to inventors that they could follow its general approach to problem solving.

Another important concept of TRIZ is that a successful system is captured through idealization. Idealization means that the system has maximum benefits and minimum costs and negative effects, and the outcome should be an ideal final result (IFR). The characteristics of an IFR are four: (i) it reduces the disadvantages of the original system; (ii) it preserves the advantages of the original system; (iii) it does not make the new system more complicated; and (iv) it does not introduce any drawbacks in the new system. When we plan for an IFR, we check for the above four characteristics and think of problem solving as a process of innovation.

Although TRIZ was originally used for product innovation, it can also be helpful in structuring a problem. The essential part of TRIZ is to overcome our psychological inertia and expand the solution space so that some creative ideas can be generated. Then we can follow the step-by-step procedure proposed by Altshuller to develop the structure of the problem.

Step by Step Structuring Process

Step 1. *Identify the Problem.*

It begins with a contradiction or dissatisfaction in our mind. It might need a group meeting or questionnaires to capture the problem in a quantitative and qualitative way. This is the step where the customer's needs and wants are recorded and the elements are identified.

Step 2. *Formulate the Problem: the Prism of TRIZ*

Restate the problem in terms of its contradictions and dissonances. Identify the problems that could occur, their consequences, and the ways in which they can occur. What, when and how the actions are selected? What are the advantages and disadvantages of the actions? This step attempts to clarify the problem and the relations among all the elements.

Step 3. *Search for Previous Successfully Solved Problem*

Here we search for some successful cases to study. Compare their structures and consider the similarities and dissimilarities with our problem.

Step 4. *Look for Analogous Solutions and Adapt Them to Generate Our Solution*

Try to extend previous analogous structures being aware of their advantages and disadvantages to remove any contradictions. Some trade-offs might need to be made so that an inventive structure can be established.

There are 40 inventive principles that can help us think better when we structure a problem as: segmentation, extraction, asymmetry, combining, universality, nesting, counterweight, inversion, spheroidality, dynamicity, partial or overdone action, moving to a new dimension, periodic action, continuity of a useful action, rushing through, converting harm into benefit, feedback, mediator, self-service, copying, homogeneity, phase transformation and so on [17]. For instance, the principle of the segmentation means dividing an object into independent parts, making an object sectional, and increasing the degree of an object's segmentation so that a problem can be broken down.

In the following paragraphs, a procedure is proposed first for hierarchic structures and then for network structures and the latter is then illustrated with an example.

Structuring Hierarchies

The process of structuring a system hierarchically is as follows:

(1) Define the goal or focus of the decision problem at the top level.

The purpose or focus will be the desired state or goal of the problem to be solved in the future. For instance, it could be a vision or a mission statement of an organization. It could also be the target value of a performance measure when the problem is solved.

(2) Break down the purpose into some supportive elements in the first level below the goal.

There are various ways to make the breakdown. The elements on the first level should be comparable and homogeneous or close in their possession of a common attribute.

The breakdown can be made from the elements in the first level into their sub-elements. For instance, a system can be broken down physically into sub-systems, units, sub-units, components, etc. On the other hand, there might be many combinations or choices in the physical integration of a system. This is the most straightforward way. When we attempt to manage the functions of a system, we characterize its performance according to its purpose. Then we break the purpose down into criteria or figures of merits, sub-criteria, etc.

It is also possible to break down purpose according to long-term planning and short-term planning time horizons. Another way is to break purpose down in terms of strategic planning, tactical planning, and operational planning in an organization.

Sometimes decomposition runs from actions to consequences. There are some policies to support the purpose, and each policy has a set of possible actions and each action has its consequences. Another way is to think of the entire hierarchic decomposition in terms of causes and effects. The relations of cause-effect can form a hierarchy, similar to a fish bone diagram in quality management.

(3) Insert actors into a suitable level.

The function of the actors is similar to a filter that screens out some influences at the upper levels. It might be more than one level of actors depending on the requirements.

(4) Establish the bottom level for choice.

The bottom level of the hierarchy could be alternatives, actions, consequences, scenarios, or policies to be chosen. These elements or actions are assumed to solve the problem if they are implemented. Hence, a more formal hierarchy can be established.

(5) Examine the hierarchic levels forward and backward.

Conceptually, the elements at the high levels can be decomposed into many elements at the lower levels, and the lower levels should support the upper levels. One usually needs to check and revise the elements, and even the levels, backward and forward iteratively to ensure the consistency of the structure. A formal hierarchy is thus determined. It is worth noting that Saaty and Kearns [18] provide 13 points to aid in structuring a hierarchy. They are more practical suggestion for constructing a hierarchy.

Structuring Networks

Because of the complex interrelations involved, it may not be easy to classify the elements by levels as in a hierarchy because of the need for feedback and for inner dependence loops and thus a network representation is more appropriate, where there is dependence of what would be upper level elements on lower level ones if structured as a hierarchy.

The process of structuring a system as a network is as follows:

(1) Categorize the elements into suitable clusters.

The elements related to a decision include goal, criteria, influence, actors, actions, and so on. Besides influence, all the rest can be grouped into a cluster based on the similar characteristics, i.e. homogenous elements are sorted. Some guidelines for breaking down the levels for a hierarchy, in Step 2 of previous section, could be helpful to categorizing the clusters in a network.

(2) Determine the influences.

The influences are different kinds of interactions among elements or clusters of elements. It can happen within a cluster, inner dependence, or between two clusters, outer dependence. One needs to check the influences carefully to ensure that the connections of that represent interactions are correctly made along with their direction.

Note that there can several networks to represent the different kinds of influence, social influence, political influence, economic influence and these are repeated in appropriate fashion for the four BOCR. The different influence criteria are called control criteria because they individually determine the way we provide judgments for that type of influence and follow it by synthesizing all the control type of influences [12].

(3) Examine the network by clusters forward and backward.

There is no clear top-down or bottom-up relations in a network. Examination of the nonlinear structure would depend on the scope of understanding of the problem by the analysts. Usually they need to sketch and revise the elements within each cluster and the relations among the clusters to make sure of the completeness and consistency of the structure.

We believe that the diversity of examples collected in books is gradually turning the process of construction of a hierarchy or a network from art to science [19].

Validation of the Structures

The structure of a hierarchy or network is a way of representing a real-world problem by the observers. A decision is similar to a model in operations research. But establishing the structure is more of an art than a science, and certain characteristics make it difficult to validate the structure.

There are some possible ways to alleviate the difficulty of validation. Daellenbach [20] addresses how to perform ongoing evaluations during the modeling process and also proposes three rules for testing validity. These rules deal with field studies so his suggestions indirectly handle validation. In addition, a valid result or outcome is not necessarily equal to a good decision. Validation might not be possible in a decision-making process, but it is needed to avoid the stigma of garbage-in garbage-out. Forecasting outcomes whose occurrence can be documented statistically is one way to increase confidence decision models. Here two guidelines to check the structure that are possibly related to validation.

(1) Is the structure logical?

This consideration is focused on the systematic representation of the influences involved so that the flow of influence among the elements systematically illustrated. The concepts of forward and backward planning might help us sharpen our logical thinking. In addition, reviewing: who, why, what, when, where, and how, might provide some clues toward planning a logical structure.

(2) Is the structure complete?

Because a structure is an abstraction of the problem, it is essential to include the most important elements and their relations in that structure to ensure completeness. It is common to investigate structures from economic, social, political, ethical and environmental points of view to ensure their completeness, but there may be other factors to consider in different situations. The point is to keep an open inquiring mind that is able to include these factors as necessary.

No matter how a structure is validated, group participation with knowledgeable people is a good way to ensure its logicality and completeness.

An Example that Leads to a Structure - US Options for Iraq's Future (as of September 11, 2007)

After the US and its allies entered Iraq on March 20, 2003, the nation which was strongly controlled by the dictator Saddam Hussein was released from his hold. Because there was no good plan to transit from dictatorship to democracy the social order collapsed and political forces disintegrated soon after the war. Although Iraq now has a form of a democratic government, that government cannot control the violence that prevails among the different factions scattered throughout the country. Gun fighting, car explosions, improvised explosive devices (IED's) have been happening everyday killing about 100 American each month (3,773 American casualties, 4072 coalition casualties as of September 10, 2007, and 27,767 Americans troops wounded in action) and 100 Iraqis every day. The cost has been enormous, so far adding up to $400 billion. Currently the US has nearly 170,000 troops deployed in Iraq, but the chaos has not abated very much. Some Americans are concerned that the situation has worsened and is beginning to look like another Vietnam. Protests are becoming widespread and more frequent in the United States.

Iraq, the home of the world's first known civilization, now has a population of 26,783,383 (40th largest country in the world). It is irrigated by two major rivers, the Euphrates and Tigris, which provide much of the agricultural capability of that nation, better than any other country in the Middle East. In addition, Iraq has an estimated 112 billion barrels of proven oil, ranking second in the world behind Saudi Arabia in the amount of oil reserves. Moreover, the US Department of Energy estimates that up to 90% of the country remains unexplored for oil. The oil attracts the interest of many countries, especially since we have learned recently with fair certainty that the current known reserves of oil will be depleted in the world around 2050. After the removal of Saddam Hussein in 2003, Iraq has had many national problems with developing a political balance, a working economy and infrastructure, and in how to use its huge reserves of oil.

The Iraq situation seems unstable and nobody knows when or if peace will be restored (the goal). Currently a new constitution has been voted in by 78% of the voters, but the three communities of Shiites, Sunnis and Kurds are separate factions that are not in agreement. In addition, the reconstruction of Iraq has been difficult due to the damage to the infrastructure brought about by the present fighting and some even dating as far back as the Iran-Iraq war. Iraq has large foreign debt payments to make.

Although Iraq is important to the US, the US is facing much trouble there as described above (Step 1). Since we are dissatisfied with the current situation, we shall try to overcome the dissatisfaction by analyzing the problem (Step 2). We also need to search for some successfully solved similar problems in history to understand it better (Step 3). We may compare the

Iraq situation with these cases (the Gulf War, Bosnia, Vietnam, the Korean War, World War II) to find similarities and dissimilarities.

After identifying all the elements, we simplify the situation and think about how to structure it. Since these elements and their relations are rather complex and interconnected, a network representation would be suitable. In the network there will be clusters of elements grouped by their characteristics. Here we set up seven clusters. Three are clusters for the nations: US, Iraq, and other influential nations with elements that are possible actions they can take, and four are clusters of social, political, economic, and military considerations.

Since our goal is to achieve peace in Iraq, we will examine the possible solutions, and their interactions with the elements in the other clusters. For the US cluster, there are four possible actions: withdraw all troops, withdraw to bases outside urban areas, increase troops until the country is brought fully under control, and pursue the status quo. For the Iraq cluster, Iraq might take actions concentrated on interior or on foreign affairs. The third cluster is the other influential nations in the world, that are stakeholders outside the US and Iraq: the Arabs, Iran, European Union, Russia, and China have some interests in Iraq, and can take actions to help with the construction of Iraq, cooperate with oil companies so Iraq can acquire a stable source of revenue, or continue with the status quo. The remaining four clusters are different considerations about the social, political, economic, and military aspects of the problem that may be relevant for the different parties. The social factors will include social value, health care, education, jobs, and safety. The economic factors consist of infrastructure establishment, oil drilling and production, agricultural productivity, and industrial recovery. Military factors include costs for the US, the casualties for the US, costs for Iraq, casualties for Iraq, and diminished violence. Political factors consist of internal relations among members of the coalition government, Iraq's relations with its neighbors, and Iraq-US relations.

The most creative aspect is coming up with the alternatives of the decision (Step 4). To create the influence links we examine the elements within and among the clusters. We find that in this complex situation all the elements in the clusters are related. There is inner dependence within all seven of the clusters. We further examine the relations among the cluster and make the outer dependence links. Only the cluster of social factors has no relations with the cluster of other nations. The seven clusters and their interactions are shown in Figure 8. After we have structured the problem, we carry out the analysis by entering pairwise comparison judgments and deriving priorities throughout the structure. We then synthesize or combine all the priorities to determine the best option for the US to follow.

Our Version of Human Values and Activities [21]

To develop our own general list of human values and activities we had to examine at length the literature of the philosophy of science, among which The Journal of Value Inquiry [22] is perhaps the most relevant. We were directed to three lists we found useful to draw upon for our work. The lists are the product of thinking in law, philosophy and anthropology. The first, done by a lawyer, is a List of Human Capabilities, included in the works of the distinguished professor of philosophy and teacher at the law school of the University of Chicago, Martha Nussbaum [23], about whom it is written that "she is America's foremost philosopher, a title retired since Ralph Waldo Emerson died in 1882". She has defended cases before the US Supreme Court based on the prestige of her innovation in human values.

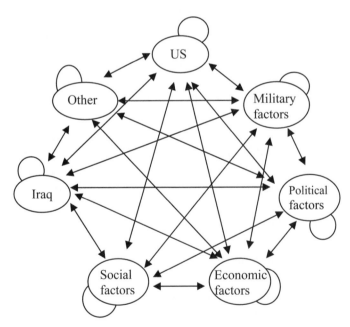

Figure 8 A Structure of Iraq's Problem

The second is a comprehensive list of values by K. Baier and N. Rescher [24] (also mentioned in Chapter 11), world-renowned philosophers of science (Rescher is also a mathematician trained at Princeton), that provides a collection of personal values (of character and personality) that an individual may prize in himself/herself and his/her associates, and also in what he/she prizes in his/her society, nation, culture, fellow men in general, and environment.

The third list, the eighty year old work, Outline of Cultural Materials (OCM) [25, 26], began in 1937 and revised in 2004, was created by many anthropologists, originally led by G.P. Murdoch at Yale. It is a manual which presents a system for categorizing cultural data regarding all aspects of human behavior. It is an ethnological and numerical classification system that provides subject indexing for human behavior, social life, customs, material products, and ecological settings. The Outline of Cultural Materials was developed in 1937 as a tool for a cross-cultural survey by the Institute of Human Relations at Yale University. It serves as a key to assembling and classifying basic information from samples of people around the world. This kind of classification system provides ways to group concepts under relatively broad topics. The outline successfully classifies material (meant to be used by those concerned with human behavior) in broad perspective according to seven basic criteria with 79 major divisions of cultural background information. They include: (1) patterned activity, (2) circumstance, (3) subject, (4) object, (5) means, (6) purpose, and (7) result. In the fifth edition [26] of the Outline as revised by experts at Yale University, the result was a new list of 81 categories with hundreds of subcategories updated to the present day.

Here we offer information on three lists that is our starting point. These lists were given as long lists of words, not tabulated and tightly organized. We have ordered, rearranged and added elements to these lists as we felt are necessary and we have ordered and arranged them for decision making purposes as shown in Tables 1 to 3. At first sight, the reader may find these lists overwhelming because they contain more than 1000 elements, but we guarantee that they give greater exposure to the scope of decision making. They are valuable to provide us with the perspective of people involved in a diversity of complex problems such politics and the environment so that our decision structures will be richer and more complete. Lists need a different way of thinking about how valuable they are. They must be read and re-read, examined, remembered and used often enough and extended when necessary so that the user's thinking grows to cope with today's changing world. To acquire this kind of familiarity, we urge the practitioner to keep them handy so they will be there when needed.

Table 1 The List of Basic Biological and Cultural Capabilities of a Human Being

Basic Capabilities	Explanation
Life	Being able to live a normal length life.
Bodily health	Adequate food and shelter.
Bodily integrity	Being able to move freely from place to place; to be secure against violent assault; having opportunities for sexual satisfaction and reproduction.
Senses, imagination, and thought	Being able to use the senses, to imagine, think and reason- to do these things in a "truly human" way; Being able to use imagination and thought in connection with experiencing and producing works and events. Being able to use one's mind in ways protected by guarantees of freedom of expression with respect to both political and artistic speech, and freedom of religious exercise. Being able to have pleasurable experiences and to avoid non-beneficial pain.
Emotions	Being able to love, grieve at their absence; in general, to love, to grieve, to experience longing, gratitude and justified anger, not blighted by fear and anxiety.
Practical reason	Being able to form a conception of the good and to engage in critical reflection about the planning of one's own life.
Affiliation	A. Being able to live with and toward others, to recognize and show concern for other human beings, to engage in various forms of social interaction; B. Having the social bases of self-respect and non-humiliation; being able to be treated as a dignified being whose worth is equal to that of others.
Other species	Being able to live with concern for and in relation to animals, plants, and the world of nature.
Play	Being able to laugh, to play, to enjoy recreational activities.
Control over one's environment	A. Political. Being able to participate effectively in political choices that govern one's life; having the right of political participation, protections of free speech and association. B. Material. Being able to hold property (both land and movable goods), not just formally but in terms of real opportunity; and having property rights on an equal basis with others.

Table 2 The Comprehensive List of Values that Individuals Bring to Society and Society Brings to the World

Values	Category	Subcategory
I. Self-oriented values	"Material" welfare	Health
		Economic security and well-being
		Personal security
	Self-respect	
	Self-reliance	
	Personal liberty	
	Self-advancement	

	Self-fulfillment	
	Skill and prowess	The intellectual virtues
		The physical virtues
		The virtues of the will
		Competence
		Inventiveness and innovativeness
		Initiative
		Being well-informed
		Faith
		Appreciation and appreciativeness
II. Group-oriented values	Respectability	
	Rectitude and personal morality	
	Reasonableness and rationality	
	The domestic virtues	
	The civic virtues	
	Conscientiousness	Devotion to family, duty
		Personal responsibility and accountability
		Devotion to principle (especially of one's religion—"the god-fearing man")
	Friendship and friendliness	Friendship proper
		Loyalty
		Friendliness, Kindliness, Helpfulness, Cooperativeness and Courteousness
		Fellow-feeling (compassion, sympathy, and "love of one's fellows"
		Gregariousness
		Receptivity
		Personal tolerance
		Patience
	Service	
	Generosity	
	Idealism	
	Recognition	
	Forthrightness	
	Fair play	
III. Society-oriented values	Social welfare	
	Equality	Tolerance
		"Fair play", Fairness
		Civil rights
	Justice	
	Liberty	
	Order	
	Opportunity	
	Charity	
	Progressivism	
	Pride in "our culture" and "our way of life"	
IV. Nation-oriented values	Patriotic virtues	National freedom and independence
		National prosperity and national achievement

		Patriotism and national pride
		Concern for the national welfare
		Loyalty (to country)
		Chauvinism
	Democracy	
	Public service	
	The "welfare of mankind"	Peace
		Material achievement and progress
		Cultural and intellectual achievement and progress
V. Mankind-oriented values	Humanitarianism and the "brotherhood of man"	
	Internationalism	
	Pride in the achievements of "the human community"	
	Reverence for life	
	Human dignity and the "worth of the individual"	
VI. Environment-oriented values	Aesthetic values (environmental beauty)	
	Novelty	

Table 3 The Cause-effect List

Cause -effect	Categories	Subcategories
Settling the environment	DEMOGRAPHY	Population, Composition of population, Birth statistics, Morbidity, Mortality, Internal migration, External migration, Population policy
	GEOGRAPHY	Location, Climate, Topography and geology, Soil, Mineral resources, Fauna, Flora, Post depositional processes
	HUMAN BIOLOGY	Anthropometry, Descriptive somatology, Genetics, Racial affinities, Ontogenetic data, Nutrition, Physiological data
	INDIVIDUATION AND MOBILITY	Personal names, Names of animals and things, Naming, Status, Role, Prestige, Talent mobility, Accumulation of wealth, Manipulative mobility, Downward mobility
	SOCIALIZATION	Techniques of inculcation, Weaning and food training, Cleanliness training, Sex training, Aggression training, Independence training, Transmission of cultural norms, Transmission of skills, Transmission of beliefs
	SOCIAL STRATIFICATION	Age stratification, Gender status, Ethnic stratification, Castes, Classes, Serfdom and peonage, Slavery
	SOCIAL CHALLENGES	Disasters, Disabilities, Alcoholism and drug addiction, Invalidism, Poverty, Dependency, Old age dependency, Delinquency
	PROPERTY	Property system, Property in movables, Real Property, Incorporeal property, Acquisition and relinquishment of property, Borrowing and lending, Renting and leasing, Inheritance, Administration
	SETTLEMENTS	Settlement patterns, Housing, Streets and traffic, Refuse disposal and sanitary facilities, Public utilities, Commercial facilities, Parks, Miscellaneous facilities,

		Urban and rural life
	TRAVEL AND TRANSPORTATION	Locomotion, Burden carrying, Weight moving, Travel , Travel services, Regulation of travel, Routes, Warehousing, Transportation
	LAND TRANSPORT	Highways and bridges, Animal transportation, Vehicles, Highway transportation, Auxiliary highway services, Railways, Rail transport, Terminal facilities, Highway and railway construction
	WATER AND AIR TRANSPORT	Boats, Water navigation, Waterways improvements, Port facilities, Water transport, Aircraft, Aviation, Airport facilities, Aair transport
	TOTAL CULTURE	Ethos, Functional and adaptational interpretations, Norms, Cultural participation, Cultural goals, Cultural identity and pride
	HISTORY AND CULTURE CHANGE	Comparative evidence, Prehistory, Traditional history, Historical reconstruction, History, Innovation, Acculturation and culture contact, Sociocultural trends, Economic planning and development, Cultural revitalization and ethnogenesis
People	REPRODUCTION	Menstruation, Conception, Pregnancy, Childbirth, Difficult and unusual births, Postnatal care, Abortion and infanticide, Illegitimacy
	SEX	Sexuality, Sexual stimulation, Sexual intercourse, General sex restrictions, Kinship regulation of sex, Premarital sex relations, Extramarital sex relations, Homosexuality, Miscellaneous sex behavior
	GENDER ROLES AND ISSUES	Male and female responsibilities, Participation in business, Order, Politics and the military
	KIN GROUPS	Rule of descent, Kindreds and ramages, Lineages, Sibs, Phratries, Moieties, Bilinear kin groups, Clans, Tribe and nation
	FAMILY	Residence, Household, Family relationships, Nuclear family, Polygamy, Extended families, Adoption
	MARRIAGE	Basis of marriage, Regulation of marriage, Mode of marriage, Arranging a marriage, Nuptials, Termination of marriage, Secondary marriage, Special unions and marriages, Celibacy
	KINSHIP	Kinship terminology, Kin relationships, Grandparents and grandchildren, Avuncular and nepotic relatives, Cousins, Parents-in-law and children-in-law, Siblings-in-law, Artificial kin relationships, Behavior toward nonrelatives
	INFANCY AND CHILDHOOD	Social placement, Ceremonial during infancy and childhood, Infant feeding, Infant care, Child care, Development and maturation, Childhood activities, Status of children
	ADOLESCENCE, ADULTHOOD, AND OLD AGE	Puberty and initiation, Status of adolescents, Adolescent activities, Majority, Adulthood, Senescence, Activities of the aged, Status and treatment of the aged
	HEALTH AND WELFARE	Philanthropic foundations, Medical research, Hospitals and clinics, Public health and sanitation, Social insurance, Public assistance, Private welfare agencies, Social work
	SICKNESS	Preventive medicine, Bodily injuries, Theory of disease, Sorcery, Magical and mental therapy,

		Psychotherapists, Medical therapy, Medical care, Medical personnel
	DEATH	Life and death, Suicide, Dying, Burial practices, Mourning, Special mortuary practices, Mortuary specialists, Social readjustments to death, Cult of the dead
Interaction of people	LANGUAGE	Speech, Vocabulary, Grammar, Phonology, Sociolinguistics, Semantics, Linguistic identification, Special languages
	COMMUNICATION	Gestures and signs, Transmission of messages, Dissemination of news and information, Press, Mail, Telephone and telegraph, Radio and television, Public opinion, Proxemics, Internet communications
	INTERPERSONAL RELATIONS	Social relationships and groups, Friendships, Cliques, Visiting and hospitality, Sodalities, Etiquette, Ethics, In-group antagonism, Brawls, Riots and banditry
	BEHAVIOR PROCESSES AND PERSONALITY	Sensation and perception, Drives and emotions, Modification of behavior, Adjustment processes, Personality development, Social personality, Personality traits, Personality disorders, Life history materials
Organizing people	COMMUNITY	Community structure, Community heads, Councils, Local officials, Police, Social control, Informal ingroup justice, Inter-community relations, Inter-ethnic relations
	TERRITORIAL ORGANIZATION	Territorial hierarchy, Towns, Cities, Districts, Provinces, Dependencies
	STATE	Citizenship, Constitution, Chief executive, Executive household, Cabinet, Parliament, Administrative agencies, International relations
	GOVERNMENT ACTIVITIES	Taxation and public income, Public finance, Public works, Research and development, Government enterprises, Government regulation, Public welfare, Public education, Miscellaneous government activities
	ARMED FORCES	Military organization, Recruitment and training, Discipline and morale, Ground combat forces, Supply and commissariat, Navy, Air force, Auxiliary corps
	ECCLESIASTICAL ORGANIZATION	Magicians and diviners, Prophets and ascetics, Priesthood, Congregations, Religious denominations, Organized ceremonial, Missions, Religious intolerance
	BUSINESS AND INDUSTRIAL ORGANIZATION	Ownership and control of capital, Individual enterprise, Corporate organization, Cooperative organization, State enterprise, Mutual aid, Competition
Occupation with food and production	FOOD QUEST	Annual cycle, Collecting, Fowling, Hunting and trapping, Marine hunting, Fishing, Fishing gear, Marine industries
	AGRICULTURE	Tillage, Agricultural science, Cereal agriculture, Vegetable production, Arboriculture, Forage crops, Floriculture, Textile agriculture, Special crops
	ANIMAL HUSBANDRY	Domesticated animals, Applied animal science, Pastoral activities, Dairying, Poultry raising, Wool production, Animal by-products
	FOOD PROCESSING	Preservation and storage of food, Food preparation, Meat packing industry, Refrigeration industry,

		Canning industry, Cereal industry, Confectionery industries, Miscellaneous food processing and packing industries
	FOOD CONSUMPTION	Gratification and control of hunger, Diet, Condiments, Eating, Food service industries, Cannibalism
	DRINK AND DRUGS	Water and thirst, Nonalcoholic beverages, Alcoholic beverage's, Beverage industries, Drinking establishments, Recreational and non-therapeutic drugs, Tobacco industry, Pharmaceuticals
	ENERGY AND POWER	Power development, Fire, Light, Heat, Thermal power, Water power, Electric power, Atomic power, Miscellaneous power production
	MACHINES	Mechanics, Industrial machinery, Electrical machines and appliances, Household machines and appliances, weighing, measuring, and recording machines, Weigh-moving machinery, Agricultural machinery, Computer technology
	TOOLS AND APPLIANCES	Weapons, General tools, Special tools, Miscellaneous hardware, Utensils, Appliances, Apparatus
	BUILDING AND CONSTRUCTION	Construction, Earth moving, Masonry, Structural steel work, Carpentry, Plumbing, Electrical installation, Miscellaneous building trades, Building supplies industries
	EQUIPMENT AND MAINTENANCE OF BUILDINGS	Grounds, Furniture, Interior decoration and arrangement, Heating and lighting equipment, Miscellaneous building equipment, Housekeeping, Domestic service, Maintenance of nondomestic buildings
	STRUCTURES	Architecture dwellings, Outbuildings, Public structures, Recreational structures, Religious and educational structures, Business structures, Industrial structures, Miscellaneous structures
	CHEMICAL INDUSTRIES	Chemical engineering, Petroleum and coal products industries, Rubber industries, Synthetics industries, Industrial chemicals, Paint and dye manufacture, Fertilizer industry, Soap and allied products, Manufacture of explosives
	CAPITAL GOODS INDUSTRIES	Hardware manufacture, Machine industries, Electrical supplies industry, Manufacture of heating and lighting appliances, Manufacture of optical and photographic equipment, Shipbuilding, Railway equipment industry, Manufacture of vehicles, Aircraft industry
	EXPLOITATIVE CHALLENGES	Land use, Water supply, Lumbering forest products, Oil and gas wells, Mining and quarrying, Special deposits, Environmental quality
	FINANCE	Accounting, Credit, Banking, Saving and investment, Speculation, Insurance, Foreign exchange, Business cycles
	EXCHANGE	Gift giving, Buying and selling , Production and supply, Income and demand, Price and value, Medium of exchange, Exchange transactions, Domestic trade, Foreign trade
	MARKETING	Mercantile business, Wholesale marketing, Retail marketing, Retail businesses, Service industries, Sales promotion, Advertising
	MILITARY	Military engineering, Military installations, Ordnance,

		TECHNOLOGY	Uniform and accouterment, Military vehicles, Naval vessels, Military aircraft, Special military equipment, Munitions industries
Sophistication		EDUCATION	Educational system, Elementary education, Liberal arts education, Vocational education, Teachers, Educational theory and methods, Students
		SCIENCES AND HUMANITIES	Logic, Philosophy, Scientific method, Humanistic studies, Science, Applied science
		TEXTS	Texts in the speaker's language, Texts translated into English, Interlinear translations
		NUMBERS AND MEASURES	Numerology, Numeration, Mathematics, Weights and measures, Ordering of time
		RECORDS	Mnemonic devices, Writing, Printing, Publishing, Photography, Sound records, Archives, Writing and printing supplies
		RESEARCH METHODS	Theoretical orientation in research and its results, Practical preparations in conducting fieldwork, Observational role in research, Interviewing in research, Tests and schedules administered in the field, Recording and collecting in the field, Historical and archival research, Organization and analysis of results of research, Archaeological survey methods, Archaeological excavation methods, Dating methods in archaeology, Laboratory analysis of materials other than dating methods in archaeology, Comparative data
		INFORMATION SOURCES	Citations of documents in the Human Relations Area Files (HRAF) collection, Additional bibliography, Information sources listed in other works, Reviews and critiques, Informants, Complete texts of HRAF documents, Field data, Fiction, Artifact and archive collections
		ORIENTATION	Identification, Maps, Place names, Glossary, Cultural summary, Coded data, Diagnostic material attributes
		ARCHAEOLOGICAL MEASURES, TECHNIQUES, AND ANALYSES	Chronologies and culture sequences, Cultural stratigraphy, Functional specialization areas, Typologies and classifications, Archaeological inventories
		IDEAS ABOUT NATURE AND PEOPLE	Ethnometeorology, Ethnophysics, Ethnogeography, Ethnobotany, Ethnozoology, Ethnoanatomy, Ethnophysiology, Ethnopsychology, Ethnosociology
		RELIGIOUS BELIEFS	General character of religion, Cosmology, Mythology, Animism, Eschatology, Spirits and gods, Luck and chance, Sacred objects and places, Theological systems
		RELIGIOUS PRACTICES	Religious experience, Prayers and sacrifices, Purification and atonement, Avoidance and taboo, Asceticism, Ecstatic religious practices, Revelation and divination, Ritual, Magic
Order and control		JUSTICE	Litigation, Judicial authority, Legal and judicial personnel, Initiation of judicial proceedings, Trial procedure, Execution of justice, Prisons and jails, Special courts
		LAW	Legal norms, Liability, Wrongs, Crime, Contracts, Agency, Organized crime
		OFFENSES AND	Sanctions, Offenses against life, Offenses against the

	SANCTIONS	person, Sex and marital offenses, Property offenses, Nonfulfillment of obligations, Offenses against the State, Religious offenses, Social offenses
	POLITICAL BEHAVIOR	Exploitation, Political intrigue, Public service, Pressure politics, Political parties, Elections, Political machines, Political movements, Revolution
	WAR	Instigation of war, Wartime adjustments, Strategy, Logistics, Tactics, Warfare, Aftermath of combat, Peacemaking, War veterans
Beauty, leisure and entertainment	ARTS	* Decorative art, * Representative art, Music, Musical instruments, Dance, Drama, Oratory, * Literature, * Literary texts, Verbal arts, Visual arts
	ADORNMENT	Ornament, Toilet, Manufacture of toilet accessories, Mutilation, Beauty specialists, Jewelry manufacture
	RECREATION	Conversation, Humor, Hobbies, Games, Gambling, Athletic sports, Rest days and holidays, Vacations, Recreational facilities
	COMMERCIALIZED ENTERTAINMENT	Spectacles, Commercialized sports, Exhibitions, Public lectures, Musical and theatrical productions, Motion picture industry, Night clubs and cabarets, Illegal entertainment, Art and recreational supplies industries

From what we know, this is an ambitious ground breaking work, first of its kind to cover the many factors that go into making decisions. We have no illusion that this work is anything but a start. There is much more work to be done on the subject of structures in decision making and what should go into them. It was not as easy to do as we thought it would be when we started because even though we have written extensively on the subject in books that are solely concerned with structures, it is an intractable undertaking to cope with all of human decision making in one chapter.

Conclusions

We structure a problem in order to understand it, solve it. It is an aid to systematize our thought processes. A geometry is necessary for us to represent our structure, a new kind of subjective geometry: a graph of a hierarchy or a network. Such a representation makes it easier for us to visualize and understand the relevant issues and their interactions and enables us to solve the problem with greater efficiency, relevance and confidence.

A hierarchic structure with its linear form helps us to recognize the essence of the world in terms of goals and purposes, particularly our own. When the interactions among the elements are complicated, a network with its nonlinear structure allows us to represent feedback and dependence relations. However, because both are an abstract representation of the real world, the best line of demarcation between a hierarchy and a network is the presence of feedback among and within clusters. The choice depends on the interactions and on our ability to simplify yet still include all the important elements and their relations. It seems that to be safe we should always be prepared to structure our problems as networks. There is a common saying that everything in the world affects everything else but to varying degrees.

We humans can transfer our knowledge from generation to generation through teaching or by recording our ideas in a book or using modern methods. This is a unique and valuable characteristic that distinguishes us from other animals since we can learn fast through such channels. The structures we develop in decision making can be used to transmit knowledge and understanding as well and can be adapted as conditions change. By becoming familiar with hierarchic and network structures we become more expert at creating decision structures [27].

References

1. Saaty, T.L. and H-S Shih (2009), Structures in Decision Making: On the Subjective Geometry of Hierarchies and Networks, *European Journal of Operational Research*

2. Garuti, C. and I. Spencer (2007), Parallels Between the Analytic Hierarchy and Network Processes (AHP/ANP) and Fractal Geometry, *Mathematical and Computer Modelling*, 46, pp. 926-934

3. Kenning, P. and H. Plassmann (2005), NeuroEconomics: An overview from an economic perspective, *Brain Research Bulletin*, 67, pp. 343-354

4. Maslow, A. H. (1943), A Theory of Human Motivation, *Psychological Review*, 50, pp. 370-396

5. Osborn, A.F. (1963), *Applied Imagination: Principles and Procedures of Creative Problem Solving*, Charles Scribner's Sons, New York

6. Saaty, T.L. (2004), Automatic decision-making: neural firing and response. *Journal of Systems Science and Systems Engineering*, Tsinghua University, Beijing, 13, 4, pp. 385-404

7. Saaty, T.L. (1980), *The Analytic Hierarchy Process*, McGraw-Hill, New York

8. Saaty, T.L. (1990), *Decision Making for Leaders: The Analytic Hierarchy Process for Decision in a Complex World*, RWS Publications, Pittsburgh, PA

9. Saaty, T.L. and E.H. Forman (1993), *The Hierarchon - A Dictionary of Hierarchies*, RWS Publications, Pittsburgh, PA

10. Saaty, T.L. and M.S. Ozdemir (2005), *The Encyclicon* RWS Publications,

Pittsburgh, PA

11. Saaty, T.L. and B. Cillo (2008), *The Encyclicon, Volume 2*, RWS Publications, Pittsburgh, PA

12. Saaty, T.L. (2005), *Theory and Applications of the Analytic Network Process: Decision Making with Benefits, Opportunities, Costs, and Risks*, RWS Publications, Pittsburgh, PA

13. Figueroa, J.D. and D.R. Wood (2004), Energy Security of the United States of America, Decision Making Class Project, University of Pittsburgh, April

14. Ross, V.E. (2006), A Model of Inventive Ideation. *Thinking Skills and Creativity*, 1, pp. 120-129

15. Altshuller, G.S. (1974), *Innovation Algorithm*, Technical Innovation Center, Worcester, MA

16. Yu, P.L. (1991), Habitual domains, *Operations Research*, 39(6), pp. 869-876

17. Altshuller, G.S. (1984), *Creativity as an Exact Science*, New York, NY: Gordon & Breach

18. Saaty, T.L. and K.P. Kearns (1985), *Analytical Planning: the Organization of Systems*, Pergamon, Oxford, UK

19. Saaty, T.L. (2001), *Creative Thinking, Problem Solving and Decision Making*, RWS Publications, Pittsburgh, PA

20. Daellenbach, H.G. (1994), *Systems and Decision Making: A Management Science Approach*, Wiley, Chichester, West Sussex, England

21. Saaty, T.L. and N. Begicevic (2010), The Scope of Human Values and Human Activities in Decision Making, *Applied Soft Computing*

22. *The Journal of Value Inquiry*, www.springerlink.com/content/102951

23. Nussbaum, M. (1999), *Sex and Social Justice*, Oxford University Press, New York, pp. 41-42

24. Baier, K., N. Rescher (1969), *Values and the Future*, New York, The Free Press

25. Murdock, G.P., C.S. Ford, A.E. Hudson, R. Kennedy, L.W. Simmons and J.W.M. Whiting (1961), Outline of Cultural Materials, In *Behavior Science Outlines*, 4th revised edition, New Haven, Connecticut: Human Relations Area Files, Inc.

26. Murdock, G.P., C.S. Ford, A.E. Hudson, R. Kennedy, L.W. Simmons and J.W.M. Whiting (2004), Outline of Cultural Materials, 5th revised edition with modifications, New Haven, Connecticut: Human Relations Area Files, Inc., <http://www.yale.edu/hraf/Ocm_xml/newOcm.xml>

27. Ellspermann, S.J., G.W. Evans and M. Basadur (2007), The impact of training on the formulation of ill-structured problems, *Omega* 35, pp. 221-236

Part III

Synthesis in Hierarchies and in Single and Multiple Networks with Benefits, Opportunities, Costs and Risks

Chapter 4 deals with hierarchic structures with judgments and their syntheses. Chapter 5 deals with network structures and the mathematical foundations of priorities and their syntheses. Chapter 6 deals with the axiomatization of the theory of the AHP/ANP.

Chapter 4

Judgment and Proportion

This chapter deals with the following ideas:
- The major categories of scales used in measurement
- The process of pairwise comparisons – this involves the assumption of dependence among the alternatives
- The fundamental scale needed to represent judgments numerically and obtain valid answers when measurements are known
- How the fundamental scale is derived from stimulus-response phenomena
- The eigenvalue representation of pairwise comparisons
- The consistency and inconsistency of judgments
- The need for closeness or homogeneity of the elements compared and the need to compare no more than about seven elements to maintain a high level of consistency
- The stability of the eigenvector under small perturbations
- The measurement of inconsistency and the consistency index and compatibility indices
- How to improve consistency and be how much when knowledge and judgment allow it
- How rate and thus rank alternatives one at a time instead of comparing them in pairs – this involves the assumption of independence among the alternatives
- Synthesis in hierarchies by weighting and adding and thus using multilinear forms
- Resource allocation using the derived priorities
- Various comments by people in the past that one cannot measure feelings
- Benefits, opportunities, costs and risks, four necessary ways to rank the alternatives and how to combine them using strategic criteria – and example of what to do about Iran done in two hours by graduate students
- Failure of the so-called multiplicative method (raising the priorities of the alternatives to the power of the priorities of their criterion and

multiplying the results to obtain the priorities) to represent
judgments correctly

- Rank reversal and how it is always wrongly preserved by rating
  alternatives one at a time thus assuming independence from newly
  arriving alternatives

Introduction

There are four stages in the development of the AHP: 1) hierarchies, 2)
networks, 3) continuous framework and 4) operators framework. They all
have useful and important interpretations that I will discuss briefly, but will
spend more time on networks, of which hierarchies are a special case.

The guiding principles of science, the criteria employed in the
acceptance as well as rejection of constructs and complexes of constructs
called theories, have been loosely enumerated as: simplicity, extensibility,
multiple connections (that a theory does not have to have one overall part
but several that are connected to one another), logical fertility (the theory
should have logical and empirical consequences), stability of interpretation
(the basic assumptions of the theory cannot be altered to suit the occasion),
causality (everything that happens has a cause), and elegance (order and
beauty). They are not clear categories with rigidly defined boundaries but
organically related requirements imposed upon the choice of constructs.

The mathematics that underlies the AHP/ANP uses multilinear
forms and their generalization to the continuous case that is more general
than the mathematics of physics. This is what I want to talk about now. In
particular, physics uses a combination of ratio scales and is a
multidimensional method of measurement and thus the result, in order to be
dimensionally valid, needs to be a formula with a single expression. In one
term of the AHP's multilinear form, the sum of the powers of its variables is
usually different from one term to another term. The multilinear form is
homogeneous (the sum of the powers of the variables is the same for each of
its terms) only when the hierarchy is complete, whereby every element in a
level is evaluated in terms of all the elements in the level immediately above.
The AHP is a unidimensional method of measurement in which one uses
absolute numbers which are dimensionless to represent dominance. These
numbers can be added and multiplied making inhomogeneous multilinear
forms (with different sums of powers of the variables in each term)
meaningful. One way to relate the AHP results to physics results is to use the

marginal benefit to cost ratio that involves both positive and negative exponents.

We said earlier that the AHP focuses on dominance matrices and their corresponding measurement. This is one of the four ways to treat data, according to a classification by R.N. Shepard [1] Taxonomy of some principal types of data and of multidimensional methods for their analysis, in proximity, dominance, profile, and conjoint measurement. This classification goes beyond L.L. Thurston's [2] comparative judgment statistical approach by relaxing the assumption of normality on the parameters, e.g. equal variance, zero covariance, and restriction of the type of comparisons. *Proximity* data occur in: 1) a square matrix whose rows and columns correspond to the same n objects. Each entry contains a measure of similarity, substitutability, affinity, confusion, association, correlation or interaction between the two objects corresponding to that entry. The entry may for example be the frequency the two objects occur or frequency of their interaction; 2) a rectangular matrix whose rows and columns correspond to different objects and the entries indicate the proximity of an object in one set to an object in the other, like indicating the preference of an individual in one set to a stimulus in the other; 3) comparison of only certain pairs that have a common property but not the others. *Dominance* data occur in 1) a single square matrix whose rows and columns correspond to the same n objects. Each cell indicates the preference for or importance of one object over another; 2) several such square matrices each obtained for example from a different person. *Profile* data occur in: a rectangular matrix whose rows correspond to n objects and columns to m variables and entries are an assignment of a value to each object on a variable. *Conjoint* data occur in a rectangular matrix whose rows correspond to n levels of one variable and columns to m levels of another variable and the entries specify the pair of values of the variables for the corresponding pair of levels. A method is called metric or non-metric depending on whether its values are or are not invariant under monotone transformations. The data belong to an ordinal scale if they are invariant under monotone transformations.

The AHP positive matrix of reciprocal paired comparisons is known as a dominance matrix. We need concepts from the arcane and less known area of mathematics for this known as order topology in which one uses order and transitivity rather than metric closeness to determine the merits of a process designed to extract rank out of numerical data.

Scales of Measurement

A scale is a set of numbers, a set of objects and an assignment of the objects to the numbers. A scale also has a more abstract meaning that only refers to the nature of the numbers used and not to the objects or to how the numbers are assigned to the objects. The class of transformations or ways to create the numbers we are willing to allow on a particular measurement defines what is called the scale of measurement for that measurement operation.

Nominal Scale: invariant under one to one correspondence where, for example, a name or telephone number is assigned to objects to help identify them.

Ordinal Scale: invariant under monotone transformations, where things are ordered by number but the magnitudes of the numbers only serve to designate order, increasing or decreasing; for example, assigning two numbers 1 and 2, to two people to indicate that one is taller than the other, without including any information about their actual heights. The smaller number may be assigned to the taller person and vice versa. Note that one cannot add ordinal numbers and get a meaningful outcome because their magnitude only indicates order but not cardinal (how much and how many) magnitude. There are scales used in science that satisfy conditions of which monotonicity is a special case. They are known as *cardinal* scales which we now introduce.

Interval Scale: invariant under a positive linear transformation; for example, the linear transformation $F = (9/5) C + 32$ for converting a Celsius to a Fahrenheit temperature reading. Note that one cannot add two readings x_1 and x_2 on an interval scale because the transformed numbers don't belong to the same scale. We have $y_1+y_2=(ax_1+b)+(ax_2+b)=a(x_1+x_2)+2b$ which is of the form $ax+2b$ and not of the form $ax+b$. However, one can take an average of such readings because dividing by 2 yields the correct form. Putting it differently, 10 degrees of temperature added to 15 degrees of temperature do not make 25 degrees of temperature. At best their sum might be 15 degrees and at worst 10 degrees.

Ratio Scale: invariant under a similarity transformation, $y=ax$, $a>0$. An example is converting weight measured in pounds P to kilograms K by using the similarity transformation $P = 2.2 K$. The ratio of the weights of the two objects is the same regardless of whether the measurements are done in pounds or in kilograms. Zero is not the measurement of anything; it applies to objects that do not have the property and, in addition, one cannot divide by zero to preserve ratios in a meaningful way. Note that one can add two readings from a ratio scale, but not multiply them because $a^2x_1x_2$ does not have the form ax. The ratio of two readings from a ratio scale such as 6 kg/ 3 kg = 2 is a number that belongs to an absolute scale that says that the 6 kg object is twice heavier than the 3 kg object. The ratio 2 cannot be changed by some formula to another number. Thus we introduce the next scale.

Absolute Scale: invariant under the identity transformation $x = x$; for example, numbers used in counting the people in a room. An absolute scale is a special instance of a ratio scale with the constant multiplier equal to one. It is dimensionless. The real numbers that all mathematics uses to solve equations belong to an absolute scale. The natural numbers and the real numbers are defined in terms of 1-1 correspondence and equivalence classes, not in terms of laying out a unit of measurement starting with an origin. There are also other less well-known scales such as the logarithmic or the log-normal scales.

Pairwise Comparisons

The world presents itself to us in three ways: as matter and energy, as feelings and behavior, and as ideas. There are two possible ways to learn about anything. One is to examine the entity in itself according what it is known to be and what properties and influence it has. The other is to study that entity relative to other similar entities and relate it to them by making comparisons.

In sum, there are two ways to perform measurement, one is by using an instrument and making the correspondence directly, and the other is by using judgment and making the correspondence indirectly. When using judgments one can either assign numbers to the objects by importing or guessing their value on some scale of measurement when there is one, or by carefully deriving a scale by considering a subset of objects in some fashion such as comparing them in pairs, thus making the correspondence indirect.

Using judgments is a questionable practice when objectivity is the norm. But we have seen that even when the numbers obtained from a standard scale are objective, their interpretation is always subjective even when it conforms to a theory that is held to be true at a particular time. Still we need to validate the use of judgments to derive tangible values to provide greater credence for their use when intangibles are involved.

When paired comparisons are made on the conscious level, they involve thought and reflection and therefore are discrete in time. But they also occur at the subconscious to perform decisions about the body: is sleep more important than eating late at night, is the body warm enough as compared with the outside temperature to go for a walk. Signals received from the body are continuously processed according to their urgency or priority. Thus, continuous paired comparisons are also part of our natural endowment. It is widely believed that the mechanisms of our conscious behavior derive from and are outward manifestations closely linked to the subconscious.

Suppose we wish to derive a scale of relative importance according to size (volume) of three apples A, B, C shown in Figure 1. Assume that their volumes are known respectively as S_1, S_2 and S_3. For each position in the matrix the volume of the apple at the left is compared with that of the apple at the top and the ratio is entered. A matrix of judgments $A=(a_{ij})$ is constructed with respect to a particular property the elements have in common. It is reciprocal, that is, $a_{ji}=1/a_{ij}$, and $a_{ii}=1$. For the matrix in Figure 1, it is necessary to make only three judgments with the remainder being automatically determined. There are $n(n-1)/2$ judgments required for a matrix of order n. Sometimes one (particularly an expert who knows well what the judgments should be) may wish to make a minimum set of judgments and construct a consistent matrix defined as one whose entries satisfy $a_{ij}a_{jk}=a_{ik}$, $i, j, k=1,...n$. To do this one can enter $n-1$ judgments in a row or in a column, or in a spanning set with at least one judgment in every row and column, and construct the rest of the entries in the matrix using the consistency condition. Redundancy in the number of judgments generally improves the validity of the final answer because the judgments of the few elements one chooses to compare may be more biased.

If we only knew the paired comparison ratios from the measurements, w_1, w_2, and w_3 how would we recover the scale values w_1, w_2, and w_3 from them? There are many ways to do that but because of possible inconsistency, only one way generalizes from consistency to inconsistency from which a scale is derived that captures transitivity of the measurements correctly. It goes as follows: If we denote the matrix of ratios (w_i/w_j) by A and the vector of priorities (w_1, w_2, w_3) by w we have $Aw=3w$ or

$$\begin{pmatrix} w_1 / w_1 & w_1 / w_2 & w_1 / w_3 \\ w_2 / w_1 & w_2 / w_2 & w_2 / w_3 \\ w_3 / w_1 & w_3 / w_2 & w_3 / w_3 \end{pmatrix} \begin{pmatrix} w_1 \\ w_2 \\ w_3 \end{pmatrix} = 3 \begin{pmatrix} w_1 \\ w_2 \\ w_3 \end{pmatrix}$$

Comparison Matrix

Given: Three apples of different sizes.

Apple A	**Apple B**	**Apple C**

We Assess Their Relative Sizes By Forming Ratios

Size Comparison	Apple A	Apple B	Apple C
Apple A	w_1/w_1	w_1/w_2	w_1/w_3
Apple B	w_2 / w_1	w_2 / w_2	w_2 / w_3
Apple C	w_3 / w_1	w_3 / w_2	w_3 / w_3

Figure 1 Reciprocal Structure of Pairwise Comparison Matrix for Apples

This is a system of homogeneous equations that defines an eigenvalue problem with an eigenvalue equal to 3 and eigenvector w that we need to solve to get w back. The question is whether 3 is an eigenvalue of A for only then can we hope to get a nonzero vector w. In general when A is not consistent its entries are not given by ratios but we must still solve the eigenvalue problem $Aw=\lambda w$.

Assume that we know the volumes of the apples so that the values we enter in Figure 2 are consistent. Apple A is twice as big in volume as apple B, and apple B is three times as big as apple C, so we enter a 2 in the (1,2) position, and so on. Ones are entered on the diagonal by default as every entity equals itself on any criterion. Note that in the (2, 3) position we can enter the value 3 because we know the judgments are consistent as they are based on actual measurements. We can deduce the value this way: from the first row A = 2B and A = 6C, and thus B = 3C.

If we did not have actual measurements, we could not be certain that the judgments in the first row are accurate, and we would not mind estimating the value in the (2, 3) position directly by comparing apple B with apple C. We are then very likely to be inconsistent. How inconsistent can we be before we think it is intolerable? Later we give an actual measure of inconsistency and argue that a consistency of about 10% is considered acceptable.

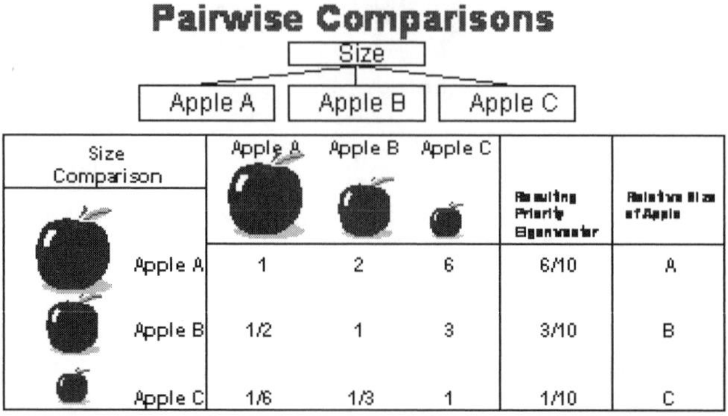

Pairwise Comparisons

Size Comparison	Apple A	Apple B	Apple C	Resulting Priority Eigenvector	Relative Size of Apple
Apple A	1	2	6	6/10	A
Apple B	1/2	1	3	3/10	B
Apple C	1/6	1/3	1	1/10	C

Figure 2 Pairwise Comparison Matrix for Apples using Judgments

We obtain from the consistent pairwise comparison matrix above a vector of priorities showing the relative sizes of the apples. Note that we do not have to go to all this trouble to derive the relative volumes of the apples. We could simply have normalized the actual measurements. The reason we did so is to lay the foundation for what to do when we have no measures for the property in question. When judgments are consistent as they are here, this vector of priorities can be obtained in two ways: dividing the elements in any column by the sum of its entries (normalizing it), or by summing the entries in each row to obtain the overall dominance in size of that alternative relative to the others and normalizing the resulting column of values. Incidentally, calculating dominance plays an important role in computing the priorities when judgments are inconsistent for then an alternative may dominate another by different magnitudes by transiting to it through intermediate alternatives. Thus the story is very different if the judgments are inconsistent, and we need to allow inconsistent judgments for good reasons. In sports, team A beats team B, team B beats team C, but team C beats team A. How would we admit such an occurrence in our attempt to explain the real world if we do not allow inconsistency? Most theories have taken a stand against such an occurrence with an axiom that assumes transitivity and prohibits intransitivity, although one does not have to be intransitive to be inconsistent in the values obtained. Others have wished it away by saying that it should not happen in human thinking. But it does, and we have a theory given below that copes with intransitivity.

The question is what numbers do we use to make the comparisons and what do we do when things being compared fall beyond the range of these numbers? It is clear that no matter what numbers we select, there will always be such things that fall outside their range. Thus we need to group things in a way that allows us to compare them with the given scale, and use a pivot or common element from one group to another group that is slightly larger or smaller and whose elements are also compared with the same scale. This is the basic idea that makes pairwise comparisons a reliable way to measure things across as wide a span as desired.

In the preface we provided the following numbers to use to represent judgments about dominance.

Table 1 Fundamental Scale of Absolute Numbers

Intensity of Importance	Definition	Explanation
1	Equal Importance	Two activities contribute equally to the objective
2	Weak or slight	
3	Moderate importance	Experience and judgment slightly favor one activity over another
4	Moderate plus	
5	Strong importance	Experience and judgment strongly favor one activity over another
6	Strong plus	
7	Very strong or demonstrated importance	An activity is favored very strongly over another; its dominance demonstrated in practice
8	Very, very strong	
9	Extreme importance	The evidence favoring one activity over another is of the highest possible order of affirmation
1.1-1.9	When activities are very close a decimal is added to 1 to show their difference as appropriate	A better alternative way to assigning the small decimals is to compare two close activities with other widely contrasting ones, favoring the larger one a little over the smaller one when using the 1-9 values

Reciprocals of above	If activity i has one of the above nonzero numbers assigned to it when compared with activity j, then j has the reciprocal value when compared with i	A logical assumption
Real numbers between the above integers		When appropriate according to the person making the comparisons because of special knowledge that person has
Ratios of measurements on a ratio scale		When measurements are available and one interprets their ratios to be equivalent to judgments (not usually recommended).

A useful observation has emerged from recent research in psychology that relates to the use of the fundamental scale of the absolute numbers 1-9 to represent judgments in making pairwise comparisons of homogeneous elements with respect to a common property. In his book The Number Sense, How the Mind Creates Mathematics [3], the mathematician and cognitive neuropsychologist Stanislas Dehaene writes "Introspection suggests that we can mentally represent the meaning of numbers 1 through 9 with actual acuity. Indeed, these symbols seem equivalent to us. They all seem equally easy to work with, and we feel that we can add or compare any two digits in a small and fixed amount of time like a computer. In summary, the invention of numerical symbols should have freed us from the fuzziness of the quantitative representation of numbers."

We demonstrate how the integers 1 to 9 used in pairwise comparison judgments can be derived from stimulus-response theory. The conditions needed for the stability of the eigenvector of priorities, known from the mathematics literature, are briefly mentioned. These conditions require that the elements being compared be homogeneous. This limits the upper value of the scale to 9. They also require that the number of elements compared be small. It is widely known that both of these conditions are intrinsic to the way in which our brains actually operate. A brief discussion is given about two ways to deal with a large number of elements.

We show here how the process of deriving a priority eigenvector that represents ratio relations among the elements of a discrete decision represented by a positive reciprocal matrix of paired comparisons based on ratios, can be extended to the continuous case to derive an eigenfunction of priorities as the solution of a functional equation also based on ratios.

From such an eigenfunction we obtain the well known Weber-Fechner law of response to stimuli as a first order approximation. We then use this response function to derive expressions for response to just noticeable successive stimuli. The ratios of these successive responses lead to the integer valued scale 1-9. By examining the sensitivity of the derived principal eigenvector to perturbations in the scale we find that the number of elements in the comparisons must be small and the values assigned must be homogeneous (of the same order of magnitude) from which we conclude that the values which begin with 1 must not go past the value 9. We also show that the upper limit of 9 does not impose a severe limit on comparisons of widely disparate elements by using clustering with a common pivot from one cluster to the next carefully constructed so the scale values of a cluster differ by just one order of magnitude from an immediately adjacent cluster.

Stimulus-Response and the Fundamental Scale

To be able to perceive and sense objects in the environment our brains miniaturize them within our system of neurons so that we have a proportional relationship between what we perceive and what is out there. Without proportionality we cannot coordinate our thinking with our actions with the accuracy needed to control the environment. Proportionality with respect to a single stimulus requires that our response to a proportionately amplified or attenuated stimulus we receive from a source should be proportional to what our response would be to the original value of that stimulus. If $w(s)$ is our response to a stimulus of magnitude s, then the foregoing gives rise to the functional equation $w(as) = b\, w(s)$. This equation can also be obtained as the necessary condition for solving the Fredholm equation of the second kind:

$$\int_a^b K(s,t)\, w(t)\, dt = \lambda_{\max}\, w(s)$$

obtained as the continuous generalization of the discrete formulation $Aw = \lambda_{\max} w$ for deriving priorities where instead of the positive reciprocal matrix A in the principal eigenvalue problem, we have a positive kernel, $K(s,t) > 0$, with $K(s,t)\, K(t,s) = 1$ that is also consistent i.e. $K(s,t)\, K(t,u) = K(s,u)$, for all s, t, and u . The solution of this functional equation in the real domain is given by

$$w(s) = Ce^{\log b \frac{\log s}{\log a}} P\left(\frac{\log s}{\log a}\right)$$

where P is a periodic function of period 1 and $P(0) = 1$. One of the simplest such examples with $u = \log s / \log a$ is $P(u) = \cos(u/2\pi)$ for which $P(0) = 1$.

The logarithmic law of response to stimuli can be obtained as a first order approximation to this solution through series expansions of the exponential and of the cosine functions as:

$$v(u) = C_1 e^{-\beta u} P(u) \approx C_2 \log s + C_3$$

$\beta = -\log b, \beta > 0$, $u = \log s / \log a$. The expression on the right is known as the Weber-Fechner law of logarithmic response $M = a \log s + b$, $a \neq 0$ to a stimulus of magnitude s. This law was empirically established and tested in 1860 by Gustav Theodor Fechner who used a law formulated by Ernest Heinrich Weber regarding discrimination between two nearby values of a stimulus. We have now shown that that Fechner's version can be derived by starting with a functional equation for stimulus response.

The integer-valued scale of response used in making paired comparison judgments can be derived from the logarithmic response function as follows. The larger the stimulus, the larger a change in it is needed for that change to be detectable. The ratio of successive just noticeable differences (the well-known "jnd" in psychology) is equal to the ratio of their corresponding successive stimuli values. Proportionality is maintained. Thus, starting with a stimulus s_0 successive magnitudes of the new stimuli take the form:

$$s_1 = s_0 + \Delta s_0 = s_0 + \frac{\Delta s_0}{s_0} s_0 = s_0(1+r)$$

$$s_2 = s_1 + \Delta s_1 = s_1(1+r) = s_0(1+r)^2 \equiv s_0 \alpha^2$$

$$\vdots$$

$$s_n = s_{n-1}\alpha = s_0 \alpha^n \ (n = 0,1,2,...)$$

We consider the responses to these stimuli to be measured on a ratio scale ($b=0$). A typical response has the form $M_i = a \log \alpha^i$, $i = 1,...,n$, or one after another they have the form:

$$M_1 = a \log \alpha, M_2 = 2a \log \alpha, ..., M_n = na \log \alpha$$

We take the ratios M_i/M_1, $i = 1,...,n$, of these responses in which the first is the smallest and serves as the unit of comparison, thus obtaining the *integer* values 1, 2, ..., n of the fundamental scale of the AHP. It appears that numbers are intrinsic to our ability to make comparisons, and that they were not an invention by our primitive ancestors. We must be grateful to them for the discovery of the symbolism. In a less mathematical vein, we note that we are able to distinguish ordinally between high, medium and low at one level and for each of them in a second level below that also distinguish between high, medium and low giving us nine different categories. We assign the value one to (low, low) which is the smallest and the value nine to (high, high) which is the highest, thus covering the spectrum of possibilities between two levels, and giving the value nine for the top of the paired comparisons scale as compared with the lowest value on the scale. Because of increase in inconsistency when we compare more than about 7 elements, we don't need to keep in mind more than 7±2 elements. This was first conjectured by the psychologist George Miller in the 1950's and explained in the AHP in the 1970's [4]. Finally, we note that the scale just derived is attached to the importance we assign to judgments. If we have an exact measurement such as 2.375 and want to use it as it is for our judgment without attaching significance to it, we can use its entire value without approximation.

A person may not be schooled in the use of numbers and there are many in our world who do not, but still have feelings, judgments and understanding that enable him or her to make accurate comparisons (equal, moderate, strong, very strong and extreme and compromises between these intensities). Such judgments can be applied successfully to compare stimuli that are not too disparate but homogeneous in magnitude. By homogeneous we mean that they fall within specified bounds. The Fundamental Scale for paired comparisons, summarizes the foregoing discussion.

No Limit on the Range of the Scale: from 1-9 to 1-∞

We can use clustering as in Figure 3 to compare a small cherry tomato with a large watermelon to show that all we need is the 1-9 scale to compare homogeneous elements and link them to other such elements successively by taking the largest element in a cluster and using it as the smallest one in the immediately next cluster. We divide all the priorities in a cluster by the priority of the pivot in that cluster, and multiply by its priority in the previous cluster. In this way, all the priorities of the clusters can be combined.

Scoring or Rating and Making Comparisons

In a rather haphazard way people have the habit of using ordinal numbers to create scales used to assign numbers to anything. In addition they perform meaningless arithmetic operation on such numbers that make no sense. A frequently used example is the psychometric scale commonly used in questionnaires the Likert scale named after Rensis Likert (1932), with the following numbers and their meaning 1. Strongly disagree 2. Disagree 3. Neither agree or disagree 4. Agree 5. Strongly Agree. It is disturbing to see such scales used in unjustifiable mathematical ways. It is not clear what a person relates such judgments to because people's likes and dislikes are so variable even about the same thing but at different times.

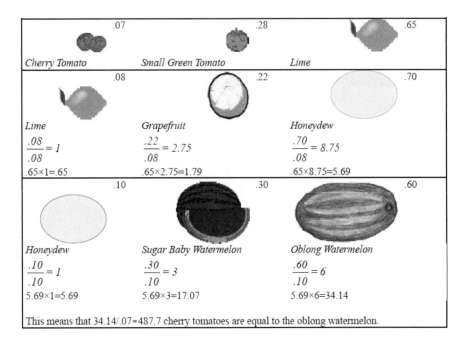

Figure 3 Clustering to Compare a Cherry Tomato with a Watermelon on the Scale 1-9

Nothing can be known in itself even if we have measurements of it. Knowing how good or bad it is requires experience with many similar things and comparisons of its measurement with their measurement. It must be related to other things and compared with them. When we assign a number to rate an alternative in a decision, we have something else in mind that we compare it with. It is an imagined ideal that we establish in our memories. This ideal can differ from person to person. In addition, the ideal is learned about and developed by examining many individual alternatives. The ideal is often improved or diminished in stature by examining new alternatives that were not known before. Thus when we rate things one at a time we compare them with an ideal that has been evolved through comparisons with many alternatives. Scoring or rating is the very rough short hand way of making comparisons. Its outcome is done for speed not for accuracy. By doing it we develop the illusion that we are able to rate an alternative independently of what other alternatives there are. But the ideal with which it is compared is already there through comparisons, and hence the assumption of independence in scoring begs the question by finding a circuitous route and instills a false way of thinking that how an alternative is rated has nothing to do with other alternatives. In addition, when we think of an alternative we are already conscious of other alternatives and rate it silently as if we are thinking of it alone, which is rarely ever the case. In fact once we have rated the first alternative, we cannot forget it when we rate the next one and the one after. All subsequent ratings depend on what passed through our minds before.

Rating is a quick but not an accurate way of ranking. If we have many alternatives, it is convenient and efficient although often misleading. It is an improvement on arbitrarily assigning ranks to alternatives without analyzing them on different criteria. Other than "illegally" manipulating ordinal numbers, it also creates the false understanding of the effect of new alternatives on the ranks of the older ones. It assumes that they have no influence unless new criteria are added or judgments are changed and that is false. Usually, when there are many copies of anything, its value is not as great as when there is only one of it. To represent the number of things as a criterion with respect to which they are evaluated makes them dependent on each other as to their number. When alternatives are dependent, one can no longer speak of preserving their ranks if new ones are added or old ones deleted. When we think of it, how we rate anything depends on how much we know about it and about other things so we can determine how good it is to satisfy our objectives. The conclusion is that assuming independence and rating things one at a time is a convenient and unscientific way to assign numbers subjectively to alternatives. The numbers are pulled out of a hat even when an expert is involved.

Prior to the AHP, people assumed that the alternatives of a decision were independent so they could rate them on several criteria one at a time. As a result adding or deleting alternatives had no effect on the ranks of the existing alternatives. But this is not true in the real world nor is it true in general. If the alternatives of a decision are compared with one another, how important any of them is depends on the quality of the alternatives with which it is compared. A poor alternative looks good when compared with still poorer ones and looks very poor when compared with good ones. Thus adding or deleting alternatives can influence the ranks of the other alternatives. Preserving rank is a matter of choice, of making assumptions of independence, and also of using ratings instead of comparisons. Alternatives may be independent but, like too many strangers in a room, they can influence the survival of each other. That is the number of alternatives affects their priority.

Let us now look at what is involved in making comparisons. When we make comparisons we limit ourselves to homogeneous alternatives in order to not make poor comparisons. We can also extend the system to non-homogeneous alternatives by using a pivot from one set to another, using care in comparing and sorting to build the homogeneous groups in an appropriate manner from the small to the larger and so on in stages.

The AHP way of comparing pairs and deriving a scale of priorities is a scientific method of creating scales that does not involve the assignment of arbitrary numbers from the top of our heads without an explicit reason. The process involves the dependence of each alternative on the quality and number of the other alternatives. The final scale may show that all the alternatives are close if they are similar, and not so close if some alternatives are much better than all the others. The values are relative. As a result the presence or absence of alternatives always has an effect on the rank of any of them. The ranking is relative to the set one has and not absolute in any sense. Reversal of ranks can occur and that is justified even when no new criteria are added or judgments changed.

The question is: which method reflects what happens in reality. The answer is easy on at least two grounds. First we are biologically endowed with the ability to make comparisons (of which we have seen that scoring is a degenerate from) which we can use ordinally even when we don't know about numbers. We simply say we prefer A to B and B to C and speak of transitivity. When we use numbers we no longer need to assume transitivity because the numbers may not tally and dominance itself may not be transitive as for example team A beats team B and team B beats team C but team C beats team A. Intransitivity is a frequent outcome in the real world that we cannot afford to ignore. Here is an example of rank reversal that paired comparisons makes clear without begging the question with weak arguments.

A typical example of rank reversal in multicriteria decisions would be to introduce more and more copies of an alternative and see it lose its rank order. A simple though perhaps not the most typical example of rank reversal occurs for another reason that has to do with limited resources to be distributed among more elements. It occurred in the presidential elections of 1991 when the entry of Ross Perot into the elections took votes away from George Herbert Bush. The prediction as to who would win the race prior to Perot's entry is shown in Figure 4. After Perot entered the race, Bush lost to Clinton as shown in Figure 5, below, because Perot took votes from Bush.

	1991 Election				
	Economy (.493)	Health (.299)	Foreign Affairs (.058)	Image (.098)	Abortion (.051)
Clinton (.44)	.327	.600	.229	.627	.550
Bush (.56)	.673	.400	.771	.373	.450

Figure 4 Presidential Elections with Standings for Bush and Clinton before Perot

But if, instead of comparing them pairwise as shown in Figure 2, we were to rate them one at a time, adding Perot would not change the rank order of Bush and Clinton and Bush would be predicted to be the winner, contrary to what happened. Rating one at a time forces rank preservation, Perot would have no effect, and Bush would be wrongly predicted to win as shown in Figure 6.

1991 Election				
Economy (.493)	Health (.299)	Foreign Affairs (.058)	Image (.098)	Abortion (.051)
Clinton (.44)	.327	.600	.229	.627	.550
Bush (.37)	.473	.300	.623	.323	.340
Perot (.19)	.200	.100	.148	.050	.110

Figure 5 Presidential Race with Three Candidates; Prediction Close to Actual Result

1991 Election				
Economy (.493)	Health (.299)	Foreign Affairs (.058)	Image (.098)	Abortion (.051)
Clinton (.66)	.485	1	.297	1	1
Bush (.89)	1	.667	1	.595	.818
Perot (.43)	.423	.166	.238	.080	.200

Figure 6 Forcing Rank Preservation by Idealizing gives Wrong Results

To force rank preservation by using ratings, start with the situation shown in Figure 4 and idealize by dividing by the larger priority in each column for the two candidates, Bush and Clinton, under each criterion. Bush would receive a larger overall priority than Clinton. We then assign Perot his proportionate value from the second figure with respect to the ideal in Figure 6. This has no effect on the ranking of Bush and Clinton, so the outcome in Figure 6 shows that Bush should be the winner.

In effect, comparisons take into consideration the relative number of people voting for the candidates by considering each criterion separately, and then weighting and combining the relative numbers. Therefore comparisons capture the outcome with greater sensitivity to dependence for each criterion.

The Eigenvalue Problem – Inconsistent Judgments

Paired comparisons as with the apples example are made by means of consistent and near consistent matrices. The latter are small perturbations of the former. The consistent set up leads to computing the principal eigenvector of the following equation written out in slightly elaborated but familiar matrix form:

$$
Aw = \begin{matrix} & A_1 & \cdots & A_n & \\ A_1 \\ \vdots \\ A_n \end{matrix}
\begin{bmatrix} w_1/w_1 & \cdots & w_1/w_n \\ \vdots & \cdots & \vdots \\ w_n/w_1 & \cdots & w_n/w_n \end{bmatrix}
\begin{bmatrix} w_1 \\ \vdots \\ w_n \end{bmatrix} = n \begin{bmatrix} w_1 \\ \vdots \\ w_n \end{bmatrix} = nw
$$

When $Aw = nw$ is written out as a system of equations we have

$$\sum_{j=1}^{n} a_{ij} w_j = nw_i \quad i = 1,\ldots,n$$

subject to: $a_{ji}=1/a_{ij}$ (or simply $a_{ij}a_{ji}=1$) known as the reciprocal condition resulting from the stronger consistency condition $a_{ij}a_{jk}=a_{ik}, i,j,k=1,\ldots,n$, and the normalization condition $\sum_{i=1}^{n} w_i = 1$.

We first show that it is necessary that the priority vector $w = (w_1,\ldots, w_n)$ of a consistent matrix also be the principal eigenvector of that matrix. Because a consistent matrix is always of the form $W = (w_i/w_j)$, and has rank one. Thus n is its largest eigenvalue and w is its corresponding eigenvector and the coefficients of W coincide with the coefficients of the matrix of ratios from the vector w. Next, we show that order holds for a consistent matrix A. Element A_i is said to *dominate* element A_j in one step, if the sum of the entries in row i of A is greater than the sum of the entries in row j. It is convenient to use the vector $e = (1,\ldots,1)^T$ to express this dominance: Element A_i *dominates* element A_j in one step if $(Ae)_i > (Ae)_j$. An element can dominate another element in more than one step by dominating other elements that in turn dominate the second element. It is known from graph theory that the number of paths of length n between two nodes is obtained from the corresponding for these nodes in the nth power of the path matrix. Thus, in our case, two-step dominance is identified by squaring the matrix and summing its rows, three-step dominance by cubing it, and so on. Thus, A_i dominates A_j in k steps if $(A^k e)_i > (A^k e)_j$. Element A_i is said simply to dominate

A_j if entry i of the vector obtained by averaging over the one step dominance vector, two step dominance vector, k step dominance vector and passing to the limit:

$$\lim_{m\to\infty} \frac{1}{m} \sum_{i=1}^{m} A^k e / e^T A^k e$$

is greater than its entry j. But this limit of weighted averages (the Cesaro sum) can be evaluated: We have for an n by n consistent matrix A: $A^{k} = n^{k-1} A$, $A=(w_i/w_j)$ and the foregoing limit is simply the eigenvector w normalized.

It is useful to summarize some of the mathematics of a derived scale involved in the multicriteria decision process, and give the corresponding generalization to the continuous case. First, we make an observation about the solvability of a system of linear algebraic equations given in matrix form. The homogeneous system $Ax = 0$ has a non-zero solution if A has no inverse A^{-1} with $AA^{-1}=A^{-1}A=I$, where I is the identity matrix, and hence the determinant of A is equal to zero. The inhomogeneous system $Ax=y$ has a non-zero solution $x=A^{-1}y$ if and only if A^{-1} exists. This means that the determinant of A is not zero. We recall that an eigenvalue λ of A is a root of the characteristic equation of A and that a right eigenvector of A is a solution x of the equation $Ax=\lambda x$ which can also be written as $(\lambda I-A)x=0$. The homogeneous eigenvalue system $(\lambda I-A)x=0$ has a solution if the determinant of $(\lambda I-A)$ which is a polynomial (the characteristic polynomial)in λ is equal to zero which is true only if λ is a zero of that polynomial. That value of λ is called an eigenvalue of the matrix A. The inhomogeneous system $(\lambda I-A)x= y$ has a non-zero solution $x=(\lambda I-A)^{-1}y$ if and only if $(\lambda I-A)^{-1}$ exists which can only be if λ is not an eigenvalue of A. The set of eigenvalues is referred to as the *spectrum* of A. It is clear that A is the kernel or focus that provides the conditions for the system of equations to have or not to have a solution. These ideas will be relevant in the generalization to the infinite case made later.   If A is simply reciprocal and positive, then

$$a_{ij} = \left(\frac{w_i}{w_j}\right)\varepsilon_{ij}, \varepsilon_{ij} = \frac{1}{\varepsilon_{ji}}, \varepsilon_{ij}>0$$

Where (ε_{ij}) is a perturbation matrix of the consistent matrix (w_i/w_j). A left eigenvector y of A is a solution of the equation $yA=\lambda y$. For a consistent matrix, the corresponding entries of the normalized left and right eigenvectors are reciprocals. The reason why we used the principal right eigenvector only in the discrete case instead of the principal left eigenvector is because it represents the priorities derived from making pairwise comparisons with respect to what dominates what with respect to a given property and by how much it dominates it. In making paired comparison judgments one must identify the smaller or lesser element and use it as a unit and then estimate how many multiples of that unit the larger element dominates it in value. We cannot do the opposite by asking what fraction of the larger element the smaller one is without first using the smaller one as the unit. Knowing that the left and right eigenvectors are reciprocals when we have consistency is useful in the continuous case.

To recover the scale from the matrix of ratios, one must solve the problem $Aw = nw$ or $(A - nI)w = 0$. This is a system of homogeneous linear equations. It has a nontrivial solution if and only if the determinant of $A-nI$ vanishes, that is, n is an eigenvalue of A. Now A has unit rank since every row is a constant multiple of the first row. Thus all its eigenvalues except one are zero. The sum of the eigenvalues of a matrix is equal to its trace, the sum of its diagonal elements, and in this case the trace of **A** is equal to n. Thus n is an eigenvalue of A, and one has a nontrivial solution. The solution consists of positive entries and is unique to within a multiplicative constant.

To make w unique, one can normalize its entries by dividing by their sum. Thus, given the comparison matrix, one can recover the scale. In this case, the solution is any column of A normalized. Note that in A the reciprocal property $a_{ji} = 1/a_{ij}$ holds; thus, also $a_{ii} = 1$. Another property of A is that it is consistent: its entries satisfy the condition $a_{jk} = a_{ik}/a_{ij}$. Thus the entire matrix can be constructed from a set of n elements which form a chain across the rows and columns.

In the general case, the precise value of w_i/w_j cannot be given, but instead only an estimate of it as a judgment. For the moment, consider an estimate of these values by an expert who is assumed to make small perturbations of the coefficients. This implies small perturbations of the eigenvalues. The problem now becomes $A'w' = \lambda_{max}w'$ where λ_{max} is the largest eigenvalue of A'. To simplify the notation, we shall continue to write $Aw = \lambda_{max}w$, where A is the matrix of pairwise comparisons. The problem now is how good is the estimate of w. Notice that if w is obtained by solving this problem, the matrix whose entries are w_i/w_j is a consistent matrix. It is a consistent estimate of the matrix A. A itself need not be consistent. In fact, the entries of A need not even be transitive; that is, A_1 may be preferred to A_2 and A_2 to A_3 but A_3 may be preferred to A_1. What we would like is a measure of the error due to inconsistency. It turns out that A is consistent if and only if $\lambda_{max} = n$ and that we always have $\lambda_{max} \geq n$.

When the measurements are not available and judgments are used the matrix takes the positive reciprocal form:

$$A = \begin{bmatrix} 1 & a_{12} & \cdots & a_{1n} \\ 1/a_{12} & 1 & \cdots & a_{2n} \\ \vdots & \vdots & \vdots & \vdots \\ 1/a_{1n} & 1/a_{2n} & \cdots & 1 \end{bmatrix}$$

Although reciprocal, with $a_{ji}=1/a_{ij}$, this matrix need not be consistent.

In general we assume that expert judgments are made to estimate the ratios of the entries in the vector w. Fundamentally the second matrix is assumed to be a small perturbation of the first matrix. There are several ways to justify the argument that in order to obtain the vector of priorities from the second matrix we must again solve the eigenvalue problem $Aw=\lambda_{max}w$. One of the simplest is a theorem which says that a small perturbation of a matrix yields a matrix whose principal eigenvalue is close to the principal eigenvalue of the unperturbed matrix.

We said earlier that an n by n matrix $A=(a_{ij})$ is consistent if $a_{ij}a_{jk}=a_{ik}$, $i,j,k=1\ldots n$ holds among its entries. We have for a consistent matrix $A^k=n^{k-1}A$, a constant times the original matrix. In normalized form both A and A^k have the same principal eigenvector. That is not so for an inconsistent matrix. A consistent matrix always has the form

$$A = (\frac{w_i}{w_j}).$$

Of course, real-world pairwise comparison matrices are very unlikely to be consistent.

In the inconsistent case, the normalized sum of the rows of each power of the matrix contributes to the final priority vector. Using Cesaro summability and the well-known theorem of Perron, we are led to derive the priorities in the form of the principal right eigenvector. Now we give an elegant mathematical discussion, based on the concept of invariance, to show why we still need for an inconsistent matrix the principal right eigenvector for our priority vector. It is clear that no matter what method we use to derive the weights w_i, we need to get them back as proportional to the expression

$$\sum_{j=1}^{n} a_{ij}w_j \quad i=1,\ldots,n,$$

that is, we must solve

$$\sum_{j=1}^{n} a_{ij} w_j = c w_i \quad i = 1, \dots, n.$$

Otherwise $\sum_{j=1}^{n} a_{ij} w_j \quad i = 1, \dots, n$

would yield another set of different weights and they in turn can be used to form new expressions

$$\sum_{j=1}^{n} a_{ij} w_j \quad i = 1, \dots, n,$$

and so on ad infinitum. Unless we solve the principal eigenvalue problem, our quest for priorities becomes meaningless.

We learn from the consistent case that what we get on the right is proportional to the sum on the left that involves the same ratio scale used to weight the judgments that we are looking for. Thus we have the proportionality constant c. A better way to see this is to use the derived vector of priorities to weight each row of the matrix and take the sum. This yields a new vector of priorities (relative dominance of each element) represented in the comparisons. This vector can again be used to weight the rows and obtain still another vector of priorities. In the limit (if one exists), the limit vector itself can be used to weight the rows and get the limit vector back perhaps proportionately. Our general problem possibly with inconsistent judgments takes the form:

$$Aw = \begin{bmatrix} 1 & a_{12} & \cdots & a_{1n} \\ 1/a_{12} & 1 & \cdots & a_{2n} \\ \vdots & \vdots & \vdots & \vdots \\ 1/a_{1n} & 1/a_{2n} & \cdots & 1 \end{bmatrix} \begin{bmatrix} w_1 \\ w_2 \\ \vdots \\ w_n \end{bmatrix} = cw$$

This homogeneous system of linear equations $Aw = cw$ has a solution w if c is the principal eigenvalue of A. That this is the case can be shown using an argument that involves both left and right eigenvectors of A. Two vectors $x = (x_1, \dots, x_n)$, $y = (y_1, \dots, y_n)$ are orthogonal if their scalar product $x_1 y_1 + \dots + x_n y_n$ is equal to zero. It is known that any left eigenvector of a matrix corresponding to an eigenvalue is orthogonal to any right eigenvector corresponding to a different eigenvalue. This property is known as biorthogonality (Horn and Johnson 1985).

Theorem *For a given positive matrix A, the only positive vector w and only positive constant c that satisfy Aw = cw, is a vector w that is a positive multiple of* *the principal eigenvector of A, and the only such c is the principal eigenvalue of A.*

Proof. We know that the right principal eigenvector and the principal eigenvalue satisfy our requirements. We also know that the algebraic multiplicity of the principal eigenvalue is one, and that there is a positive left eigenvector of A (call it z) corresponding to the principal eigenvalue. Suppose there is a positive vector y and a (necessarily positive) scalar d such that $Ay=dy$. If d and c are not equal, then by biorthogonality y is orthogonal to z, which is impossible since both vectors are positive. If c and d are equal, then y and w are dependent since c has algebraic multiplicity one, and y is a positive multiple of w. This completes the proof.

Inconsistency and the Need for the Elements to be Close Enough (Homogeneous) to Make Meaningful Comparisons

The numerical judgments use the fundamental scale of absolute numbers (invariant under the identity transformation). From logarithmic stimulus-response theory that we do not go into here, we learn that a stimulus compared with itself is always assigned the value 1 so the main diagonal entries of the pairwise comparison matrix are all 1. We also learn that we must use integer values for the comparisons. The numbers 3, 5, 7, and 9 correspond to the verbal judgments "moderately more dominant", "strongly more dominant", "very strongly more dominant", and "extremely more dominant" (with 2, 4, 6, and 8 for compromise between the previous values). Reciprocal values are automatically entered in the transpose position. Consistency of the set of judgments is measured by the consistency ratio (C.R.), which we explain now.

In order to get some feel for what the consistency index $\mu \equiv (\lambda_{max} - n)/(n-1)$ discussed in details later might be telling us about a positive n-by-n reciprocal matrix A, consider the following simulation: choose the entries of A above the main diagonal at random from the 17 values $\{1/9, 1/8, \ldots, 1, 2, \ldots, 8, 9\}$. Then fill in the entries of A below the diagonal by taking reciprocals. Put ones down the main diagonal and compute the consistency index. Do this 50,000 times and take the average, which we call the random index. Table 2 shows the values obtained from one set of such simulations and also their first order differences, for matrices of size 1, 2,…,15.

Figure 7 is a plot of the first two rows of Table 2. It shows the asymptotic nature of random inconsistency.

Table 2 Random Index

Order	1	2	3	4	5	6	7	8	9	10	11	12	13	14	15
R.I.	0	0	0.52	0.89	1.11	1.25	1.35	1.40	1.45	1.49	1.52	1.54	1.56	1.58	1.59
First Order Differences		0	0.52	0.37	0.22	0.14	0.10	0.05	0.05	0.04	0.03	0.02	0.02	0.02	0.01

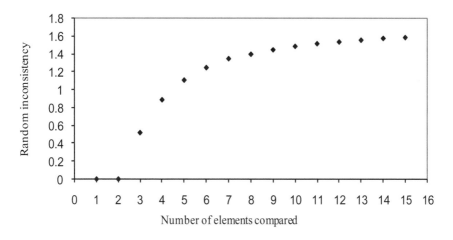

Figure 7 Plot of Random Inconsistency

Since it would be pointless to try to discern any priority ranking from a set of random comparison judgments, we should probably be uncomfortable about proceeding unless the consistency index of a pairwise comparison matrix is very much smaller than the corresponding random index value in Table 2. The consistency ratio (C.R.) of a pairwise comparison matrix is the ratio of its consistency index μ to the corresponding random index value in Table 2. The notion of order of magnitude is essential in any mathematical consideration of changes in measurement. When one has a numerical value say between 1 and 10 for some measurement and one wants to determine whether change in this value is significant or not, one reasons as follows: A change of a whole integer value is critical because it changes the magnitude and identity of the original number significantly. If the change or perturbation in value is of the order of a percent or less, it would be so small (by two orders of magnitude) and would be considered negligible. However if this perturbation is a decimal (one order of magnitude smaller) we are likely to pay attention to modify the original value by this decimal without losing the significance and identity of the original number as we first understood it to be. Thus in synthesizing near consistent judgment values, changes that are too large can cause dramatic change in our understanding, and values that are too small cause no change in our understanding. We are left with only values of one order of magnitude smaller than we can deal with incrementally to change our understanding. It follows that our allowable consistency ratio should be not more than about .10. The requirement of 10% cannot be made smaller such as 1% or .1% without trivializing the impact of inconsistency. But inconsistency itself is important because without it, new knowledge that changes preference cannot be admitted. Assuming that all knowledge should be consistent contradicts experience that requires continued revision of understanding.

If the C.R. is larger than desired, we do three things: 1) Find the most inconsistent judgment in the matrix (for example, that judgment for which $\varepsilon_{ij}=a_{ij}w_j/w_i$ is largest), 2) Determine the range of values to which that judgment can be changed corresponding to which the inconsistency would be improved, 3) Ask the judge to consider, if he can, changing his judgment to a plausible value in that range. If he is unwilling, we try with the second most inconsistent judgment and so on. If no judgment is changed the decision is postponed until better understanding of the stimuli is obtained. Judges who understand the theory are always willing to revise their judgments often not the full value but partially and then examine the second most inconsistent judgment and so on. It can happen that a judge's knowledge does not permit one to improve his or her consistency and more information is required to improve the consistency of judgments.

Before proceeding further, the following observations may be useful for a better understanding of the importance of the concept of a limit on our ability to process information and also change in information. The quality of response to stimuli is determined by three factors. Accuracy or validity, consistency, and efficiency or amount of information generated. Our judgment is much more sensitive and responsive to large perturbations. When we speak of perturbation, we have in mind numerical change from consistent ratios obtained from priorities. The larger the inconsistency and hence also the larger the perturbations in priorities, the greater is our sensitivity to make changes in the numerical values assigned. Conversely, the smaller the inconsistency, the more difficult it is for us to know where the best changes should be made to produce not only better consistency but also better validity of the outcome. Once near consistency is attained, it becomes uncertain which coefficients should be perturbed by small amounts to transform a near consistent matrix to a consistent one. If such perturbations were forced, they could be arbitrary and thus distort the validity of the derived priority vector in representing the underlying decision.

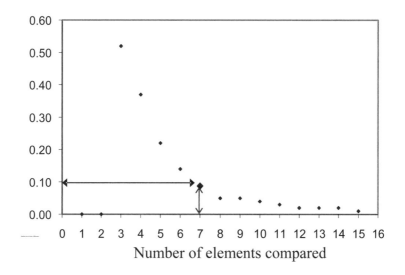

Figure 8 Plot of First Differences in Random Inconsistency

The third row of Table 2 gives the differences between successive numbers in the second row. Figure 8 is a plot of these differences and shows the importance of the number seven as a cutoff point beyond which the differences are less than 0.10 where we are not sufficiently sensitive to make accurate changes in judgment on several elements simultaneously.

What is useful and powerful in regard to perturbation from consistency is the following theorem that lends strong credibility to the foregoing line of thinking. Stability of the principal eigenvector when making reciprocal paired comparisons imposes a condition on why there is a limit on the number of things to be compared and at the same time maintain a reasonable degree of consistency. It highlights the importance of homogeneity. To a first order approximation, perturbation Δw_1 in the principal right eigenvector w_1 due to a perturbation ΔA in the matrix A where A is consistent is given by J.H. Wilkinson [5]:

$$\Delta w_1 = \sum_{j=2}^{n} (v_j^T \Delta A w_1 / (\lambda_i - \lambda_j) v_i^T w_j) w_j$$

Here T indicates transposition and v is the left eigenvector of A. The eigenvector w_1 is insensitive to perturbation in A, if 1) the number of terms n is small, 2) if the principal eigenvalue λ_1 is separated from the other eigenvalues λ_j, here assumed to be distinct (otherwise a slightly more complicated argument given below can be made) and, 3) if none of the products $v_j^T w_j$ of left and right eigenvectors is small but if one of them is small, they are all small. However, $v_1^T w_1$, the product of the normalized left and right principal eigenvectors of a consistent matrix is equal to n that as an integer is never very small. If n is relatively small and the elements being compared are homogeneous, none of the components of w_1 is arbitrarily small and correspondingly, none of the components of v_1^T is arbitrarily small. Their product cannot be arbitrarily small, and thus w is insensitive to small perturbations of the consistent matrix A. The conclusion is that n *must be small*, and one must compare *homogeneous* elements.

When the eigenvalues have greater multiplicity than one, the corresponding left and right eigenvectors will not be unique. In that case the cosine of the angle between them which is given by $v_i^T w_i$ corresponds to a particular choice of w_i and v_i. Even when w_i and v_i correspond to a simple λ_i they are arbitrary to within a multiplicative complex constant of unit modulus, but in that case $| v_i^T w_i |$ is fully determined. Because both vectors are normalized, we always have $| v_i^T w_i | < 1$.

When is a Positive Reciprocal Matrix Consistent?

Let $A = [a_{ij}]$ be an n-by-n positive reciprocal matrix, so all $a_{ii} = 1$ and $a_{ij} = 1/a_{ji}$ for all $i, j = 1, \ldots, n$. Let $w = [w_i]$ be the Perron vector of A, let $D = \text{diag}(w_1, \ldots, w_n)$ be the n-by-n diagonal matrix whose main diagonal entries are the entries of w, and set $E \equiv D^{-1}AD = [a_{ij} w_j / w_i] = [\varepsilon_{ij}]$. Then E is similar to A and is a positive reciprocal matrix since $\varepsilon_{ji} = a_{ji} w_i / w_j = (a_{ij} w_j / w_i)^{-1} = 1/\varepsilon_{ij}$. Moreover, all the row sums of E are equal to the Perron eigenvalue of A:

$$\sum_{j=1}^{n} \varepsilon_{ij} = \sum_{j} a_{ij} w_j / w_i = [Aw]_i / w_i = \lambda_{\max} w_i / w_i = \lambda_{\max}.$$

The computation

$$n\lambda_{\max} = \sum_{i=1}^{n}(\sum_{j=1}^{n}\varepsilon_{ij}) = \sum_{i=1}^{n}\varepsilon_{ii} + \sum_{\substack{i,j=1\\i\neq j}}^{n}(\varepsilon_{ij}+\varepsilon_{ji})$$

$$= n + \sum_{\substack{i,j=1\\i\neq j}}^{n}(\varepsilon_{ij}+\varepsilon_{ij}^{-1}) \geq n + (n^2 - n)/2 = n^2$$

reveals that $\lambda_{\max} \geq n$. Moreover, since $x + 1/x \geq 2$ for all $x > 0$, with equality if and only if $x = 1$, we see that $\lambda_{\max} = n$ if and only if all $\varepsilon_{ij} = 1$, which is equivalent to having all $a_{ij} = w_i/w_j$.

The foregoing arguments show that a positive reciprocal matrix A has $\lambda_{\max} \geq n$, with equality if and only if A is consistent. As our measure of deviation of A from consistency, we choose the *consistency index*

$$\mu \equiv \frac{\lambda_{\max} - n}{n - 1}.$$

We have seen that $\mu \geq 0$ and $\mu = 0$ if and only if A is consistent. These two desirable properties explain the term "n" in the numerator of μ; what about the term "n-1" in the denominator? Since trace $A = n$ is the sum of all the eigenvalues of A, if we denote the eigenvalues of A that are different from $\lambda_{\max}$

by $\lambda_2, ..., \lambda_{n-1}$, we see that $n = \lambda_{\max} + \sum_{i=2}^{n}\lambda_i$, so $n - \lambda_{\max} = \sum_{i=2}^{n}\lambda_i$ and

$\mu = -\frac{1}{n-1}\sum_{i=2}^{n}\lambda_i$ is the negative average of the non-principal eigenvalues of A.

It is an easy, but instructive, computation to show that $\lambda_{\max} = 2$ for every 2-by-2 positive reciprocal matrix:

$$\begin{bmatrix} 1 & \alpha \\ \alpha^{-1} & 1 \end{bmatrix}\begin{bmatrix} 1+\alpha \\ (1+\alpha)\alpha^{-1} \end{bmatrix} = 2\begin{bmatrix} 1+\alpha \\ (1+\alpha)\alpha^{-1} \end{bmatrix}$$

Thus, every 2-by-2 positive reciprocal matrix is consistent.

Not every 3-by-3 positive reciprocal matrix is consistent, but in this case we are fortunate to

$$A = \begin{bmatrix} 1 & a & b \\ 1/a & 1 & c \\ 1/b & 1/c & 1 \end{bmatrix},$$

have again explicit formulas for the eigenvalue and eigenvector. For we have

$$\lambda_{\max} = 1 + d + d^{-1}, \; d = (ac/b)^{1/3}$$

and

$$w_1 = bd/(1+bd+\frac{c}{d}), \quad w_2 = c/d(1+bd+\frac{c}{d}), \quad w_3 = 1/(1+bd+\frac{c}{d}).$$

Note that $\lambda_{max} = 3$ when d = 1 or c = b/a, which is true if and only if A is consistent.

Consistency, Compatibility and Proportionality

To establish order in the mind requires consistent thinking. But to be consistent means that we do not change our minds and learn and grow. Therefore we need a moderate amount of inconsistency to expand our thinking. What effect does inconsistency have on ordering things? Proportion is the comparative relation between things. It is a part, or share in relation to the whole. It is balance or symmetry. Consistency is conformity with previous practice. To be able to perceive and sense objects in the environment our brains miniaturize them within our system of neurons so that we have a proportional relationship between what we perceive and what is out there. Without proportionality we cannot coordinate our thinking with our actions with the accuracy needed to control the environment. Proportionality with respect to a single stimulus requires that our response to a proportionately amplified or attenuated stimulus we receive from a source should be proportional to what our response would be to the original value of that stimulus. If $w(s)$ is our response to a stimulus of magnitude s, then the foregoing gives rise to the functional equation $w\ (as) = b\ w\ (s)$. Thus miniaturization implies proportionality that implies consistency.

CONSISTENCY implies measurability where $a_{ij} = \dfrac{w_i}{w_j}$ **and hence also proportionality on a scale. Conversely, proportionality implies consistency.**

Reciprocal nonnegative matrices may have complex eigenvalues. Hence, they have no simple generic characterization. However, we note that since the maximum eigenvalue lies between the largest and the smallest row sums, a matrix whose columns are identical has an eigenvalue which is equal to the sum of any of its columns. Also we shall see that a small perturbation leaves the maximum eigenvalue close to its value, and that the remaining eigenvalues are perturbed away from zero, and their sum is real.

If we write $\varepsilon_{ij} = 1 + \delta_{ij}$ with $\delta_{ij} > -1$ we have

$$\mu = \frac{1}{n(n-1)} \sum_{1 \le i < j \le n} \left[\delta_{ij}^2 - \frac{\delta_{ij}^3}{1 + \delta_{ij}} \right]$$

Theorem *Let* $\delta = \max_{i,j} \delta_{ij}$ *then*

$$\lambda_{\max} - n < \frac{1}{n} \sum_{1 \le i < j \le n} \delta_{ij}^2 \le \frac{(n-1)}{2} \delta^2$$

Thus if the perturbation (or judgmental error) is small and the number of elements being compared is also <u>small</u> (e.g., less than 10) then the departure of $\lambda_{\max}$ from n is also small. Again we note that to remain near consistency we need to keep n small. For example, $\delta = 0.1$, $n = 7$ give $\lambda_{\max} - n < 0.04$ and $\delta = 0.9$, $n = 7$ give $\lambda_{\max} - n < 2.43$.

From $a_{ij}a_{jk} = a_{ik}$, we have, on using the reciprocal property $a_{ji} = 1/a_{ij}$, that $a_{ij}a_{jk}a_{ki} = 1$. Thus consistency for a reciprocal matrix means that all cycles of length three have unit intensity.

Assuming $|\delta_{ij}| < 1$, and considering triangular cycles we have

$$a_{ij}a_{jk}a_{ki} = (1 + \delta_{ij})(1 + \delta_{jk})(1 - \delta_{ik}) \approx 1 + \delta_{ij} + \delta_{jk} - \delta_{ik}$$

and, since $\lambda_{\max} = \sum_{j=1}^{n} \varepsilon_{ij}$, we have

$$\sum_{i,j,k} a_{ij}a_{jk}a_{ki} = n^2 \lambda_{\max}$$

For $i \ne j$, $j \ne k$, $i \ne k$, this sum becomes $n^2(\lambda_{\max} - n) + n(n-1)(n-2)$, since by putting $a_{pp} = 1$, $a_{pq} = a_{qp}^{-1}$ we have $n^2 + 2n(n-1)$ terms whose value is unity. Averaging over the number of terms, i.e., $n(n-1)(n-2)$, the result is $[n/(n-2)][(\lambda_{\max} - n)/(n-1)] + 1$ valid for $n \ge 3$. In any case it is $\lambda_{\max} - n$ that is of interest to us as it also appears in these global considerations of consistency.

Compatibility and Consistency

Consistency is concerned with the compatibility of a matrix of the ratios constructed from a principal right eigenvector with the matrix of judgments from which it is derived. Compatibility is concerned with two different vectors. If the matrix of judgments is inconsistent, is it compatible with the matrix of eigenvector ratios? The following theorem and the table following it show that there is a relation between consistency and compatibility. Comparison of the two indices suggests that for the cases of $n = 3,4,5$ the Compatibility Index should have a smaller value than 1.1.

   Let $W = (w_i/w_j)$ be the matrix of ratios of the principal right eigenvector $w = (w_1,...,w_n)$ of the positive reciprocal matrix A and λ_{max} be the corresponding principal eigenvalue and let $\sum_{i=1}^{n} w_i = 1$. We define the Compatibility Index (S.I.) of a matrix of judgments and the matrix of derived eigenvector ratios as $S.I. = \frac{1}{n^2} e^T A o W^T e$, where o denotes the Hadamard or elementwise product of the two matrices.

Theorem : $\frac{1}{n^2} e^T A o\ W^T e = \frac{\lambda_{max}}{n}$

Proof: From $Aw = \lambda_{max} w$ we have

$$\sum_{j=1}^{n} a_{ij} w_j = \lambda_{max} w_i$$

and $\frac{1}{n^2} e^T A o W^T e = \frac{1}{n^2} \sum_{i=1}^{n}\sum_{j=1}^{n} a_{ij} \frac{w_j}{w_i} = \frac{\lambda_{max}}{n}$

Table 3 gives information on compatibility and consistency for different size judgment matrices.

Table 3 Relationship between Consistency and Compatibility for a Different Number of Elements

Number of Elements (n)	Compatibility Index (S.I.)	λ_{max}	$C.I. = \dfrac{\lambda_{max} - n}{n - 1}$	R.I.	$C.R. = \dfrac{C.I}{R.I}$
3	1.017	3.052	0.026	0.52	0.05
4	1.053	4.214	0.071	0.89	0.08
5	1.089	5.444	0.111	1.11	0.10
6	1.104	6.625	0.125	1.25	0.10
7	1.116	7.810	0.135	1.35	0.10
8	1.123	8.980	0.140	1.40	0.10
9	1.129	10.160	0.145	1.45	0.10
10	1.134	11.341	0.149	1.49	0.10
11	1.137	12.510	0.151	1.51	0.10
12	1.141	13.694	0.154	1.54	0.10
13	1.144	14.872	0.156	1.56	0.10
14	1.146	16.041	0.157	1.57	0.10
15	1.147	17.212	0.158	1.58	0.10

In the preface we gave an area estimation example that demonstrated the validity of the pairwise comparisons matrix to which the reader may apply the compatibility index for actual and derived vector to see how close they are. Here are two more examples.

Optics Example

Four identical chairs were placed on a line from a light source at the distances of 9, 15, 21, and 28 yards. The purpose was to see if one could stand by the light and look at the chair and compare their relative brightness in pairs, fill in the judgment matrix and obtain a relationship between the chairs and their distance from the light source. This experiment was repeated twice with different judges whose judgment matrices we now give.

Relative visual brightness (1st Trial)

	C_1	C_2	C_3	C_4
C_1	1	5	6	7
C_2	1/5	1	4	6
C_3	1/6	1/4	1	4
C_4	1/7	1/6	1/4	1

Relative visual brightness (2nd Trial)

	C_1	C_2	C_3	C_4
C_1	1	4	6	7
C_2	1/4	1	3	4
C_3	1/6	1/3	1	2
C_4	1/7	1/4	1/2	1

The judges of the first matrix were the author's young children, ages 5 and 7 at that time, who gave their judgments qualitatively. The judge of the second matrix was the author's wife, who was not present during the children's judgment process.

Relative brightness eigenvector (1st Trial)	Relative brightness eigenvector (2nd Trial)
0.61	0.62
0.24	0.22
0.10	0.10
0.05	0.06

λ_{max} = 4.39, C.I. = 0.13, C.R.= 0.14 λ_{max} = 4.10, C.I. = 0.03, C.R.= 0.03

Inverse square law of optics

Distance	Normalized distance	Square of normalized distance	Reciprocal of previous column	Normalized reciprocal	Rounding off
9	0.123	0.015 129	66.098	0.607 9	0.61
15	0.205	0.042 025	23.79	0.218 8	0.22
21	0.288	0.082 944	12.05	0.110 8	0.11
28	0.384	0.147 456	6.78	0.062 3	0.06

First and second trial eigenvectors should be compared with the last column of this table calculated from the inverse square law in optics. It is interesting and important to observe that the judgments have captured a natural law here. It would seem that they could do the same in other areas of perception or thought, as we shall see later.

Note that sensitivity of the results as the object is very close to the source, for then it absorbs most of the value of the relative index and a small error in its distance from the source yields great error in the values. What is noteworthy from this sensory experiment is the observation or hypothesis that the observed intensity of illumination varies (approximately) inversely with the square of the distance. The more carefully designed the experiment, the better the results obtained from the visual observations.

The RMS of (0.62, 0.22, 0.10, 0.06) and (0.61, 0.22, 0.11, 0.06) is $\{1/4[(0.01)^2 + 0 + (0.01)^2+0]\}^{1/2}$ = 2.23x10^{-3}. The MAD is as follows. The differences between the two vectors are given by (0.01, 0, −0.01, 0). The median of these numbers is 0+0/2 = 0. The deviations about this median are

(0.01, 0, −0.01, 0). Their absolute value is taken and the median of the result is (0.01+0)/2 = 0.005 = 5x10⁻³. The significance of both RMS and MAD may be determined by dividing their values by the average value of the vector components which is simply $1/n$, where n is the number of components. Two vectors are nearly the same if either or both ratios are, for example, less than 0.1.

Relative Consumption of Drinks

Table 4 shows how an audience of about 30 people, using consensus to arrive at each judgment, provided judgments to estimate the dominance of the consumption of drinks in the United States (which drink is consumed more in the US and how much more than another drink?). The derived vector of relative consumption and the actual vector, obtained by normalizing the consumption given in official statistical data sources, are at the bottom of the table.

Drink Consumption in the U.S.	Coffee	Wine	Tea	Beer	Sodas	Milk	Water
Coffee	1	9	5	2	1	1	1/2
Wine	1/9	1	1/3	1/9	1/9	1/9	1/9
Tea	1/5	2	1	1/3	1/4	1/3	1/9
Beer	1/2	9	3	1	1/2	1	1/3
Sodas	1	9	4	2	1	2	1/2
Milk	1	9	3	1	1/2	1	1/3
Water	2	9	9	3	2	3	1

The derived scale based on the judgments in the matrix is:

Coffee	Wine	Tea	Beer	Sodas	Milk	Water
.177	.019	.042	.116	.190	.129	.327

with a consistency ratio of .022.
The actual consumption (from statistical sources) is:

.180	.010	.040	.120	.180	.140	.330

Table 4 Relative Consumption of Drinks

The Compatibility of Several (Ratio) Scales

Consider now the case of two vectors $p = (p_1, ..., p_n)$ and $q = (q_1, ..., q_n)$ each of which consists of single readings each on one of n scales as in the case of a patient who takes several tests measured in different ways. How should we judge how close p and q are? We first consider the ratios $\dfrac{p_i}{q_i}$ and form the sum $\dfrac{1}{2n}\sum_{i=1}^{n}\left(\dfrac{p_i}{q_i}+\dfrac{q_i}{p_i}\right)$ and require that it be close to one. If on the other hand we can determine through paired comparisons that the properties have different priorities given by a normalized vector $\alpha = (\alpha_1, ..., \alpha_n)$, then we require that

$$\frac{1}{2}\sum_{i=1}^{n}\alpha_i\left(\frac{p_i}{q_i}+\frac{q_i}{p_i}\right)$$

be close to one. If we have multiple readings on each property, we could use the same analysis for each as in the previous discussion for a single attribute and add the outcomes and require the total not exceed 1.10. For a mixed vector with several readings each on a different property some of which are measured on the same ratio scale, we compare these readings as before. Finally we add the different indices derived for the different ratio scales and take their average for an overall index that should be no more than 1.10.

The foregoing discussion assumes that the measurements are independent of one another. If there is dependence among the factors it can be captured in part through α_i above. Measurements from several different ratio scales may be multiplied to form a single new ratio scale. This product may be compared with a similar product by forming the expression

$$\frac{1}{2}\left[\frac{p_1 p_2 \cdots p_n}{q_1 q_2 \cdots q_n}+\frac{q_1 q_2 \cdots q_n}{p_1 p_2 \cdots p_n}\right]$$

that should be close to one.

How to Improve Consistency when the Judgments and Understanding Allow It-The Gradient

For a given positive reciprocal matrix $A= [a_{ij}]$ and a given pair of distinct indices $k > l$, define $A(t)= [a_{ij}(t)]$ by $a_{kl}(t) \equiv a_{kl} + t$, $a_{lk}(t) \equiv (a_{lk} + t)^{-1}$, and $a_{ij}(t) \equiv a_{ij}$ for all $i \neq k$, $j \neq l$, so $A(0) = A$. Let $\lambda_{max}(t)$ denote the Perron eigenvalue of $A(t)$ for all t in a neighborhood of $t = 0$ that is small enough to ensure that all entries of the reciprocal matrix $A(t)$ are positive there. Finally, let $v = [v_i]$ be the unique positive eigenvector of the positive matrix A^T that is normalized so that $v^T w = 1$. Then a classical perturbation formula [6] tells us that

$$\frac{d\lambda_{\max}(t)}{dt}\bigg|_{t=0} = \frac{v^T A'(0)w}{v^T w} = v^T A'(0)w = v_k w_l - \frac{1}{a_{kl}^2} v_l w_k.$$

We conclude that

$$\frac{\partial \lambda_{\max}}{\partial a_{ij}} = v_i w_j - a_{ji}^2 v_j w_i \text{ for all } i,j=1,\ldots,n.$$

Because we are operating within the set of positive reciprocal matrices we have:

$$\frac{\partial \lambda_{\max}}{\partial a_{ji}} = -\frac{\partial \lambda_{\max}}{\partial a_{ij}} \text{ for all } i \text{ and } j.$$

Thus, to identify an entry of A whose adjustment within the class of reciprocal matrices would result in the largest rate of change in $\lambda_{\max}$ we should examine the $n(n-1)/2$ values $\{v_i w_j - a_{ji}^2 v_j w_i\}, i > j$ and select (any) one of largest absolute value [7]. We had proposed using the judgment which when divided by the ratio of the corresponding values from the eigenvector is the largest (smallest) when it fact it should be equal to one. It is significant to note here that if one compares more than about seven elements in a homogeneous group, the rise in inconsistency is generally so small that it is then difficult to determine which judgment should be changed [4]. In no case should one force improvement in inconsistency unless one's understanding, more or less, permits that change.

Rating Alternatives One at a Time

People are able to make two kinds of comparisons - absolute and relative. In absolute comparisons, people compare alternatives with a standard in their memory that they have developed through experience. In relative comparisons, they compared alternatives in pairs according to a common attribute.

People use ratings to rank independent alternatives one at a time in terms of rating intensities for each of the criteria. An intensity is a range of variation of a criterion that enables one to distinguish the quality of an alternative for that criterion. An intensity may be expressed as a numerical range of values if the criterion is measurable or defined in qualitative terms.

For example, if ranking students is the objective and one of the criteria on which they are to be ranked is performance in mathematics, the mathematics ratings might be: excellent, good, average, below average, poor; or, using the usual school terminology, A, B, C, D and F. Relative comparisons are first used to set priorities on the ratings themselves. If desired, one can fit a continuous curve through the derived intensities. This concept may go against our socialization. However, it is perfectly reasonable to ask how much an A is preferred to a B or to a C. The judgment of how much an A is preferred to a B might be different under different criteria. Perhaps for mathematics an A is very strongly preferred to a B, while for physical education an A is only moderately preferred to a B. So the end result might be that the ratings are scaled differently. For example one could have the scale values for the ratings as shown in Table 5:

Table 5 Examples of Scale Values for Ratings

	Math	Physical Education
A	0.50	0.30
B	0.30	0.30
C	0.15	0.20
D	0.04	0.10
E	0.01	0.10

The alternatives are then rated or ticked off one at a time using the intensities. We will illustrate ratings with an example. A firm evaluates its employees for raises. The criteria are dependability, education, experience, and quality. Each criterion is subdivided into intensities, standards, or subcriteria (Figure 9). The managers set priorities for the criteria by comparing them in pairs. They then pairwise compare the intensities according to priority with respect to their parent criterion (as in Table 6) or with respect to a subcriterion if they are using a deeper hierarchy. The priorities of the intensities are divided by the largest intensity for each criterion (second column of priorities in Figure 9).

Table 6 shows a paired comparison matrix of intensities with respect to dependability. The managers answer the question: which intensity is more important and by how much with respect to dependability. The priorities of the intensities for each criterion are divided by the largest one and multiplied by the priority of the criterion. Finally the managers rate each individual (Table 7) by assigning the intensity rating that applies to him or her under each criterion. The scores of these intensities are each weighted by the priority of its criterion and summed to derive a total ratio scale score for the individual (shown on the right of Table 7). These numbers belong to an absolute scale, and the managers can give salary increases precisely in proportion to the ratios of these numbers. Adams gets the highest score and

Kesselman the lowest. This approach can be used whenever it is possible to set priorities for intensities of criteria; people can usually do this when they have sufficient experience with a given operation. This normative mode requires that alternatives be rated one by one without regard to how many there may be and how high or low any of them rates on prior standards. Some corporations have insisted that they no longer trust the normative standards of their experts and that they prefer to make paired comparisons of their alternatives. Still, when there is wide agreement on standards, the absolute mode saves time in rating a large number of alternatives.

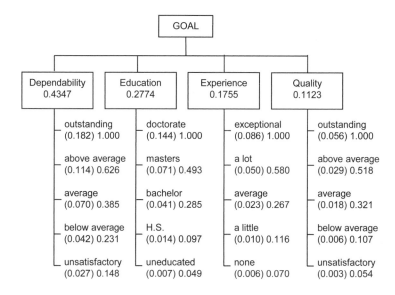

Figure 9 Hierarchy with Absolute Measurement

Table 6 Ranking Intensities: Which intensity is preferred most with respect to dependability and how strongly?

Dependability	Outstand-ing	Above Average	Average	Below Average	Unsatis-factory	Priorities	Idealized Priorities
Outstanding	1.0	2.0	3.0	4.0	5.0	0.419	1.000
Above Avg	1/2	1.0	2.0	3.0	4.0	0.263	0.628
Average	1/3	1/2	1.0	2.0	3.0	0.160	0.382
Below Avg.	1/4	1/3	1/2	1.0	2.0	0.097	0.232
Unsatisfactory	1/5	1/4	1/3	1/2	1.0	0.062	0.148

C.R. = 0.015

Table 7 Rating Alternatives

Employees	Dependability .4347	Education .2774	Experience .1775	Quality .1123	Total
1. Adams, V	Outstanding	Bachelor	A Little	Outstandin	0.646
2. Becker, L	Average	Bachelor	A Little	Outstandin	0.379
3. Hayat, F	Average	Masters	A Lot	Below	0.418
4. Kessel, S	Above	H.S.	None	Average	0.369
5. O'Shea, K	Average	Doctorate	A Lot	Above	0.605
6. Peters, T	Average	Doctorate	A Lot	Average	0.583
7. Tobias, K	Above	Bachelor	Averag	Above	0.456

Nonlinearity and Multilinear Forms in the AHP

Hierarchic composition produces sums of products of priorities. These define a special kind of mathematical function known as a multilinear form. It is useful for us to examine briefly how these forms that arise here naturally, may tell us something useful about the real world. This subject is wide open for investigation.

A **monomial** is a single term that is a product of one coefficient and several variables each with an exponent indicating a power (often restricted to be a non-negative integer) of that variable. Examples are $-3x^5, a^2x^3y^2, -a$. A **polynomial** is the sum or difference of monomials as $-5x^3y^7z^2+2xy^4+7$ from which we can define a polynomial in one variable as $2x^4-x^2+x+1$. A polynomial is a rational integral algebraic expression with nonnegative powers of the variables. The coefficients of a polynomial can be real or complex. A **multinomial** is another term for polynomial, although one would prefer the former to apply to several variables and the latter to a single variable. A **form** is a polynomial in several variables in which the sum of the powers of the variables in each term is equal to that in any other term. A form is binary, ternary etc depending on whether it has two, three etc. variables. It is linear, quadratic etc the sum of the degrees of the variables that is the same in each term. For example $7xz-3y^2+2yz$ is a ternary quadratic form. A **multilinear** form is a form in which the variables are divided into sets so that in each term a variable from every set appears to the first power. It has the general form

$$\sum_{i,j,\ldots,l=1}^{n} a_{ij\ldots l} x_i y_j \ldots z_l$$

with m sets of variables with n variables in each set, $x_1, x_2, \ldots, x_n; y_1, y_2, \ldots, y_n; z_1, z_2, \ldots, z_n$ and because it is linear in the variables of each set, it is called a multilinear form. When $m=1$, the form

$$\sum_{i=1}^{n} a_i x_i$$

is known as a linear form. When $m=2$, the form

$$\sum_{i,j=1}^{n} a_{ij} x_i y_i$$

is known as a bilinear form. Any form can be obtained from a multilinear form by identifying certain of the variables. Conversely, transforming any form to a multilinear form is carried out by polarization. For example $x_1^2 + 2x_1 x_2 + x_2^2$ can be written as a multilinear form $x_1 y_1 + x_1 y_2 + x_2 y_1 + x_2 y_2$ with y_1 identified with x_1 and y_2 identified with x_2. A multilinear form is a particular case of a multilinear mapping or operator (not defined here) as a result of which one can think of it as symmetric, skew symmetric, alternating, symmetrized and skew symmetrized forms. Let us now turn to hierarchies using more uniform notation.

Hierarchic composition yields multilinear forms which are of course nonlinear and have the form

$$\sum_{i_1,\cdots,i_p} x_1^{i_1} x_2^{i_2} \cdots x_p^{i_p}$$

The richer the structure of a hierarchy in breadth and depth the more complex are the derived multilinear forms from it. There seems to be a good opportunity to investigate the relationship obtained by composition to covariant tensors and their algebraic properties. More concretely we have the following covariant tensor for the priority of the ith element in the hth level of the hierarchy.

$$w_i^h = \sum_{i_2,\cdots,i_{h-1}=1}^{N_{h-1},\cdots,N_1} w_{i_1 i_2}^{h-1} \cdots w_{i_{h-2} i_{h-1}}^{2} w_{i_{h-1}}^{1} \quad i_1 \equiv i$$

The composite vector for the entire hth level is represented by the vector with covariant tensorial components. Similarly, the left eigenvector approach to a hierarchy gives rise to a vector with contravariant tensor components. Tensors, are generalizations of scalars (which have no indices), vectors (which have a single index), and matrices or arrays (which have two indices) to an arbitrary number of indices. They are widely known and used in physics and engineering.

Another interpretation follows the lines of polynomial approximation. We see above that polynomials in one and in several variables are intimately linked to multilinear forms. The **Weierstrass approximation theorem** states that every continuous function defined on an interval $[a,b]$ can be uniformly approximated as closely as desired by a polynomial function. These ideas will be discussed again later in the book.

The Analytic Hierarchy Process and Resource Allocation

Intangible resources such as quality, care, attention, and intelligence are often needed to develop a plan, design a system or solve a problem. Thus far, resource allocation models have not dealt with intangibles directly, but rather by assigning them worth in terms of such phenomena as time and money. Although there is no direct scale of measurement for an intangible, it can be measured in relative terms together with tangibles. A ratio scale of priorities can thus be derived for both. These priorities serve as coefficients in an optimization framework to derive relative amounts of resources to be allocated. For intangible resources, because there is no unit of measurement, no absolute amount of a resource can be specified. However, in the presence of tangibles, it becomes possible to compute their absolute equivalents because of the proportionality inherent in their priorities. The coefficients of a mathematical linear programming (LP) model can be represented with priorities obtained with relative (i.e., pairwise comparisons) measurement. The result is that when measurement scales exist, the solution to the relative linear programming (RLP) model (with coefficients normalized to unity to make them correspond to priorities obtained with relative measurement) and the solution to the absolute linear programming (LP) model (the "usual" model with measurements on physical scales are the same to within a multiplicative constant. It is then possible to construct LP models using solely relative measurement to optimize the allocation of intangible resources, as can be seen below.

It is significant to note that all coefficients in the relative formulation are unit free, although their relative magnitudes are preserved. Thus, the underlying magnitudes they represent can be compared in pairs.

There are three places where intangibles can arise in an LP model, the objective function and in estimating the left side and the right side of the coefficients of the constraints. The most common is in the objective function wherein the coefficients can be estimated as priorities, with the rest of the model formulated in the usual way. This presents no practical complications since the solution is the same if the objective function coefficients are given in relative terms, which is tantamount to dividing by a constant. For general treatment and examples, see Saaty, Vargas and Dellmann [8].

	Traditional LP	⇔	Relative LP

Decision Variables: $\bar{x} = (\bar{x}_1, \cdots, \bar{x}_n)^T$ $\qquad$ $\bar{w} = (w_1, \cdots, w_n)^T$

Objective Function: $\sum_j c_j x_j \rightarrow {}_R c_j = \dfrac{c_j}{\sum_k |c_k|} \rightarrow \sum_j {}_R c_j w_j$

Constraints: $\sum_j a_{ij} x_j \le b_i \rightarrow \left\{ \begin{array}{l} {}_R a_{ij} = \dfrac{a_{ij}}{\sum_k |a_{ik}|} \\[2mm] {}_R b_i = \dfrac{\dfrac{b_i}{\sum_k |a_{ik}|}}{\sum_h \dfrac{|b_h|}{\sum_k |a_{hk}|}} \\[2mm] w_j = \dfrac{x_j}{\sum_h \dfrac{|b_h|}{\sum_k |a_{hk}|}} \end{array} \right\} \rightarrow \sum_j {}_R a_{ij} w_j \le {}_R b_i$

Primal:

$$Max \sum_j c_j x_j \qquad\qquad Max \sum_j {}_R c_j w_j$$

$$s.t.: \sum_j a_{ij} x_j \le b_i \qquad \Leftrightarrow \qquad s.t.: \sum_j {}_R a_{ij} w_j \le {}_R b_i$$

$$x_j \ge 0 \qquad\qquad w_j \ge 0$$

Dual:

$$Min \sum_i b_i y_i \qquad\qquad Min \sum_i {}_R b_i v_i$$

$$s.t.: \sum_i a_{ij} y_i \ge c_j \qquad \Leftrightarrow \qquad s.t.: \sum_i {}_R a_{ij} v_i \ge {}_R c_j$$

$$y_i \ge 0 \qquad\qquad v_j \ge 0$$

Judgments, Feelings and Measurement

Because decision making involves judgments, preferences, feelings, and risk taking, it appears that it belongs in part to meta rational thinking. In rational thinking one uses logic based on explicit assumptions to derive one's conclusions. In decision making one elicits information about comparisons and preferences that belong to the domain of feelings and emotions.

In Chapter 2 we had quotations against and for quantifying feelings. In addition to A. F. MacKay [9] mentioned and Le Shan and Margenau [11] mentioned in that chapter, Davis and Hersh [10] write, "If you are more of a human being, you will be aware there are such things as emotions, beliefs, attitudes, dreams, intentions, jealousy, envy, yearning, regret, longing, anger, compassion and many others. These things —the inner world of human life— can never be mathematized."

The Nobel Laureate, Henri Bergson [12] writes: But even the opponents of psychophysics do not see any harm in speaking of one sensation as being more intense than another, of one effort as being greater than another, and in thus setting up differences of quantity between purely internal states. Common sense, moreover, has not the slightest hesitation in giving its verdict on this point; people say they are more or less warm, or more or less sad, and this distinction of more and less, even when it is carried over to the region of subjective facts and unextended objects, surprises nobody.

A question that puzzles all of us brought up in the use of models is that usually a model is based on data from measurement that anyone can validate on their own. In the AHP we rely on the judgment of people. Where does this judgment originate, and how can we trust the subjective understanding of people to tell us something "objective" about the real world? We must assume that any understanding registers somewhere in our nervous system and we carry it with us. In the end we are the ones who provide the criteria and ways of understanding. At bottom all knowledge is subjectively derived. In this regard psychologists make the distinction between our cognitive and our affective (feeling) abilities. The changes in state of an organism due to the dynamic stresses in the psychological situation experienced are directly apprehended as sensations or perceptions belonging to our cognitive ability. The state itself is apprehended as feeling (affect), a global effect arising from a pattern of visceral impulses that is not easily localizable.

While "thinking" is generally thought to be carried out in the neo-cortex of the brain, feelings and partly emotions are associated with the autonomic (sympathetic and parasympathetic) nervous system that in part is known to operate independently of the thought processes of the brain. There is very little conscious control over many activities of the autonomic nervous system. It is as if there are two persons in each of us. One that looks out at the environment to give us information for survival of hazards, and another that looks inside to keep our system running. The sympathetic division, located in the spinal cord from its first thoracic to its third lumbar segments prepares the body in times of stress by dilating the blood vessels in the heart, muscles, and other vital organs, speeding the heart and blood flow (by stimulating production of adrenaline that liberates sugar from the liver) and constricting it in the skin. The parasympathetic division has two parts one originating in the midbrain, pons and medulla and consists of four cranial nerves mostly opposing sympathetic action as needed, and the other division comes from cells in the second, third and fourth segments of the sacral part of the spinal cord both stimulating parts of the body and inhibiting others like constricting the bronchi in the lungs.

Most animals have small brains but have effective autonomic systems to run their bodies, perhaps better in some ways than we have. Our brain looks out to the environment to provide data for adjustment and survival. Philosophically, decision making must be subject to the laws of science but its assumptions cannot be stated explicitly because of the use of feelings and intuition to express preference. Science has not yet learned enough about where emotions and feelings fit rationally into our system of logical thinking.

It has been pointed out to this author that there is a classification of types or levels of consciousness that originated in India which shows that truth belongs to different domains of existence of which logical thinking is only a part and not necessarily the ultimate means of discovering ideas and meaning. They are: 1) physical (matter and energy in the form of solids, liquids and gasses), 2) etheric (electromagnetic, subatomic particles), 3) emotional (feeling, emotion, desire, imagination, personal power), 4) mental (intellectual, understanding, beliefs, thoughts, knowledge, and cognitive processes), 5) causal (personal individuality, the enlivening source of life and consciousness), 6) physical to causal (the personality as a unit is made of several bodies: the mental/intellectual, the emotional, the etheric and the physical), 7) the different bodies combined, 8) manasic (consciousness of a bigger reality beyond the physical world), 9) social or religious buddhic/christic, (wider consciousness beyond individuality and integration with others with love and harmony), 10) atmic (identification not with individuals, not with groups, but with all pervading life-equanimity and peacefulness towards all.) Atmic consciousness is characterized by omnipotence and an extreme power of will that makes nearly all possible is that of pure equanimity with undifferentiated awareness - identification, not with individuality, not with groups of beings, but with all pervading life itself. It is the transcendence of both pain and bliss, extremely intense peace, 11) monadic (the generator of consciousness for all the previous levels, the power station from which will, love and intelligence are derived), and 12) logoic (the universal God consciousness encompassing all the beings living on the multiple levels mentioned above of which we are the atoms.) Decision making, even as we try to explain it with logic, belongs to the tenth or atmic level of consciousness.

Benefits, Opportunities, Costs, and Risks – The Ratio and Total Formulas

The synthesized results of the alternatives for each of the four control merits of benefits (B), opportunities (O), costs (C) and risks (R) are combined, along traditional benefit to cost ratio analysis used in economics, to obtain a ratio outcome by taking the quotient of the benefits times the opportunities to the costs times the risks for each alternative thus forming the formula that represents marginal returns (BO/CR). If desired, the results for the alternatives are normalized to determine the best outcome. This formula is only useful when one is certain that the relative measurements are commensurate, that is, of the same order of magnitude. In other words it is meaningless to divide thousands of dollars for benefits, by pennies for costs that is tantamount to dividing by numbers close to zero.

There is another more reliable way to combine the B, O, C, and R over the long run that gives the total outcome. The top ranked alternative is rated (not compared) for each of the B, O, C and R with respect to strategic criteria that are needed to determine the merits of any decision. From this rating one then obtains normalized respective weights, b, o, c and r and computes the total outcome bB+oO-cC-rR for each alternative, possibly yielding negative values. Note in evaluating the benefits (opportunities) ones responds to the question of dominance: which alternative contributes the most benefits (opportunities), whereas for costs (risks) one responds to the question which alternative costs (is subject to greater risks) more, which is opposite in sense to the benefits and opportunities and must be subtracted from them. It is known that the ranks obtained from ratio and total syntheses need not coincide.

We note that there is no advantage in using the weights b, o, c and r in the formula (BO/CR) because we would be multiplying the result for each alternative by the same constant bo/cr. Because all values lie between zero and one, we have from the series expansions of the exponential and logarithmic functions the approximation:

$$\frac{bBoO}{cCrR} = \exp(\log bB + \log oO - \log cC - \log rR) \approx 1 + (\log bB + \log oO - \log cC - \log rR) + \ldots \approx$$
$$1 + (bB - 1) + (oO - 1) - (cC - 1) - (rR - 1) = 1 + bB + oO - cC - rR$$

Because the constant one is added to the overall value of each alternative we can eliminate it. The approximate result is that the ratio formula is similar (but not identical, nor particularly numerically close) to the total formula with equal weights assumed for the B, O, C, and R. Note that the total outcome formula is related to the residual probabilities formula that always gives positive answers needed in probabilities: $bB + oO + c(1-C) + r(1-R) = bB + oO - cC - rR + c + r$ in which the costs and risks are subtracted from one and in the end it turns out that the same constant $c + r$ is added to the priority of every alternative. However, this last formula may be useful in situations involving BOCR that predict proportionate voting or other type of outcomes measured with positive numbers or statistics.

A Full BOCR Example for a Hierarchy: AHP Analysis of Strategies Towards Iran

The threat of war in Iran is a complex and controversial issue, involving many actors in different regions and several possible courses of action. Nearly 40 people were involved in the exercise. They were divided into groups of 4 or 5 and each of these groups worked out the model and derived results for a designated merit: benefits, opportunities, costs or risks. In the end there were two outcomes for each merit which were combined using the geometric mean (proven to be the only way to combine individual judgments to produce a representative group judgment that satisfies the reciprocal relation) and then the four resulting outcomes were combined into a single overall outcome as described below. It should be understood that this is only an exercise to illustrate use of the method and no real life conclusions should be drawn from it primarily because it did not involve political expert and negotiators from all the interested parties. Its conclusions should be taken as hypotheses to be further tested.

Creating the Model

A model for determining the policy to pursue towards Iran seeking to obtain weapon grade nuclear material was designed using a benefits, opportunities, costs, and risks model. The benefits model shows which alternative would be most beneficial, the opportunities model shows which alternative has the greatest potential for benefits, the costs model (costs may include monetary, human and intangible costs) shows which alternative would be most costly and the risks model shows which alternative has the highest potential costs.

Strategic Criteria

Strategic Criteria are used to evaluate the BOCR merits of all decisions by a decision maker. They are the overriding criteria that individuals corporations or governments use to determine which decision to make first, and what are the relative advantages and disadvantages of that decision.

For policy towards Iran, the BOCR model structured by the group is evaluated using the strategic criteria of *World Peace* (0.361), *Regional Stability* (0.356), *Reduce Volatility* (0.087) and *Reduce Escalation of Middle East Problem* (0.196). The priorities of the strategic criteria indicated in parentheses next to each, are obtained from a pairwise comparisons matrix with respect to the goal of long term peace in the world.

Control Criteria

The BOCR model is evaluated using the control criteria: *Economic, Political, Rule of Law* and *Security*. They are the criteria for which we are able to represent the different kinds of influences that we are able to perceive which later need to be combined into an overall influence using AHP/ANP calculations.

Actors

The countries mainly concerned with this problem are: the *US, Iran, Russia & China, Middle East* countries and *Israel*.

Alternatives

The group identified six Alternatives:
(1) It is reasonable to undertake *Aerial Strikes* towards Iran
(2) *Economic Sanctions* should be applied against Iran
(3) The Actors should carry out *Ground Invasion* of Iran
(4) *Israeli Action* towards Iran
(5) To do *Nothing*, leaving everything so as it is
(6) To make efforts to make a *Regime Change*

BOCR Models

With a view to saving space we do not give all the hierarchies and their matrices of judgments. In this exercise it was determined to keep the structure simple by using the same structure for all four merits (see Figure 10) albeit with different judgments. In particular for the costs and risks one asks the question which is more (not less) costly or risky, and in the end subtract the corresponding values from those of benefits and opportunities. The analysis derives four rankings of the alternatives, one for each of the BOCR merits. Following that one must obtain priorities for the BOCRs themselves in terms of the strategic criteria and use the top ranked alternative for each merit in order to think about that merit and then use those priorities to weigh and synthesize the alternatives. The priorities of the alternatives are proportional to the priority of the top ranked alternative, thus they would all be multiplied by the same number that is the priority of the merit.

It is important to note again that usually for a general decision problem each merit would have a different structure than the other merits. However, for the sake of expediency in this decision, the group decided to use the same structure with the appropriate formulation of the questions to provide the judgments.

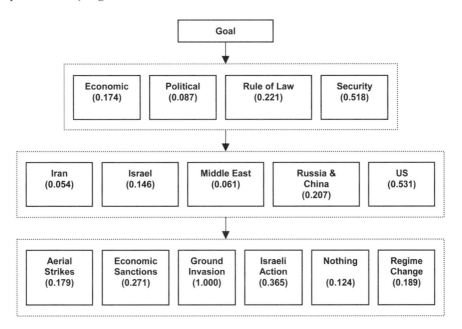

Figure 10 Costs Hierarchy to Choose the Best Strategy towards Iran

Judgments and Comparisons

As previously mentioned, a judgment is an expression of opinion about the dominance (importance, preference or likelihood) of one element over another. It is done every day through verbal expression that has some quantitative significance that we need to use to combine the many dominance judgments involved in a decision. The set of all such judgments in making comparisons with respect to a single property or goal can be represented by means of a square matrix in which the set of elements is compared. It is a way of organizing all the judgments with respect to some property to be processed and synthesized along with other matrices of comparisons involved in the decision. Each judgment represents the dominance of an element in the left column of the matrix over an element in the row on top. It reflects the answers to two questions: which of the two elements is more important with respect to a higher level criterion, and how strongly.

As usual with the AHP, in the models of benefits, opportunities, cost, and risks the group compared the criteria and subcriteria according to their relative importance with respect to the parent element in the adjacent upper level. For example, the entries in the matrix shown in Table 8 are responses to the question: which control criterion is more important with respect to choosing the best strategy towards Iran and how strongly? Here economic costs are moderately more important than political costs and are assigned the absolute number 3 in the (1,2) or first-row second-column position. Three signifies three times more. The reciprocal value is automatically entered in the (2,1) position, where political costs on the left are compared with economic costs at the top. Similarly a 5, corresponding to strong dominance or importance, is assigned to security costs over political costs in the (4,2) position, and a 2, corresponding to weak or slight dominance, is assigned to the costs of rule of law over political costs in the (3,2) position with corresponding reciprocals in the transpose positions of the matrix.

The group first made all the comparisons using semantic terms from the fundamental scale and then translated them to the corresponding numbers.

Table 8 Judgment Matrix for the Control Criteria of the Costs Hierarchy

Choosing best strategy towards Iran (costs)	Economic	Political	Rule of Law	Security	Normalized Priorities
Economic	1	3	½	1/3	0.173
Political	1/3	1	½	1/5	0.087
Rule of Law	2	2	1	1/3	0.222
Security	3	5	3	1	0.518

C.R. = 0.049

For example, where we compare security costs with economic costs and with political costs, we have the respective judgments 3 and 5. Now if $x=3y$ and $x=5z$ then $3y=5z$ or $y=5/3z$. If the judges were consistent, economic costs would be assigned the value 5/3 instead of the 3 given in the matrix. Thus the judgments are inconsistent. In fact, we are not sure which judgments are the accurate ones and which are the cause of the inconsistency. However, these can be determined in a systematic way and improved by interrogating the decision maker.

The process is repeated for all the matrices by asking the appropriate dominance or importance question. For example, the entries in the judgment matrix shown in Table 9 are responses to the question: which party is more committed to ensure security?

Table 9 Judgment Matrix of Subcriteria with Respect to Security Costs

Security Costs	Iran	Israel	Middle East	Russia & China	U.S.	Normalized Priorities
Iran	1	1/8	1/3	1/6	1/9	0.029
Israel	8	1	4	1/2	1/7	0.138
Middle East	3	1/4	1	1/5	1/7	0.054
Russia & China	6	2	5	1	1/6	0.182
U.S.	9	7	7	6	1	0.597

C.R. = 0.1

Here US security costs are regarded as extremely more important than the security costs for Iran, and 9 is entered in the (5,1) position and 1/9 in the (1, 5) position.

In comparing the six strategies (alternatives) towards Iran, we asked members of the decision group which strategy in their opinion would be more costly for each of the actors. For example, for the USA, we obtained a matrix of paired comparisons in Table 10 in which Ground Invasion is the most expensive strategy. On the contrary, regime change and doing nothing are the least costly ones. In this example the criteria (here the different countries) are assumed to be independent of the alternatives and hence the priorities of alternatives are given in ideal form by dividing by the largest priority among them. Here ground invasion would be the most costly.

Tables 11, 12 and 13 give the priorities obtained from all the comparisons for the BOCR.

Table 10 Relative Costs of the Strategies for the U.S

Strategies costs for the U.S.	Aerial Strikes	Economic Sanctions	Ground Invasion	Israeli Action	Nothing	Normalized Priorities	Idealized Priorities
Aerial Strikes	1	1/3	1/7	1/2	3	0.087	0.164
Economic Sanctions	3	1	1/6	2	3	0.160	0.301
Ground Invasion	7	6	1	6	7	0.533	1.000
Israeli Action	2	1/2	1/6	1	3	0.122	0.229
Nothing	1/3	1/3	1/7	1/3	1	0.058	0.108
Regime Change	1/3	1/3	1/6	1/4	1/3	0.040	0.075

C. R. = 0.08

Each column in Table 11 gives in bold face the priorities of the control criteria with respect to which the comparisons are made. For example economic has the value 0.047 under opportunities obtained by comparing it in a matrix with Political, Rule of Law and security whose priorities are also shown in bold face. These priorities sum to one. We do likewise under opportunities costs and risks. The priorities of the actors are given under the priority of each of the control criteria in the same column. At the bottom of Table 12 are given the overall priorities of the actors with respect to each of the BOCR obtained by weighting by the priority of the control criteria and adding in the same column. We do not yet combine numbers in the same row but only in the same column. Similarly in Table 12 for the actors and the alternatives. At the bottom of Table 12 we have the overall idealized weights of the alternatives for each of the BOCR. In Table 13 we rate the top alternative for each BOCR merit with respect to each of the strategic criteria using a rating scale derived from comparisons. Usually and for greater precision one should develop a different rating scale for each criterion or subcriterion, but we have simplified the analysis here by adopting a single scale for all the strategic criteria. We then weight the ratings by the priorities of the strategic criteria and add to obtain a weight for each BOCR merit. Finally we normalize these four values to obtain the priorities b,o,c, and r. We then use these priorities in Table 14 to synthesize the idealized weights of the alternatives according to the marginal formula that represents short term solution and the total formula that represents long term solution to the problem.

Table 11 Priorities of the Actors with respect to Control Criteria of BOCR groups

		BENEFITS	OPPORTUNITIES	COSTS	RISKS
Control Criteria	Actors				
Economic		**0.047**	**0.626**	**0.174**	**0.209**
	Iran	0.031	0.066	0.129	0.321
	Israel	0.259	0.041	0.036	0.126
	Middle East	0.166	0.233	0.087	0.306
	Russia & China	0.095	0.120	0.425	0.075
	US	0.449	0.540	0.324	0.173
Political		**0.128**	**0.156**	**0.087**	**0.033**
	Iran	0.043	0.201	0.082	0.506
	Israel	0.311	0.125	0.226	0.145
	Middle East	0.133	0.494	0.067	0.248
	Russia & China	0.079	0.090	0.152	0.045
	US	0.433	0.090	0.483	0.056
Rule of Law		**0.246**	**0.043**	**0.222**	**0.066**
	Iran	0.031	0.114	0.044	0.317
	Israel	0.347	0.415	0.218	0.118
	Middle East	0.132	0.169	0.060	0.443
	Russia & China	0.101	0.051	0.119	0.059
	US	0.389	0.251	0.559	0.063
Security		**0.579**	**0.175**	**0.518**	**0.692**
	Iran	0.068	0.131	0.029	0.200
	Israel	0.115	0.298	0.138	0.200
	Middle East	0.165	0.308	0.054	0.200
	Russia & China	0.407	0.106	0.181	0.200
	US	0.245	0.156	0.597	0.200
OVERALL					

	Iran	0.031	0.100	0.054	0.243
	Israel	0.259	0.115	0.204	0.177
	Middle East	0.166	0.284	0.153	0.240
	Russia & China	0.095	0.110	0.275	0.159
	US	0.449	0.390	0.314	0.180

Table 12 Priorities of the Alternatives with Respect to the Actors in BOCR Groups

Actors	Alternatives	BENEFITS	OPPORTUNITIES	COSTS	RISKS
Iran		**0.031**	**0.100**	**0.054**	**0.243**
	Aerial Strikes	1.000	0.078	0.115	0.701
	Economic Sanctions	1.000	0.452	0.260	1.000
	Ground Invasion	1.000	0.057	1.000	0.294
	Israeli Action	1.000	0.142	0.149	0.762
	Nothing	1.000	1.000	0.068	0.239
	Regime Change	1.000	0.220	0.362	0.882
Israel		**0.259**	**0.115**	**0.204**	**0.177**
	Aerial Strikes	0.214	0.359	0.212	0.240
	Economic Sanctions	0.463	0.069	0.120	0.209
	Ground Invasion	0.128	0.228	0.355	0.385
	Israeli Action	0.070	0.104	1.000	1.000
	Nothing	0.177	0.062	0.210	0.153
	Regime Change	1.000	1.000	0.130	0.052
Middle East		**0.166**	**0.284**	**0.153**	**0.240**
	Aerial Strikes	0.095	0.168	0.257	0.186
	Economic Sanctions	0.357	0.676	0.132	0.073
	Ground Invasion	0.159	0.196	1.000	0.328
	Israeli Action	0.131	0.062	0.483	1.000
	Nothing	1.000	0.371	0.111	0.068
	Regime Change	0.702	1.000	0.175	0.045
Russia & China		**0.095**	**0.110**	**0.275**	**0.159**
	Aerial Strikes	0.778	0.141	0.114	0.190
	Economic Sanctions	0.825	0.259	0.215	0.057
	Ground Invasion	0.331	0.174	1.000	0.379
	Israeli Action	1.000	0.122	0.160	1.000
	Nothing	0.559	1.000	0.071	0.072
	Regime Change	0.303	0.154	0.411	0.086
US		**0.449**	**0.390**	**0.314**	**0.180**
	Aerial Strikes	0.167	1.000	0.164	0.133
	Economic Sanctions	0.231	0.094	0.301	0.076
	Ground Invasion	0.130	0.285	1.000	0.388
	Israeli Action	0.165	0.050	0.229	1.000
	Nothing	1.000	0.150	0.108	0.079
	Regime Change	0.130	0.417	0.075	0.038

OVERALL					
	Aerial Strikes	0.402	0.891	0.179	0.259
	Economic Sanctions	0.586	0.496	0.271	0.221
	Ground Invasion	0.258	0.378	1.000	0.368
	Israeli Action	0.414	0.136	0.365	1.000
	Nothing	1.000	0.666	0.124	0.112
	Regime Change	0.651	1.000	0.189	0.165

Table 13 Ratings of Strategic Criteria for BOCR merits

VeryHigh (1), High (0.619), Medium (0.381), Low (0.238), VeryLow (0.143).

	World peace (0.362)	Regional Stability (0.356)	Reduce Volatility (0.087)	Reduce Escalation of the Middle East Conflict (0.196)	Priorities	Normalized Priorities
Benefits	Very High	High	High	Medium	0.710	0.254
Opportunities	Medium	Low	Medium	Medium	0.330	0.118
Costs	Very High	Very High	Very High	Medium	0.878	0.314
Risks	Very High	Very High	Very High	Medium	0.878	0.314

Table 14 Synthesis of the Alternatives' Overall Priorities for the Four BOCR Merits

	BENEFITS	OPPORTUNITIES	COSTS	RISKS	BO/CR	bB+oO-cC-rR
	b=0.254	o=0.118	c=0.314	r=0.314		
Aerial Strikes	0.402	0.891	0.179	0.259	7.711	0.069
Economic Sanctions	0.586	0.496	0.271	0.221	4.841	0.053
Ground Invasion	0.258	0.378	1.000	0.368	0.265	-0.319
Israeli Action	0.414	0.136	0.365	1.000	0.155	-0.308
Nothing	1.000	0.666	0.124	0.112	**48.077**	**0.258**
Regime Change	0.651	1.000	0.189	0.165	20.814	0.172

Next, we rate the top outcome for each of the BOCR against the strategic criteria using the five-level ratings scale obtained from paired comparisons: The synthesized Rating Results are shown in Table 14. We want to evaluate or rate the top alternative for Benefits and that for opportunities against the strategic criteria as to how they help with respect to each criterion. We also want to rate the top alternatives for the costs and risks as to how much they hurt or damage with respect to each criterion. This yields the priorities of the BOCR before normalization.

Benefits and Opportunities are positive merits, whereas Costs and Risks are negative. The overbalance of weights is negative for Ground Invasion and Israeli Action and is positive for Aerial Strikes, Economic Sanctions, doing Nothing and Regime Change. As a result, in the current situation doing Nothing turns out to be the best alternative and Ground Invasion is the worst.

Sensitivity Analysis

There are many ways for doing sensitivity analysis, we show one of them here. Sensitivity graphs for BOCR groups are shown in Figures 11, 12, 13 and 14 respectively. From the software program Superdecisions we see that the results obtained by perturbing the priorities of each of the benefits and opportunities, costs and risks are stable. The model is sensitive to changes of priorities in the BOCR merits. As the priority of Costs increases, the alternative 'Israeli Action' becomes more preferred than 'Ground Invasion' and 'Aerial Strikes' becomes more important than 'Economic Sanctions'. On the other hand, as the priority of Risks increases, the last two alternatives 'Israeli Action' and 'Ground Invasion' trade places in the overall order of ranking. Results obtained for Benefits and Opportunities are stable and 'Nothing' remains the best alternative.

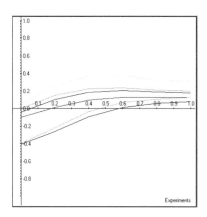
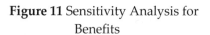
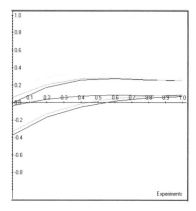

Figure 11 Sensitivity Analysis for   **Figure 12** Sensitivity Analysis for
Benefits   Opportunities

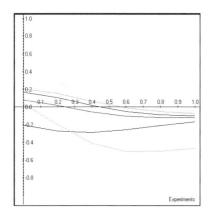

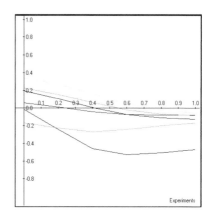

Figure 13 Sensitivity Analysis for
Costs

Figure 14 Sensitivity Analysis for
Risks

Why the Multiplicative Approach Does not Work

In the so-called multiplicative approach to the AHP the judgments for each alternative with respect to a criterion are multiplied in each row and then normalized to obtain the priorities. In addition, different vectors derived this way for the alternatives with respect to several criteria are synthesized not by weighting and adding but by raising each priority of an alternative to the power of its corresponding criterion and then multiplying the corresponding values for each alternative. The multiplicative approach was promoted by some people and later withdrawn because of the problems described below. It is a method that has no legitimacy in multicriteria decisions. There are examples to show that the multiplicative approach gives different final priorities to alternatives than the usual additive approach in which the priorities are multiplied by the weights of the criteria instead of raising them to the power of the weight of the corresponding criterion.

First, the multiplicative method has serious mathematical difficulties. First and rather seriously, raising the priority of an alternative to the power of its corresponding criterion contradicts the very essence of prioritization. Here is a simple example. Assume that an alternative has a priority .2 with respect to each of two criteria whose respective priorities are.3 and .5. It is logical to assume that this alternative should have a higher priority with respect to the more important criterion, the one with the value of .5, after the weighting is performed. But $.2^{.5} < .2^{.3}$ and alas it does not, it has a smaller priority. One would think that the procedure of ranking in this way would have been abandoned at first knowledge of this observation. Its advocates say no decision theory is perfect. What would happen to mathematics if such an excuse were given to justify all its wrong ideas of which there are many more than there are correct ones? Keep them all in because no mathematics is perfect? Would the reader recommend using the multiplicative method knowing this counter intuitive behavior? There have been loud cries made against it at institutes of learning in parts of the world where people who had been using "conventional" AHP are now being told they are required by the terms of the contract with one international organization to use the multiplicative method if funding is to be expected.

Second, the multiplicative method does not synthesize values correctly from the same scale of measurement on several criteria. To be credible, prioritization with paired comparisons needs to reproduce simple arithmetic operations on tangibles in relative terms as they should come out. We will give an example to illustrate this point better. First we show how the AHP does it in Table 15 and then comment about the difficulty with using the proposed multiplicative way of synthesizing priorities.

Table 15 Unnormalized Criteria and Alternative Weights From Measurements in Same Dollar Scale for both Criteria

Alternatives	Criterion C_1 Unnormalized weight = 1.0	Criterion C_2 Unnormalized weight = 1.0	Weighted Sum Unnormalized	Normalized or Relative values
A_1	200	150	350	350/1300=.269
A_2	300	50	350	350/1300=.269
A_3	500	100	600	600/1300=.462
Totals	1000	300	1300	1

Relative values require that criteria be examined as to their relative importance with respect to each other (on the average or on the whole). What is the relative importance of a criterion, or what numbers should the tangible criteria be assigned that reflect their relative importance? In conventional AHP when the values of the alternatives are measured on the same scale for several criteria, it is necessary that these criteria have priorities that reflect the proportion of the sum of the values under them to the total under all criteria. Multiplying the relative values of the alternatives by the relative values of the criteria and adding gives the final column of Table 16. The outcome coincides with the last column of Table 15.

Table 16 Normalized Criteria Weights and Normalized Alternative Weights
From Measurements in Same Scale (Additive Synthesis)

Alternatives	Criterion C_1 Normalized weight = 1000/1300=0.7692	Criterion C_2 Normalized weight = 300/1300=0.2308	Weighted Sum
A_1	200/1000	150/300	350/1300=.269
A_2	300/1000	50/300	350/1300=.269
A_3	500/1000	100/300	600/1300=.462

If we raise the unnormalized priorities of the alternatives to the power of their respective criteria, multiply (which causes the problem no matter what weight we choose for the criteria) and take the square root because there are two criteria (take the nth root when there are n criteria), as the multiplicative approach would have us do, whether we normalize or do not normalize, we cannot replicate the results obtained from the measurement values. In fact the problem is to find weights for the criteria that would produce the right outcome. We believe that it is not possible. A mathematical approach to find such values for the criteria would involve solving a system of simultaneous equations that is over determined and therefore has no solution. In the additive case of the AHP, where x_j is the weights of the jth criterion and a_{ij} is the weight of the ith alternative with respect to the jth criterion, we can determine the x_j for tangibles as follows:

$$\sum_j a_{ij} x_j \Big/ \sum_i a_{ij} = \sum_j a_{ij} \Big/ \sum_i \sum_j a_{ij}$$

from which we get

$$x_j = \sum_j a_{ij} \Big/ \sum_i \sum_j a_{ij}$$

If the outcome does not work for tangibles, how can one be sure that it is any better for intangibles?

Third, in justifying the theory in a mathematical context, the invariance principle is the most important. Priorities are derived from judgments in a special way. It involves a composition of priorities vectors given as the columns of a matrix according to certain rules. For example in additive composition, priority vectors are weighted (multiplied) by the priority of the element with respect to which they were derived and then summed over all such elements to obtain an overall composite priority vector. In particular, the columns of a judgment matrix are themselves priority vectors with respect to each element represented at the top of the matrix, and their composition, by multiplying by the priority of that element and adding across the elements, yields the composite priority vector of all the elements. In the additive case, what we just described above can be written as $\sum_{j=1}^{n} a_{ij} w_j = c w_i$ i=1,...,n where c > 0 (which may be taken as c = 1) is a constant of proportionality so that the derived vector is a similarity transformation of the original vector and thus both belong to the same ratio scale. This is the principle of invariance of priorities. The foregoing problem has a unique solution in eigenvectors.

To apply this principle to multiplicative composition we need to solve a corresponding invariance requirement:

$$(\prod_{j=1}^{n} a_{ij}^{\ w_j})^{1/n} = c w_i \quad i=1,...,n \text{ or on taking logarithms on both sides,}$$

$\dfrac{1}{n} \sum_{j=1}^{n} w_j \log a_{ij} = \log c + \log w_i$. This problem does not have a solution and thus is not a justifiable way for deriving priorities. Let us illustrate with a simple example.

The 2x2 matrix: $\begin{matrix} & A_1 & A_2 \end{matrix}$ $\begin{matrix} A_1 \\ A_2 \end{matrix} \begin{pmatrix} 1 & 4 \\ 1/4 & 1 \end{pmatrix}$ is consistent and its priorities (A_1, A_2) = (.8, .2) obtained by normalizing either column, are the same for the additive and the geometric mean methods. In additive composition we have: A_1 = 1 x .8 + 4 x .2 = 1.6 and A_2 = ¼ x .8 + 1 x .2 = .4 and normalized again gives (A_1, A_2) = (.8, .2), and the priority vector is invariant under weighting and adding. Note here that each a_{ij} is weighted by the corresponding priority w_j.

In the multiplicative case we have A_1 = ($1^{.8}$ x $4^{.2}$)$^{1/2}$ = 1.149 and A_2 = (¼$^{.8}$ x $1^{.2}$)$^{1/2}$ = 0.574 and normalized (A_1,A_2) = (.666,.333) ≠ (.8,.2) and using it as priority vector gives rise to a new priority vector for the alternatives and so on. The same is true if we do not normalize the derived vectors. Thus using the multiplicative method to generate priorities does not satisfy the invariance principle. To see that this is not true even in the limit we substitute values for our 2x2 case in the logarithmic system of equations above. We have $A_1 = \dfrac{1}{2}(.8\log 1 + .2\log 4) = \log c + \log .8$, from which log c = 0.362, and $A_2 = \dfrac{1}{2}(.8\log \dfrac{1}{4} + .2\log 1) = \log c + \log .2$, from which log c = 1.055 and there is no unique solution. We conclude that in general the multiplicative approach does not lead to priorities invariant under composition not even for a single judgment matrix. More generally, a vector obtained by additive composition for a multicriteria priority problem can also be shown to be an invariant composite vector (the principal eigenvector) of a column stochastic supermatrix of a network of which the matrix of a hierarchy is a particular case.

Examples of Rank Reversal

There have been numerous examples cited in the literature by investigators in economics and in decision theory that give examples of rank reversal, that utility theorists themselves have written about and some have told this author that they cannot all be justified by adding criteria or changing judgments. In one instance a professor of economics unknown to this author called by telephone to say that it needs to be known by researchers. In another instance another professor told this author he thought adding the criterion "uniqueness" would take care of rank reversal in the case of copies. When told that "uniqueness" implies dependence of an alternative on the other alternatives even if it is their number, he reflected on it for more than a month and later wrote from Rome that he agreed, it did imply dependence and could not be used as a criterion.

In mathematics it is sufficient to give a single counter example to topple an assumption. I had thought to include several examples including copies, phantoms, decoys, and others studied systematically by people who worked in utility theory. My colleagues suggested that one is enough, but I have included two. Here is an example with explanation. It is an illustration of something that happens in the real world as practiced by people in marketing. A phantom alternative A_3 is publicized in the media to bring about rank reversal between A_1 and A_2 with the ideal mode. We begin with A_1 dominating A_2. Introducing A_3 we obtain reversal in the rank of A_2 over A_1 once with A_3 between A_1 and A_2 and once ranking the last of the three. This is the case of a phantom alternative (a car) that is more expensive and thus less desirable but has the best quality. People bought A_1 because it is cheaper but A_2 is a much better car on quality. Knowing that a (considerably) more expensive car A_3 will be on the market that also has a slightly better quality than A_2 makes people shift their preference to A_2 over A_1 without anything happening that causes them to change the relative importance of the criteria: cost and quality. Car A_3 is called a phantom because it is never made, it is proposed in advertising in a way to induce people to change their overall choice, although their preferences remain the same as before.

Alternatives	0.5	0.5	Composition	Normalized Weights	
A1	1	0.6	0.8	0.533	A1>A2
A2	0.4	1	0.7	0.467	
	1.4	1.6	1.5		

Alternatives	0.5	0.5	Composition	Normalized Weights	
A1	1	0.3	0.65	0.322	
A2	0.4	0.99	0.695	0.344	A2>A3>A1
A3	0.35	1	0.675	0.334	
	1.75	2.29	2.02		

Alternatives	0.55	0.45	Composition	Normalized Weights	
A1	1	0.6	0.82	0.550	A1>A2
A2	0.4	1	0.67	0.450	
			1.49		

Alternatives	0.55	0.45	Composition	Normalized Weights	
A1	1	0.1	0.595	0.327	
A2	0.4	0.99	0.6655	0.366	A2>A1>A3
A3	0.2	1	0.56	0.308	
			1.8205		

Here is a second example for which the reader can construct a corresponding real life set up. We begin with two alternatives A and B as above. We have:

	Efficiency (.5)					Cost (.5)				Composite Ideal		
	0.5	0.5				0.5	0.5					
	A	B	Norm	Ideal		A	B	Norm	Ideal	Comp Dist	Comp	Renorm.
A	1	3	0.75	1	A	1	0.5	0.33	0.5	0.542	0.75	0.5294
B	0.333	1	0.25	0.333	B	2	1	0.67	1	0.458	0.6667	0.4706
									1	1.4167	1	

and the distributive mode gives A = .54 and B = .46 while the normalized ideal mode gives A = .53 and B = .47. Now, if we add C that is a relevant alternative under efficiency, because it dominates both A and B we obtain:

	Efficiency (.5)					Cost (.5)					Comp Dist	Composite Ideal	
	A	B	C	Norm	Ideal	A	B	C	Norm	Ideal		Comp Renorm.	
A	1	3	0.5	0.3	0.5	1	0.5	4	0.308	0.5	0.3038	0.500	0.304
B	0.333	1	0.167	0.1	0.17	2	1	8	0.615	1	0.3577	0.583	0.354
C	2	6	1	0.6	1	0.25	0.13	1	0.077	0.125	0.3385	0.563	0.342
						3.25	1.63	13			1	1.64581	

Now, the distributive mode gives A=.30, B=.36 and C=.34 with rank reversal between A and B, and the normalized ideal mode gives A=.30, B=.35 and C=.34 again with rank reversal. There is rank reversal with both the distributive and ideal modes because C is dominant with respect to efficiency.

References

1. Shepard, R.N. (1972), ed., *Multidimensional Scaling: Theory and Applications in the Behavioral Sciences*, Vol. 1, Seminar Press, New York
2. Thurston, L.L. (1927) A Law of Comparative Judgment, *Psychological Review* **34**, pp. 273–286
3. Dahaene, S. (1997), *The Number Sense, How the Mind Creates Mathematics*, Oxford University Press
4. Saaty, T.L. and Ozdemir, M. (2003), Negative priorities in the Analytic Hierarchy Process, *Mathematical and Computer Modeling*, Vol. 37, pp. 1063-1075.
5. Wilkinson, J.H. (1965), Th*e Algebraic Eigenvalue Problem*, Clarendon Press, Oxford
6. Horn, R.A. and Johnson, C.R. (1985), *Matrix Analysis*, Cambridge University Press, New York
7. Harker, P.T. (1987), "The Theory of Ratio Scale Estimation: Saaty's Analytic Hierarchy Process", *Management Science*, vol. 33, No. 14, pp. 1383-1403
8. Saaty, T.L., Vargas, L.G., Dellmann, K. (2003), "The allocation of

intangible resources: the analytic hierarchy process and linear programming", *Socio-economic Planning Sciences*, Vol. 37, pp.169-84

9. MacKay, A.F., (1980) *Arrow's Theorem: The Paradox of Social Choice - A Case Study in the philosophy of Economics*, New Haven and London: Yale University Press

10. Davis, P.J. and R. Hersh (1986), *Descartes Dream*, Harcourt Brace and Jovanovich, New York

11. Leshan, L. and Margenau, H, (1983) *Einstein's Space and Van Gogh's Sky: Physical Reality and Beyond*, Macmillan 1st Collier Books

12. Bergson, H. (1910), The intensity of psychic states, *Time and Free Will: An Essay on the Immediate Data of Consciousness*, translated by F. L. Pogson, M. A. London: George Allen and Unwin, 1–74

Chapter 5

Feedback Network

This chapter deals with the following ideas:

- How to group priorities derived in a network into a supermatrix so they can be synthesized
- Illustration with examples of a hierarchy and a holarchy
- A classification of hierarchies according to their connections
- The control hierarchy with its control criteria indication and the type of influence that one must consider in giving all the judgments in a network e.g., economic influence or political influence or social influence or technological influence and so on. These control criteria may be subdivided into subcriteria and the networks and judgments constructed with respect to these subcriteria instead of the criteria.
- Comparisons of the influence of all the clusters on each cluster are made according to the control criterion and the resulting priorites are used to weight the corresponding blocks of the supermatrix thus making it column stochastic.
- The supermatrrix is then raised to powers and one of two two kinds of limits may be the result
- Benefits, opportunities, costs and risks (BOCR), that are the merits which the alternatives of a decision present us with. Each of these four BOCR has several control criteria and subcriteria, and each has a network for which the alternatives are ranked and combined. The result is four rankings of the alternatives one for each of the BOCR. How to rate the top alternative for each of the four with respect to strategic criteria and combine them is discussed and illustrated.
- Some results are then obtained for hierarchies
- A comprehensive example with BOCR is provided in analyzing what the Ford Motor Company should do about its Explorer model with the difficulties it presented to driving customers

Introduction

Many decision problems cannot be structured hierarchically because they involve the interaction and dependence of higher-level elements on lower-level elements. Not only does the importance of the criteria determine the importance of the alternatives as in a hierarchy, but also the importance of the alternatives themselves determines the importance of the criteria. Two bridges, both strong, but the stronger is also uglier, would lead one to choose the strong but ugly one unless the criteria themselves are evaluated in terms of the bridges, and strength receives a smaller value and appearance a larger value because both bridges are strong. Feedback enables us to factor the future into the present to determine what we have to do to attain a desired future.

The feedback structure does not have the linear top-to-bottom form of a hierarchy but looks more like a network, with cycles connecting its components of elements, which we can no longer call levels, and with loops that connect a component to itself. It also has sources and sinks. A **source** node is an origin of paths of influence (importance) and never a destination of such paths. A **sink** node is a destination of paths of influence and never an origin of such paths. A full network can include source nodes; intermediate nodes that fall on paths from source nodes, lie on cycles, or fall on paths to sink nodes; and finally sink nodes. Some networks can contain only source and sink nodes. Still others can include only source and cycle nodes or cycle and sink nodes or only cycle nodes. A decision problem involving feedback arises often in practice. It can take on the form of any of the networks just described. The challenge is to determine the priorities of the elements in the network and in particular the alternatives of the decision. Because feedback involves cycles, and cycling can be an infinite process, the operations needed to derive the priorities become more demanding than has been familiar with hierarchies. Unraveling their intricacies is challenging to the intellect and is essential for making the computations precise.

At present, in their effort to simplify and deal with complexity, people who work in decision making use mostly very simple hierarchic structures consisting of a goal, criteria, and alternatives. Yet, not only are decisions obtained from a simple hierarchy of three levels different from those obtained from a multilevel hierarchy, but also decisions obtained from a network can be significantly different from those obtained from a more complex hierarchy. We cannot collapse complexity artificially into a simplistic structure of two levels, criteria and alternatives, and hope to capture the outcome of interactions in the form of highly condensed judgments that correctly reflect all that goes on in the world. We must learn to decompose these judgments through more elaborate structures and organize our reasoning and calculations in sophisticated but simple ways to serve our understanding of the complexity around us. Experience indicates that it is not very difficult to do this although it takes more time and effort. Indeed, we must use feedback networks to arrive at the kind of decisions needed to cope with the future.

To test for the mutual independence of elements such as the criteria, one proceeds as follows: Construct a zero-one matrix of criteria against criteria using the number one to signify dependence of one criterion on another, and zero otherwise. A criterion need not depend on itself as an industry, for example, may not use its own output. For each column of this matrix, construct a pairwise comparison matrix only for the dependent criteria, derive an eigenvector, and augment it with zeros for the excluded criteria. If a column is all zeros, then assign a zero vector to represent the priorities. The question in the comparison would be: For a given criterion, which of two criteria depends more on that criterion with respect to the goal or with respect to a higher-order controlling criterion?

In this chapter we lay out the theoretical foundations for the kinds of structures and matrices of derived ratio scales associated with feedback networks from which we obtain the priorities for a decision.

The Supermatrix of a Feedback System [1]

Assume that we have a system of N components where the elements in each component interact or have an influence on some or all of the elements of another component with respect to a property governing the interactions of the entire system, such as energy or capital or political influence (see Figure 1). *Note that the network connecting the components of a decision system must always be connected. It cannot be divided into two or more disconnected parts, otherwise they cannot communicate with each other and it is pointless to ask for the influence of one part on another because there can never be any.* There are three kinds of components in Figure 1.

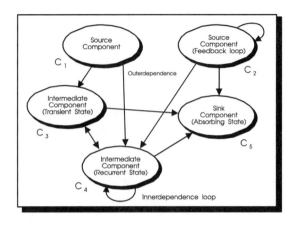

Figure 1 Components of a Feedback Network

Those components which no arrow enters are known as **source** components such as C_1 and C_2. Those from which no arrow leaves are known as **sink** components such as C_5;and finally those which arrows both enter and exit leave are known as **transient** components such as C_3 and C_4. In addition C_3 and C_4 form a **cycle** of two components because they feed back and forth into each other. C_2 and C_4 have **loops** that connect them to themselves. They are **inner dependent**. All other connections represent dependence between components which are thus known to be **outer dependent**. An example of dependence between components is the input-output of materials among industries. The electric industry supplies electricity to other industries including itself. But it depends more on the coal industry than on its own electricity for operation and also more on the steel industry for its turbines.

In general, a network consists of components and elements in these components. But in creating structures to represent problems there may be larger parts to consider than components. According to size, we have a **system** that is made up of **subsystems**, with each subsystem made up of **components**, and each component made up of **elements**. We might consider that the whole need not be equal to the sum of its parts but may, due to synergy, be larger or smaller in the sense of contributing to a goal. Sometimes we refer to a set of objects contained in a larger one as elements when in fact they may be components. The context would make this clear.

We denote a component of a decision network by C_h, h=1, ... m, and assume that it has n_h elements, which we denote by $e_{h1}, e_{h2}, ..., e_{hm_h}$. The influences of a given set of elements in a component on any element in the system are represented by a priority vector derived from paired comparisons in the usual way of the AHP. It is these derived vectors, how they are grouped and arranged, and then how to use the resulting structure which turns out to be a matrix, that interests us here. This matrix is thus used to represent the flow of influence from a component of elements to itself as in the loop which flows back to C_4 above, or from a component from which an arrow is directed out to another component. Sometimes, as with hierarchies, one is concerned with the influence of the component at the end of an arrow on the component from which the arrow begins; one must decide on one or the other. The influence of elements in the network on other elements in that network can be represented in the following **supermatrix:**

$$
W = \begin{array}{c} \\ C_1 \\ \\ \\ C_2 \\ \\ \\ \vdots \\ \\ C_m \\ \\ \end{array}
\begin{array}{c}
e_{11} \\ e_{12} \\ \vdots \\ e_{1L} \\ e_{21} \\ e_{22} \\ \vdots \\ e_{2n_2} \\ \vdots \\ e_{m1} \\ e_{m2} \\ \vdots \\ e_{mn_m}
\end{array}
\left[
\begin{array}{cccc}
W_{11} & W_{12} & \cdots & W_{1m} \\
\\
W_{21} & W_{22} & \cdots & W_{2m} \\
\\
\vdots & \vdots & \ddots & \vdots \\
\\
W_{m1} & W_{m2} & \cdots & W_{mm}
\end{array}
\right]
$$

A typical entry W_{ij} in the supermatrix, is called a **block** of the supermatrix. It is a matrix of the form

$$
W_{ij} = \begin{bmatrix}
w_{i_1 j_1} & w_{i_1 j_2} & \cdots & w_{i_1 j_{n_j}} \\
w_{i_2 j_1} & w_{i_2 j_2} & \cdots & w_{i_2 j_{n_j}} \\
\vdots & \vdots & \vdots & \vdots \\
w_{i_{n_i} j_1} & w_{i_{n_i} j_2} & \cdots & w_{i_{n_i} j_{n_j}}
\end{bmatrix}
$$

Each column of W_{ij} is a principal eigenvector of the influence (importance) of the elements in the *ith* component of the network on an element in the *jth* component. Some of its entries may be zero corresponding to those elements that have no influence. Thus we do not need to use all the elements in a component when we make the paired comparisons to derive the eigenvector, but only those that have a non-zero influence. Figures 2 and 3, with their accompanying supermatrices, represent a hierarchy and a holarchy of *m* levels. As with any supermatrix, an entry in each of the foregoing two supermatrices is a block W_{ij} positioned where the *ith* component or level is connected to and influences the *jth* level immediately above. The entry in the last row and column of the supermatrix of a hierarchy is the identity matrix *I*.

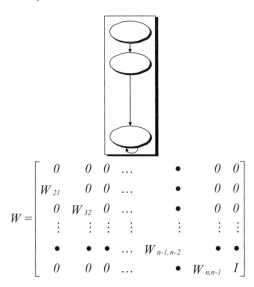

$$W = \begin{bmatrix} 0 & 0 & 0 & \ldots & \bullet & 0 & 0 \\ W_{21} & 0 & 0 & \ldots & \bullet & 0 & 0 \\ 0 & W_{32} & 0 & \ldots & \bullet & 0 & 0 \\ \vdots & \vdots & \vdots & \vdots & \vdots & \vdots & \vdots \\ \bullet & \bullet & \bullet & \ldots & W_{n-1,n-2} & \bullet & \bullet \\ 0 & 0 & 0 & \ldots & \bullet & W_{n,n-1} & I \end{bmatrix}$$

Figure 2 The Structure and Supermatrix of a Hierarchy

It corresponds to a loop at the bottom level, used to show that each element depends only on itself, is a necessary aspect of a hierarchy (or any sink) when viewed within the context of the supermatrix. The entry in the first row and last column of a holarchy is nonzero because the top level depends on the bottom level. Again we did not use identity matrices on the diagonal to make easier to see later on how cycling takes place through powers of the matrix. Both types of supermatrices will occur again in the book.

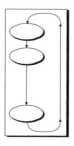

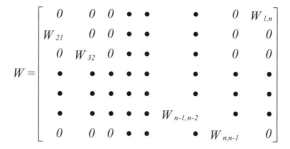

$$W = \begin{bmatrix} 0 & 0 & 0 & \bullet & \bullet & & \bullet & 0 & W_{1,n} \\ W_{21} & 0 & 0 & \bullet & \bullet & & \bullet & 0 & 0 \\ 0 & W_{32} & 0 & \bullet & \bullet & & \bullet & 0 & 0 \\ \bullet & \bullet & \bullet & \bullet & \bullet & & \bullet & \bullet & \bullet \\ \bullet & \bullet & \bullet & \bullet & \bullet & & \bullet & \bullet & \bullet \\ \bullet & \bullet & \bullet & \bullet & \bullet & W_{n-1,n-2} & & \bullet & \bullet \\ 0 & 0 & 0 & \bullet & \bullet & & \bullet & W_{n,n-1} & 0 \end{bmatrix}$$

Figure 3 The Structure and Supermatrix of a Holarchy

A network may be generated from a hierarchy by increasing the hierarchy's connections gradually so that pairs of components are connected as desired and some components have an inner dependence loop. This suggests the following classification of hierarchies modified to become networks with feedback. This classification is not used in this book but may serve some need in the future.

A Classification of Hierarchies

We introduce the following terminology for special kinds of hierarchies and their modifications to a feedback system. A *hierarchy* is a structure with a goal at the top. A *suparchy* (Figure 4a) is a structure that is like a hierarchy except that it has no goal but has a feedback cycle between the top (superior) two levels. An *intarchy* (Figure 4b) is a hierarchy with a feedback cycle between two consecutive intermediate levels. A *sinarchy* (Figure 4c) is a hierarchy with a feedback cycle between the last two (bottom or sink) levels. We also use the terms neosuparchy, neointarchy, and neosinarchy for a hierarchy whose top, middle, or lower levels, no matter how many, are connected in such a way that they form a cycle.

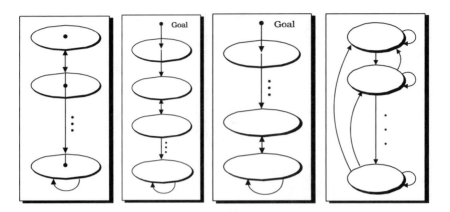

Figure 4 (a) A Suparchy, (b) An Intarchy, (c) A Sinarchy and (d) A Hiernet

A *hiernet* is a network arranged vertically to facilitate remembering its levels (Figure 4d). It is possible for a system to have interactive components, which as a whole influence another such interactive system of components as in Figure 5. In this figure we have a reducible network because there is no path that connects the bottom group of two components to the top group of three components.

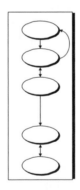

Figure 5 Interactive System of Components

Note that wherever there is a cycle in a network, its priorities take precedence over whatever leads into it, and that the priorities of what leads into a cycle may be ignored and that part of the structure discarded for limit results. However, a cycle can lead into noncycling terminal nodes or portions of a hierarchy, and its priorities have an effect on the limit priorities of the outcome. To summarize, an intarchy and a sinarchy can be truncated and the top parts discarded. Thus for a sinarchy it is sufficient to simply compute the supermatrix for the bottom two levels. Similar observations apply to neo structures.

The Control Hierarchy and What Question to Ask

For clarity and greater precision, the influence represented in all the derived eigenvectors of priorities entered in a supermatrix must be measured according to a single criterion, such as economic influence. Another supermatrix may represent social influence, and so on. We call such criteria with respect to which influence is represented in individual supermatrices **control criteria**. Because we need to combine all such influences obtained from the limits of the several supermatrices in order to obtain a measure of the priority of **overall influence**, we need to group the control criteria in a structure that allows us to derive priorities for them and use these priorities to weight the corresponding individual supermatrix limits and add. Such a structure of control criteria may itself be elaborate. For simplicity we call the structure of control criteria a **control hierarchy**. Analysis of priorities in a system can be thought of in terms of a control hierarchy with dependence among its bottom-level alternatives arranged as a network (Figure 6). Dependence can occur within the components and between them. A control hierarchy at the top may be replaced by a control network with dependence among its components. More generally, one can have a cascading set of control networks, the outcome of one used to synthesize the outcomes of what it controls. For obvious reasons relating to the complexity of exposition, apart from a control hierarchy, we will not discuss such complex control structures here. A control hierarchy can also be involved in the networks of its criteria with feedback involved.

A component in the ANP is a collection of elements whose function derives from the synergy of their interaction and hence has a higher-order function not found in any single element. A component is like the audio or visual component of a television set or like an arm or a leg, consisting of muscle and bone, in the human body. A mechanical component has no synergy value but is simply an aggregate of elements and is not what we mean by a component. The components of a network should generally be synergistically different from the elements themselves. Otherwise they would be a mechanical collection with no intrinsic meaning.

Principia Mathematica Decernendi

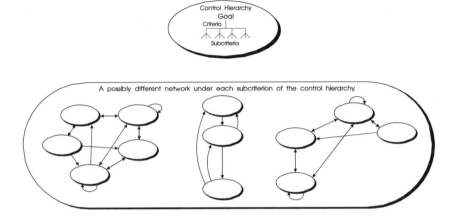

Figure 6 Control Hierarchy with Dependence Among its Bottom-level
Alternatives Arranged as a Network

The criteria in the control hierarchy that are used for comparing the components are usually the major parent criteria whose subcriteria are used to compare the elements in the component. Thus the criteria for comparing the components need to be more general than those of the elements because of the greater functional complexity of the components.

There are two types of control criteria (subcriteria). A control criterion may be directly connected to the structure as the goal of a hierarchy if the structure is in fact a hierarchy. In this case the control criterion is called a comparison-"linking" criterion. Otherwise a control criterion does not connect directly to the structure but "induces" comparisons in a network. In that case the control criterion is called a comparison-"inducing" criterion.

The **generic question** to be answered by making pairwise comparisons is: Given a control criterion (subcriterion), a component (element) of the network, and given a pair of components (element), how much more does a given member of the pair influence that component (element) with respect to the control criterion (subcriterion) than the other member?

The material from here on is essential for our purpose but is of a highly technical nature. It explains how a supermatrix that is either positive or non-negative and stochastic is central to obtaining priorities in decision making with dependence and feedback. There are also some interesting theorems about hierarchies.

The Benefits, Opportunities, Costs and Risks and Their Merit Ratings

Any decision has several favorable and unfavorable **concerns** to consider. Some of these are sure things, others are less certain and have a likelihood of materializing. The favorable sure concerns are called **benefits** while the unfavorable ones are called **costs**. The uncertain concerns of a decision are the positive **opportunities** that the decision might create and the negative **risks** that it can entail. Each of these four concerns utilizes a separate structure for the decision, beginning with a benefits control structure and the network of interdependencies that belongs under each benefit control criterion, and ending with a risks control structure. We refer to the four concerns collectively as **BOCR**, having used the initials of the positive ones (benefits and opportunities) before the initials of the negative ones (costs and risks). Each of these concerns contributes to the merit of a decision and must be evaluated (rated) individually on a set of (prioritized) criteria that is used to also rate any other decision. We call these ratings **merits** and refer to the evaluation criteria to derive them as **merit criteria**. Examples of merit criteria are: satisfaction, happiness, convenience, fulfillment, order, harmony, peace, power, efficiency, social good, progress, wealth and so on. They must themselves be prioritized for frequent use in all decisions. In this manner we can synthesize the outcome of the alternatives for each of the BOCR structures, to obtain their **overall synthesis**. We note that for costs and risks one must ask which is more costly and which is more risky (not which is less costly and which is less risky) because in paired comparisons we can only estimate how much more the dominant member of a pair has a property as a multiple of how much the less dominant one has it and not the other way around. The priorities of the alternatives are now obtained from the reciprocals of their final synthesized values in the costs and the risks structures. This is in conformity with using actual measurement such as dollars on several criteria and inverting the final outcome. The computer program for the ANP does this automatically after all the judgments have been made.

Priorities in the Supermatrix

We are interested in deriving limit priorities of influence from the supermatrix to capture all the interaction among its elements and components. To obtain such priorities the supermatrix must first be transformed to a matrix each of whose columns sums to unity in order for its powers to converge. It is known as a *column stochastic* or simply a **stochastic** matrix. *If the matrix is stochastic, the limit priorities can be viewed in a way to depend on the concepts of reducibility, primitivity, and cyclicity of the matrix.*

The question arises as to whether there is a natural way (a scientific on top of a mathematical justification) to transform a given supermatrix whose columns usually sum to more than one, to a stochastic matrix. The priority of an element in a component is an inadequate indicator of its priority in the entire set of components. The highest priority element in a component need not be the highest priority element in the set of components. This is obvious because each component has a highest ranked element and they cannot all be first in the system. Thus we need to compare the components themselves according to their influence on each component in the supermatrix with respect to a higher order control criterion. The comparisons give rise to a derived vector of priorities of the influence of all the components (on the left of the supermatrix) on each component on top. This is done as many times as there are components. The resulting vectors are each used to weight the blocks of matrices that fall in the column under the given component. The first entry of the vector is multiplied by all the elements in the first block of that column, the second by all the elements in the second block of the column and so on. In this manner we weight the blocks in each column of the supermatrix. The result is known as the **weighted supermatrix** which is now stochastic. It is this stochastic matrix that we can work with to derive the desired priorities by transforming it to a **limit matrix** described below. This matrix yields the long-run or limit priority of influence of each element on every other element.

Remark: By way of further elaboration on rendering the supermatrix stochastic we note that it may be that only some elements of a component have an influence on some elements of another component in which case zeros are entered where there is no influence. Or it may even be that no element of a component influences a given element of another (there would be zeros for all the priorities represented by that vector) or only some elements influence it (there would be zeros for the priorities of the elements that do not influence it in the priority vector). In the case where an entire vector, but not all vectors in that component, is zero, the weighted column of the supermatrix must be renormalized. It is appropriate to say here that if all the elements of a component have zero influence on all the elements of a second component, the priority of influence of the first component itself on the second must also be equal to zero. However, this is not true when some or all the elements of the first component have an influence on some or all of those of the second. That is why the renormalization of some columns is essential and natural in making the weighted supermatrix stochastic.

We note that if the component of the alternatives of a decision is a sink of the network, and the other components do not depend on it, it need not be included in the supermatrix, and its priorities are used in the process of synthesis after limit priorities have been obtained for the relevant components of the supermatrix. This enables one to ensure rank preservation when desired by using the ideal mode of the AHP. If the component of alternatives is not a sink then it must be kept in the supermatrix whose priorities are analogous to the distributive mode and hence rank may legitimately be allowed to reverse.

On the Limit Supermatrix and its Cesaro Sum

Why do we need to raise the supermatrix to powers? It is because we wish to capture the transmission of influence along all possible paths of the supermatrix. The entries of the weighted supermatrix itself give the direct influence of any element on any other element. But an element can influence a second element indirectly through its influence on some third element and then by the influence of that element on the second. There are potentially many third elements. One must consider every such possibility of a third element. All indirect influences of pairs of elements through an intermediate third element are obtained by squaring the weighted supermatrix and so on for higher power as known in graph theory about the powers of the path matrix. Again the influence of one element on another can occur by considering a third element that influences a fourth element, which in turn influences the second element. All such influences are obtained from the cubic power of the matrix, and so on. Thus we have an infinite sequence of influence matrices: the matrix itself, its square, its cube, etc., denoted by W^k $k=1,2,...$. If we take the limit of the average of a sequence of N of these powers of the supermatrix (known as the Cesaro sum), $\lim_{k \to \infty} \left(\frac{1}{N} \right) \sum_{k=1}^{N} W^k$, does the result converge and is the limit unique? How do we compute this limit to obtain the desired priorities? It is known in mathematical analysis that if a sequence converges to a limit then its Cesaro sum converges to the same limit. Since the sequence is defined by the powers of the matrix, it is sufficient to find out what the limit of these powers is. It may well be that the sequence does not converge to a unique limit but its Cesaro sum averages out over the different limits of the sequence obtaining a unique limit. As we shall see, both these cases occur for our supermatrix when it is raised to powers. First we note from the Jordan Canonical Form of a stochastic matrix W, that $\lim_{k \to \infty} W^k$ generally exists. It is known that W is similar to its Jordan matrix J if there is a nonsingular matrix P such the $J=PWP^{-1}$. Thus raising W to limiting powers is equivalent to raising J to limiting powers. So what does J look like? With every square matrix is associated a unique Jordan matrix that has the following form: It consists of square blocks whose principal diagonals lie on its principal diagonal. All entries that lie outside these blocks are equal to zero. All entries that lie in a block are zero except for the principal diagonal all of whose entries are the same and are equal to an eigenvalue of W, and all entries in the diagonal immediately above the principal diagonal are equal to one. The matrix W is said to be the direct sum of its Jordan blocks. Without too much detail, it is clear that $\lim_{k \to \infty} W^k$ exists if, (a) no eigenvalue of W has modulus greater than one, (b) W has no eigenvalue of modulus one other than $\lambda = 1$, and if $\lambda = 1$ is an eigenvalue as it is with the stochastic matrix W, it has only 1-by-1 blocks in the Jordan Canonical Form. In fact one can define a limit in the sense of Cesaro when case (b) is not satisfied. To know that the limit exists and to derive that limit are different matters. We now derive this limit.

Unfolding the Complexity of Functions of W

There are five parts to the mathematics of this story; four are described in this chapter and the fifth is discussed in my book, *The Brain: Unraveling the Mystery of How it Works* [2]. The first has to do with matrices eigenvalues and eigenvectors, the second with functions of matrices discussed here, the third with the characterization of a nonnegative matrix, its principal eigenvalue and eigenvector, the fourth with stochastic matrices and Markov chains, and the fifth and final one with Dirac type distributions (generalized functions) and neural firings which is discussed in my book on the brain [2].

Three leading mathematicians of the last century laid the foundations for the theory of matrices by generalizing on the solvability of systems of linear algebraic equations. They were the Irish mathematician William Rowan Hamilton (1805-1865) and the two English mathematicians James Joseph Sylvester (1814-1897) and Arthur Cayley (1821-1891). Hamilton, at the age of 21, became the Royal Astronomer of Ireland, holding the position until his death. Sylvester was a poet, a wit, and one of the great creators of terms in mathematics. During his stay (1877-1883), he gave Johns Hopkins University in Baltimore its reputation in mathematics. Cayley followed an early career as a lawyer with a chair in mathematics at Cambridge. A famous result, known as the Hamilton-Cayley theorem, will be used later. Sylvester gave us his powerful formula to represent a function $f(W)$ of a matrix W, and in particular $f(W)=W^\infty$.

The two names that need to be mentioned in the third part of the story are those of the German mathematicians Oskar Perron (1880-1975) and Georg Ferdinand Frobenius (1849-1917). The first proved in 1907 that a matrix of positive entries always has a real positive and simple eigenvalue λ_{max} called the principal eigenvalue of the matrix, which strictly dominates in modulus all the other eigenvalues. With this eigenvalue is associated a principal eigenvector that is positive and unique to within multiplication by a positive constant. In 1912 Frobenius extended and amplified Perron's result. He arrived at a similar conclusion for a nonnegative matrix that is irreducible, except that now the principal eigenvalue need not strictly dominate the moduli of the other eigenvalues but may be equal to them, and the corresponding eigenvector is nonnegative.

The fourth part of our story derives from the study of Markov chains and processes. Andre Andreevich Markov (1856-1922) was probably the first person to draw attention to stochastic matrices because of his work on probabilistic chains of transition (known as Markov chains) among the different states of a system. In this type of analysis one is often interested in steady state or limiting probabilities when they exist and in how to obtain them.

The theory of eigenvalues is essential for characterizing the different cases that arise in calculating W. Here are some useful facts that one needs to know. The principal eigenvalue λ_{max} of a nonnegative matrix lies between the maximum and the minimum of the row sums. Because the eigenvalues are the same for a given matrix and for the transpose of that matrix, λ_{max} also lies between the maximum and the minimum of the column sums. Thus if a nonnegative matrix is column stochastic (each of its columns sums to one), as is the supermatrix, its maximum and minimum column sums are equal to one and hence its maximum eigenvalue is one. If it is nonnegative but not everywhere positive, then the moduli of some of the other eigenvalues may be equal to one. If the matrix is irreducible, then the theorem of Frobenius assures us that $\lambda_{max}=1$ is a simple root; but if the matrix is reducible, then $\lambda_{max}=1$ may be a simple or a multiple root.

To see that one is an eigenvalue of a stochastic supermatrix W we note that the vector $e=(1,...,1)$ is a left eigenvector of such a matrix with eigenvalue one. An eigenvalue can be obtained by summing each column of the matrix thus obtaining a vector whose scalar product with the corresponding normalized eigenvector yields the desired eigenvalue. Thus from

$$\sum_{j=1}^{n} a_{ij} w_j = \lambda_{w_i}, i = 1,...n$$

we have on summing with respect to i and interchanging sums and remembering that the sum of the w_j is equal to one, we have:

$$\sum_{j=1}^{n} w_j \sum_{i=1}^{n} a_{ij} = \lambda$$

For a column stochastic matrix, we may take w as the vector e normalized so that $w_j = 1/n$ and the second sum on the left is equal to one and thus summing over j gives the desired result $\lambda=1$. Because the maximum and minimum column sums of a column stochastic matrix are equal to one, $\lambda=1$ must be its maximum or principal eigenvalue.

On The Roots of Unity [1]

If the characteristic equation of a nonnegative matrix A has the form $\lambda^n-1=0$ or even if it factors into the product of several factors one of which is $\lambda^k-1=0$, the roots of the characteristic polynomial have a special property.

By the fundamental theorem of algebra, $\lambda^n-1=0$ has exactly n roots. By De Moivre's theorem for the representation of a complex number z we have:

$$z = a + bi = r(\cos \theta + i \sin \theta) = r e^{i\theta}$$

$$r = \sqrt{a^2 + b^2}$$

$$\theta = \arctan \frac{b}{a}$$

We can show by series expansion that we also have $z = re^{i\theta}$. We can represent each root of unity (of $\lambda^n - 1 = 0$) in the polar form $\lambda = re^{i\theta}$, from which we have $\lambda^k = r^k e^{i\theta k}$. Consider a complex number z whose representation is given by

$$z = \cos\frac{2\pi}{n} + i\,\sin\frac{2\pi}{n} = e^{2\pi i/n}$$

where z is an nth root of unity since:

$$z^n = (\cos\frac{2\pi}{n} + i\,\sin\frac{2\pi}{n})^n = (e^{\frac{2\pi i}{n}})^n = e^{2\pi i} = \cos\,2\pi + i\,\sin\,2\pi = 1$$

For every integer m we have $(z^m)^n = (z^n)^m = 1$, and z^m is also an nth root of unity. In particular $z, z^2, \ldots, z^{n-1}, z^n$ are all distinct nth roots of unity. If, for example, two powers of z are the same, we have $z^s = z^t$, $t > s$, and we have

$$1 = z^{t-s} \equiv z^p = \cos\frac{2\pi p}{n} + i\,\sin\frac{2\pi p}{n}, \cos\frac{2\pi p}{n} = 1, \sin\frac{2\pi p}{n} = 0$$

having equated real and imaginary parts. Since $\sin\dfrac{2\pi p}{n} = 0$, it follows that

$\dfrac{2\pi p}{n}$ is a multiple $q\pi$ of π, and substitution yields $\cos\,q\pi = 1$, which implies

that q is an even integer, $q=2r$, from which we have $\dfrac{2p}{n} = 2r$ or $p=nr$. But

$1 \le p = t-s \le n-1$, and we have a contradiction. Thus $z, z^2, \ldots, z^{n-1}, z^n$ are distinct and are all the roots of $\lambda^n = 1$. The moduli of all these n roots are equal to one. In general, when there are c such roots, they are given as follows: $\lambda_1 = \lambda_{max}, \lambda_2 = \lambda_{max}z, \ldots, \lambda_c = \lambda_{max}z^{c-1}$ where $z = e^{2\pi i/c}$ and $i = \sqrt{-1}$.

On the Multiplicity of a Root

We will be concerned with the multiplicity of $\lambda_{max} = 1$ for our stochastic supermatrix W. If λ_{max} is a multiple root of multiplicity k of a characteristic polynomial, then $(\lambda-\lambda_{max})^k$ is one of the factors of that polynomial. One way to find k is to apply the derivative over and over again to the point where λ_{max} is no longer a root of the resulting polynomial. Thus if λ_* is a root of multiplicity k of a polynomial $f(\lambda)$, then on differentiating f with respect to λ once we have $f'(\lambda)=(\lambda-\lambda^*)^k \, g'(\lambda)+k(\lambda-\lambda^*)^{k-1}g(\lambda)=(\lambda- \lambda^*)^{k-1}[(\lambda- \lambda^*)g'(\lambda)+kg(\lambda)]$ and the quantity in brackets is not divisible by $\lambda-\lambda^*$ and thus $f'(\lambda)$ has λ^* as a root of multiplicity $k-1$. The process can be continued k times, until λ^* disappears as a root and we would then know the multiplicity k.

How to Compute the Functions of a Matrix [3]

Many real-life problems are solved mathematically by considering functions of an operator. The classic example is solving a system of linear inhomogeneous equations given in matrix operator form as $Ax=y$. Solving such a system requires that a certain function of A, namely its inverse A^{-1} should exist. Using it we have for the solution: $x =A^{-1}y$. In the case of the supermatrix W, what we want is the limit of W^k as $k \to \infty$. This is another kind of function. Thus it is useful to have a general way to calculate a function of a matrix A.

Consider the polynomial

$$f(x)= a_n x^n + a_{n-1} x^{n-1} + \cdots + a_1 x_1 + a_0$$

The function $f(x)$ is completely determined by its values for $n+1$ or more arbitrary but distinct values of x. The $n+1$ values of x and the $n+1$ corresponding values of $f(x)$ lead to a system of $n+1$ linear equations in a_i, $i=0,1,...,n$, making it possible to obtain a unique solution to the system of $n+1$ coefficients and thus determine $f(x)$ uniquely. If two polynomials of degree n coincide in $n+1$ or more values, then they must be identical. Otherwise their difference is a polynomial of degree no more than n and, by the fundamental theorem of algebra, cannot have more than n roots, contradicting the fact that this difference has at least $n+1$ roots.

The following representation of a polynomial is known as the Lagrange interpolation formula (identity), named after Joseph Louis Lagrange (1736-1813), a mathematician of Italian-French ancestry who worked in the court of Frederick the Great and moved to Paris after Frederick's death. This formula enables one to compute the values of a polynomial $f(x)$ of degree not more than n at any point by simply knowing its values at $n+1$ points, $x_1, ..., x_{n+1}$:

$$f(x) = \sum_{i=1}^{n+1} f(x_i) \frac{(x-x_1)...(x-x_{i-1})(x-x_{i+1})...(x-x_{n+1})}{(x_i-x_1)...(x_i-x_{i-1})(x_i-x_{i+1})...(x_i-x_{n+1})}$$

$$= \sum_{i=1}^{n+1} f(x_i) \prod_{j \neq i} (x - x_j) / \prod_{j \neq i} (x_i - x_j)$$

It has a form that is a polynomial of degree n in x, and by the foregoing discussion, uniquely represents $f(x)$. If the degree of $f(x)$ does not exceed n-1, the upper limit of the sum would be n, which is its usual form in the literature. Note on the right that only $f(x_i)$ depends on the form of f and not its multiplying factor, which is a polynomial of degree n-1.

If instead of the variable x we use a matrix A, then because of the analogy between the algebras of the two polynomials we can write for a polynomial in A of degree less than or equal to n

$$f(A) = \sum_{i=1}^{n+1} f(x_i) \prod_{j \neq i} (x_j I - A) / \prod_{j \neq i} (x_j - x_i)$$

For matrices the x_i are the eigenvalues λ_i.

Sylvester showed that this relation holds for the general case of an entire function of A (an analytic function whose power series expansion converges in the entire plane). He observed that a power A^k of A, when represented in this way, is for each term a polynomial of degree n-1 in A, and the sum simplifies to a polynomial in A. Thus a power series that converges everywhere can also be represented by this expression.

Traditionally this formula for distinct roots of a matrix and more generally for a diagonizable matrix is written as follows:

$$f(A) = \sum_{i=1}^{n} f(\lambda_i) Z(\lambda_i)$$

where

$$Z(\lambda_i) = \frac{\prod_{j \neq i} (\lambda_j I - A)}{\prod_{j \neq i} (\lambda_j - \lambda_i)}$$

The $Z(\lambda_i)$ can be shown to be complete orthogonal idempotent matrices of A; that is, they have the properties $\sum_{i=1}^{k} Z(\lambda_i) = I$, $Z(\lambda_i) Z(\lambda_j) = 0$, $i \neq j$, $Z^2(\lambda_i) = Z(\lambda_i)$, where I and 0 are the identity and null matrices, respectively. The first relation follows by substituting I for $f(A)$ above. The second follows from the observation that two such products involve all the factors of the characteristic polynomial in A which vanishes by the Hamilton-Cayley theorem. The Hamilton-Cayley theorem says that the characteristic equation is identically equal to the zero matrix if λ is replaced by A, and the constant term is multiplied by the identity matrix I, thus yielding a matrix equation.

It is not difficult to show, as in the Hamilton-Cayley theorem, that a polynomial in a single variable with scalar coefficients and the same polynomial with a square matrix replacing the variable have analogous algebras. Thus it is meaningful to form a polynomial in a matrix and treat the polynomial much as one does polynomials in a single variable.

On multiplying both sides of the first equation successively by each of the n $Z(\lambda_i)$, each time applying the orthogonality condition, the third relation (idempotence) follows.

If $f(A) = A^k$ and all eigenvalues are distinct, we have:

$$A^k = \sum_{i=1}^{n} \lambda_i^k Z(\lambda_i) = \sum_{i=1}^{n} \lambda_i^k \frac{\prod_{j \neq i}(\lambda_j I - A)}{\prod_{j \neq i}(\lambda_j - \lambda_i)}$$

In this formula each term consists of a product of a function of one of the characteristic roots and of a polynomial of degree at most $(n\text{-}1)$ in A. Thus, for example, if we want to evaluate W^k as $k \rightarrow \infty$, it is sufficient to examine what happens to $\lim_{k \to \infty} \lambda_i^k, i = 1,...,n$. In each of these terms we may replace an eigenvalue by its complex number representation $re^{i\theta}$. In that case we would be concerned with r^k as $k \rightarrow \infty$, since $e^{i\theta k} = \cos\theta\ k + i\ \sin\theta\ k$, which oscillates and is bounded. Thus in the limit the outcome depends on the value of r. Now as $k \rightarrow \infty$ we have

$$r^k = \begin{cases} 0 & r < 1 \\ 1 & r = 1 \\ \infty & r > 1 \end{cases}$$

Now $\lambda_{\max} = 1$ may be a simple or a multiple root. The case of multiple roots is covered by another form of Sylvester's formula which we now give.

Note that in Lagrange's formula the terms involving $(x - x_i)$ in the numerator and $(x_i - x_i)$ in the denominator were excluded only once because the values x_i were all distinct. If x_i is a repeated value of multiplicity k, how do we exclude it k times? Obviously, to exclude it $k\text{-}1$ additional times, we must differentiate the right side $k\text{-}1$ times and divide by $(k - 1)!$. This is done for each multiple root.

We have for multiple characteristic roots what is known as the confluent form of Sylvester's theorem:

$$f(A) = \sum_{i=1}^{k} T(\lambda_i) = \sum_{i=1}^{k} \frac{1}{(m_i - 1)!} \frac{d^{m_i - 1}}{d\lambda^{m_i - 1}} f(\lambda)(\lambda I - A)^{-1} \frac{\prod_{i=1}^{n}(\lambda - \lambda_i)}{\prod_{i=m_{i+1}}^{n}(\lambda - \lambda_i)} \Bigg|_{\lambda = \lambda_i}$$

where k is the number of distinct roots and m_i is the multiplicity of the root λ_i. Now what to do about $(\lambda I - A)^{-1}$?

From the relation of the inverse of A to the adjoint of A, i.e., $A^{-1} = \dfrac{adj\ A}{\det\ A}$, or $A\ adj\ A = (\det\ A)I$, we may similarly write, using $F(\lambda)$ for the adjoint of $(\lambda I - A)$:

$$(\lambda I - A)\ F(\lambda) = \Delta(\lambda)I, \Delta(\lambda) = (\lambda - \lambda_1)...(\lambda - \lambda_n)$$

$$\text{and } (\lambda I - A)^{-1} = \frac{F(\lambda)}{\Delta \lambda}$$

Thus

$$T(\lambda_i) = f(\lambda_i)Z_{m_i - 1}(\lambda_i) + f'(\lambda_i)Z_{m_i - 2} + \frac{f''(\lambda_i)}{2!}Z_{m_i - 3}(\lambda_i) + ... + \frac{f^{m_i - 1}(\lambda_i)}{(m-1)!}Z_0(\lambda_i)$$

$$Z_{m_i}(\lambda_i) = \frac{1}{m_i!} \frac{d^{m_i}}{d\lambda^{m_i}} \frac{F(\lambda)}{\Delta_{m_i}(\lambda)} \Bigg|_{\lambda = \lambda_i}$$

where

$$F^{(m)}(\lambda_i) = m!(-1)^{n-m-1} (\lambda_i I - A)^{m_i - m - 1} \prod_{j \neq i}(\lambda_j I - A)$$

gives the mth-order derivative of F, and

$$\Delta_{m_i}(\lambda) = \prod_{j \neq i}(\lambda - \lambda_j)$$

Note, for example, that

$$Z_i(\lambda) = \frac{d}{d\lambda} \frac{F(\lambda)}{\Delta(\lambda)} = \frac{\Delta(\lambda)F'(\lambda) - F(\lambda)\Delta'(\lambda)}{[\Delta(\lambda)]^2}$$

For distinct roots we have:

$$(\lambda I - A)^{-1} = \frac{F(\lambda)}{\Delta(\lambda)} = \frac{C_1}{\lambda - \lambda_1} + \frac{C_2}{\lambda - \lambda_2} + ... + \frac{C_n}{\lambda - \lambda_n}$$

The right side is a rational fraction decomposition of the middle term. If we multiply the two sides of the last equation by $\lambda - \lambda_i$, we obtain

$$C_i = \frac{F(\lambda_i)}{\Delta'(\lambda_i)}, \Delta'(\lambda_i) = \frac{d\Delta(\lambda)}{d\lambda}\Big|_{\lambda = \lambda_i}$$

where $\Delta'(\lambda)$ is the derivative of $\Delta(\lambda)$.

We have for $(\lambda I - A)^{-1}$, known as the resolvent of A:

$$(\lambda I - A)^{-1} = \sum_{i=1}^{n} \frac{F(\lambda_i)}{\Delta'(\lambda_i)\,(\lambda - \lambda_i)}$$

We also have

$$f(A) = \sum_{i=1}^{n} \frac{f(\lambda_i)F(\lambda_i)}{\Delta'(\lambda_i)}$$

This result, together with the relation $f(\lambda)=(\lambda I-A)^{-1}\Delta\lambda$, is suggestive of a similar representation for a function of a general operator other than a matrix. In that case the multiplicity of roots is not the main concern, but, with regard to the existence of $(\lambda I-A)^{-1}$, what kind of spectral values there are and where they are located in the complex plane are the serious concerns.

The Values of $\lim\limits_{k \to \infty} W^k$

The theory reveals what one must do to obtain the limit of W^k. There are essentially three cases to consider: 1) $\lambda_{max}=1$ is a simple root and there are no other roots of unity, or, 2) there are other roots of unity that cause cycling, whether $\lambda_{max}=1$ simple or multiple, and 3) $\lambda_{max}=1$ is a multiple root.

The concept of an irreducible-reducible matrix is due to Frobenius. A nonnegative matrix (a_{ij}) is irreducible if the graph (with as many nodes as the order of the matrix, and for any pair of nodes i and j there is an arc directed from i to j if $a_{ij}>0$, otherwise there is no arc from i to j) corresponding to that matrix is strongly connected (there is a sequence of arcs, often called a path, from any node to any other node.) Thus an irreducible matrix cannot have source or sink nodes. Algebraically, a nonnegative matrix W is **irreducible** if it cannot be reduced or decomposed into the form

$$\begin{bmatrix} W_1 & 0 \\ W_2 & W_3 \end{bmatrix}$$

where W_1 and W_3 are square submatrices. Otherwise, it is said to be **reducible**. W is irreducible if and only if $(I + W)^n > 0$ (for proof see Appendix 1). An irreducible matrix has a largest eigenvalue λ_{max} that is simple. If W is stochastic then we know that $\lambda_{max}=1$. An irreducible matrix is either primitive (some power of W is positive; $W^{n^2-2n+1} > 0$ always), or cyclic, which means that it has other eigenvalues that are roots of one; cases 1) or 2) above. If W is reducible, $\lambda_{max}=1$ may be simple with no other roots of unity, and case 1) applies, or multiple with no other roots of unity, and case 3) applies; otherwise if there are other roots of unity, then case 2) applies.

The limit priorities are found in the row corresponding to the element they represent. They are normalized for the elements in each component to determine their relative priorities. We now state what the solution is in the three cases.

1) When there are no other roots of unity and $\lambda_{max}=1$ is the dominant (in modulus) simple root, and because $f(\lambda) = \lambda^k$, the only root to the power k that does not tend to zero as $k \to \infty$ in Sylvester's formula is $1^k \to 1$. We have

$$W^k \to \frac{\prod_{j \neq i}(\lambda_j I - W)}{\prod_{j \neq i}(\lambda_j - \lambda_i)} = \frac{Adjoint(I - W)}{\Delta'(I)}$$

A more convenient, better known, and simpler outcome for case 1) is obtained as we now show.

If the nonnegative matrix W is primitive then [4] $\lim_{k \to \infty} W^k = we^T$ where to form the matrix we^T, w is the (column) right principal eigenvector of W and because W is stochastic $e^T = (1,...,1)$ is its (row) left principal eigenvector. Thus again we have the answer for $\lambda_{max}=1$ when W *is* primitive. This outcome can be shown to be the same as the previous one involving the adjoint of W. What is most characteristic of this outcome is that it is a stochastic matrix all of whose columns are identical i.e., all the entries in any single row are the same. If we multiply we^T on the right by the stochastic matrix W we still obtain we^T indicating that the limit has been attained. With a computer, and particularly because the product of stochastic matrices is stochastic, it is sufficient to raise the primitive stochastic matrix W to large powers to get a good approximation to the limit outcome.

2) Let us first show with an example what cycling means. We have:

$$W = \begin{bmatrix} 0 & W_{12} & 0 \\ 0 & 0 & W_{23} \\ W_{31} & 0 & 0 \end{bmatrix}; \quad W^2 = \begin{bmatrix} 0 & 0 & W_{12}W_{23} \\ W_{23}W_{31} & 0 & 0 \\ 0 & W_{31}W_{12} & 0 \end{bmatrix}$$

$$W^3 = \begin{bmatrix} W_{12}W_{23}W_{31} & 0 & 0 \\ 0 & W_{23}W_{31}W_{12} & 0 \\ 0 & 0 & W_{31}W_{12}W_{23} \end{bmatrix}$$

$$W^{3k} = \begin{bmatrix} (W_{12}W_{23}W_{31})^k & 0 & 0 \\ 0 & (W_{23}W_{31}W_{12})^k & 0 \\ 0 & 0 & (W_{31}W_{12}W_{23})^k \end{bmatrix}$$

$$W^{3k+1} = \begin{bmatrix} 0 & (W_{12}W_{23}W_{12})^k W_{12} & 0 \\ 0 & 0 & (W_{23}W_{31}W_{12})^k W_{23} \\ (W_{31}W_{12}W_{23})^k W_{31} & 0 & 0 \end{bmatrix}$$

$$W^{3k+2} = \begin{bmatrix} 0 & 0 & (W_{12}W_{23}W_{31})^k W_{12}W_{23} \\ (W_{23}W_{31}W_{12})^k W_{23}W_{31} & 0 & 0 \\ 0 & (W_{31}W_{12}W_{23})^k W_{31}W_{12} & 0 \end{bmatrix}$$

In this case we do not have a single limit answer because by raising the matrix W to powers, it passes through the three different cyclic forms or phases shown, each of which tends to its own limit that is different from the other two. What we do then for a limiting outcome is to take the average of the three limits which is their Cesaro sum.

Let us compute the average limit value for the case of a cycle of length c by taking the average over large powers of each of the consecutive phases of the cycle. We have formally

$$\frac{1}{c}[(W^c)^\infty + (W^{c+1})^\infty + \dots + (W^{c+c-1})^\infty] = \frac{1}{c}(I + W + \dots + W^{c-1})(W^c)^\infty, c \geq 2$$

which is the answer for case 2.

Although a computer can be programmed to go through a cycle by raising the matrix to powers, it may be useful to show what the theory has to say about finding c.

Assume that there are c such roots, let W be irreducible, and let $\lambda^n + a_1\lambda^{n_1} + a_2\lambda^{n_2} + ... + a_k\lambda^{n_k}$ be the characteristic polynomial of W where $n > n_1 > n_2 > ... > n_k$ and $a_t \neq 0, t = 1, 2, ..., k$.

Now consider $c = g.c.d.(n - n_1, n_1 - n_2, ..., n_{k-1} - n_k)$ where g.c.d. stands for the greatest common divisor.

Note that if $n_k=0$, then $a_k\lambda^{n_k} = a_k$, and the last term in the g.c.d. is n_{k-1}.

If, for example, the characteristic polynomial of W is given by:
$$\lambda^{13} + 2\lambda^{10} + 5\lambda^4$$
then $c=3$ since 13-10=3 and 10-4=6. However, if the characteristic polynomial is $\lambda^{13} + a_1\lambda^{10} + a_2\lambda^4 + a_3$, a_1, a_2, $a_3 \neq 0$ then $c=1$.

3) If the stochastic matrix W is reducible, then $(I+W)^{n-1}>0$ does not hold, and we need the characteristic equation to determine if $\lambda_{max}=1$ is a simple or a multiple root. In the former case we would still have the same answer as in case 1). In the latter, the limit priorities are obtained by using Sylvester's formula with $\lambda_{max}=1$ a multiple root of multiplicity n_1. We have:

$$W^\infty = n_1 \frac{d^{(n_1-1)}}{d\lambda^{(n_1-1)}}(\lambda I - W)^{-1}\Delta(\lambda) / \frac{d^{n_1}}{d\lambda^{n_1}}\Delta(\lambda)\big|_{\lambda=1} = \infty$$

$$n_1 \sum_{k=0}^{n_1}(-1)^k \frac{n_1!}{(n_1-k)!} \frac{\Delta^{(n_1-k)}(\lambda)}{\Delta^{(n_1)}(\lambda)}(\lambda I - W)^{-k-1}\big|_{\lambda=1} =$$

$$n_1 \sum_{k=n_1-1}^{n-1} \sum_{h=0}^{k-n_1+1} \frac{(k-h)!}{(k-n_1+1-h)!}p_h W^{n-1-k} / \sum_{h=0}^{n-n_1} p_h \frac{(n-h)!}{(n-n_1-h)!}$$

where

$$\Delta(\lambda) \equiv \text{Det}(\lambda I - W) = \lambda^n + p_1\lambda^{n-1} + ... + p_n$$

and the limit outcome is a polynomial in W. It is a sufficient but not a necessary condition. We shall see in the next section that with hierarchies the power can be much less than prescribed by the above formula. This approach for raising matrices to powers was developed more than a century ago when computers had not yet been invented. Although we have given an algorithm for computing the characteristic polynomial and another for calculating the eigenvalues, it is tedious to do that in general. Isaacson and Madsen [5], in writing about use of the direct approach to obtain limit results in the reducible case, say, "Actually for many examples it is almost impossible" (p. 92). They then develop a special procedure to deal with the problem.

We note that in this particular case of dealing with limits, if we multiply both sides of the reducible case by $\lim_{k\to\infty} W^k$, we would still have $\lim_{k\to\infty} W^k$ on the left. On the right, a large power of W, because it converges to a limit, would absorb the other factors involving powers of W. It would thus factor out leaving a finite sum of terms that is a constant multiplier which we can ignore because we are only interested in the proportionality of the limit outcome in the resulting matrix. It is thus again computationally sufficient when W is reducible and acyclic to raise it to large powers.

The excellent ANP software *Super Decisions* developed by Rozann W. Saaty and William Adams does these calculations automatically without having to go through the different cases. It first tests for irreducibility, and unless there is cyclicity for which the Cesaro sum would be calculated, they obtain the outcome for primitivity as the limit powers of W. If irreducibility fails, they again raise W to large powers. The result is that in all cases the matrix is raised to powers with the Cesaro sum used when there is cycling, recognized by noting that successive powers of the matrix yield different limit outcomes.

Our analysis narrows the possibilities to two cases for computation. We raise the stochastic matrix W to large powers and read off the priorities. If the powers do not converge to a single matrix whose successive values improve in accuracy, we know that the outcome belongs to a cycle whose length is determined by taking successive large powers of W. In that case, we take the average (Cesaro sum) of the successive matrices of an entire cycle for the final priorities.

Application to Hierarchies

Let us look at hierarchies.

Lemma: *The supermatrix W of a hierarchy is reducible.*

Proof: Its graph is not strongly connected because there is no path from the bottom to the top.

Theorem 1 *The characteristic polynomial of the n by n supermatrix W of a hierarchy is given by* $\lambda^{n_c} (\lambda - 1)^{n_a}$, $n_c + n_a = n$,*where n_c is the number of elements above the level of alternatives, and n_a is the number of alternatives in a hierarchy.*

Proof: Consider row cofactor expansion of the determinant. By the lemma, all elements above the main diagonal in W are zero, and this is also the case for λI-W. Thus, except for λ in the (1, 1) position, all elements in the first row are zero, and hence they and their cofactors make no contribution to the determinant. If we strike out the first row and first column, then the top row of the surviving cofactor again has λ in its (1,1) position and zeros for the remaining elements in the row. In this manner the process is continued. Note that the diagonal elements corresponding to the alternatives are each equal to (λ-1), and all elements to its right in that row are again zero. Thus the determinant of (λI-W) has the form given in the theorem.

Corollary: $\lambda_{max} = 1$ *is a multiple root of the supermatrix of a hierarchy whose multiplicity is equal to the number of alternatives.*

Theorem 2 *The composite vector of a hierarchy of n levels is the entry in the (m,1) position of* W^k, $k \geq m - 1$.

Proof: The supermatrix of a hierarchy of m levels (Figure 2) is stochastic, reducible, and acyclic. In this case it is easy to see that the formula in case 3 simplifies to $W^{\infty} = W^k$, for k m -1, where

$$
W^k = \begin{bmatrix}
0 & 0 & \cdots & 0 & 0 & 0 \\
0 & 0 & \cdots & 0 & 0 & 0 \\
\vdots & \vdots & \ddots & \vdots & \vdots & \vdots \\
0 & 0 & \cdots & 0 & 0 & 0 \\
W_{m,m-1}W_{m-1,m-2}\cdots W_{32}W_{21} & W_{m,m-1}W_{m-1,m-2}\cdots W_{32} & \cdots & W_{m,m-1}W_{m-1,m-2} & W_{m,m-1} & I
\end{bmatrix}
$$

It is easy to show by induction on multiplying blocks while raising W to powers that when the power k=m-1 is reached, further multiplication does not produce a new outcome. Because the number of components far exceeds the total number of elements in each component, this number is always less than the number $n\text{-}n_a$ assured by the outcome we gave for Sylvester's formula.

The foregoing theorem shows that hierarchic composition is a result of raising W to powers. It also shows that to obtain the final priorities, the submatrices of the supermatrix corresponding to higher levels of the hierarchy are arranged from right to left as influence is transmitted from top to bottom. This leads us to the observation that the submatrices on a path leading to a cycle in a network would be multiplied on the right by the submatrices corresponding to the blocks in the cycle and eventually by their limit. Since this limit is stochastic with identical columns, the outcome of multiplying it matrix on the right by a stochastic matrix is the limit itself. Thus in a feedback network with cycles, influence along a path leading into a cycle is cancelled by the influences in that cycle and the paths from source nodes have no effect on the outcome priorities of the network. For a path leading to a sink (such as the alternatives of a decision) from a cycle, the opposite is true. This is because the influence matrices of the blocks on the path multiply the limit matrix of the cycle on the left and thus makes a contribution to the outcome.

An Example of a Reducible Matrix with a Multiple Root: Hierarchic Composition from the Supermatrix

Our simplest example of the multiple root (and hence reducible) case is a hierarchy. In practice the structure of a decision problem is often a hierarchy or a simple modification of a hierarchy, so that a feedback cycle is required at some point as in the holarchy in Figure 3. In a hierarchy when one is using time periods for projection purposes, the time periods both influence and depend on the criteria in the level under them. A cycle between the two top levels of the hierarchy is then needed. In that case it is simpler to first evaluate the limit outcome of the cycle between the two levels, and then use the resulting weights of the criteria to proceed downward in the hierarchy. Consider the first supermatrix W of a hierarchy with two criteria and two alternatives below on the left and the supermatrix $\lambda I - W$ on the right.

$$
\begin{pmatrix} 0 & 0 & 0 & 0 & 0 \\ 0.2 & 0 & 0 & 0 & 0 \\ 0.8 & 0 & 0 & 0 & 0 \\ 0 & 0.1 & 0.6 & 1 & 0 \\ 0 & 0.9 & 0.4 & 0 & 1 \end{pmatrix}
\begin{pmatrix} \lambda & 0 & 0 & 0 & 0 \\ -0.2 & \lambda & 0 & 0 & 0 \\ -0.8 & 0 & \lambda & 0 & 0 \\ 0 & -0.1 & -0.6 & -1+\lambda & 0 \\ 0 & -0.9 & -0.4 & 0 & -1+\lambda \end{pmatrix}
$$

We know that we are in case 3) because the supermatrix of a hierarchy is reducible, and has no cycles. We have two ways to get the limit. The first is to multiply the matrix by itself. Since it has three components (goal, criteria and alternatives), it is enough to square it to get the answer. We can get the same outcome with Sylvester's formula. It can take more work because for this case it turns out that we need to cube the matrix. We have $\Delta(\lambda)=\lambda^5-2\lambda^4+\lambda^3$, and

$$
(\lambda I - W)^{-1} = \begin{pmatrix}
\dfrac{\lambda^2-2\lambda^3+\lambda^4}{\lambda^3-2\lambda^4+\lambda^5} & 0 & 0 & 0 & 0 \\
\dfrac{0.2\lambda-0.4\lambda^2+0.2\lambda^3}{\lambda^3-2\lambda^4+\lambda^5} & \dfrac{\lambda^2-2\lambda^3+\lambda^4}{\lambda^3-2\lambda^4+\lambda^5} & 0 & 0 & 0 \\
\dfrac{0.8\lambda-1.6\lambda^2+0.8\lambda^3}{\lambda^3-2\lambda^4+\lambda^5} & 0 & \dfrac{\lambda^2-2\lambda^3+\lambda^4}{\lambda^3-2\lambda^4+\lambda^5} & 0 & 0 \\
\dfrac{-0.5\lambda+0.5\lambda^2}{\lambda^3-2\lambda^4+\lambda^5} & \dfrac{-0.1\lambda^2+0.1\lambda^3}{\lambda^3-2\lambda^4+\lambda^5} & \dfrac{-0.6\lambda^2+0.4\lambda^3}{\lambda^3-2\lambda^4+\lambda^5} & \dfrac{\lambda^3+\lambda^4}{\lambda^3-2\lambda^4+\lambda^5} & 0 \\
\dfrac{-0.5\lambda+0.5\lambda^2}{\lambda^3-2\lambda^4+\lambda^5} & \dfrac{-0.9\lambda^2+0.9\lambda^3}{\lambda^3-2\lambda^4+\lambda^5} & \dfrac{-0.4\lambda^2+0.4\lambda^3}{\lambda^3-2\lambda^4+\lambda^5} & 0 & \dfrac{-\lambda^3+\lambda^4}{\lambda^3-2\lambda^4+\lambda^5}
\end{pmatrix}
$$

The formula for case 3) gives

$$
\frac{2B^{(1)}(\lambda)}{\Delta^{(2)}(\lambda)}\Big|_{\lambda=1}=W^3 = \begin{pmatrix} 0 & 0 & 0 & 0 & 0 \\ 0 & 0 & 0 & 0 & 0 \\ 0 & 0 & 0 & 0 & 0 \\ 0.5 & 0.1 & 0.6 & 1 & 0 \\ 0.5 & 0.9 & 0.4 & 0 & 1 \end{pmatrix}
$$

The last two rows are precisely the hierarchic composition we obtain by raising W to the second power because the matrix remains the same for $k>2$.

Inner Dependence of Criteria

Consider a three-level hierarchy with a goal, criteria, and alternatives. Assume that the criteria are dependent among themselves. The supermatrix representation is given by:

$$W = \begin{pmatrix} 0 & 0 & 0 \\ X & Y & 0 \\ 0 & Z & I \end{pmatrix}$$

where X is the column vector of priorities of the criteria with respect to the goal, Y is the matrix of column eigenvectors of interdependence among the criteria, and Z is the matrix of column eigenvectors of the alternatives with respect to each criterion. W is a column stochastic matrix obtained by appropriate weighting of the matrices corresponding to interactions between levels.

The kth power of W that captures rank dominance along paths of length k is given by:

$$W^k = \begin{pmatrix} 0 & 0 & 0 \\ Y^{k-1}X & Y^k & 0 \\ Z\sum_{i=0}^{n-2} Y^i X & Z\sum_{i=0}^{n-1} Y^i & I \end{pmatrix}$$

and the priorities are obtained from the limit of W^k as $k \rightarrow \infty$. We have:

$$W^\infty = \begin{pmatrix} 0 & 0 & 0 \\ 0 & 0 & 0 \\ Z(I-Y)^{-1}X & Z(I-Y)^{-1} & I \end{pmatrix}$$

Note that if $Y=0$, and hence the criteria are independent among themselves, the weights of the alternatives are given by ZX, the result of the additive model obtained by hierarchic composition. Also when Y is not zero but is a small perturbation in a neighborhood of the null matrix, the additive model would be a good representation of the limit priorities, and hierarchic composition is still valid. It is only when Y is a large perturbation away from zero that the supermatrix solution should be used. In general, unless there are strong dependencies among the criteria, the additive model is an adequate estimate of the priorities in a hierarchy. Otherwise the criteria should be redefined to ensure the independence of the new set.

The Consistency of a System

We want to represent both the inconsistency along paths beginning with a goal and the inconsistency in cycles. For paths we want the initial, not the limit, priorities of the elements. For cycles we want the limit priorities of the elements. We need to weight inconsistency by the weight of the corresponding elements. Also we need the influence priority of a component containing an element used to compare elements in another component, on that component. In the end we need to weight by the priorities K_C of the supercriteria in the control hierarchy.

$$C_S = \sum_{\substack{control \\ criteria}} K_C \sum_{\substack{all \\ chains}} (\sum_{j=1}^{h} \sum_{i=1}^{n_{ij+1}} w_{ij}\mu_{ij+1} + \sum_{\substack{control \\ criteria}} K_C \sum_{k=1}^{S} \sum_{j=1}^{n_k} w_{jk} \sum_{h=1}^{|C_h|} w_{(k)(h)}\mu_k(j,h)$$

where $n_j=j=1,2,\ldots,h$ is the number of elements in the jth level and μ_{ij+1} is the consistency index of all elements in the $(j+1)^{st}$ level with respect to the ith criterion of the jth level. In the second term, $w_{(k)(h)}$ is the priority of the influence of the hth component on the kth component and w_{jk} is the limit priority of the jth element in the kth component. In the case of a hierarchy, there are no cycles and the second term is equal to zero. As in the measurement of consistency of a hierarchy, this index must be divided by the corresponding index with random inconsistencies.

Judgments: Their Quality and Number

The number of judgments and their validity are two constant concerns particularly to users of the ANP. One would prefer not to tax the energy of the decision maker. One may be willing to spend more time on an important decision but may not have the desire to confirm the obvious by putting forth too much effort. This kind of concern is legitimate. Also, no one would argue that with less information provided, the decision may not be as certain as it would be if an exhaustive analysis were made. Sometimes it should be possible to do a back-of-the-envelope estimation to determine whether a certain outcome is worth pursuing. Then the staff can spend more time verifying and validating the decision with a thorough development. What methods can we use to expedite decision making without loss of validity? That will be our concern in this section.

The following ideas can be used to control the number of judgments in the model:

1. Good results are the outcome of good judgments, and there is no good, ready-made substitute for that knowledge. The more complex the problem, the more complex its structure and the more judgments are needed. Patience is a virtue in any creative effort.
2. Make a smaller model.
3. Reduce the number of components.

4. Reduce the number of elements in each component.
5. Pairwise compare the control criteria and subcriteria and eliminate those with small priorities, since there is no feedback among them.
6. Pairwise compare the components influence on each component and compute the limit priorities of the resulting supermatrix. Drop those components whose limit weight is very small relative to the others.
7. Assign priorities geometrically using the software by adjusting the relative length of bars associated with the elements. It can also be done arithmetically by assigning them numbers that are then normalized and introduced into the supermatrix.
8. With confidence in the accuracy of the knowledge available, in each set of paired comparisons one can fill in the judgments in one row of the matrix or fill in any set of n-1 judgments that form a spanning tree.
9. Distribute the judgment effort among experts specialized in those parts of the problem. Only the most important parts of the problem should be considered by the entire group.
10. Combine benefits, costs, and risks in each judgment and use only one model.

The most scientific approach would be to apply Harker's algorithm for incomplete judgments and use our ratio scale metric to add the next most important judgments until diminishing returns indicate that one should stop. Here is a description of that procedure.

A Method for Incomplete Comparisons

Harker [6,7] suggests the following:
-   Have the decision maker provide judgments such that at least one judgment is answered in each column, yielding a matrix with some unknown ratio elements.
-   Enter zero for any missing judgment in that matrix and add the number of missing judgments in each row to the diagonal element in the row, producing a new matrix A.
-   Calculate the weight w:

$$\lim_{k \to \infty} \frac{A^k e}{e^T A^k e} = cw$$

-   Use the resulting w_i/w_j as a suggested value for the missing judgments to make it consistent with the judgments already provided.

- Guide the decision maker to make additional judgments that have the greatest influence on the weight w. One chooses for the next judgment that entry (i,j), with the largest sum of the absolute values of the coefficients of the gradient of w with respect to (i,j) calculated using the following formula:

  x: right principal eigenvector = w, in AHP notation $Ax = \lambda_{max}\, x$

  y: left principal eigenvector $y^T A = \lambda_{max}\, y$

$$D^A_{\lambda_{max}} = \left[\frac{\partial \lambda_{max}}{\partial_{ij|}} i, j\right] = \left[(y_i x_j) - (y_j x_i)/a^2_{ij}, j > i\right]$$

where y is normalized so that $y^T x = 1$. When an original $a_{ij} = 0$, it is replaced by the corresponding ratio w_i/w_j from w.

Then $D^A_x = \left[\dfrac{\partial x}{\partial_{ij}} \mid j > i\right]$ is the matrix of gradients for the

weights x and is given by:

$$\left[\begin{array}{cc} \left(\tilde{A} - \lambda_{max}\tilde{I}\right)^{-1} & \tilde{D}^A_{\lambda_{max}} x - \tilde{z} \\ e & 0 \end{array}\right]$$

where

$I = n \times n$ identity matrix

$e = n$ dimensional row vector of ones

$z = (z_k) = n$ dimensional column vector defined by:

$$z_k = \begin{cases} x_j & \text{if } k = i \\ -x_i / a^2_{ij} & \text{if } k = j \\ 0 & \text{otherwise} \end{cases}$$

~ denotes the matrix or vector with its last row deleted.

D^A_x is a column vector whose elements can either be positive or negative, and their sum is zero.

- We then follow this process. Identify an element of the gradient which is too large in proportion with its corresponding eigenvector element. For example, adding a large negative gradient value to a small eigenvector element may give a negative value. If such an element exists, decide on a proportion (say, 50%) and apply it to all gradient elements for all missing entries.

- If the number of gradient elements that require adjustment is more than one, choose that with the smallest proportion to apply to all gradient elements. This ensures the non-negativity of the elements of the new eigenvector to be computed next.

- Compute the potentially new eigenvector for each missing entry by adding elementwise the gradient vector to the most recent eigenvector.

- Compute compatibility between each of the potentially new eigenvector representing each missing entry (say p_{ij}) and the most recent eigenvector w, as follows:
  - Construct the matrix of ratios for p_{ij} and w.
  - Compute the metric for each missing entry.

$$\text{Metric } (i, j) = \frac{1}{n^2} \, e^T P_{ij} - W^T e$$

where n = the number of elements in the component
   e = a column vector of 1's
   P_{ij} = the matrix of ratios for p_{ij}
   W^T = the transpose of the matrix of ratios for w
   e^T = a row vector of 1's

- Rank the missing entries according to their metric
- Guide the decision maker to provide a judgment for the entry with the largest metric.

The decision maker may decide to stop the questioning or continue according to whether the metric comparison of the new and old eigenvector is less than a predetermined value such as 1.1. One should keep in mind that redundancy is needed to ensure that the outcome has practical validity and hence one may need to add more than a single additional judgment.

An Example

Consider the matrix of Table 1 with initial judgments:

Table 1 Initial Judgment Set

	A	B	C	D
A	1	2	1/7	5
B	1/2	1	0	0
C	7	0	1	0
D	1/5	0	0	1

Applying the Harker's ideas above to this matrix, we have for the initial calculations, shown in Table 2:

Table 2 Initial Calculations

Element	Gradient Absolute Sum	Ratio Metric
(1,2)	0.0271	1.0081
(1,3)	0.8739	1.8466
(1,4)	0.0104	1.0013
(2,3)	**1.4241**	**8.4838**
(2,4)	0.0111	1.0051
(3,4)	0.0025	1.0000

Here the user is invited to provide a judgment in the (2,3) position which has the largest metric value. Assume that the judgment is 1/5 which gives the following new matrix (Table 3).

Table 3 New Judgment Set

	A	B	C	D
A	1	2	1/7	5
B	1/2	1	1/5	0
C	7	5	1	0
D	1/5	0	0	1

The new calculations are exhibited in Table 4. This shows that the next judgment is in the (3,4) position because we already have a judgment in the (1,4) position. Assume that the judgment is 8 for this position. Compute the eigenvector and check its compatibility with the previous eigenvector. If they are acceptably close, stop. Otherwise, continue. The process needs refinements to make it work successfully all the time.

Table 4 New Calculations

Element	Gradient Absolute Sum	Ratio Metric
(1,2)	0.4261	15.0431
(1,3)	1.2518	1.4560
(1,4)	0.3994	2.9926
(2,3)	0.6131	1.1385
(2,4)	0.3859	2.2172
(3,4)	**0.3962**	**2.9019**

Feedback Can Cause an Unimportant Element to Become Important

The following example illustrates how an element e_{12} that has low priority in its component (Table 5) but has high priority of influence on elements in other components obtains a high overall priority in the limit (Table 6). The idea is that intuitively one may assume that at first glance that element is unimportant relative to its component, and therefore perhaps unimportant overall, but finds with the ANP that it is the most important element. Here we give the initial and the limit supermatrices. We also learn from this example that while in a hierarchy we can proceed downward by ignoring the judgments of subcriteria and alternatives under a low priority criterion, we cannot do the same in a feedback process because an initially unimportant criterion may become more important in the cycling and limit operations.

Table 5 The Supermatrix of Column Eigenvectors

	e_{11}	e_{12}	e_{13}	e_{21}	e_{22}	e_{31}	e_{32}	e_{41}	e_{42}
e_{11}	0.021	0.025	0.028	0.025	0.018	0.022	0.026	0.020	0.028
e_{12}	0.005	0.005	0.005	0.189	0.245	0.243	0.225	0.241	0.246
e_{13}	0.223	0.220	0.217	0.119	0.071	0.068	0.082	0.073	0.059
e_{21}	0.219	0.214	0.222	0.000	0.000	0.277	0.277	0.222	0.250
e_{22}	0.031	0.036	0.028	0.000	0.000	0.056	0.056	0.111	0.083
e_{31}	0.208	0.214	0.214	0.266	0.276	0.000	0.000	0.250	0.286
e_{32}	0.042	0.036	0.036	0.067	0.056	0.000	0.000	0.083	0.048
e_{41}	0.188	0.219	0.219	0.278	0.278	0.267	0.278	0.000	0.000
e_{42}	0.063	0.031	0.031	0.056	0.056	0.067	0.056	0.000	0.000

Table 6 The Limit Supermatrix

	e_{11}	e_{12}	e_{13}	e_{21}	e_{22}	e_{31}	e_{32}	e_{41}	e_{42}
e_{11}	0.024	0.024	0.024	0.024	0.024	0.024	0.024	0.024	0.024
e_{12}	0.159	0.159	0.159	0.159	0.159	0.159	0.159	0.159	0.159
e_{13}	0.125	0.125	0.125	0.125	0.125	0.125	0.125	0.125	0.125
e_{21}	0.183	0.183	0.183	0.183	0.183	0.183	0.183	0.183	0.183
e_{22}	0.047	0.047	0.047	0.047	0.047	0.047	0.047	0.047	0.047
e_{31}	0.187	0.187	0.187	0.187	0.187	0.187	0.187	0.187	0.187
e_{32}	0.044	0.044	0.044	0.044	0.044	0.044	0.044	0.044	0.044
e_{41}	0.193	0.193	0.193	0.193	0.193	0.193	0.193	0.193	0.193
e_{42}	0.038	0.038	0.038	0.038	0.038	0.038	0.038	0.038	0.038

Actual Relative Market Share Based on Sales

Estimating the Relative Market Share of Walmart, Kmart and Target

The object is to estimate the market share of Walmart, Kmart, and Target without using dollar values in the estimate. The network for the ANP model shown in Figure 7 describes well the influences that determine the market share of these companies. We will not use space in this chapter to describe the clusters and their nodes in great detail.

The Unweighted Supermatrix

The unweighted supermatrix is constructed from the priorities derived from the different pairwise comparisons. The nodes, grouped by the clusters they belong to, are the labels of the rows and columns of the supermatrix. The column of priorities for a node at the top of the supermatrix includes the priorities of the nodes on the left side of the matrix that have been pairwise compared as to their influence with respect to market share on that node. The sum of these priorities is equal to one. The supermatrix of the network of Figure 7 is shown in Table 7. We have broken the matrix into two parts because it is wider than the page we are writing on.

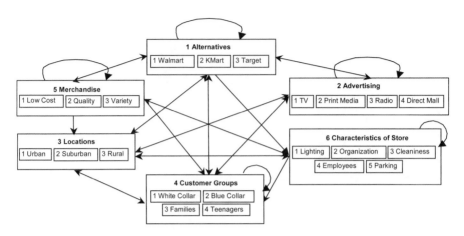

Figure 7 The Clusters and Nodes of a Model to Estimate the Relative Market Share of Walmart, Kmart and Target

It is clear that this matrix is not column stochastic and its blocks under each cluster at the top need to be weighted by the priorities of the influence with respect to market share of the clusters at the left on the cluster to which they fall under.

Table 7 The Unweighted Supermatrix, Displayed in Two Parts

		1 Alternatives			2 Advertising				3 Locations		
		1 Walmart	2 KMart	3 Target	1 TV	2 Print Media	3 Radio	4 Direct Mail	1 Urban	2 Suburban	3 Rural
1 Alternatives	1 Walmart	0.000	0.833	0.833	0.687	0.540	0.634	0.661	0.614	0.652	0.683
	2 KMart	0.750	0.000	0.167	0.186	0.297	0.174	0.208	0.268	0.235	0.200
	3 Target	0.250	0.167	0.000	0.127	0.163	0.192	0.131	0.117	0.113	0.117
2 Advertising	1 TV	0.553	0.176	0.188	0.000	0.000	0.000	0.000	0.288	0.543	0.558
	2 Print Media	0.202	0.349	0.428	0.750	0.000	0.800	0.000	0.381	0.231	0.175
	3 Radio	0.062	0.056	0.055	0.000	0.000	0.000	0.000	0.059	0.053	0.048
	4 Direct Mail	0.183	0.420	0.330	0.250	0.000	0.200	0.000	0.273	0.173	0.219
3 Locations	1 Urban	0.114	0.084	0.086	0.443	0.126	0.080	0.099	0.000	0.000	0.000
	2 Suburb	0.405	0.444	0.628	0.387	0.416	0.609	0.537	0.000	0.000	0.000
	3 Rural	0.481	0.472	0.285	0.169	0.458	0.311	0.364	0.000	0.000	0.000
4 Cust.Groups	1 White	0.141	0.114	0.208	0.165	0.155	0.116	0.120	0.078	0.198	0.092
	2 Blue	0.217	0.214	0.117	0.165	0.155	0.198	0.203	0.223	0.116	0.224
	3 Families	0.579	0.623	0.620	0.621	0.646	0.641	0.635	0.656	0.641	0.645
	4 Teens	0.063	0.049	0.055	0.048	0.043	0.045	0.041	0.043	0.045	0.038
5 Merchandise	1 Low Cost	0.362	0.333	0.168	0.000	0.000	0.000	0.000	0.000	0.000	0.000
	2 Quality	0.261	0.140	0.484	0.000	0.000	0.000	0.000	0.000	0.000	0.000
	3 Variety	0.377	0.528	0.349	0.000	0.000	0.000	0.000	0.000	0.000	0.000

6 Charact.	1 Lighting	0.000	0.000	0.000	0.000	0.000	0.000	0.000	0.000	0.000	0.000
	2 Org.	0.000	0.000	0.000	0.000	0.000	0.000	0.000	0.000	0.000	0.000
	3 Clean	0.000	0.000	0.000	0.000	0.000	0.000	0.000	0.000	0.000	0.000
	4 Employ.	0.000	0.000	0.000	0.000	0.000	0.000	0.000	0.000	0.000	0.000
	5 Parking	0.000	0.000	0.000	0.000	0.000	0.000	0.000	0.000	0.000	0.000

		4 Custom. Groups				5 Merchandise			6 Characteristics of Store				
		1 White Collar	2 Blue Collar	3 Familie	4 Teens	1 Low Cost	2 Quality	3 Variety	1 Light.	2 Organiz.	3 Clean	4 Employees	5 Park
1 Alternat.	1 Walmart	0.637	0.661	0.630	0.691	0.661	0.614	0.648	0.667	0.655	0.570	0.644	0.558
	2 KMart	0.105	0.208	0.218	0.149	0.208	0.117	0.122	0.111	0.095	0.097	0.085	0.122
	3 Target	0.258	0.131	0.151	0.160	0.131	0.268	0.230	0.222	0.250	0.333	0.271	0.320
2 Advertis.	1 TV	0.323	0.510	0.508	0.634	0.000	0.000	0.000	0.000	0.000	0.000	0.000	0.000
	2 Print Med.	0.214	0.221	0.270	0.170	0.000	0.000	0.000	0.000	0.000	0.000	0.000	0.000
	3 Radio	0.059	0.063	0.049	0.096	0.000	0.000	0.000	0.000	0.000	0.000	0.000	0.000
	4 Direct Mail	0.404	0.206	0.173	0.100	0.000	0.000	0.000	0.000	0.000	0.000	0.000	0.000
3 Locations	1 Urban	0.167	0.094	0.096	0.109	0.268	0.105	0.094	0.100	0.091	0.091	0.111	0.067
	2 Suburban	0.833	0.280	0.308	0.309	0.117	0.605	0.627	0.433	0.455	0.455	0.444	0.293
	3 Rural	0.000	0.627	0.596	0.582	0.614	0.291	0.280	0.466	0.455	0.455	0.444	0.641
4 Customer Groups	1 White Col.	0.000	0.000	0.279	0.085	0.051	0.222	0.165	0.383	0.187	0.242	0.165	0.000
	2 Blue Collar	0.000	0.000	0.649	0.177	0.112	0.159	0.165	0.383	0.187	0.208	0.165	0.000
	3 Families	0.857	0.857	0.000	0.737	0.618	0.566	0.621	0.185	0.583	0.494	0.621	0.000
	4 Teenagers	0.143	0.143	0.072	0.000	0.219	0.053	0.048	0.048	0.043	0.056	0.048	0.000
5 Merch.	1 Low Cost	0.000	0.000	0.000	0.000	0.000	0.800	0.800	0.000	0.000	0.000	0.000	0.000
	2 Quality	0.000	0.000	0.000	0.000	0.750	0.000	0.200	0.000	0.000	0.000	0.000	0.000
	3 Variety	0.000	0.000	0.000	0.000	0.250	0.200	0.000	0.000	1.000	0.000	0.000	0.000
6 Character.	1 Lighting	0.000	0.000	0.000	0.000	0.000	0.000	0.000	0.000	0.169	0.121	0.000	0.250
	2 Organiz.	0.000	0.000	0.000	0.000	0.000	0.000	0.000	0.251	0.000	0.575	0.200	0.750
	3 Cleanli.	0.000	0.000	0.000	0.000	0.000	0.000	0.000	0.673	0.469	0.000	0.800	0.000
	4 Employee	0.000	0.000	0.000	0.000	0.000	0.000	0.000	0.000	0.308	0.304	0.000	0.000
	5 Parking	0.000	0.000	0.000	0.000	0.000	0.000	0.000	0.075	0.055	0.000	0.000	0.000

The Cluster Matrix

The cluster themselves must be compared to establish their relative importance and use their priorities to weight the supermatrix to make it column stochastic. A cluster impacts another cluster with respect to market share when it is linked from it, that is, when at least one node in the source cluster is linked to nodes in the target cluster. The clusters linked from the source cluster are pairwise compared for the importance of their impact on it with respect to market share, resulting in the column of priorities for that cluster in the cluster matrix. The process is repeated for each cluster in the network to obtain the priorities shown in Table 8. An interpretation of the priorities in the first column is that Merchandise (0.442) and Locations

(0.276) have the most impact on Alternatives, (the three competitors) with respect to market share.

Table 8 The Cluster Matrix

	1 Alternatives	2 Advertising	3 Locations	4 Customer Groups	5 Merchandise	6 Charact. of Store
1 Alternatives	0.137	0.174	0.094	0.057	0.049	0.037
2 Advertising	0.091	0.220	0.280	0.234	0.000	0.000
3 Locations	0.276	0.176	0.000	0.169	0.102	0.112
4 Customer Groups	0.054	0.429	0.627	0.540	0.252	0.441
5 Merchandise	0.442	0.000	0.000	0.000	0.596	0.316
6 Characteristics of Store	0.000	0.000	0.000	0.000	0.000	0.094

The Weighted Supermatrix

The weighted supermatrix shown in Table 9 is obtained by multiplying each entry in a block of the component at the top of the supermatrix by the priority of influence of the component on the left from the cluster matrix in Table 8. For example, the first entry, 0.137, in Table 8 is used to multiply each of the nine entries in the block (Alternatives, Alternatives) in the unweighted supermatrix shown in Table 7. This gives the entries for the (Alternatives, Alternatives) component in the weighted supermatrix of Table 9. Each column in the weighted supermatrix has a sum equal to 1, and thus the matrix is column stochastic and converges to a single vector or is periodic in which case the average is usually used..

Table 9 Weighted Supermatrix (Given in two parts because it is too wide to display in one piece)

		1 Alternatives			2 Advertising				3 Locations		
		1 Walmart	2 KMart	3 Target	1 TV	2 Print Media	3 Radio	4 Direct Mail	1 Urban	2 Suburban	3 Rural
1 Alternatives	1 Walmart	0.000	0.114	0.114	0.120	0.121	0.110	0.148	0.058	0.061	0.064
	2 KMart	0.103	0.000	0.023	0.033	0.066	0.030	0.047	0.025	0.022	0.019
	3 Target	0.034	0.023	0.000	0.022	0.037	0.033	0.029	0.011	0.011	0.011
2 Advertising	1 TV	0.050	0.016	0.017	0.000	0.000	0.000	0.000	0.080	0.152	0.156
	2 Print Media	0.018	0.032	0.039	0.165	0.000	0.176	0.000	0.106	0.064	0.049
	3 Radio	0.006	0.005	0.005	0.000	0.000	0.000	0.000	0.016	0.015	0.014
	4 Direct Mail	0.017	0.038	0.030	0.055	0.000	0.044	0.000	0.076	0.048	0.061
3 Locations	1 Urban	0.031	0.023	0.024	0.078	0.028	0.014	0.022	0.000	0.000	0.000

	2 Suburban	0.112	0.123	0.174	0.068	0.094	0.107	0.121	0.000	0.000	0.000
	3 Rural	0.133	0.130	0.079	0.030	0.103	0.055	0.082	0.000	0.000	0.000
4 Cust.Groups	1 White Collar	0.008	0.006	0.011	0.071	0.086	0.050	0.066	0.049	0.124	0.058
	2 Blue Collar	0.012	0.011	0.006	0.071	0.086	0.085	0.112	0.140	0.073	0.141
	3 Families	0.031	0.033	0.033	0.267	0.356	0.275	0.350	0.411	0.402	0.404
	4 Teenagers	0.003	0.003	0.003	0.021	0.024	0.019	0.023	0.027	0.028	0.024
5 Merchandise	1 Low Cost	0.160	0.147	0.074	0.000	0.000	0.000	0.000	0.000	0.000	0.000
	2 Quality	0.115	0.062	0.214	0.000	0.000	0.000	0.000	0.000	0.000	0.000
	3 Variety	0.166	0.233	0.154	0.000	0.000	0.000	0.000	0.000	0.000	0.000
	1 Lighting	0.000	0.000	0.000	0.000	0.000	0.000	0.000	0.000	0.000	0.000
	2 Organization	0.000	0.000	0.000	0.000	0.000	0.000	0.000	0.000	0.000	0.000
	3 Cleanliness	0.000	0.000	0.000	0.000	0.000	0.000	0.000	0.000	0.000	0.000
	4 Employees	0.000	0.000	0.000	0.000	0.000	0.000	0.000	0.000	0.000	0.000

		4 Customer Groups				5 Merchandise			6 Characteristic of Store				
		1 White Collar	2 Blue Collar	3 Familie	4 Teens	1 Low Cost	2 Quality	3 Variety	1 Light'ng	2 Organ.	3 Clean	4 Employees	5 Pkg
1 Alternat.	1 Walmart	0.036	0.038	0.036	0.040	0.033	0.030	0.032	0.036	0.024	0.031	0.035	0.086
	2 KMart	0.006	0.012	0.012	0.009	0.010	0.006	0.006	0.006	0.004	0.005	0.005	0.019
	3 Target	0.015	0.007	0.009	0.009	0.006	0.013	0.011	0.012	0.009	0.018	0.015	0.049
2 Advertising	1 TV	0.076	0.119	0.119	0.148	0.000	0.000	0.000	0.000	0.000	0.000	0.000	0.000
	2 Print Med.	0.050	0.052	0.063	0.040	0.000	0.000	0.000	0.000	0.000	0.000	0.000	0.000
	3 Radio	0.014	0.015	0.012	0.023	0.000	0.000	0.000	0.000	0.000	0.000	0.000	0.000
	4 Direct Mail	0.095	0.048	0.040	0.023	0.000	0.000	0.000	0.000	0.000	0.000	0.000	0.000
3 Locations	1 Urban	0.028	0.016	0.016	0.018	0.027	0.011	0.010	0.016	0.010	0.015	0.018	0.031
	2 Suburban	0.141	0.047	0.052	0.052	0.012	0.062	0.064	0.071	0.051	0.074	0.073	0.135
	3 Rural	0.000	0.106	0.101	0.098	0.063	0.030	0.029	0.076	0.051	0.074	0.073	0.295
4 Cust Grps	1 White Col.	0.000	0.000	0.151	0.046	0.013	0.056	0.042	0.247	0.082	0.156	0.107	0.000
	2 Blue Collar	0.000	0.000	0.350	0.096	0.028	0.040	0.042	0.247	0.082	0.134	0.107	0.000
	3 Families	0.463	0.463	0.000	0.398	0.156	0.143	0.157	0.119	0.257	0.318	0.400	0.000
	4 Teenagers	0.077	0.077	0.039	0.000	0.055	0.013	0.012	0.031	0.019	0.036	0.031	0.000
5 Merchand	1 Low Cost	0.000	0.000	0.000	0.000	0.000	0.477	0.477	0.000	0.000	0.000	0.000	0.000
	2 Quality	0.000	0.000	0.000	0.000	0.447	0.000	0.119	0.000	0.000	0.000	0.000	0.000
	3 Variety	0.000	0.000	0.000	0.000	0.149	0.119	0.000	0.000	0.316	0.000	0.000	0.000
6 Charact.	1 Lighting	0.000	0.000	0.000	0.000	0.000	0.000	0.000	0.000	0.016	0.017	0.000	0.097
	2 Organiz.	0.000	0.000	0.000	0.000	0.000	0.000	0.000	0.035	0.000	0.079	0.027	0.290
	3 Cleanli.	0.000	0.000	0.000	0.000	0.000	0.000	0.000	0.092	0.044	0.000	0.110	0.000
	4 Employee	0.000	0.000	0.000	0.000	0.000	0.000	0.000	0.000	0.029	0.042	0.000	0.000
	5 Parking	0.000	0.000	0.000	0.000	0.000	0.000	0.000	0.010	0.005	0.000	0.000	0.000
	5 Parking	0.000	0.000	0.000	0.000	0.000	0.000	0.000	0.000	0.000	0.000		

The limit supermatrix is not shown here to save space. It is obtained from the weighted supermatrix by raising it to powers until all columns are identical to within a certain decimal place. From the top part of the first column of the limit supermatrix we get the priorities we seek for Alternatives and normalize them.

Synthesized Results From The Limit Supermatrix and Actual Relative Market Share

The relative market shares of the alternatives Walmart, Kmart and Target from the limit supermatrix are: 0.057, 0.024 and 0.015. When normalized they are 0.599, 0.248 and 0.154.

Table 10 The Synthesized Results for the Alternatives

Alternatives	Values from Limit Supermatrix	Actual Values July13, 1998	Normalized Values from Supermatrix	Actual Market Share as Dollar Sales Normalized
Walmart	0.057	58 billion $	0.599	54.8
KMart	0.024	27.5 billion $	0.248	25.9
Target	0.015	20.3 billion $	0.254	19.2

The object was to estimate the market share of Walmart, Kmart, and Target. The normalized results from the model were compared with sales as reported in the Discount Store News of July 13, 1998, p.77, of $58, $27.5 and $20.3 billions of dollars respectively. Normalizing the dollar amounts shows their actual relative market shares to be 54.8, 25.9 and 19.2. The relative market share from the model was compared with the sales values by constructing a pairwise comparisons matrix from the results vector in column 2 and a pairwise comparisons matrix from the results vector in column 4 and computing the compatibility index. The index value is equal to 1.016. As that is about 1.01 the ANP results may be said to be close to the actual relative market share.

A Complete BOCR Example: The Ford Explorer Case

Introduction / Background

The analysis in this section is based on a study done in June 2001 by J. P. Alberio and S. Mulani. On August 9, 2000 the companies Firestone and Ford announced a recall of 6.5 million tires that contained a safety-related defect. The recall was the result of an abnormally high rate of tread separations that caused catastrophic rollover crashes that maimed and killed drivers and passengers.

In May 2001, the Ford Motor Company also announced a new recall of 13 million tires from the Ford Explorer models and the termination of the business relationship with Firestone. It also announced in March 2001 that the company would redesign the Explorer model (creating the new Explorer) adding a wider body and incorporating some "rollover" features. We investigate here whether that was the right decision?

There are several key players in the tire separation tread case. The first is the company that designed and manufactured the tires: Firestone. The second is the company that designed and manufactured the vehicles: Ford Motor Company. The third is the governmental regulation agency: the National Highway Safety Administration (NHTSA).

Creating the Model

The model for finding the optimal decision for the Ford Motor Company regarding the Explorer/Firestone conflict was designed using BOCR model. No Opportunities were included because it was thought that the decision should be corrective. The Benefits indicate advantages obtained from the decision, whereas Costs and Risks reflect current and potential negative effects. There are different clusters defined under Benefits, Costs and Risks. In the models of Benefits and Risks, the control criteria are social and economic, whereas Costs model has an additional political control criterion. Although the clusters and the specific elements assigned to each network vary due to their interactions, the following general definitions apply to all.

Alternatives

The alternative choices cluster includes:
- Discontinue Explorer production.
- Redesign the Explorer model.
- Maintain the production of Explorer Model.
- Maintain the production of Explorer Model, but change the tire supplier.

Stakeholders

The stakeholders include people or groups that would be impacted by the alternative decisions made by the Ford Motor Company. The elements in this cluster are:

- Customers: current and potential buyers
- Community: people who may not be a customer but could be affected by the alternative decisions
- Employees: the Ford Motor Company employees, including labor and management
- Nation's Highway Safety Agency: government agency

Tire Suppliers

This cluster considers current and potential tire suppliers for the Ford Motor Company. The elements in this cluster are: Firestone, Goodyear, Michelin, and Other Tire Suppliers.

Competition

The competition cluster includes other SUV brands and models owned by the Ford Motor Company and other companies. The nodes of this cluster are:

- Ford's other SUV brands (e.g. Escape)
- Ford affiliates' SUV brands (e.g. Land Rover)
- Other companies' SUV brands (e.g. GM, Honda, Lexus, Dodge, etc)

Public Relation

This cluster considers elements that would impact relationships between the company and the stakeholders. The elements in this cluster are:

- Image: image of the company in public
- Trust: reliability of the name of the company
- Accountability: how the company reacts to community threats caused by its products
- Legal Matters: current and potential lawsuits filed against the company

Brand Image

The Brand Image cluster describes major aspects of the products that would impact image of the company. The elements in this cluster are:
Quality, Safety, Prestige, and Service.

Cost of Resources

The cost of resources refers to those costs that the Ford Motor Company may incur when choosing the alternative decisions. The nodes of this cluster are:

- Layoff costs: the cost that the company would incur in case it decides to reduce the number of employees.
- Launching costs: the cost that the company would incur in case it decides to launch a new product.
- Write-off costs: the cost that the company would incur in case it decides to reduce the inventory of discontinued products
- Production costs: the cost that the company incurs during the production stage

Resources

Resources cluster includes Revenues, Production Capacity, and Market Share.

Procedure

In order to rate the Benefits, Costs and Risks in the decision, three strategic criteria were considered: Domestic Issues, International Relations and Human Well-Being. For Domestic Issues, the subcriteria were: a) Ford Motor Company's reputation, b) Car's Industry reputation and c) US Government's reputation. In the case of International Relations, the subcriteria used were: a) Relationship with customers in other countries, b) Relationship with suppliers in other countries and c) Relationship with other countries' governments. Finally, in the case of Human Well-Being, the subcriteria were: a) Future Safety Factors, b) Confidence in government agencies and c) Confidence in the Justice system.

Benefits Model

Benefits in our model are gains and advantages from making a given decision, partitioned into two categories: economic and social. Economic benefits refer to a decision's positive effect on stakeholders, tire suppliers, competition and resources. Social benefits describe a decision's positive effect on stakeholders, tire suppliers, competition and resources.

The dependencies of clusters in the Economic Benefits network are shown in Figure 8.

The Stakeholders cluster, obviously, refers to the people or group of people who could potentially benefit economically, based on different decision alternatives taken by the Ford Motor Company. This cluster also affects the Competition cluster, because the decisions made may drive the stakeholders to provide economic benefit to anyone of the competitors. The Stakeholders cluster also affects the Resources cluster. The Resources cluster refers to the internal resources that the company has. For example, revenue of the company would be impacted by some of the actions taken by the stakeholders.

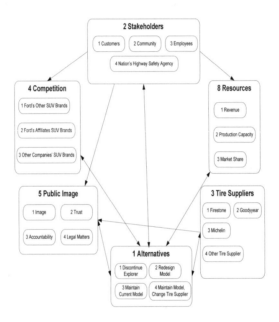

Figure 8 Economic Benefits Network

The Tire Suppliers cluster refers to tire companies that may gain economically based on the decision alternatives taken by Ford. This cluster would also affect the Public Image cluster; more specifically, legal matters.

The Stakeholders and Tire Suppliers clusters have more inter-links than the other clusters. This is due to the nature of the network of Economic Benefits, which usually has more impact on a person or a group of persons.

In this particular network, there is no inner-dependence in any of the clusters.

The table below shows the result for the Economic Benefits network. It is computed along the lines of the market share example worked out in detail in the previous section.

Table 11 Final Result from the Economic Benefits Network

Graphics	Alternatives	Priority	Ranking
	1. Discontinue Explorer	0.48	1
	2. Redesign Model	0.18	3
	3. Maintain Current Model	0.06	4
	4. Maintain Model, Change Tire Supplier	0.28	2

The dependencies of clusters in the Social Benefits model are shown in Figure 9. Table 12 summarizes the results obtained from the Social Benefits network.

Figure 9 Social Benefits Network

Table 12 Final Result from the Social Benefits Network

Graphics	Alternatives	Priority	Ranking
	1. Discontinue Explorer	0.55	1
	2. Redesign Model	0.32	2
	3. Maintain Current Model	0.01	4
	4. Maintain Model, Change Tire Supplier	0.12	3

Synthesis of Priorities in the Benefits Model

Both networks in the Benefits model have independent results that feed into the higher-level network (the overall benefits network). The combined results from Economic Benefits and Social Benefits networks are shown in Table 13:

Table 13 Synthesized Judgments in the Benefit Model

Alternative	Economic Benefit Priority (0.80)	Social Benefit Priority (0.20)	Overall Priority	Overall Ranking
1. Discontinue Explorer	0.48	0.55	0.49	1
2. Maintain Model, Change Tire Supplier	0.28	0.12	0.25	2
3. Redesign Model	0.18	0.35	0.21	3
4. Maintain Current Model	0.06	0.01	0.05	4

This result indicates that the alternative decision of discontinuing the Explorer gives the highest benefits, both from the economic and social standpoints.

Another observation is that the overall priority 0.49 for the first ranked alternative, i.e. to discontinue the Explorer, is significantly larger than 0.25 the priority of the next alternative to Maintain the Model but change the Tire Suppliers.

Costs Model

The costs are divided into Economic, Political and Social, which comprise the control criteria for this model. Economic Costs are the costs in which a monetary value can be assigned to the production and advertising costs involved on the redesign of the Ford Explorer. Political Costs can be defined as the intangible costs due to the decision taken, such as breaking the long standing relationship between Ford and its tire supplier. Social Costs are defined as the expense (pain) to society in terms of stakeholder exposure to decisions made regarding the Ford Explorer.

The dependencies of clusters in the economic costs model are shown in Figure 10.

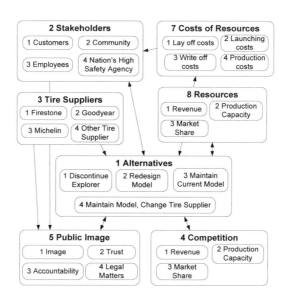

Figure 10 Economic Costs Network

Table 14 shows the result from the Economic Costs network.

Table 14 Final Results from Economic Costs Network

Alternatives	Priority	Ranking
1 Discontinue Explorer	0.14	4
2 Redesign Model	0.37	1
3 Maintain Current Model	0.32	2
4 Maintain Model, Change Tire Supplier	0.17	3

The dependencies of clusters in the Political Costs model are shown in Figure 11.

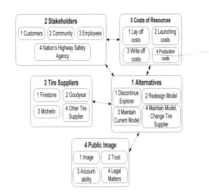

Figure 11 Political Costs Network

Table 15 summarizes the results from the network of Political Costs.

Table 15 Final Results from the Political Costs Network

Alternatives	Priority	Ranking
1 Discontinue Explorer	0.08	3
2 Redesign Model	0.00	4
3 Maintain Current Model	0.10	2
4 Maintain Model, Change Tire Supplier	0.82	1

Social Costs Clusters

The dependencies of clusters in the economic risks model are shown in Figure 12.

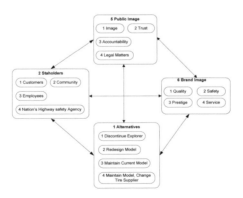

Figure 12 Social Costs Network

Table 16 summarizes the results from the network of Social Costs.

Table 16 Final Result in Social Costs Network

Alternatives	Priority	Ideal	Ranking
1 Discontinue Explorer	0.052	0.10	4
2 Redesign Model	0.54	1.00	1
3 Maintain Current Model	0.18	0.33	3
4 Maintain Model, Change Tire Supplier	0.23	0.43	2

Synthesis of Judgments in the Costs Model

The combined results from Economic Cost, Political Cost and Social Cost networks can be seen in the following table:

Table 17 Synthesized results for Costs

Alternative	Economic Costs Priority (0.66)	Political Costs Priority (0.08)	Social Costs Priority (0.26)	Overall Priority	Overall Ranking
1. Discontinue Explorer	0.14	0.08	0.05	0.45	1
2. Maintain Model, Change Tire Supplier	0.17	0.82	0.23	0.24	2
3. Maintain Current Model	0.32	0.10	0.18	0.19	3
4. Redesign Model	0.37	0.00	0.54	0.11	4

This result indicates that from the Costs Model point of view, the alternative decision of discontinuing the Explorer gives the highest cost for the Ford Company, and the Redesign alternative would have the smallest impact on the company's costs.

Risks Model

Unlike the Benefits and Costs models, the Risks model is slightly different. Risks are defined as the negative uncertainties in the decisions taken by the Ford Motor Company regarding the Ford Explorer/Firestone matters.

Risks are classified into two categories, Economic and Social. Economic Risks refer to financial risks that may be incurred as a result of the decisions taken by the Ford Motor Company. For example, if the decision is to discontinue the Explorer, there is a risk that Ford would jeopardize its relationship with Firestone which may impact Firestone's relation on other

Ford brands. Social Risks describe other than financial risks that may be incurred as a result of the decision taken by Ford. For example, if the decision is to maintain the current Explorer model, there is a risk that the number of accidents happening to customers who drive this car would increase.

Networks of the Economic and Social Risks are exhibited in Figure 13 and Figure 14 respectively. Tables 18 and 19 summarize the results from the Economic and Social Risks networks.

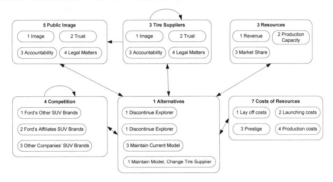

Figure 13 Economic Risks Network

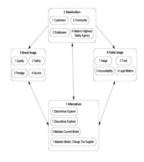

Figure 14 Social Risks Network

Table 18 Final Result in Economic Risks Network

Alternatives	Priority	Ranking
1 Discontinue Explorer	0.19	4
2 Redesign Model	0.35	1
3 Maintain Current Model	0.20	3
4 Maintain Model, Change Tire Supplier	0.25	2

Table 19 Final Result in Social Benefits Network

Alternatives	Priority	Ranking
1 Discontinue Explorer	0.10	3
2 Redesign Model	0.60	1
3 Maintain Current Model	0.05	4
4 Maintain Model, Change Tire Supplier	0.24	2

Synthesis of Judgments in the Risks Model

The combined results from Economic Risks and Social Risks networks are shown in Table 20:

Table 20 Synthesized Judgments from the Risks Model

Alternative	Economic Risks Priority (0.25)	Social Risks Priority (0.75)	Overall Priority	Overall Ranking
5. Maintain Current Model	0.20	0.05	0.49	1
6. Discontinue Explorer	0.20	0.10	0.29	2
7. Maintain Model, Change Tire Supplier	0.25	0.24	0.15	3
8. Redesign Model	0.35	0.60	0.08	4

The least risky alternative would be to redesign the model, with overall priority of 0.08. In this alternative, the driven force is the Social Risks whose contribution is 0.60 which is in contrast with the Economic Risks contribution of 0.35, and with Social Risks having nearly twice the influence than Economic Risks.

Strategic Criteria and Final Priorities of the Alternatives

The strategic criteria in this case have a hierarchical structure shown in Figure 15. The priorities of these criteria are shown in Table 21.

To rate the top outcome for each of the BCR against the strategic criteria we use the five-level ratings scale obtained from paired comparisons shown above the table.

To obtain priorities of all the alternatives we use the formula: $bB-cC-rR$. Here, $b = 0.49$, $c = 0.40$, $r = 0.11$ are used to weight the vectors B, C and R for the alternatives shown in Table 22 and obtain the overall priorities of the alternatives.

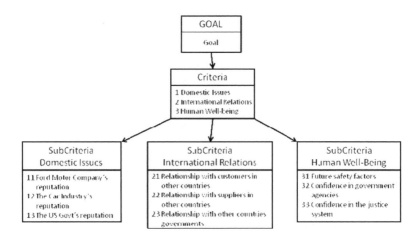

Figure 15 Strategic criteria and subcriteria

Table 21 Ratings with respect to Strategic Criteria for BCR merits

VeryHigh (0.50), High (0.29), Medium (0.12), Low (0.06), VeryLow (0.03).

	Domestic Issues (0.22)			International Relations (0.07)			Human Well-Being (0.71)		
Strategic Criteria Priorities									
Strategic Sub-criteria Local Priorities	Ford Motor Company's Reputation (0.73)	The Car Industry's Reputation (0.08)	The US Govt's Reputation (0.19)	Relationship with customers in other countries (0.64)	Relationship with suppliers in other countries (0.10)	Relationship with other countries governments (0.26)	Future safety factors (0. 73)	Confidence in government agencies (0.19)	Confidence in the justice system (0.08)
Strategic Sub-criteria Global Priorities	Ford Motor Company's Reputation (0.16)	The Car Industry's Reputation (0.02)	The US Govt's Reputation (0.04)	Relationship with customers in other countries (0.04)	Relationship with suppliers in other countries (0.01)	Relationship with other countries governments (0.02)	Future safety factors (0.52)	Confidence in government agencies (0.13)	Confidence in the justice system (0.06)
Benefits 0.49	Very High	High	Medium	Medium	Low	Medium	Very High	Very High	High
Costs 0.40	Very High	Medium	Low	High	Very Low	Low	Very High	Very Low	Very Low
Risks 0.11	Medium	Low	Very Low	Low	Medium	Low	Medium	Medium	Very Low

Table 22 Vectors of Priorities for the Alternatives for BC and R

	B	C	R
Discontinue Explorer	0.21	0.18	0.14
Redesign Model	0.08	0.05	0.04
Maintain Current Model	0.02	0.08	0.24
Maintain Model, Change the Supplier	0.11	0.10	0.07

The final priorities of the alternatives are shown in Table 23. Benefits is a positive merit, whereas Costs and Risks are negative ones.

Table 23 Final Priorities of the Alternatives

	B/CR	bB-cC-rR
Discontinue Explorer	8.21	0.01
Redesign Model	48.03	0.02
Maintain Current Model	1.17	-0.05
Maintain Model, Change the Supplier	15.45	0.01

The second alternative, i.e. Redesign Model has the highest ranking with overall priority of 0.02 in the right column of Table 23. The benefit of this alternative is not very attractive with an overall value close to zero. In fact, the benefit is the second lowest among the alternatives. However, both its costs and risks are extremely low and offset the also low benefits and contribute to the end result, which drive this alternative to be the best option for the Ford Motor Company to take.

As affirmed by the result of this model using the standard formula (bB-cC-rR), the worst alternative, i.e. Maintain Current Model has the least benefit (0.02) and the highest risk (0.24).

For marginal analysis, the formula B/CR was used. Here we obtain the same results, i.e. Redesign Model has the highest priority and Maintain Current Model – the smallest.

Sensitivity Analysis

In order to determine when different alternatives become preferred, sensitivity analysis was made by varying different weights and ratings in the model.

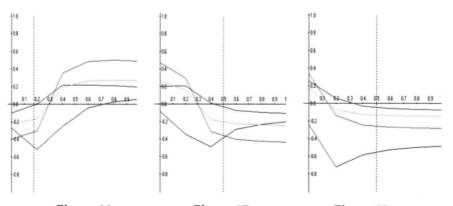

Figure 16	Figure 17	Figure 18

Sensitivity graph for Benefits Sensitivity graph for Costs Sensitivity graph for Risks

Sensitivity graphs for Benefits, Costs and Risks are shown in Figures 16, 17 and 18 respectively. The order of the curves from top to bottom is as in the last column of Table 23.

References

1. Dickson, L.E. (1939), *New First Course in the Theory of Equations*, John Wiley & Sons, Inc., New York
2. Saaty, T.L (2000), *The Brain: Unraveling the Mystery of How it Works*, RWS Publications, Pittsburgh, PA
3. Fraser, R.A., W.J. Duncan and A.R. Collarm (1955), *Elementary Matrices*, Cambridge University Press, London
4. Horn, R.A. and C.R. Johnsonm (1992) *Matrix Analysis*, Cambridge University Press
5. Isaacson, D.L. and R.W. Madsen (1976), *Markov Chains: Theory and Applications*, John Wiley & Sons, New York
6. Harker, P.T. (1987), *Incomplete Pairwise Comparisons in the Analytic Hierarchy Process*, Mathematical Modeling 9/11, pp. 837-848
7. Harker, P.T. (1987), *Alternative Modes of Questioning in the Analytic Hierarchy Process*, Mathematical Modeling 9, pp. 353-360

Chapter 6

Axioms and Theorems

This chapter deals with the following ideas:
- Axioms of the AHP/ANP and some important theorems that follow from them
- The reciprocal axiom regarding pairwise measurements
- The homogeneity axiom regarding the closeness of the elements in the comparisons
- The structure axiom regarding hierarchies and networks
- The expectations axiom regarding judgments and structure

Introduction

Let $\mathfrak{A}$ be a finite set of n elements called alternatives. Let $\mathfrak{S}$ be a set of properties or attributes with respect to which elements in $\mathfrak{A}$ are compared. A *property* is a feature that an object or individual possesses even if we are ignorant of this fact, whereas an *attribute* is a feature we assign to some object: it is a concept. Here we assume that properties and attributes are interchangeable, and we generally refer to them as criteria. A *criterion* is a primitive concept.

When two objects or elements in $\mathfrak{A}$ are compared according to a criterion C in $\mathfrak{S}$, we say that we are performing binary comparisons. Let $>_C$ be a binary relation on $\mathfrak{A}$ representing "more preferred than" or "dominates" with respect to a criterion C in $\mathfrak{S}$. Let $\sim_C$ be the binary relation "indifferent to" with respect to a criterion C in $\mathfrak{S}$. Hence, given two elements, $A_i, A_j \; \varepsilon \; \mathfrak{S}$, either $A_i >_c A_j$ or $A_j >_c A_i$ or $A_i \sim_c A_j$ for all $C \in \mathfrak{S}$. We use $A_i \geq_c A_j$ to indicate more preferred or indifferent. A given *family of binary relations* $.>_C$ with respect to a criterion C in $\mathfrak{S}$ is a primitive concept. We shall use this relation to derive the notion of priority or importance both with respect to one criterion and also with respect to several.

Let $\mathfrak{F}$ be the set of mappings from $\mathfrak{A} \times \mathfrak{A}$ to R^+ (the set of positive reals). Let $f : \mathfrak{S} \to \mathfrak{F}$. Let $P_C \; \varepsilon \; f(C)$ for $C \; \varepsilon \; \mathfrak{S}$. P_C assigns a positive real number to every pair $(A_i, A_j) \; \varepsilon \; \mathfrak{A} \times \mathfrak{A}$. Let $P_C(\; A_i, A_j \;) \; a_{ij} \; \varepsilon \; R^+$, $A_i, A_j \; \varepsilon \; \mathfrak{A}$. For each $C \; \varepsilon \; \mathfrak{S}$, the triple $(\mathfrak{A} \times \mathfrak{A}, R^+, P_C)$ is a *fundamental* or *primitive scale*. A fundamental scale is a mapping of objects to a numerical system.

Definition: For all $A_i, A_j \; \varepsilon \; \mathfrak{A}$ and $C \; \varepsilon \; \mathfrak{I}$
$\qquad A_i >_C A_j \qquad$ if and only if $P_C(A_i, A_j) > 1$,
$\qquad A_i \sim_C A_j \qquad$ if and only if $P_C(A_i, A_j) = 1$.
$\qquad$ If $A_i >_C A_j$, we say that A_i dominates A_j with respect to $C \; \varepsilon \; \mathfrak{I}$. Thus P_C represents the intensity or strength of preference for one alternative over another.

Reciprocal Axiom

Axiom 1: For all A_i, $A_j \; \varepsilon \; \mathfrak{A}$ and $C \; \varepsilon \; \mathfrak{I}$
$$P_C(A_i, A_j) = 1/P_C(A_j, A_i)$$
$\qquad$ Whenever we make paired comparisons, we need to consider both members of the pair to judge the relative value. The smaller or lesser one is first identified and used as the unit for the criterion in question. The other is then estimated as a not necessarily integer multiple of that unit. Thus, for example, if one stone is judged to be five times heavier than another, then the other is automatically one fifth as heavy as the first because it participated in making the first judgment. The comparison matrices that we consider are formed by making paired reciprocal comparisons. It is this simple yet powerful means of resolving multicriteria problems that is the basis of the AHP.
$\qquad$ Let $A = (a_{ij}) \; / \; (P_C(A_i, A_j))$ be the set of paired comparisons of the alternatives with respect to a criterion $C \; \varepsilon \; \mathfrak{I}$. By Axiom 1, A is a positive reciprocal matrix. The object is to obtain a *scale of relative dominance* (or *rank order*) of the alternatives from the paired comparisons given in A.
$\qquad$ There is a natural way to derive the relative dominance of a set of alternatives from a pairwise comparison matrix A.

Definition: Let $R_{M(n)}$ be the set of $(n \times n)$ positive reciprocal matrices $A = (a_{ij}) \; /$ $(P_C(A_i, A_j))$ for all $C \; \varepsilon \; \mathfrak{I}$. Let $[0,1]^n$ be the n-fold cartesian product of $[0,1]$ and let $\psi(A) : R_{M(n)} \to [0,1]^n$ for $A \; \varepsilon \; R_{M(n)}$, $\psi(A)$ is an n-dimensional vector whose components lie in the interval $[0,1]$. The triple $(R_{M(n)}, [0,1]^n, \psi)$ is a *derived scale*. A derived scale is a mapping between two numerical relational systems.
$\qquad$ It is important to point out that the rank order implied by the derived scale ψ may not coincide with the order represented by the pairwise

comparisons. Let $\psi_i(A)$ be the ith component of $\psi(A)$. It denotes the relative dominance of the ith alternative. By definition, for $A_i, A_j \in \mathfrak{A}$, $A_i >_c A_j$ implies $P_c(A_i, A_j) > 1$. However, if $P_c(A_i, A_j) > 1$, the derived scale could imply that $\psi_j(A) > \psi_i(A)$. This occurs if row dominance does not hold, i.e., for $A_i, A_j \in \mathfrak{A}$, and $C \in \mathfrak{S}$, $P_c(A_i, A_j) \geq P_c(A_j, A_k)$ does not hold for all $A_k \in \mathfrak{A}$. In other words, it may happen that $P_c(A_i, A_j) > 1$, and for some $A_k \in \mathfrak{A}$ we have

$$P_c(A_i, A_k) < P_c(A_j, A_k)$$

A more restrictive condition is the following:

Definition: The mapping P_c is said to be *consistent* if and only if $P_c(A_i, A_j)P_c(A_j, A_k) = P_c(A_i, A_k)$ for all i, j, and k. Similarly the matrix A is consistent if and only if $a_{ij}a_{jk} = a_{ik}$ for all i, j, and k.

If P_c is consistent, then Axiom 1 automatically follows and the rank order induced by ψ coincides with pairwise comparisons.

Luis Vargas has proposed, through personal communication with the author, that the following "behavioral" independence axiom could be used instead of the more mathematical reciprocal axiom that would then follow as a theorem. However, the reciprocal relation does not imply independence as defined by him, and unless one wishes to assume independence, one should retain the reciprocal axiom.

Two alternatives A_i and A_j are said to be mutually independent with respect to a criterion $C \in \mathfrak{S}$ if and only if, for any A_k the paired comparison of the component $\{A_i, A_j\}$ with respect to A_k satisfies

$$P_c[\{A_i, A_j\}, A_k] = P_c(A_i, A_k) P_c(A_j, A_k)$$

and

$$P_c[A_k, \{A_i, A_j\}] = P_c(A_k, A_i) P_c(A_k, A_j)$$

A set of alternatives is said to be independent if they are mutually independent.

Axiom 1: All the alternatives in $\mathfrak{A}$ are independent.

Hierarchic Axioms

Definition: A *partially ordered set* is a set S with a binary relation $\leq$ which satisfies the following conditions:

a. *Reflexive*: For all $x \in S$, $x \leq x$,

b. *Transitive*: For all $x, y, z \in S$, if $x \leq y$ and $y \leq z$ then $x \leq z$,

c. *Antisymmetric*: For all $x, y \in S$, if $x \leq y$ and $y \leq x$ then $x = y$ (x and y coincide).

Definition: For any relation $x \leq y$ (read, y includes x) we define $x < y$ to mean that $x \leq y$ and $x \neq y$. y is said to *cover* (*dominate*) x if $x < y$ and if $x < t < y$ is possible for no t.

Partially ordered sets with a finite number of elements can be conveniently represented by a directed graph. Each element of the set is represented by a vertex so that an arc is directed from y to x if $x < y$.

Definition: A subset E of a partially ordered set S is said to be *bounded* from above (below) if there is an element $s \in S$ such that $x \leq s$ ($\geq s$) for every $x \in E$. The element s is called an upper (lower) bound of E. We say that E has a supremum (infimum) if it has upper (lower) bounds and if the set of upper (lower) bounds U (L) has an element u_1(l_1) such that $u_1 \leq u$ for all $u \in U$ ($l_1 \geq l$ for all $l \in L$).

Definition: Let $\mathfrak{H}$ be a finite partially ordered set with largest element b. The set $\mathfrak{H}$ is a *hierarchy* if it satisfies the following conditions:

1. There is a partition of $\mathfrak{H}$ into sets called levels $\{L_k = 1, 2, ..., h\}$, where $L_1 = \{b\}$.
2. $x \in L_k$ implies $x^- \subseteq L_{k+1}$, where $x^- = \{y \mid x$ covers $y \}$, $k = 1, 2, ..., h-1$.
3. $x \in L_k$ implies $x^+ \subseteq L_{k-1}$, where $x^+ = \{y \mid y$ covers $x \}$, $k = 2, 3, ..., h$.

Definition: Given a positive real number $\varrho \geq 1$, a nonempty set $x^- \subseteq L_{k+1}$ is said to be ϱ-homogeneous with respect to $x \in L_k$ if for every pair of elements $y_1, y_2 \in x^-$, $1/\varrho \leq P_C (y_1, y_2) \leq \varrho$. In particular the reciprocal axiom implies that $P_C (y_i, y_i) = 1$.

Axiom 2: Given a hierarchy $\mathfrak{H}$, $x \in \mathfrak{H}$ and $x \in L_k$, $x^- \subseteq L_{k+1}$ is ϱ-homogeneous for $k = 1, ..., h-1$.

Homogeneity is essential for comparing similar things, as the mind tends to make large errors in comparing widely disparate elements. For example, we cannot compare a grain of sand with an orange according to size. When the disparity is great, the elements are placed in separate components of comparable size, giving rise to the idea of levels and their decomposition. This axiom is closely related to the well-known Archimedean property which says that forming two real numbers x and y with $x < y$, there is an integer n such that $nx \geq y$, or $n \geq y/x$.

The notions of fundamental and derived scales can be extended to $x \in L_k$, $x'' \subseteq L_{k+1}$ replacing $\mathfrak{S}$ and $\mathfrak{A}$, respectively. The derived scale resulting from comparing the elements in x^- with respect to x is called a *local derived scale* or *local priorities*. Here no irrelevant alternative is included in the comparisons, and such alternatives are assumed to receive the value of zero in the derived scale.

Given L_k, $L_{k+1} \subseteq \mathfrak{H}$, let us denote the local derived scale for $y \, \varepsilon \, x^-$ and $x \, \varepsilon \, L_k$ by $\psi_{k+1}(y \mid x)$, $k = 2, 3, ..., h-1$. Without loss of generality we may assume that $\sum y \varepsilon x^- \psi_{k+1}(y \mid x) = 1$. Consider the matrix $\psi_k(L_k \mid L_{k-1})$ whose columns are local derived scales of elements in L_k with respect to elements in L_{k-1}.

Definition: A set $\mathfrak{A}$ is said to be *outer dependent* on a set $\mathfrak{Z}$ if a fundamental scale can be defined on $\mathfrak{A}$ with respect to every $C \, \varepsilon \, \mathfrak{Z}$.

Decomposition implies containment of the small elements by the large components or levels. In turn, this means that the smaller elements depend on the outer parent elements to which they belong, which themselves fall in a large component of the hierarchy. The process of relating elements (e.g., alternatives) in one level of the hierarchy according to the elements of the next higher level (e.g., criteria) expresses the outer dependence of the lower elements on the higher elements. This way comparisons can be made between them. The steps are repeated upward in the hierarchy through each pair of adjacent levels to the top element, the focus or goal.

The elements in a level may depend on one another with respect to a property in another level. Input-output dependence of industries (e.g., manufacturing) demonstrates the idea of inner dependence. This may be formalized as follows:

Definition: Let $\mathfrak{A}$ be outer dependent on $\mathfrak{Z}$. The elements in $\mathfrak{A}$ are said to be *inner dependent* with respect to $C \, \varepsilon \, \mathfrak{Z}$ if for some $A \, \varepsilon \, \mathfrak{A}$, $\mathfrak{A}$ is outer dependent on A.

Axiom 3: Let $\mathfrak{H}$ be a hierarchy with levels L_1, L_2, ..., L_h. For each L_k, $k = 1, 2, ..., h-1$,

1. L_{k+1} is outer dependent on L_k
2. L_k is not outer dependent on L_{k+1}
3. L_{k+1} is not inner dependent with respect to any $x \, \varepsilon \, L_k$.

Principle of Hierarchic Composition

If Axiom 3 holds, the global derived scale (rank order) of any element in $\mathfrak{H}$ is obtained from its component in the corresponding vector of the following:

$\psi_1(b) = 1$

$\psi_2(L_2) = \psi_2(b^- \mid b)$

.   .

.   .

.   .

$\psi_k(L_k) = \psi_k(L_k \mid L_{k-1}),\ \psi_{k-1}(L_{k-1}), k=3,\ldots,h$

Were one to omit Axiom 3, the Principle of Hierarchic Composition would no longer apply because of outer and inner dependence among levels or components which need not form a hierarchy. The appropriate composition principle is derived from the supermatrix approach explained below, of which the Principle of Hierarchic Composition is a special case.

At the risk of repeating what we said in chapter 3, a hierarchy is a special case of a system, defined as follows:

Definition: Let $\mathfrak{S}$ be a family of nonempty sets $\mathfrak{I}_1, \mathfrak{I}_2, \ldots, \mathfrak{I}_n$ where $\mathfrak{I}_i$ consists of the elements $\{e_{ij}, j = 1,\ldots, m_i \}$, $i = 1,2,\ldots,n$. $\mathfrak{S}$ is a system if it is a directed graph whose vertices are $\mathfrak{I}_i$ and whose arcs are defined through the concept of outer dependence; thus, given two components $\mathfrak{I}_i$ and $\mathfrak{I}_j \ \varepsilon \ \mathfrak{S}$, there is an arc from $\mathfrak{I}_i$ to $\mathfrak{I}_j$ if $\mathfrak{I}_j$ is outer dependent on $\mathfrak{I}_i$.

Axiom 3′: Let $\mathfrak{S}$ be a system consisting of the subsets $C_1, C_2,\ldots C_n$. For each C_i there is some C_j so that either C_i is outer dependent on C_j or C_j is outer dependent on C_i, or both.

Note that C_i may be outer dependent on C_i, which is equivalent to inner dependence in a hierarchy. Actually Axiom 3′ would by itself be adequate without Axiom 3. We have separated them because of the importance of hierarchic structures, which are more widespread at the time of this writing than are systems with feedback.

Many of the concepts derived for hierarchies also relate to systems with feedback. Here one needs to characterize dependence among the elements. We now give a criterion for this purpose.

Let $D_A \subseteq \mathfrak{A}$ be the set of elements of $\mathfrak{A}$ outer dependent on $A \, \varepsilon \, \mathfrak{A}$. Let $\psi_{A_i,C}(A_j)$, $A_j \, \varepsilon \, \mathfrak{A}$ be the derived scale of the elements of $\mathfrak{A}$ with respect to A_i $\varepsilon \, \mathfrak{A}$, for a criterion $C \, \varepsilon \, \mathfrak{I}$. Let $\psi_C(A_j)$, $A_j \, \varepsilon \, \mathfrak{A}$ be the derived scale of the elements of $\mathfrak{A}$ with respect to a criterion $C \, \varepsilon \, \mathfrak{I}$. We define the dependence weight

$$\Phi_C(A_j) = \sum_{A_i \in D_{A_j}} \Psi_{A_i C}(A_j) \Psi_C(A_i)$$

If the elements of $\mathfrak{A}$ are inner dependent with respect to $C \, \varepsilon \, \mathfrak{I}$, then $\Psi_C(A_i) \neq \Psi_C(A_j)$ for some $A_j \, \varepsilon \, \mathfrak{A}$.

Expectations

Expectations are beliefs about the rank of alternatives derived from prior knowledge. Assume that a decision maker has a ranking, arrived at intuitively, of a finite set of alternatives $\mathfrak{A}$ with respect to prior knowledge of criteria $\mathfrak{I}$. Expectations are not only about the structure of a decision and its completeness, but also about the judgments and their redundancy to capture reality and inconsistency that should be improved with redundancy.

Axiom 4:

1. Completeness : $\mathfrak{I} \subset \mathfrak{H} - L_h$, $\mathfrak{A} = L_h$.
2. Rank: To preserve rank independently of what and how many other alternatives there may be. Alternatively, to allow rank to be influenced by the number and the measurements of alternatives that are added to or deleted from the set.

This axiom simply says that those thoughtful individuals who have reasons for their beliefs should make sure that their ideas are adequately represented for the outcome to match these expectations; i.e., all criteria are represented in the hierarchy. It assumes neither that the process is rational nor that it can accommodate only a rational outlook. People could have expectations that are branded irrational in someone else's framework. It also says that the rank of alternatives depends both on the expectations of the decision maker and on the nature of a decision problem. Finally, we also have expectations about the judgments and their adequacy and consistency to capture the situation under study.

Results from the Axioms

Note that if Pc is consistent, then Axiom 1 follows, i.e., consistency implies the reciprocal property. The first few theorems below are based on this more restrictive property of consistency.

They show that paired comparisons and the principal eigenvector are useful in estimating ratios. We use perturbation arguments to demonstrate that the principal eigenvector solution is the appropriate way to derive rank order from inconsistent data. They also show that the eigenvector is stable to small perturbations in the data where the number of elements compared is small. These results are also obtained by means of graph theoretic arguments. Let $R_{C(n)} \subset R_{M(n)}$ be the set of all (n by n) consistent matrices.

A few facts from matrix algebra will be useful.

If $^3A^3$ is the determinant of A, and if $\lambda_1, ..., \lambda_n$ are the eigenvalues of A, then $^3A^3 = \lambda_1 ... \lambda_n$. This follows from the fact that the characteristic polynomial of A satisfies the relation, $^3\lambda I - A^3 = (\lambda - \lambda_1) ... (\lambda - \lambda_n)$, and on putting $\lambda = 0$, we have $^3A^3 = (-1)^n {}^3 A^3 = (-1)^n \lambda_1 ... \lambda_n$ and the result follows. It is now clear that a matrix is singular if and only if at least one of its eigenvalues is zero.

The trace of a matrix A denoted by Trace (A), is the sum of its diagonal coefficients. We want to show that Trace (A) is equal to the sum of the eigenvalues of A. We proceed by induction. When A is 2 by 2 we have $^3\lambda I - A^3 = \lambda^2 - (a_{11} + a_{22})\lambda - a_{21}a_{12}$. For a 3 by 3 matrix we extend the 2 by 2 case by a third row and third column and calculate the determinant by using either the third row or third column. Only the term $\lambda - a_{33}$ contributes to the terms λ^3 and λ^2. Multiplication by λ gives $\lambda^3 - (a_{11} + a_{22})\lambda^2 - a_{21}a_{12}\lambda$. Multiplication by $-a_{33}$ contributes $-a_{33}\lambda^2 + ...$. Hence, the coefficient of λ^2 would be $-(a_{11} + a_{22} + a_{33})$. It is clear that if this reasoning is true for n=k it is also true for n=k+1 and hence it is true in general. Thus, $\lambda^{n-1} \sum_{i=1}^{n} a_{ii}$ equals the term $\lambda^{n-1} \sum_{i=1}^{n} \lambda_i$ in the expansion of $(\lambda - \lambda_1)$

$...(\lambda - \lambda_n)$, and Trace $(A) = \sum_{i=1}^{n} \lambda_i$.

Theorem 1 (Consistency and Rank) *Let $A \ \varepsilon \ R_{M(n)}$. $A \ \varepsilon \ R_{C(n)}$ if and only if rank $(A) = 1$.*

Proof If $A \ \varepsilon \ R_{C(n)}$, then $a_{ij}a_{jk} = a_{ik}$ for all i, j and k. Hence, given a row of A, a_{i1}, a_{i2}, ..., a_{in}, all other rows can be obtained from it by means of the relation $a_{jk} = a_{ik} / a_{ij}$ and rank $(A) = 1$.

Let us now assume that rank $(A) = 1$. Given a row a_{jh} ($j \varepsilon i$, $h = 1,2,...,n$), $a_{jh} = Ma_{ih}$ ($h = 1,2,...,n$) where M is a positive constant. Also, for any reciprocal matrix, $a_{ii} = 1$ ($i = 1,2,...,n$). Thus, for $i=h$ we have $a_{ji} = Ma_{ii} = M$ and $a_{jh} = a_{ji}a_{ih}$ for all i, j and k, and A is consistent.

Theorem 2 (Consistency and the Principal Eigenvalue) *Let $A \varepsilon R_{M(n)}$. $A \varepsilon R_{C(n)}$ if and only if its principal eigenvalue λ_{max} is equal to n.*

Proof By Theorem 1 we have rank$(A) = 1$. Also, all eigenvalues of A but one

vanish. Since Trace $(A) = \displaystyle\sum_{i=1}^{n} a_{ii} = n$ and Trace $(A) = \sum_k \lambda_k = n$, then $\lambda_{max} \equiv \lambda_1$

$= n$.

If $\lambda_{max} = n$, then

$$n\lambda_{max} = \sum_{i,j=1}^{n} a_{ij}w_j w_i^{-1} = n + \sum_{1\leq i<j\leq n} (w_j w_i^{-1} + a_{ji}w_i w_j^{-1})$$

$$\equiv n + \sum_{1\leq i\leq j\leq n} (y_{ij} + 1 / y_{ij}).$$

Since $y_{ij} + y_{ij}^{-1} \geq 2$, and $n\lambda_{max} = n^2$, equality is uniquely obtained on putting $y_{ij} = 1$, i.e. $a_{ij} = w_i/w_j$. The condition $a_{ij}a_{jk} = a_{ik}$ holds for all i, j and k, and the result follows.

Theorem 3 (Ratios and Consistency) *Let $A = (a_{ij}) \varepsilon R_{C(n)}$. There exists a function $\psi = (\psi_1, \psi_2,..., \psi_n)$, $\psi : R_{C(n)} [0,1]^n$ such that*

(i) *$a_{ij} = \psi_i(A)/\psi_j(A)$,*

(ii) *The relative dominance of the ith alternative, $\psi_i(A)$, is the ith component of the principal right eigenvector of A,*

(iii) *Given two alternatives A_i, $A_j \varepsilon \mathfrak{A}$, $A_i \gtrsim A_j$ if and only if $\psi_i(A) \geq \psi_j(A)$.*

Proof $A \varepsilon R_{C(n)}$ implies that $a_{ij} = a_{ik}a_{jk}^{-1}$ for all k, and each i and j. Also by Theorem 1, we have rank $(A) = 1$ and we can write $a_{ij} = x_i/x_j$, where $x_i, x_j > 0$ ($i,j = 1, 2, ..., n$). Multiplying A by the vector $x^T = (x_1, x_2,..., x_n)$, we have $Ax = nx$. Dividing both

sides of this expression by $\displaystyle\sum_{i=1}^{n} x_i$ and writing $w = x / \displaystyle\sum_{i=1}^{n} x_i$, we have $Aw = nw$

and $\displaystyle\sum_{i=1}^{n} w_i = 1$. By Theorem 2, n is the largest positive real eigenvalue of A and

w is its corresponding right eigenvector. Since $a_{ij} = x_i/x_j = w_i/w_j$ for all i and j, we have $\psi_i(A) = w_i$, $i=1,2,...,n$ and (i) and (ii) follow.

By Axiom 1, for A ε $R_{C(n)}$, $A_i \gtrsim A_j$, if and only if, $a_{ij} \geq 1$ for all i and j. Hence we have $\psi_i(A) \geq \psi_j(A)$ for all i and j.

It is unnecessary to invoke the Perron-Frobenius theorem given at the end of this chapter, to ensure the existence and uniqueness of a largest positive real eigenvalue and its corresponding eigenvector. We have already proved the existence of an essentially unique solution in the consistent case. A similar result follows using the perturbation argument given below.

Theorem 4 *Let A ε $R_{C(n)}$, and let $\lambda_1 = n$ and $\lambda_2 = 0$ be the eigenvalues of A with multiplicity 1 and $(n-1)$, respectively.*
Given $\varepsilon > 0$, there is a $\delta = \delta(\varepsilon) > 0$ such that if
$$| a_{ij} + \tau_{ij} - a_{ij} | = | \tau_{ij} | \leq \delta \quad \text{for } i,j = 1,2,...,n,$$
the matrix $B = (a_{ij} + \tau_{ij})$ has exactly $1 + (n-1)$ eigenvalues in the circles $^3\mu - n^3 < \varepsilon$ and $^3\mu - 0^3 < \varepsilon$, respectively.

Proof Let $\varepsilon_0 = n/2$, and let $\varepsilon < n/2$. The circles C_1: $^3\mu - n^3 = \varepsilon$ and C_2: $^3\mu - 0^3 = \varepsilon$ are disjoint. Let $f(\mu, A)$ be the characteristic polynomial of A. Let $r_j = \min^3 f(\mu, A)^3$ for μ on C_j. Note that $\min^3 f(\mu, A)^3$ is defined because f is a continuous function of μ, and $r_j > 0$ since the roots of $f(\mu, A) = 0$ are the centers of the circles.

$f(\mu, B)$ is a continuous function of the $1 + n^2$ variables μ and $a_{ij} + \tau_{ij}$, $i, j = 1, 2,..., n$, and for some $\delta > 0$, if $^3\tau_{ij}^3 \leq \delta$, $i,j = 1,2,...,n$, then $f(\mu, B) \neq 0$ for μ on any C_j, $j = 1,2$.

From the theory of functions of a complex variable, the number of roots μ of $f(\mu, B) = 0$ which lie inside C_j, $j = 1,2$, is given by
$$n_j(B) = \frac{1}{2\pi i} \int_{C_j} \frac{f'(\mu, B)}{f(\mu, B)} d\mu, \quad j = 1,2, .$$
This number is also a continuous function of the n^2 variables $a_{ij} + \tau_{ij}$ with $^3\tau_{ij}^3 \leq \delta$.

For $B = A$, we have $n_1(A) = 1$ and $n_2(A) = n-1$. Since $n_j(B)$, $j = 1,2$, is continuous, it cannot jump from $n_j(A)$ to $n_j(B)$ and the two must be equal and have the value $n_1(B) = 1$ and $n_2(B) = n-1$, for all B with $^3a_{ij} + \tau_{ij} - a_{ij}^3 \leq \delta$, $i, j = 1,2,...,$ n.

Theorem 5 (The Haunting Theorem; perturbation of the consistent case) *Let A ε $R_{C(n)}$ and let w be its principal right eigenvector. Let $\Delta A = (\delta_{ij})$ be a matrix of perturbations of the entries of A such that $A' = A + \Delta A$ ε $R_{M(n)}$, and let w' be its* *principal right eigenvector. Given $\varepsilon > 0$, there exists a $\delta > 0$ such that $^3\delta_{ij}{}^3 \leq \delta$ for all i and j, then $^3w'_i - w_i{}^3 \leq \varepsilon$ for all $i = 1,2,..., n$.*

Proof By Theorem 4, given $\varepsilon > 0$, there exists a $\delta > 0$ such that if $^3\delta_{ij}{}^3 \leq \delta$ for all i and j, the principal eigenvalue of A' satisfies $^3\lambda_{max}-n^3 \leq \varepsilon$. Let $\Delta A = \tau B$. Wilkinson (1965) has shown that for a sufficiently small τ, λ_{max} can be given by a convergent power series $\lambda_{max} = n + k_1\tau + k_2\tau^2 + ...$. Now, $\lambda_{max} \rightarrow n$ as $\tau \rightarrow 0$, and $^3\lambda_{max} - n^3 = o(\tau) \leq \varepsilon$.

Let w be the right eigenvector corresponding to the simple eigenvalue n of A. Since n is a simple eigenvalue, $(A - nI)$ has at least one nonvanishing minor of order $(n-1)$. Suppose, without loss of generality, that this minor lies in the first $(n-1)$ rows of $(A-nI)$. From the theory of linear equations, the components of w may be taken to be $\left(A_{n1},..., A_{nn} \right)$ where A_{ni} denotes the cofactor of the (n,i) element of $(A - nI)$, and is a polynomial in n of degree not greater than $(n-1)$.

The components of w' are polynomials in λ_{max} and τ, and since the power series expansion of λ_{max} is convergent for all sufficiently small τ, each component of w' is represented by a convergent power series in τ. We have
$$w' = w + \tau z_1 + \tau^2 z_2 + ... \text{ and } ^3 w' - w^3 = o(\tau) \leq \varepsilon.$$
By Theorems 4 and 5, it follows that a small perturbation A' of A transforms the eigenvalue problem $(A - nI)w = 0$ to the eigenvalue problem $(A - \lambda_{max}I)w = 0$.

Theorem 6 (Ratio Estimation). *Let $A \varepsilon R_{M(n)}$, and let w be its principal right eigenvector. Let $\varepsilon_{ij} = a_{ij}w_iw_j{}^{-1}$, for all i and j, and let $1 - \tau < \varepsilon_{ij} < 1 + \tau$, $\tau > 0$, for all i and j. Given $\varepsilon > 0$ and $\tau < \varepsilon$, there exists a $\delta > 0$ such that for all $(x_1,x_2,...,x_n)$, $x_i > 0$, $i = 1,2,...,n$, if*

$$1 - \delta < \frac{a_{ij}}{x_i / x_j} < 1 + \delta \qquad \textit{for all } i \textit{ and } j, \qquad (2)$$

then

$$1 - \varepsilon < \frac{w_i / w_j}{x_i / x_j} < 1 + \varepsilon \qquad \textit{for all } i \textit{ and } j, \qquad (3)$$

Proof Substituting $a_{ij} \varepsilon_{ij}{}^{-1}$ for w_i/w_j in (3) we have
$$\left| \frac{w_i / w_j}{x_i / x_j} - 1 \right| = \left| \frac{1}{\varepsilon_{ij}} \frac{a_{ij}}{x_i / x_j} - 1 \right| \leq \frac{1}{\varepsilon_{ij}} \left| \frac{a_{ij}}{x_i / x_j} - 1 \right| + \left| \frac{1}{\varepsilon_{ij}} - 1 \right|.$$

By definition $\varepsilon_{ij} = 1/\varepsilon_{ji}$ for all i and j, and we have

$$\left|\frac{w_i/w_j}{x_i/x_j} - 1\right| = \varepsilon_{ij}\left|\frac{a_{ij}}{x_i/x_j} - 1\right| + |\varepsilon_{ij} - 1| < (1+\tau)\delta + \tau.$$

Given $\varepsilon > 0$ and $0 < \tau < \varepsilon$, there exists a $\delta = (\varepsilon - \tau)/(1+\tau) > 0$ such that (2) implies (3).

This theorem says that if the paired comparison coefficient a_{ij} is close to an underlying ratio x_i/x_j then so is w_i/w_j and may be used as an approximation for it.

Theorem 7 *Let $A = (a_{ij}) \varepsilon R_{M(n)}$. Let λ_{max} be its principal eigenvalue and let w be its corresponding right eigenvector with $\Sigma^n_{i=1} w_i = 1$, then $\lambda_{max} \geq n$.*

Proof Let $a_{ij} = w_i w_j^{-1} \varepsilon_{ij}$, $i, j = 1,2,...,n$. Since $Aw = \lambda_{max}w$, and $\displaystyle\sum_{i,j=1}^{n} a_{ij}w_j = \lambda_{max}$, we have

$$\lambda_{max} - n = \sum_{i,j=1}^{n} a_{ij}w_j - n = \sum_{i,j}\varepsilon_{ij} - n.$$

by definition, the matrix $(\varepsilon_{ij}) \varepsilon R_{M(n)}$. We have $\varepsilon_{ii} = 1$ for all i, and $\varepsilon_{ij} > 0$ for all i and j. Hence, we have $\displaystyle\sum_{i,j=1}^{n}\varepsilon_{ij} - n = \sum_{i \neq j}\varepsilon_{ij} > 0$ and the result follows.

Theorem 8 *Let $A \varepsilon R_{M(n)}$. Let λ_{max} be the principal eigenvector of A, and let w be its corresponding right eigenvector with $\Sigma^n_{i=1}w_i = 1$. $\mu = (\lambda_{max} - n)/(n-1)$ is a measure of the average departure from consistency.*

Proof For $A \varepsilon R_{C(n)} \subset R_{M(n)}$, by Theorem 2 we have $\lambda_{max} = n$, and hence, $\mu = 0$.

For $A \varepsilon R_{M(n)} - R_{C(n)}$, let $a_{ij} = w_i w_j^{-1} \varepsilon_{ij}$ for all i and j. We have

$$\lambda_{max} = \sum_{j=1}^{n} a_{ij}\frac{w_j}{w_i} = \sum_{j=1}^{n}\varepsilon_{ij},$$

$$n\lambda_{max} = \sum_{i,j=1}^{n}\varepsilon_{ij} = n + \sum_{1 \leq i < j \leq n}\left(\varepsilon_{ij} + \frac{1}{\varepsilon_{ij}}\right),$$

$$\frac{\lambda_{max} - n}{n-1} = -1 + \frac{1}{n(n-1)}\sum_{1 \leq i < j \leq n}\left(\varepsilon_{ij} + \frac{1}{\varepsilon_{ij}}\right).$$

As $\varepsilon_{ij} \to 1$, i.e., consistency is approached, $\mu \to 0$. Also, μ is convex in ε_{ij}, since $(\varepsilon_{ij} + 1/\varepsilon_{ij})$ is convex, and has its minimum at $\varepsilon_{ij} = 1$, $i,j = 1,2,...,n$. Thus, μ is small or large depending on ε_{ij} being near to or far from unity, respectively, i.e. near to or far from consistency, and the result follows.

Note that $\Sigma^{n}_{i,j=1} a_{ij} w_j w_i^{-1} - n^2 = n(n-1)\mu$ is also a measure of the departure from consistency.

It is also possible to show that $(A-nI)w = 0$ is transformed into $(A-\lambda_{max}I)w = 0$ by means of graph theoretic concepts.

Definition The intensity of judgments associated with a path from i to j called the *path intensity* is equal to the products of the intensities associated with the arcs of that path.

Definition A *cycle* is a path of pairwise comparisons which terminates at its starting point.

Theorem 9 *If $A \varepsilon R_{C(n)}$, the intensities of all cycles are equal to a_{ii}, $i = 1,2,...,n$.*

Proof $A \varepsilon R_{C(n)}$, implies $a_{ij}a_{jk} = a_{ik}$ for all i,j and k. Hence, we have $a_{ii} = a_{ij}a_{jk}a_{ki} = 1$ for all $i = 1,2,...,n$. By induction, if $a_{ii_1}...a_{i_{n-1}i} = 1$ for all $i_1...i_{n-1}$, then $a_{ii_1}...a_{i_{n-1}i_n}a_{i_ni} = a_{ii_n}a_{i_ni} = 1$ and the result follows.

Theorem 10 *If $A \varepsilon R_{C(n)}$, the intensities of all paths from i to j are equal to a_{ij}.*

Proof Follows from $a_{ij} = a_{ik}a_{kj}$ for all i,j and k.

Corollary 10.1 *If $A \varepsilon R_{C(n)}$, the entry in the (i,j) position can be represented as the intensity of paths of any length starting with i and terminating with j.*

Proof Follows from Theorem 10.

Corollary 10.2 *If $A \varepsilon R_{C(n)}$, the entry in the (i,j) position is the <u>average intensity</u> of paths of length k from i to j, and $A^k = n^{k-1}A$ $(k \geq 1)$.*

Proof According to Theorem 10, the intensity of a path of any length from i to j is equal to a_{ij}. An arbitrary entry of A^k is given by

$$a_{ij}^{(k)} = \sum_{i_1=1}^{n}\sum_{i_2=1}^{n}\cdots\sum_{i_{k-1}=1}^{n} a_{ii_1}a_{i_1i_2}\cdots a_{i_{k-1}j}.$$

Since $a_{ij}a_{jk} = a_{ik}$ for all i,j and k we have

$$a_{ij}^{(k)} = \sum_{i_1=1}^{n} \sum_{i_2=1}^{n} \cdots \sum_{i_{k-1}=1}^{n} a_{ij} = n^{k-1} a_{ij}.$$

By induction, if $a_{ij}^{(k)} = n^{k-1} a_{ij}$ for $k = 1,2,...,m-1$, for $k = m$ we have

$$a_{ij}^{(m)} = \sum_{i_1=1}^{n} \cdots \sum_{i_{m-1}=1}^{n} a_{ii_1} \cdots a_{i_{m-1}j} = n^{m-2} \sum_{i_{m-1}=1}^{n} a_{ii_{m-1}} a_{i_{m-1}j} = n^{m-1} a_{ij}.$$

Hence, we have

$$a_{ij} = \frac{1}{n^{m-1}} a_{ij}^{(m)} \quad \text{for all} \quad m \geq 1,$$

and the result follows.

A shorter proof would be to use Theorem 3 with $a_{ij} = w_i/w_j$ and induction.

Theorem 11 *If $A \, \varepsilon \, R_{C(n)}$ a_{ij} is given by the average of all path intensities starting with i and terminating with j.*

Proof By Corollary 10.2 of Theorem 10, we have

$$a_{ij} = \frac{1}{n^{m-1}} \sum_{i_1=1}^{n} \cdots \sum_{i_{m-1}=1}^{n} a_{ii_1} \cdots a_{i_{m-1}j} .$$

Hence, $a_{ij} = \lim_{m \to \infty} \dfrac{1}{n^{m-1}} a_{ij}^{(m)}$, and the result follows.

Theorem 12 *If $A \, \varepsilon \, R_{C(n)}$ the scale of relative dominance is given by any of its normalized columns, and coincides with the principal right eigenvector of A.*

Proof Let a^j be the jth column of A.

$$A \bullet a^j = \left(\sum_{k=1}^{n} a_{ik} a_{kj} \right) \ (i,j = 1,2,...,n), \ = \left(\sum_{k=1}^{n} a_{ij} \right) = (n a_{ij}) \ (i,j = 1,2,...,n),$$

and any column of A (whether or not it is normalized to unity) is a solution of the eigenvalue problem $Ax = nx$. By Corollary 2 of Theorem 6 we have $A^k = n^{k-1}A$.

$$\psi(A) = \lim_{m \to \infty} \frac{1}{m} \sum_{k=1}^{n} \frac{A^k e}{e^T A^k e} = \lim_{m \to \infty} \frac{1}{m} \sum_{k=1}^{n} \frac{Ae}{e^T Ae} = \frac{Ae}{e^T Ae}.$$

Therefore,

$$\psi_i(A) = \sum_{j=1}^{n} a_{ij} \bigg/ \sum_{i,j=1}^{n} a_{ij} = \frac{a_{ih}\left(\sum_{j=1}^{n} a_{hj}\right)}{\left(\sum_{i=1}^{n} a_{ih}\right)\left(\sum_{j=1}^{n} a_{hj}\right)} = \frac{a_{ih}}{\sum_{i=1}^{n} a_{ih}}$$

for all i and h, and the result follows.

Corollary 12.1 *The principal eigenvector is unique to within a multiplicative constant.*

Proof Follows from Theorem 12.

Theorem 13 *If $A \, \varepsilon \, R_{M(n)}$ the intensity of all paths of length k from i to j is given by*

$$\sum_{i_1=1}^{n} \sum_{i_2=1}^{n} \cdots \sum_{i_{k-1}=1}^{n} a_{ii_1} a_{i_1 i_2} \cdots a_{i_{k-1}j}.$$

Proof It is known that the number of arc progressions of length k between any two vertices of a directed graph whose incidence matrix is V is given by v^k. If in addition each arc has associated a number (≥ 1) with it representing the intensity (or capacity) of the arc, then v^k represents the intensity of all arc progressions of length k between two vertices.

Let $V = A$. The entries of A^k give the intensity of all paths of length k between two vertices. Let $A^k = (a_{ij}^{(k)})$. By construction we have

$$a_{ij}^{(k)} = \sum_{i_1=1}^{n} \cdots \sum_{i_{k-1}=1}^{n} a_{ii_1} \cdots a_{i_{k-1}j}$$

and the result follows.

Corollary 13.1 *Let $A \, \varepsilon \, R_{M(n)}$. If there is some k_o for which $a_{ih}^{(k)} \geq a_{jh}^{(k)}$ for all h, then $a_{ih}^{(k)} \geq a_{jh}^{(k)}$ for all $k \geq k_o$.*

Proof If one row dominates another, multiplying both by a fixed set of priorities (columns of a matrix), yields a new matrix in which the same row dominance is preserved.

Note that this is a sufficient condition for convergence to the eigenvector, but not necessary. Here is a counterexample. Any reciprocal matrix whose principal eigenvector is the vector $(1,1,...,1)$ converges to this vector without row dominance but oscillates from power to power as the following matrix does:

$$\begin{pmatrix} 1 & 2 & 1/2 \\ 1/2 & 1 & 2 \\ 2 & 1/2 & 1 \end{pmatrix}$$

It has no clear dominance nor do its powers.

Corollary 13.2 *Let $A \ \varepsilon \ R_{M(n)}$. If there is some k for which $a_{ih}^{(k)} \geq a_{jh}^{(k)}$ for all h, then $a_{ih}^{(k)} \geq a_{jh}^{(k)}$ 1 for all $k \geq K$. The principal right eigenvector of A is given.*

Theorem 14 *Let $\mathfrak{A}2$ be a finite set of n elements $A_1, A_2, ..., A_n$, and let $C \ \varepsilon \ \mathcal{C}$ be a criterion which all the elements in $\mathfrak{A}$ have in common. Let A be the resulting matrix of pairwise comparisons. The ith component of the principal right eigenvector of the reciprocal pairwise comparison matrix A gives the relative dominance (rank order) of A_i, $i = 1,2,...,n$.*

Proof The principal right eigenvector of A is given by

$$w_i = \lim_{m \to \infty} \frac{a_{ih}^{(m)}}{\sum_{j=1}^{n} a_{jh}^{(m)}}, \quad i=1,2,...,n$$

for any $h = 1,2,...,n$. We also have

$$w_i = \lim_{m \to \infty} \frac{\sum_{j=1}^{n} a_{ij}^{(m)}}{\sum_{i,j=1}^{n} a_{ij}^{(m)}}, \quad i=1,2,...,n$$

Thus, the relative dominance of an alternative along all paths of length $k \leq m$ is given by

$$\frac{1}{m} \sum_{k=1}^{m} \frac{a_{ih}^{(k)}}{\sum_{i=1}^{n} a_{ih}^{(k)}}.$$

Let

$$s_k = \frac{a_{ih}^{(k)}}{\sum_{i=1}^{n} a_{ih}^{(k)}} \quad and \quad t_m = \frac{1}{m} \sum_{k=1}^{m} s_k.$$

It can be shown that if $\lim\limits_{k \to \infty} s_k$ exists then $\lim\limits_{m \to \infty} t_m$ also exists and the two limits coincide. By Theorem 14, we have $s_k \to w$ as $k \to \infty$, where w is the principal right eigenvector of A. Thus $t_m \to \infty$ as $m \to \infty$ and $\psi_i(A) = w_i$, $i = 1,2,...,n$.

This theorem highlights the fact that the right eigenvector gives the relative dominance (rank order) of each alternative over the other alternatives along paths of arbitrary length. It holds for a reciprocal matrix A which need not be consistent.

We have mentioned that deriving ratio scales in the AHP does not rely on the theorem of Perron because the AHP is based on ratio judgments and their perturbations. However, for completeness, we include the more general Perron-Frobenius Theorem and a short and elegant proof of that theorem due to J.P. Keener [1].

Theorem 15 *If the (nontrivial) matrix A has nonnegative entries, then there exists an eigenvector* w *with nonnegative entries, corresponding to a positive eigenvalue* λ. *Furthermore, if the matrix A is irreducible, the eigenvector* w *has strictly positive entries, is unique and simple, and the corresponding eigenvalue is the largest eigenvalue of A in absolute value.*

Proof Let Σ be the set of all nonnegative vectors with unit sum entries. for each vector s in the set Σ let σ^* be the positive number for which $As \leq \sigma s$ whenever $\sigma \geq \sigma^*$. If s has zero entries then σ^* may be infinite. Since Σ is a closed and bounded set, the smallest value of σ^* is attained for some vector s^* in Σ. To see that s^* is a positive eigenvector of A, suppose that $As^* \leq \sigma^* s^*$ but s^* is not an eigenvector of A. Then some, but not all, of the relations in the statement $As^* \leq \sigma^* s^*$ are equalities. (If there were no equalities, the number σ^* would be incorrectly chosen). After permutation, we can write the relations $As^* \leq \sigma^* s^*$ be written as

$$A_{11}s_1 + A_{12}s_2 < \sigma^* s_1,$$
$$A_{21}s_1 + A_{22}s_2 = \sigma^* s_2$$

Since A is irreducible, (cannot be partitioned into the form $\begin{bmatrix} A_1 & 0 \\ A_2 & A_3 \end{bmatrix}$ where A_1 and A_3 are square matrices and 0 is the zero matrix) A_{21} is not identically zero, and one can reduce at least one component of the vector s_1, thereby changing at least one of the equalities to a strict inequality, without changing any of the original strict inequalities. After this change in s^* one rescales the vector to sum to one. Proceeding inductively, the vector s^* is repeatedly modified until all of the relations in $A\mathbf{s}^* \leq \sigma^*\mathbf{s}^*$ are strict inequalities. But this contradicts the definition of σ^* and the first part is proven.

To prove uniqueness, note that a nonnegative eigenvector $\mathbf{w}$ must have all positive entries. Suppose there are two linearly independent eigenvectors of A, $\mathbf{w}_1$ and $\mathbf{w}_2$, satisfying $A\mathbf{w}_1 = \lambda_1\mathbf{w}_1$, and $A\mathbf{w}_2 = \lambda_2\mathbf{w}_2$, and suppose that $\mathbf{w}_1$ has strictly positive entries. If the entries of $\mathbf{w}_2$ are all of one sign, then without loss of generality they can be taken as positive. The vector $\mathbf{w}(t) = \mathbf{w}_1 - t\mathbf{w}_2$ has nonnegative entries for all t in some range $0 \leq t \leq t_0$ with $t_0 > 0$, and $\mathbf{w}(t_0)$ has some zero entries but is not identically zero, while for $t > t_0$, $\mathbf{w}(t)$ has some negative entries. Then $A\mathbf{w}(t_0) = \lambda_1(\mathbf{w}_1 - t_0\lambda_2/\lambda_1\mathbf{w}_2)$ has only positive entries. By the maximality of t_0, it must be that $|\lambda_2| < |\lambda_1|$. But if both $\mathbf{w}_1$ and $\mathbf{w}_2$ have only positive entries, we can interchange them in the above argument to conclude that $|\lambda_1| < |\lambda_2|$, a contradiction. Thus the positive eigenvector is unique and all other eigenvectors have eigenvalues that are smaller in absolute value. To see that the largest eigenvalue is simple, note that if $\mathbf{w}_2$ is a generalized eigenvector of A satisfying $A^k\mathbf{w}_2 = \lambda_1^k\mathbf{w}_2$ for some $k > 1$, then $A^k w(t_0) = \lambda_1^k w(t_0)$ is strictly positive, contradicting the definition of t_0.

References

1. Keener, J.P. (1993), "The Perron-Frobenius Theorem and the Ranking of Football Teams", *SIAM Review* 35/1, pp. 80-93
2. Saaty, T.L., (2000), *The Brain, Unraveling the Mystery of How it Works: The Neural Network Process*, RWS Publications, Pittsburgh, PA
3. Saaty, T.L. (1986), "Axiomatic Foundation of the Analytic Hierarchy Process", *Management Science* 32/7, pp. 841-855
4. Saaty, T.L. (1987), "Rank According to Perron: a New Insight", *Math. Magazine* 60, pp. 211
5. Saaty, T.L. (1990), *Multicriteria Decision Making*, RWS Publications, Pittsburgh, PA

Part IV

Group Decision Making, Validation, Applications to Resource Allocation and Conflict Resolution and Multi-Decisions Decision Making

Chapter 7 deals with multiple judgments for each pairwise comparison and also with the judgments of many people. It is followed by chapter 8 which is concerned with numerous examples and applications validating the numerical process of the AHP/ANP. Chapters 9 and 10 involve some theory and illustrative examples of applications to resource allocation and to conflict resolution respectively. In Chapter 11, we are concerned with a very important subject of making a decision to rand the urgency of acting on many decisions by prioritizing them as political bodies must do.

Chapter 7

Possibility of Constructing Group Preference

This chapter deals with the following ideas:
- How to construct a representative judgment for a group from several pairwise comparisons made by individuals to satisfy the reciprocal property
- How to derive a priority function from such group judgments that satisfies four important conditions some or all of which cannot be satisfied by only using judgments which only say that A is preferred to B or B to A without giving a number for such preference
- The end result is that by using the AHP one can construct a social welfare function that is free of fundamental difficulties encountered otherwise in practice

Introduction

The problem of social choice consists of developing a procedure or a rule for collective choice that can assist in aggregating individual preferences in the "best way" that represents the preferences of the group as a whole. An aggregation procedure that produces a group choice is considered *satisfactory* if: 1) It responds, at least not negatively, to changes in individual preferences, 2) It reflects the collective opinion of the individuals, and 3) It provides ranking for the various alternatives of a decision that the group faces. A social welfare function is a collective choice rule restricted to the set of orderings of a set of alternatives.

Let A denote a *finite* set consisting of at least three alternatives or outcomes and let M be a set of m individuals whose ordinal preferences (e.g., a preferred to b but not by how much) on A form a *weak order*. A binary relation R is a *weak order* if it is *transitive*, i.e., if xRy and yRz then xRz, and *strongly complete*, i.e., for all x and y, either xRy or yRx, x may be the same as y. For *strict* preference we write xPy, i.e., xRy but not yRx, and for *indifference* we write xIy, i.e., xRy and yRx.

Let R denote the set of all ordered m-tuples $\mathbf{R} = (R_1, R_2, \ldots, R_m)$, where R_k represents the orderings of the kth individual, $k=1,\ldots,m$. A *social welfare function* is a mapping of a subset D of R into a subset of the set of all orderings of A, i.e., a social welfare function transforms a collection of rankings **R** by individuals into a collective or social ranking *R*. In his seminal work, Arrow [1] imposed the following four conditions (referred to as *Arrow's conditions*) to be satisfied by a social welfare function:

Unrestricted Domain: The domain D of the social welfare function must contain all logically possible combinations of individual orderings.

Pareto Principle (Unanimity): For any pair x and y in A, if for each individual k, xP_ky then xPy, i.e., if each individual prefers x to y then the group must prefer x to y.

Independence from Irrelevant Alternatives: Let R and R' be two social binary relations obtained by the social welfare function from two sets of preferences $\mathbf{R}=(R_1,R_2,\ldots,R_m)$ and $\mathbf{R'}=\left(R_1',R_2',\ldots,R_m'\right)$ made by the individuals. If for all pairs of alternatives x and y in a subset S of A, xR_ky if and only if $xR_k'y$ for all k is true then xRy if and only if $xR'y$.

Non-dictatorship: There is no one individual d whose preferences coincide with the preferences imputed to the group by the social welfare function, i.e., for every element **R** in the domain of the social welfare function, there is no d such that if xP_dy then xPy for all alternatives x, $y \in$ A. Thus the preferences of the group are not dictated by or are identical to the preferences of any member or members of the group.

Arrow proved what is now known as the Impossibility Theorem in which he showed that *there does not exist a social welfare function that satisfies all four conditions at once.*

Preferences in Arrow's conditions are ordinal, i.e., either something is preferred to something else or it is not, but the intensity of preference is not considered. Thus, there are two ways of looking at the literature on social welfare functions and impossibility theorems depending on the type of preferences used, ordinal or cardinal. In the latter the intensity of preference is expressed numerically.

For ordinal preferences, there is a vast literature in which people have modified the foregoing conditions to develop both possibility and impossibility theorems. In Chapter 1 of [2], Campbell and Kelly provide an excellent review of the literature on impossibility theorems that are a consequence of relaxing Arrow's initial conditions. For cardinal preferences, the literature on cardinal impossibility theorems revolves around the type of scale (ordinal, interval and ratio) used to represent an individual's preferences. All the approaches *assume* that individual cardinal preference functions exist.

Here we show that it is possible to *construct* a non-dictatorial social welfare function by first starting with pairwise relative preferences from an absolute scale and then derive a relative absolute scale of cardinal preferences. The use of paired comparisons makes it possible to restrict the unanimity condition thus admitting non-dictatorship. This chapter is organized as follows. Next, we introduce the notation that will be used in the remainder of the chapter and summarize different attempts to construct a social welfare function when the individual preferences are measured in different scales. Later we represent individual preferences with absolute scales through pairwise comparisons (a pairwise cardinal preference relation) and show that there exists an aggregation principle for the pairwise preference relations that satisfies all of Arrow's conditions. Thereafter, we present an aggregation principle that transforms pairwise preference relations into a cardinal relation that also satisfies Arrow's conditions.

Cardinal Preference Relations

Let C denote the set of all possible functions from A to the set **R** of real numbers. A scale is a triplet consisting of a set of objects, a set of numbers and a mapping from the objects to the numbers that is invariant under a specified type of transformation. For example, ordinal, interval, ratio and absolute scales are invariant under monotone, affine (positive linear), similarity and identity transformations, respectively. There are many other scales of which a well-known one that is too weak to be useful in this study is the nominal scale that is invariant under one-to-one correspondence.

Thus, to identify a scale to represent preferences we define a cardinal preference relation over A as a subset W of C that satisfies the following conditions:
1. W is nonempty;
2. If $w, v \in W$, there is a transformation ϕ, such that for all $A_i \in A$, $v(A_i) = \phi[w(A_i)]$;
3. If $w \in W$, then v defined by $v(A_i) = \phi[w(A_i)]$, for all $A_i \in A$, also belongs to W.

ϕ is called an invariance transformation. An invariance transformation defines the kind of scale used.

As mentioned above, if ϕ is any monotone transformation, the scale is ordinal. Goodman and Markowitz [3] assumed that preferences are expressed by means of a value function invariant under monotone transformations. They showed that if ϕ is also linear, then no social welfare function is possible. However, if ϕ is a positive similarity transformation then the only possible social welfare function is the product of the welfare functions of the individuals.

If ϕ is a monotonic affine transformation then interval scales are used. Samuelson [4] conjectured that Arrow's impossibility theorem should hold when individuals and the group express their "cardinal" preferences by the von-Neumann-Morgenstern (v-NM) utility functions known to belong to an interval scale. Campbell [5] made a convincing case for the possibility of using intensity of preference in the formulation of the impossibility theorem, but he did not specify the type of function to be used. Kalai and Schmeidler [6] proved Samuelson's conjecture: *If the set of alternatives contains 4 or more elements, then an aggregation procedure is continuous, satisfies cardinal independence from irrelevant alternatives and also satisfies unanimity if and only if it is cardinally dictatorial.*

If ϕ is a similarity transformation (invariant under multiplication by a positive number) then the scales involved are ratio scales. DeMeyer and Plott [7] showed by using "relative intensity" of preferences, invariant under similarity transformations, that a non-dictatorial social welfare function exists, and that their result is an extension of Nash's solution of the bargaining problem in which the welfare of a group is maximized by considering the payoffs resulting from the product of individual utilities [8]; a similar result was obtained by Kaneko and Nakamura [9].

By assuming that individual utility functions belong to the same ratio scale, a restriction known as ratio scale full comparability (RSFC), Kevin Roberts [10] showed that if a social welfare function satisfies the conditions of unrestricted domain, i.e., all possible utility functions are considered, independence from irrelevant alternatives, the weak Pareto condition of strict preference, and invariance under positive similarity transformations, then there exists a social welfare function that preserves positive proportionality known as *homothetic* (i.e., $f(x) \geq f(y) \Leftrightarrow f(\lambda x) \geq f(\lambda y)$ for all $\lambda > 0$) that is not dictatorial.

The main theme emerging from these works is that in order for a non-dictatorial social welfare function to exist, it must at least be invariant under similarity transformations, i.e., belong to a ratio scale.

In general, a procedure for aggregating cardinal preferences is by definition a function φ from an m-fold Cartesian product of C to C; i.e., $\varphi:C^m \to C$, is a social *welfare function*. As in the ordinal case where a preference profile is denoted by $\mathbf{R}=(R_1,...,R_m)$, here we use $W = (W_1,...,W_m) \in C^m$ and call it a *cardinal profile*. For a nonempty subset A of A and W in C, $W|_A$ denotes the cardinal preferences induced by W in A. Arrow's conditions can now be stated as follows.

Unrestricted Domain: An aggregation procedure φ is said to satisfy the condition of *unrestricted domain* if its domain is all of C^m.

Pareto Principle: An aggregation procedure $\varphi:C^m \to C$ satisfies unanimity if and only if for any pair A_i and A_j of A and any cardinal profile $W=(W_1,...,W_m) \in C^m$ and $W_k(A_i) \geq W_k(A_j)$ for all $k \in M$ implies $W(A_i) \geq W(A_j)$, where $W \equiv \varphi(W)$.

Independence from Irrelevant Alternatives: An aggregation procedure is said to satisfy *cardinal independence from irrelevant alternatives* (CIIA) if for any subset **A** of A with three elements, and for any two cardinal profiles **W** and V: $W|_A = V|_A$ implies $\varphi(W)|_A = \varphi(V)|_A$.

Non-Dictatorship: An aggregation procedure φ is *cardinally non-dictatorial* if there is no group member $d \in M$ such that for all the profiles $W \in C^m$, $\varphi(W) = W_d$, i.e., φ is the projection of W on the dth coordinate.

Absolute Scale Paired Comparison Preferences

Cognitive psychologists consider comparisons and in particular paired comparisons as innate to people's cognitive processes [11]. The question is how to make meaningful numerical paired comparisons that reflect strength of preference (dominance) and also how to synthesize comparisons into a unique unidimensional scale that captures the order represented in the comparisons.

The simplest type of numerical paired comparisons that one can think of is to obtain the measurement of two objects with respect to a tangible attribute on a ratio scale and form their ratio to discover how many times one object possesses the attribute more than the other. Being dimensionless, this ratio belongs to an absolute scale and represents the intensity of the dominance of one object over the other for that attribute. It is not unreasonable to accept the fact that an expert can estimate the true ratio, which is dimensionless, in the form of an absolute number provided that they are within the threshold of perception and experience of that expert. Such a number indicates how many times one object *dominates* another on that scale. Similarly, it is not unreasonable to think that the same process may also work for judgments involving two intangibles. However, to be convincing, it would need validation in practice by making predictions whose outcome is numerical and known. There are numerous examples in which the market share in relative dollars of different companies has been estimated through paired comparisons. These comparisons are estimates of the demonstrated dominance of the companies with respect to various intangible activities. This is the subject with which we are concerned in the multicriteria measurement theory known as the Analytic Hierarchy Process (AHP) [12], [13]) and its generalization to dependence and feedback, the Analytic Network Process [14] often used in decision-making.

A fundamental question is: Can paired comparisons, measured on an absolute scale, be used to represent strength of preference? In utility theory, intensity of preference is understood in the following way. Sarin [15] wrote: "… the meaning of intensity of preference is limited to observations regarding the relative "closeness" or "similarity" of preferences for consequences, rather than to absolute statements that one consequence is twice as good as another." This statement refers to the use of v-NM utility functions to represent strength of preference. These functions belong to interval scales. But that is not what we do here where we, in fact, make the absolute statements <u>excluded</u> by Sarin. The priority functions synthesized from the paired comparisons are not subject to the same conditions as utility functions would be, were they to be used to represent the strength of preference with regard to closeness. Rather, as we show later, they belong to a relative scale that is invariant under the identity transformation, and thus they belong to absolute scales. The condition given by Sarin [15] for v-NM utilities to represent strength of preference is that "… a decision maker's preference differences between two acts given a state of the world s_l should be independent of the common outcomes outside s_l." According to Sarin, a value function v represents the judgment that if the preference difference between consequences r and r' exceeds the difference preference between consequence t and t' then $v(r)-v(r')>v(t)-v(t')$. Because we are not using interval scales but relative absolute scales one would expect this condition to be $v(r)/v(r')>v(t)/v(t')$. In fact we represent the strength of preference using pairwise absolute scale judgments that are estimates of the ratios $v(r)/v(r')$.

Paired comparison judgments can be consistent or inconsistent. Consistency means that if A is preferred x times more than B and B is preferred y times more than C, then A must be preferred xy times more than C. If in comparing A with C, a different value than xy is used, that judgment is said to be inconsistent. The consistency of paired comparisons is defined in a precise mathematical way. There are two types of inconsistency considered in the literature of the AHP. The first, called *ordinal inconsistency* (team A beats team B, team B beats team C but team C beats team A) is the familiar concept of intransitivity that violates order relations and is axiomatized away in the non-AHP literature to avoid circular reasoning. The second, called *cardinal inconsistency* or simply *inconsistency*, violates numerical order relations. The AHP assumes that people are usually inconsistent, particularly when estimating preferences among intangibles, and makes it possible to measure and decide despite inconsistency. A modicum of inconsistency allows people to readjust their thinking in light of new information and thus anchors decision making in the reality of people's behavior rather than in what seems mathematically convenient. As we said earlier, inconsistency enables one to derive a social welfare function from aggregated individual judgments that is non-dictatorial.

As previously stated, A denotes a *finite* set of n alternatives. Let F denote the set of functions from A×A to the set of positive real numbers $\mathbf{R}^+$. When a pairwise relation P is applied on a set of alternatives, e.g., $P(A_i,A_j)$, it is referred to as a *pairwise comparison* or *judgment* in which the (pairwise) dominance of A_i over A_j or A_j over A_i is expressed numerically on an absolute scale. A *reciprocal pairwise relation* P over A×A is an element of F that satisfies the following conditions:

a. For all $A_i \in A$, $P(A_i,A_i)=1$.
b. For all $A_i,A_j \in A$, $i \neq j$, $P(A_i,A_j)P(A_j,A_i)=1$, i.e., $P(A_j,A_i)=1/P(A_i,A_j)$.

Let P be the set of all reciprocal pairwise preference relations. There are $n(n-1)/2$ paired comparisons of n elements that define these relations. Denote by P_k the reciprocal pairwise relation associated with the kth member of a group of m members. A *reciprocal pairwise profile* is given by the sets of reciprocal pairwise preference relations $\mathbf{P}=(P_1,P_2,\ldots,P_m)\in P^m$ defined by the m members of the group. In general, for any two alternatives i and j, $P_h(A_i,A_j)\neq P_k(A_i,A_j)$ for $h \neq k$, for at least two members of the group. If they are equal for the entire group then the group agrees on their common value. A procedure for aggregating or synthesizing pairwise preference relations by m individuals on the same two elements is by definition a function γ_P from a subset of the m-fold Cartesian product P^m to P. We denote the restriction of the reciprocal pairwise profile **P** to a subset **A** of A by **P**|A.

Definition: A reciprocal pairwise relation P_k is said to be *consistent* if and only if $P_k(A_i,A_j)P_k(A_j,A_s)=P_k(A_i,A_s)$ for all i, j and s.

Definition: P_k is said to satisfy *pairwise preference* of alternative A_i over alternative A_j if and only if $P_k(A_i,A_j)>1$.

Analogous to *Arrow's conditions,* we introduce the following definitions for pairwise comparisons.

Unrestricted Domain: A pairwise preference aggregation procedure is said to satisfy the condition of *unrestricted domain* if its domain is all of P^m.

Pareto Principle: A pairwise preference aggregation procedure $\gamma_P:P^m{\to}P$ satisfies *pairwise unanimity* if and only if for some pair A_i and A_j of A and any reciprocal pairwise profile **P**, $P_k(A_i,A_j)\geq1$ for all $k{\in}M$, implies $P(A_i,A_j)\geq1$, where $P = \gamma_P$ (**P**).

Independence from Irrelevant Alternatives: A pairwise aggregation procedure γ_P is said to satisfy *pairwise cardinal independence from irrelevant alternatives* (PCIIA) if for any subset **A** of A with three elements and for any two reciprocal pairwise profiles **P** and **Q**: **P**|A = **Q**|A implies γ_P (**P**)|A = γ_P (**Q**)|A.

Non-Dictatorship: A pairwise aggregation procedure γ_P is said to be *pairwise cardinally non-dictatorial* if there is no group member $d{\in}M$ such that for all $P{\in}P^m$, γ_P (P) = P_d.

For reciprocal pairwise preference relations not all aggregation procedures are appropriate. Aczél and Saaty ([16]) showed that the only aggregation procedure γ that satisfies separability: $\gamma(x_1,...,x_m)=g(x_1){\circ}...{\circ}g(x_m)$, unanimity: $\gamma(x,...,x)=x$, homogeneity: $\gamma(\lambda x_1,...,\lambda x_m)=\lambda\gamma(x_1,...,x_m)$, $\lambda{>}0$, and the reciprocal property: $\gamma(1/x_1,...,1/x_m)=1/\gamma(x_1,...,x_m)$, is the geometric mean where $\gamma(x_1,\ldots,x_m) = \left(\displaystyle\prod_{k=1}^{m} x_k\right)^{1/m}$. Aczél and Alsina [17] extended this result

to the case where the individuals have different importance a_k , thus

$$\gamma(x_1,\ldots,x_m) = \left(\prod_{k=1}^{m} x_k^{a_k}\right)^{1/m} .$$

It follows that the *only* aggregation procedure that should be used for *reciprocal* pairwise preference relations is the geometric mean, which we show next satisfies *Arrow's conditions*.

The condition of unrestricted domain is automatically satisfied because the aggregation procedure is defined on all pairwise reciprocal profiles without restriction.

Theorem 1: *The geometric mean aggregation procedure* $\gamma_P : P^m \to P$ *satisfies pairwise unanimity, pairwise independence from irrelevant alternatives and is non-dictatorial.*

Proof: Given $P \in P^m$ such that for any pair A_i and A_j of A, $P_k(A_i, A_j) > 1$ for all $k \in M$, then by definition,

$$\gamma_P(\mathbf{P})(A_i, A_j) = \left[\prod_{k=1}^{m} P_k(A_i, A_j)\right]^{\frac{1}{m}} > 1$$

and γ_P satisfies pairwise unanimity.

Let **P** and **Q** be two reciprocal pairwise profiles. Let $a_{ij}^{(k)} \equiv P_k(A_i, A_j)$ and $b_{ij}^{(k)} \equiv Q_k(A_i, A_j)$. Let $A = \{A_i, A_j, A_l\} \subset$ A. If $P|_A$ = $Q|_A$, then $a_{ij}^{(k)} = b_{ij}^{(k)}$, $a_{il}^{(k)} = b_{il}^{(k)}$ and $a_{jl}^{(k)} = b_{jl}^{(k)}$, for all k, and $\gamma_P(\mathbf{P})|_A$ = $\gamma_P(\mathbf{Q})|_A$ follows.

Note that the only condition that would lead to dictatorship is that the judgments of an individual (the dictator) coincide with the geometric mean of the judgments of all the other individuals.

Thus, the following condition seems natural:

Individuality Axiom: No individual has pairwise judgments that coincide with the geometric mean of the judgments of the other individuals.

Thus, the geometric mean gives rise to an aggregate (*social*) reciprocal pairwise relation. Next, we show that it is possible to construct a social welfare function from this relation that also satisfies *Arrow's conditions*. First, we demonstrate that an individual's welfare function associated with a reciprocal pairwise relation, because of the need to capture overall dominance from pairwise dominance, must be derived in the form of the principal right eigenvector of the matrix defined by that reciprocal preference relation. Second, we show that the principal right eigenvector of the matrix corresponding to the aggregate reciprocal pairwise relation is non-dictatorial.

Absolute Cardinal Preference Relations

Recall, that a cardinal preference relation is invariant under transformations that define the scale in which the preferences are measured. Thus, if the transformation under which it is invariant is the identity then preferences are measured on an absolute scale. Let W denote the set of all absolute cardinal preference relations over A. We define an absolute cardinal preference relation W over A as a cardinal preference relation that satisfies the following conditions:

1. W is nonempty;
2. If $w, v \in W$, for all $A_i \in \mathbf{A}$, $v(A_i) \equiv w(A_i)$,

and hence, W contains one and only one element.

Let $w_k = (w_{1k}, w_{2k}, \ldots, w_{nk})^T$, where the superscript T denotes the transpose of the vector, be the absolute cardinal preference relation of the kth individual. Let the matrix $w = (w_1, \ldots, w_m)$ be an absolute cardinal profile. Traditionally, a social welfare function is a mapping from W^m to W. However, we start by establishing a correspondence between the set of reciprocal pairwise preference relations P and the set of absolute cardinal relations W. Then we establish a mapping from P^m to W. Let P_C and P_I denote the sets of consistent and inconsistent pairwise preference relations, respectively.

Consistent Pairwise Preference Relations

Theorem 2: *Given $P \in P_C$ there exists an absolute cardinal relation $w \in W$, such that if for any i and j, $P(A_i,A_j)>1$, then $w(A_i)>w(A_j)$. Conversely, for any absolute cardinal relation $w \in W$ there exists a unique consistent pairwise relation P such that for all i and j,* $P(A_i, A_j) = \dfrac{w(A_i)}{w(A_j)}$.

Proof: If $P \in P_C$ then the pairwise comparisons satisfy $P(A_i,A_j)P(A_j,A_i) = P(A_i,A_l)$, for all i, j and l. Thus, for any i and j, we have

$$P(A_i, A_j) = \frac{P(A_i, A_l)}{P(A_j, A_l)},$$

for all l, i.e., $\dfrac{P(A_i, A_1)}{P(A_j, A_1)} = \dfrac{P(A_i, A_2)}{P(A_j, A_2)} = \cdots = \dfrac{P(A_i, A_m)}{P(A_j, A_m)} = c$, where $c > 0$ is a

constant. Thus, we write $w(A_i) \equiv cP(A_i, A_1)$. If $P(A_i, A_j) > 1$,

then $P(A_i, A_j) = \dfrac{P(A_i, A_1)}{P(A_j, A_1)} = \dfrac{w(A_i)}{w(A_j)} > 1$. The converse is true by construction. Let

$P(A_i, A_j) \equiv \dfrac{w(A_i)}{w(A_j)}$ for all i and j. By definition, P is a consistent pairwise

relation uniquely determined by w.

Inconsistent Pairwise Preference Relations

To derive the absolute cardinal relation associated with an inconsistent but reciprocal pairwise relation P, i.e., $P \in P_I$ we need to extend the concept of dominance. We will be brief in summarizing the ideas needed because they have been worked out in detail in the literature ([13, 18]).

The study of transitivity takes one to the concept of transition in the form of preference of one alternative over another possibly through intermediate alternatives. A convenient way to represent the transitivity of dominance is via a directed graph whose nodes, representing the alternatives, are connected by weighted arcs indicating the intensity of dominance of one alternative over another. The product of the intensities along the arcs in a path from a node to another, represent the dominance of the starting node over the terminal node along that path. From this follows the representation of dominance with a matrix, known as a dominance path matrix, with the coefficient $a_{ij}^{(s)}$ of its sth power representing dominance along a path from i to j of length s. For each such matrix, the dominance of an alternative is given as the sum of the elements in its corresponding row divided by the total sum of the rows (a normalization operation). The sum of all such dominances along paths of length 1, 2, and so on has a limit as a Cesaro sum. That limit is the principal eigenvector of the matrix of preferences. We now formalize the foregoing through construction to demonstrate the existence of an absolute cardinal relation associated with each inconsistent pairwise relation.

Let $a_{ijk} \equiv P_k(A_i, A_j)$ be the relative dominance of A_i over A_j by individual k, $k = 1, ..., m$. To simplify the notation, let the matrix corresponding to the reciprocal pairwise relation of the kth member be denoted by (a_{ijk}). The relative dominance of A_i over A_j by individual k along paths of length s is given by

$$\frac{\displaystyle\sum_{j=1}^{n} a_{ijk}^{(s)}}{\displaystyle\sum_{i=1}^{n}\sum_{j=1}^{n} a_{ijk}^{(s)}}, \quad k = 1, ..., m$$

where $a_{ijk}^{(s)}$ is the (i,j) entry of the sth power of the matrix (a_{ijk}). The *total dominance* of alternative i over all other alternatives along paths of all lengths is given by

$$\sum_{s=1}^{\infty} \frac{\displaystyle\sum_{j=1}^{n} a_{ijk}^{(s)}}{\displaystyle\sum_{i=1}^{n}\sum_{j=1}^{n} a_{ijk}^{(s)}}, \quad k = 1, ..., m,$$

a series whose sum is given by the Cesaro sum

$$w_k(A_i) = \lim_{p \to \infty} \frac{1}{p} \sum_{s=1}^{p} \frac{\displaystyle\sum_{j=1}^{n} a_{ijk}^{(s)}}{\displaystyle\sum_{i=1}^{n}\sum_{j=1}^{n} a_{ijk}^{(s)}}, \quad k = 1, ..., m.$$

Cesaro' summability ensures that this limit is the same as that of the sequence of powers of the path matrix, i.e.,

$$\lim_{p \to \infty} \frac{1}{p} \sum_{s=1}^{p} \frac{\displaystyle\sum_{j=1}^{n} a_{ijk}^{(s)}}{\displaystyle\sum_{i=1}^{n}\sum_{j=1}^{n} a_{ijk}^{(s)}} = \lim_{s \to \infty} \frac{\displaystyle\sum_{j=1}^{n} a_{ijk}^{(s)}}{\displaystyle\sum_{i=1}^{n}\sum_{j=1}^{n} a_{ijk}^{(s)}}, \quad k = 1, ..., m.$$

This formulation which emphasizes the idea of derived overall dominance is a variant of the well-known theorem of Oskar Perron for positive matrices in which it is demonstrated that this limit converges to the principal right eigenvector of the matrix [19]. Thus, for a given reciprocal pairwise cardinal preference relation $P_k \in P$, the absolute cardinal relation w_k associated with it is the principal right eigenvector of the matrix (a_{ijk}), and for $w_k = \left(w_k(A_1), ..., w_k(A_n) \right)$, $\sum_{j=1}^{n} a_{ijk} w_k(A_j) = \lambda_{\max} w_k(A_i)$, $i=1,...,n$, where $\lambda_{\max}$ is the principal eigenvalue of the matrix (a_{ijk}). For a consistent pairwise relation P_k the corresponding matrix of pairwise comparisons is given by $\left(a_{ijk} \equiv \dfrac{w_k(A_i)}{w_k(A_j)} \right)$, and the associated absolute cardinal relation w_k coincides with the principal right eigenvector and and also with the geometric mean of the rows of the matrix. DeMeyer and Plott [7] assumed consistency by using w_{ik} / w_{jk} to represent preferences and assumed that w_{ik} is known.

Construction of a Social Welfare Function

We have shown that there is a correspondence between a reciprocal pairwise preference relation and its corresponding matrix, and that an absolute cardinal relation is realized through the principal right eigenvector of that matrix.

We can now approach the problem of constructing a social welfare function in two ways depicted in the following diagram (Figure 1) where $\sigma_P = \omega_2 \circ \gamma_P$ is the synthesis that first maps pairwise profiles **P** to a social pairwise relation and then maps that to a final social welfare function w (measured on an absolute scale), and $\sigma_W = \gamma_W \circ \omega_1$ is the synthesis that first maps each individual pairwise relation to its individual absolute cardinal relation and then maps all the individual cardinal relations to a final social welfare function w (measured on an absolute scale). Note that the two outcomes σ_P and σ_W may not coincide.

In the previous section we showed that the aggregation procedure for reciprocal pairwise profiles γ_P, namely, the geometric mean, yields a social reciprocal pairwise relation that maps the space of individuals paired comparisons P^m into the space of social paired comparisons P (Figure 2).

Individual paired comparisons   Individual cardinal relations

$$\mathbf{P} = (P_1, ..., P_m) \in \mathsf{P}^m \quad \xrightarrow{\omega_1} \quad \mathbf{W} = (W_1, ..., W_m) \in \mathsf{W}^m$$

$$\downarrow \gamma_P \qquad \sigma_P \quad \sigma_W \qquad \qquad \downarrow \gamma_W$$

$$P = \{P(A_i, A_j)\} \in \mathsf{P} \quad \xrightarrow{\omega_2} \quad w \in \mathsf{W}$$

Social paired comparisons   The final social welfare function

$$\gamma_P : \mathsf{P}^m \to \mathsf{P}, \gamma_W : \mathsf{W}^m \to \mathsf{W}$$

$$\omega_1 : \mathsf{P}^m \to \mathsf{W}^m, \omega_2 : \mathsf{P} \to \mathsf{W}$$

$$\sigma_P : \mathsf{P}^m \to \mathsf{W}, \sigma_W : \mathsf{P}^m \to \mathsf{W}$$

$$\sigma_P = \omega_2 \circ \gamma_P \text{ and } \sigma_W = \gamma_W \circ \omega_1$$

Figure 1 Mapping of Priority and Judgment Spaces

Individual paired comparisons

$$\mathbf{P} = (P_1, ..., P_m) \in \mathsf{P}^m$$

$$\downarrow \gamma_P$$

$$P = \{P(A_i, A_j)\} \in \mathsf{P}$$

Social paired comparisons

Figure 2 Geometric Mean of Paired Comparisons

The social welfare function is realized by the principal right eigenvector of the matrix associated with the mapping $\sigma_P = \omega_2 \circ \gamma_P$ (Figure 3).

Individual paired comparisons

$$\mathbf{P} = (P_1, ..., P_m) \in \mathsf{P}^m$$

$$\downarrow \gamma_P \qquad \qquad \sigma_P$$

$$P = \{P(A_i, A_j)\} \in \mathsf{P} \quad \xrightarrow{\omega_2} \quad w \in \mathsf{W}$$

Social paired comparisons   The final social welfare function

Figure 3 The Social Welfare Mapping σ_P

Formally, this can be summarized as follows. Let γ_P be the geometric mean aggregation procedure from P^m to P, i.e., γ_P (**P**)=P. Let ω_2 be a mapping from P to Ω that assigns to each P in P the principal right eigenvector w of the corresponding matrix $(a_{ij} \equiv P(A_i, A_j))$, i.e. $\omega_2(P) \equiv w$. Let σ_P be the aggregation procedure from P^m to Ω. σ_P assigns reciprocal pairwise profiles **P** to absolute cardinal relations w, i.e., σ_P(**P**)=$(\omega_2 \circ \gamma_P)$(**P**)=$\omega_2(\gamma_P$(**P**))= $\omega_2(P)$=w.

We define Arrow's conditions for this mixed aggregation procedure as follows:

Unrestricted Domain: An aggregation procedure σ_P is said to satisfy the condition of *unrestricted domain* if its domain is all of P^m.

Pareto Principle: An aggregation procedure $\sigma_P : P^m \rightarrow W$ satisfies *unanimity* if and only if for any pair A_i and A_j of A and any reciprocal pairwise profile **P**, $P_k(A_i, A_j) \geq 1$ for all $k \in M$, implies $w(A_i) \geq w(A_j)$, where $w = \sigma_P$ (**P**).

Independence from Irrelevant Alternatives: An aggregation procedure σ_P is said to satisfy *cardinal independence from irrelevant alternatives* (CIIA) if for any subset **A** of A with three elements and for any two reciprocal pairwise profiles **P** and **Q**: $P|_A = Q|_A$ implies $w|_A = v|_A$, where $w = \sigma_P$ (**P**) and $v = \sigma_P$ (**Q**).

Non-Dictatorship: A pairwise aggregation procedure σ_P is said to be *cardinally non-dictatorial* if there is no group member $d \in M$ such that for all $P \in P^m$, σ_P P) = w_d.

We now show that this composite aggregation procedure σ_P in fact satisfies *Arrow's conditions*. We can distinguish two mutually exclusive situations: consistent (P_C^m) and inconsistent (P_I^m) pairwise profiles, i.e. $P^m = P_C^m \cup P_I^m$. The latter require a slight modification of two conditions to make it compatible with the requirements of the much stronger absolute cardinal scale instead of an ordinal one.

Consistent Profiles

Figure 4 depicts the restrictions of the mappings $\omega_1, \omega_2, \gamma_P$ and γ_W to the space of consistent profiles P_C^m.

Individual paired comparisons	Individual cardinal relations
$\mathbf{P} = (P_1,...,P_m) \in \mathbf{P}_C^m$ $\xrightarrow{\omega_1}$	$\mathbf{W} = (W_1,...,W_m) \in \mathbf{W}^m$
$\downarrow \gamma_P \qquad\qquad \sigma_P \quad \sigma_W$	$\downarrow \gamma_W$
$P = \{P(A_i, A_j)\} \in \mathbf{P}_C \qquad \xrightarrow{\omega_2}$	$w \in \mathbf{W}$
Social paired comparisons	The final social welfare function

Figure 4 Restrictions of Priority and Judgment Mappings to Consistent Profiles

When σ_P is restricted to consistent profiles, the resulting absolute cardinal relation w can be obtained as the geometric mean of the rows of the group matrix and coincides with the geometric mean of the individual welfare functions associated with the individual pairwise preference relations, i.e., $\sigma_P(\mathbf{P}) = \sigma_W(\mathbf{P})$. We have

$$\sigma_P(\mathbf{P}) = (\omega_2 \circ \gamma_P)(\mathbf{P}) = \omega_2(P) = w,$$

$$\sigma_W(\mathbf{P}) = (\gamma_W \circ \omega_1)(\mathbf{P}) = \gamma_W(\omega_1(P_1),...,\omega_1(P_m)) = \gamma_W(w_1,...,w_m) = \left[\prod_{k=1}^{m} w_k\right]^{1/m} \text{ and we have}$$

$$w = \left[\prod_{k=1}^{m} w_k\right]^{1/m}.$$

In addition, because the geometric mean satisfies *Arrow's conditions*, $\sigma_P = \sigma_W$ also satisfies these conditions.

Inconsistent Profiles

Figure 5 depicts the restrictions of the mappings $\omega_1, \omega_2, \gamma_P$ and γ_P to the space of inconsistent profiles $\mathbf{P}_I^m$.

Individual paired comparisons	Individual cardinal relations
$\mathbf{P} = (P_1,...,P_m) \in \mathbf{P}_I^m$ $\xrightarrow{\omega_1}$	$\mathbf{W} = (W_1,...,W_m) \in \mathbf{W}^m$
$\downarrow \gamma_P \qquad\qquad \sigma_P \quad \sigma_W$	$\downarrow \gamma_W$
$P = \{P(A_i, A_j)\} \in \mathbf{P}_I \qquad \xrightarrow{\omega_2}$	$w \in \mathbf{W}$
Social paired comparisons	The final social welfare function

Figure 5 Restrictions of Priority and Judgment Mappings to Inconsistent Profiles

When σ_P and σ_W are defined on inconsistent reciprocal pairwise profiles, unanimity and CIIA do not always hold. With consistency $P_k(A_i,A_j) \geq 1$ for all k always implies $w_k(A_i) \geq w_k(A_j)$ for all i and j. With inconsistency unanimity may break down and we need to define conditions under which this also holds.

Pairwise Dominance: A pairwise relation P_k is said to satisfy *pairwise dominance* if for all pairs of alternatives i and j, either:

$$P_k(A_i, A_l) \geq P_k(A_j, A_l) \text{ for all } l, \text{ or } P_k(A_j, A_l) \geq P_k(A_i, A_l), \text{ for all } l.$$

This condition says that given any two rows of the matrix associated with the pairwise relation, one row always dominates another row elementwise. Pairwise dominance implies transitivity; i.e., if row i dominates row j and row j dominates row k, then row i dominates row k.

Let P_k be a pairwise relation that satisfies pairwise dominance. Let $w_k = \omega_2(P_k)$ be the corresponding absolute cardinal relation. By construction, if for a pair of alternatives i and j, we have $P_k(A_i,A_l) \geq P_k(A_j,A_l)$ for all l then the corresponding cardinal relation satisfies $w_k(A_i) \geq w_k(A_j)$.

A reciprocal pairwise profile satisfies pairwise dominance if all its pairwise preference relations satisfy pairwise dominance. This means that if alternative i is preferred to alternative j then alternative i is preferred to the other alternatives more than alternative j is preferred to them. Using this condition the Pareto principle can now be modified as follows.

Pareto Principle with Pairwise Dominance: An aggregation procedure $\gamma_P : P^m \to P$ satisfies *strong unanimity* if and only if for any pair A_i and A_j of A and any reciprocal pairwise profile **P**, $P_k(A_i,A_l) \geq P_k(A_j,A_l)$ for all l and all $k \in M$, implies $P(A_i,A_l) \geq P(A_j,A_l)$ for all l, where $\gamma_P(\mathbf{P}) = P \in P$.

Note that for pairwise profiles, strong unanimity implies unanimity. To see this, we substitute $l = j$ in $P_k(A_i,A_l) \geq P_k(A_j,A_l)$, we have $P_k(A_i,A_j) \geq P_k(A_j,A_j) = 1$ for all k, and $P(A_i,A_j) \geq P(A_j,A_j) = 1$ follows.

Let $P_D \subset P$ be the set of reciprocal pairwise preference relations that satisfy pairwise dominance. Let $\sigma_P |_D : P^m \to W$ be the restriction of σ_P to $P_D^m \subset P^m$.

Theorem 3: *The geometric mean aggregation procedure γ_P restricted to $P_D^m \subset P^m$ satisfies strong unanimity.*

Proof: Let $\mathbf{P} = (P_1,...,P_m) \in \mathbf{P}_D^m \subset \mathbf{P}^m$ be a reciprocal profile that satisfies pairwise dominance. Then, for any pair of alternatives i and j, $P_k(A_i, A_l) \geq P_k(A_j, A_l)$, for all l and k, we have

$$\gamma_P(\mathbf{P})(A_i, A_l) = \left[\prod_{k=1}^{m} P_k(A_i, A_l) \right]^{\frac{1}{m}} \geq \left[\prod_{k=1}^{m} P_k(A_j, A_l) \right]^{\frac{1}{m}} = \gamma_P(\mathbf{P})(A_j, A_l)$$

or $P(A_i, A_l) \geq P(A_j, A_l)$ for all l and the geometric mean satisfies strong unanimity.

Theorem 4: *The aggregation procedure $\sigma_{P|D}:P^m \to W$ satisfies unanimity and cardinal independence from irrelevant alternatives.*

Proof: Let $\mathbf{P}=(P_1,...,P_m)$ be a reciprocal cardinal profile. From Theorem 3, γ_P satisfies strong unanimity, i.e., for every pair of alternatives (i,j), $\gamma_P(\mathbf{P})(A_i, A_l) \geq \gamma_P(\mathbf{P})(A_j, A_l)$ for all l, or $a_{il}=P(A_i, A_l) \geq P(A_j, A_l)=a_{jl}$ for all l, and hence, by construction $\sum_{l=1}^{n} a_{il} w(A_l) \geq \sum_{l=1}^{n} a_{jl} w(A_l)$ or $w(A_i) \geq w(A_j)$ and $\sigma_{P|D}$ satisfies unanimity.

Let $\mathbf{P}$ and $\mathbf{Q}$ be two reciprocal pairwise profiles and let w and v be the corresponding absolute cardinal relations, respectively. If for any subset $\mathbf{A}$ of $\mathbf{A}$ with three elements $\mathbf{P}|_\mathbf{A} = \mathbf{Q}|_\mathbf{A}$ is true, then by Theorem 1 the geometric mean aggregation procedure satisfies pairwise independence from irrelevant alternatives and hence $\gamma_P(\mathbf{P})|_\mathbf{A} = \gamma_P(\mathbf{Q})|_\mathbf{A}$. Let $\gamma_P(\mathbf{P})=P$ and $\gamma_P(\mathbf{Q})=Q$, and let $w = \omega_2(P)$ and $v = \omega_2(Q)$. We have

$$\sigma_P|_D(\mathbf{P})|_\mathbf{A} = (\omega_2 \circ \gamma_P)(\mathbf{P})|_\mathbf{A} = \omega_2(\gamma_P(\mathbf{P})|_\mathbf{A}) = \omega_2(\gamma_P(\mathbf{Q})|_\mathbf{A}) = (\omega_2 \circ \gamma_P)(\mathbf{Q})|_\mathbf{A} = \sigma_P|_D(\mathbf{Q})|_\mathbf{A}$$

and thus $w|_\mathbf{A} = v|_\mathbf{A}$.

Theorem 5 (Cardinal Possibility for Paired Comparisons): *The aggregation procedure $\sigma_{P|D}:P^m \to W$ with the condition of individuality is non-dictatorial.*

Proof: Let $\mathbf{P} = (P_1,...,P_m) \in \mathbf{P}_D^m$ and $w = \sigma_P(\mathbf{P}) \in W$. $\sigma_{P|D}:P^m \to W$ is dictatorial if there is a member d of the group for which $\sigma_P(\mathbf{P})=w_d$. For this to happen, the following must hold: $\sigma_P(\mathbf{P})=\omega_2(\gamma_P(\mathbf{P}))=\omega_2(P_d)$ and $w(A_i)=w_d(A_i)$ for all i. But by Theorem 1 and the condition of individuality, the geometric mean aggregation procedure γ_P is non-dictatorial, i.e., $\gamma_P(\mathbf{P}) \neq P_d$, from which we have $\sigma_P(\mathbf{P})=\omega_2(\gamma_P(\mathbf{P})) \neq \omega_2(P_d)$ and hence, $\sigma_{P|D}:P^m \to W$ is non-dictatorial.

Conclusions

Strong unanimity and pairwise preference relations are restrictions of Arrow's conditions. It is clear that Arrow's conditions are too general to hold for preferences expressed on more refined scales such as an absolute scale. Hence, they need to be restricted in order for possibility to hold. We have shown by construction that with reciprocal pairwise preference relations (a restriction of ordinal preference relations) represented on an absolute scale with the unanimity condition replaced by strong unanimity, a non-dictatorial social welfare function exists.

References

1. Arrow, K.J. (1963), *Social Choice and Individual Values.* 2nd ed. New York: Wiley
2. Arrow, K.J., A.K. Sen, and K. Suzumura, ed. (2002) *Handbook of Social Choice and Welfare.* 1st ed. Handbooks in Economics, ed. M.D. Intriligator. Vol. 19., Elsevier: New York, pp. 633
3. Goodman, L.A. and H. Markowitz (1952), "Social Welfare Functions Based on Individual Rankings." *American Journal of Sociology,* **58**(3): pp. 257-262
4. Samuelson, P., *Arrow's Mathematical Politics,* in *Human Values and Economic Policy,* S. Hook, Editor (1967), New York University Press: New York. p. 41-51
5. Campbell, D.E. (1973), "Social Choice and Intensity of Preference." *Journal of Political Economy,* **81**(1): pp. 211-218
6. Kalai, E. and D. Schmeidler (1977), "Aggregation Procedure for Cardinal Preferences: A Formulation and Proof of Samuelson's Impossibility Conjecture." *Econometrica,* **45**(6): pp. 1431-1438
7. DeMeyer, F. and C.R. Plott (1971), "A Welfare Function Using "Relative Intensity" of Preference." *Quarterly Journal of Economics,* **85**(1): pp. 179-186
8. Nash, J. (1950), "The Bargaining Problem." *Econometrica,* **18**: pp. 155-162.
9. Kaneko, M. and K. Nakamura (1979), "The Nash Social Welfare Function." *Econometrica,* **47**(2): pp. 423-436
10. Roberts, K.W.S. (1980), "Interpersonal Comparability and Social Choice Theory." *The Review of Economic Studies,* **27**(2): pp. 421-439
11. Blumenthal, A.L. (1977), *The Process of Cognition.* Englewood Cliffs, NJ: Prentice-Hall

12. Saaty, T.L. (1977), "A Scaling Method for Priorities in Hierarchical Structures." *Journal of Mathematical Psychology*, **15**: pp. 234-281

13. Saaty, T.L. (1980), *The Analytic Hierarchy Process*. New York: McGraw Hill

14. Saaty, T.L. (2001), *The Analytic Network Process*. Pittsburgh, PA: RWS Publications

15. Sarin, R.K. (1982), "Strength of Preference and Risky Choice." *Operations Research*, **30**(5): pp. 982-997

16. Aczel, J., and T.L. Saaty (1983), "Procedures for Synthesizing Ratio Judgments." *Journal of Mathematical Psychology*, **27**: pp. 93-102

17. Aczel, J., and C. Alsina (1986), "On Synthesis of Judgments." *Socio-Economic Planning Sciences*, **20**: pp. 333-339

18. Harary, F. (1972), *Graph Theory*. Reading, Massachusetts: Addison-Wesley Publishing Co. Inc.

19. Perron, O. (1907), "Zur Theorie der Matrices." *Math. Ann.*, **64**: pp. 248-263

Chapter 8

Validation Examples of the Analytic Hierarchy Process and Analytic Network Process

This chapter deals with the following ideas:
- What are some real-life examples that help increase our confidence that the judgments of the AHP and their outcomes are not simply an excuse for using subjectivity that could amount to garbage in garbage out?
- Numerous examples ranging from a single matrix of comparisons to hierarchies and networks of elaborate kinds are provided to make the point that expert judgment is our main guide to understand and interpret the world in a rational way that is finer and more accurate than using words and language.

Introduction

One way to validate a scientific theory is to show that the results predicted by the theory give correct answers; that is, that they match known results. In the Analytic Hierarchy Process (AHP) this usually means finding examples with measures in an already known scale. To validate AHP priority vectors against measures from known scales the measures must first be normalized by dividing by their sum. When the two vectors are the same, or close, then one can say the results of the AHP model have been validated. The AHP and its generalization, the Analytic Network Process (ANP) can be validated at several levels ranging from priority vectors derived from pairwise comparison matrices to the synthesized priorities for a hierarchical model, to the priorities derived for the elements in an ANP network from the limiting supermatrix (perhaps most impressively validated by estimating market share of companies using intangible factors), to the overall results from complex ANP models involving several levels of networks. Many validation examples are presented along with a discussion of the compatibility index that can be used to measure closeness of priority vectors.

"Scientific truth, that is to say the validity of an accepted theory, depends on two important kinds of factors: the guiding principles...and what we

have called the process of empirical verification...these two factors are crucial in the establishment of any theory relating to any kind of knowledge."

According to LeShan and Margenau [1], quoted above, scientific theories must be verified against things that happen in the real world and must follow the guiding principles of science that have been loosely enumerated as *simplicity, extensibility, multiple connections, logical fertility, stability of interpretation, causality,* and *elegance.*

In science, validation is a central concern. It is as relevant in the social sciences, although more difficult to do, as it is in the physical sciences. Validating subjective observations made by experts or by experienced people with their perceptions is what we intend to deal with here. A decision theory that hides behind subjectivity and a claim to being normative (i.e., the theory specifies what is good for you) has no way of being validated even when it claims success. One cannot help but be struck by the rather precise way in which people using AHP are able to understand influences that they have internalized over a period of time. They can capture the importance of these influences by making pairwise comparison judgments expressed using the AHP fundamental scale in a matrix which results in a priority vector or in a hierarchical AHP model composed of a number of pairwise comparison matrices. Priority vectors can be compared to measures that have been transformed into relative form–that is, they have been normalized so that they sum to 1.

Rational decision-making is a talent we must encourage if we want to be more effective in implementing our ideas in the real world with its risks and resistance to change. There are two kinds of decisions. One is to determine what we prefer the most, known as *normative* decision making and the other is how to make a best choice given all the influences in the world around us that can affect the optimality of any choice we make, known as *descriptive* decision making. When we think about normative decisions it is easy to see why we do not wish anything to happen that can undermine the best choice we make and thus if we choose an alternative, we do not want it to be influenced by other alternatives that arrive (or occur to us) later. That is why preserving rank when a new alternative is added or an old one deleted is essential for this kind of thinking. Descriptive statements are falsifiable statements that attempt to describe the real world as it is. Normative statements legislate how things ought to be, what is good and what is bad; what is right and what is wrong. Normative statements can never be proven to be correct and workable, but only disproved with examples of what they recommended failing. A useful way to show their falsehood is by pointing to real life occurrences that they violate in spite of their claims.

But in reality how good any choice we make depends on how well we know our alternatives as compared with each other and with others outside the collection being compared so we can rank them as to how good they are. The drawback is that our knowledge of the alternatives may be very limited. It is known in practice that new alternatives can influence what we thought of in ranking other alternatives one by one earlier. Yet normative theories want to overlook that in all situations. A descriptive approach to decision making must cover both the normative and the descriptive ways of thinking. Such a theory must allow for enforcing the stability of choices in certain decisions and for their potential variability in others.

Decision-making involves prioritizing our ideas according to the circumstances we face now or might face in the future. A fundamental problem in decision-making is how to measure intangible criteria and how to interpret measurements of tangibles correctly so they can be combined with those of intangibles to yield sensible, not arbitrary numerical results. A crucial test is whether actual measurements can be used precisely as they are when needed.

The AHP/ANP is fundamentally a way to measure intangible factors by using pairwise comparisons with judgments that represent the dominance of one element over another with respect to a property that they share. Sometimes, when there is urgency, examples are worked out by knowledgeable people without entering all the judgments but only contrasting ones that form a spanning tree which covers all the elements thus shortening the time in which the exercise is done. The AHP/ANP has found useful applications in decision making which involves numerous intangibles. It is a process of laying out a structure of all the essential factors that influence the outcome of a decision. Numerical pairwise comparison judgments are then elicited to express people's understanding of the importance, preference or likely influence of these elements on the final outcome obtained by synthesizing the priorities derived from different sets of pairwise comparisons. Sensitivity analysis is performed in the end to determine the stability of the outcome to wide perturbations in the judgments. The process has been validated in practice in many ways as we show in the next section.

The AHP uses additive synthesis which means multiplying the priorities of the alternatives by those of their respective criteria and adding.

It was once proposed by F. Lootsma of Delft that it would be better to use multiplicative synthesis by raising the alternative priorities to the power of their respective criterion priorities and multiplying the resulting priorities of the alternatives. He had a few advocates who published on it, but no one has promoted this idea since T. Saaty brought to the attention of Lootsma and others several years ago that an alternative with the same priority (value less than one) under two criteria when raised to the respective powers of the criteria would result in the alternative under the larger priority criterion receiving a smaller value—contradicting common sense. Consider for example raising the fraction ½ to the power of .7 (which yields .6156) and then to the power of .3 (which yields .8123). Because of this, multiplicative synthesis is not a viable option for synthesis.

Single Matrix Validation Examples

In this section we illustrate the validation of the AHP/ANP with a variety of example for pairwise comparison matrices, hierarchies and networks. Because the process deals with the idea of dominance in the forms of importance, preference and likelihood, when importance is applied to the criteria and preference to the alternatives we have a normative outcome which as we said above has no way to defend its validity except for counter examples in real life. For that we mention a statement made by Buede and Maxwell [2] who performed many experiments to compare the outcomes of different methods and used their preferred approach known as Multi-attribute Value Theory (MAVT) as the basis for the comparisons of the methods. They wrote: *"These experiments demonstrated that the MAVT and AHP techniques, when provided with the same decision outcome data, very often identify the same alternatives as 'best'. The other techniques are noticeably less consistent with MAVT, the Fuzzy algorithm being the least consistent."*

In its descriptive/predictive form the AHP generally uses importance for the dominance among the criteria and likelihood for dominance among the alternatives.

We already gave the example of the relative sizes of areas in the preface. Here are others.

Relative Weights of Objects

The matrix below gives the estimated pairwise comparisons of the weights of the five objects lifted by hand, made by the then President of the Diners Club, a friend of the author. The two vectors appear to be very close but are they really close? To determine closeness of two priority vectors one must use the Compatibility Index in chapter 4.

Table 1 Pairwise Comparisons of the Weights of Five Objects

Weight	Radio	Type-writer	Large Attache Case	Projector	Small Attache Case	Eigen-vector	Actual Relative Weights
Radio	1	1/5	1/3	1/4	4	.09	.10
Typewriter	5	1	2	2	8	.40	.39
Large Attache Case	3	1/2	1	1/2	4	.18	.20
Projector	4	1/2	2	1	7	.29	.27
Small Attache Case	1/4	1/8	1/4	1/7	1	.04	.04

Relative Electric Consumption of Household Appliances

In Table 2 we have paired comparisons done by students in Electrical Engineering estimating the consumption of electricity of common household appliances. How compatible are the derived and actual vectors?

Table 2 Relative Electricity Consumption (Kilowatt Hours) of Household Appliances

Annual Electric Consumption	Elec. Range	Refrig	TV	Dish Wash	Iron	Radio	Hair Dryer	Eigen-vector	Actual Relative Weights
Electric Range	1	2	5	8	7	9	9	.393	.392
Refrigerator	1/2	1	4	5	5	7	9	.261	.242
TV	1/5	1/4	1	2	5	6	8	.131	.167
Dishwasher	1/8	1/5	1/2	1	4	9	9	.110	.120
Iron	1/7	1/5	1/5	1/4	1	5	9	.061	.047
Radio	1/9	1/7	1/6	1/9	1/5	1	5	.028	.028
Hair-dryer	1/9	1/9	1/8	1/9	1/9	1/5	1	.016	.003

The hairdryer is of such a small magnitude that it probably should have been left out of the other homogeneous comparisons.

Relative Wealth of Seven Nations

This exercise shown in Tables 2 and 3 was done on an airplane in 1973 by Thomas Saaty and Mohammad Khouja [3] by simply using their common knowledge about the relative power and standing of these countries in the world and without referring to any specific economic data related to GNP values.

Table 3 Paired Comparisons of the Relative Wealth of Seven Nations

	U.S	U.S.S.R	China	France	U.K	Japan	W.Germany
U.S	1	4	9	6	6	5	5
U.S.S.R	1/4	1	7	5	5	3	4
China	1/9	1/7	1	1/5	1/5	1/7	1/5
France	1/6	1/5	5	1	1	1/3	1/3
U.K	1/6	1/5	5	1	1	1/3	1/3
Japan	1/5	1/3	7	3	3	1	2
W.Germany	1/5	1/4	5	3	3	1/2	1

Table 4 The Relative Priorities Compared with the Actual Values Normalized

	Normalized Eigenvector	Actual GNP (1972)	Normalized GNP Values
U.S	.427	1,167	.413
U.S.S.R	.23	635	.225
China	.021	120	.043
France	.052	196	.069
U.K	.052	154	.055
Japan	.123	294	.104
W. Germany	.094	257	.091

Hierarchic Validation Examples

Here we give four hierarchic examples that gave results close to what the values actually were or what expert people thought was appropriate and all the works were published in refereed journals.

World Chess Championship Outcome Validation – Karpov-Korchnoi Match

The following criteria and hierarchy were used to predict the outcome of world chess championship matches using judgments of ten grandmasters in the then Soviet Union and the United States who responded to questionnaires they were mailed. The predicted outcomes that included the number of games played, drawn and won by each player either was exactly as they turned out later or adequately close to predict the winner. The outcome of this exercise was notarized before the match took place. The notarized statement was mailed to the editor of the *Journal of Behavioral*

Sciences 1980 [4], along with the paper later. See also the coauthored book by Saaty and Vargas: Prediction, Projection and Forecasting [5]. The prediction was that Karpov would win by 6 to 5 games over Korchnoi, which he did. In Table 5 we have the different criteria or factors used to judge the winner by world Chess masters in reply to a questionnaire. Figure 1 represents the layout of the decision.

Table 5 Definitions of Chess Factors

T (1)   Calculation (Q): The ability of a player to evaluate different alternatives or strategies in light of prevailing situations.

B (2)   Ego (E): The image a player has of himself as to his general abilities and qualification and his desire to win.

T (3)   Experience (EX): A composite of the versatility of opponents faced before, the strength of the tournaments participated in, and the time of exposure to a rich variety of chess players.

B (4)   Gamesmanship (G): The capability of a player to influence his opponent's game by destroying his concentration and self-confidence.

T (5)   Good Health (GH): Physical and mental strength to withstand pressure and provide endurance.

B (6)   Good Nerves and Will to Win (GN): The attitude of steadfastness that ensures a player's health perspective while the going gets tough. He keeps in mind that the situation involves two people and that if he holds out the tide may go in his favor.

T (7)   Imagination (IW: Ability to perceive and improvise good tactics and strategies.

T (8)   Intuition (IN): Ability to guess the opponent's intentions.

T (9)   Game Aggressiveness (GA): The ability to exploit the opponent's weaknesses and mistakes to one's advantage. Occasionally referred to as "killer instinct."

T (10) Long Range Planning (LRP): The ability of a player to foresee the outcome of a certain move, set up desired situations that are more favorable, and work to alter the outcome.

T (1 1) Memory M: Ability to remember previous games.

B (12) Personality (P): Manners and emotional strength, and their effects on the opponent in playing the game and on the player in keeping his wits.

T (13)   Preparation (PR): Study and review of previous games and ideas.

T (14) Quickness (Q): The ability of a player to see clearly the heart of a complex problem.

T (15) Relative Youth (RY): The vigor, aggressiveness, and daring to try new ideas and situations, a quality usually attributed to young age.

T (16) Seconds (S): The ability of other experts to help one to analyze strategies between games.

B (17) Stamina (ST): Physical and psychological ability of a player to endure fatigue and pressure.

T (18) Technique M: Ability to use and respond to different openings, improvise middle game tactics, and steer the game to a familiar ground to one's advantage.

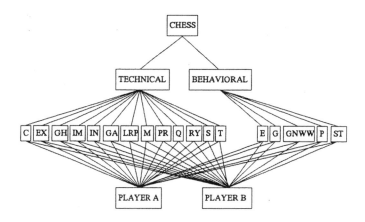

Figure 1 The Chess Decision Prediction Hierarchy

Monetary Exchange Rate – Dollar versus the Yen

In the late 1980's three economists at the University of Pittsburgh, Professors A. Blair, R. Nachtmann, and J. Olson, worked with Thomas Saaty [6] on predicting the yen/dollar exchange rate. The paper was published in *Socio-Economic Planning Sciences*. The predicted value was fairly close to the average value for a considerable number of months after that. Figure 2 represents the structure of the decision and gives the outcome at the bottom.

Number of Children in Rural Indian Families

In a hierarchy whose goal is the optimal family size in India (from a study published in the Journal of Mathematical Sociology [7]), there were four major criteria of Culture (with subcriteria: Religion, Women Status, Manlihood), Economic factors (with subcriteria: Cost of child Rearing, Old Age security, Labor, Economic Improvement, Prestige and Strength),Demographic factors (with subcriteria: Short Life Expectancy, High Infant Mortality) and the Availability and acceptance of Contraception (with subcriteria: High Level of Availability and Acceptance of contraception, Medium level of Availability and Acceptance of contraception, low level of Availability and Acceptance of contraception. At the bottom three alternatives were considered: Families with 3 or Less Children, Families with 4 to 7 Children, and Families with 8 or More Children. The outcome of this example for reasons explained in the research paper had two projections of 5.6 and 6.5 children per family (due to regional differences.) The actual value we obtained from the literature after the study was done were 6.8 births per woman in 1972 and 5.6 in 1978.

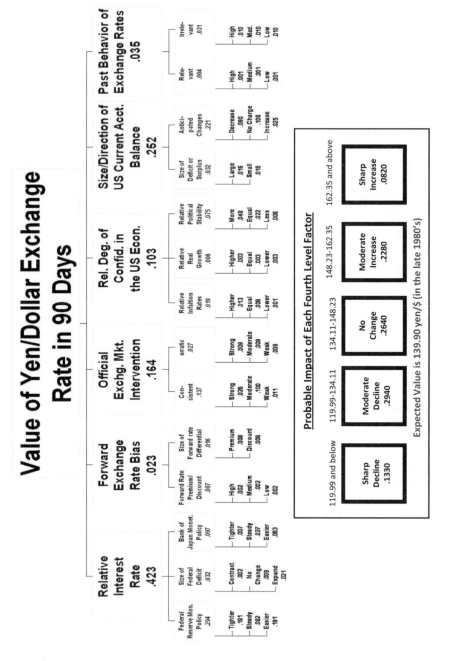

Figure 2 The Yen/Dollar Exchange Rate

Decision by the US Congress on China Joining the World Trade Organization (WTO) in May 2000 [8]

Briefly, the alternatives of the decision are:

1. *Passage of a clean PNTR bill:* Congress grants China Permanent Normal Trade Relations status with no conditions attached. This option would allow implementation of the November 1999 WTO trade deal between China and the Clinton administration. China would also carry out other WTO principles and trade conditions.

2. *Amendment of the current NTR status bill:* This option would give China the same trade position as other countries and disassociate trade from other issues. As a supplement, a separate bill may be enacted to address other matters, such as human rights, labor rights, and environmental issues.

3. *Annual Extension of NTR status:* Congress extends China's Normal Trade Relations status for one more year, and, thus, maintains the status quo.

Four hierarchies shown in the figure below were considered whose outcomes were combined as briefly outlined to derive the final priorities that show how Congress was going to vote and in fact China was later admitted to the WTO. Figure 3 and 4 summarize the results.

How to derive the priority shown next to the goal of each of the four hierarchies in Figure 3 is outlined in the table below. We rated each of the four merits: benefits, costs, opportunities and risks of the dominant PNTR alternative, as it happens to be in this case, in terms of intensities for each assessment criterion. The intensities, Very High, High, Medium, Low, and Very Low were themselves prioritized in the usual pairwise comparison matrix to determine their priorities. We then assigned the appropriate intensity for each merit on all assessment criteria. The outcome is as found at the bottom row of Table 6.

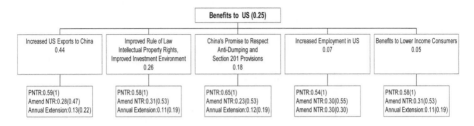

Benefits Synthesis (Ideal): PNTR 1.00 Amend NTR 0.51 Annual Extension 0.21

Opportunities Synthesis (Ideal): PNTR 1 Amend NTR 0.43 Annual Extension 0.13

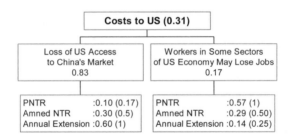

Costs Synthesis (which is more costly, Ideal): PNTR 0.31 Amend NTR 0.50 Annual Extension 0.87

Risks Synthesis (more risky, Ideal): PNTR 0.54 Amend NTR 0.53 Annual Extension 0.58

Figure 3 Hierarchies for Rating Benefits, Costs, Opportunities and Risks

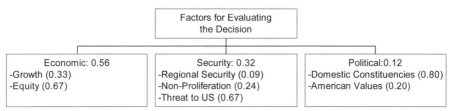

Figure 4 Prioritizing the Strategic Criteria to be Used in Rating the BOCR

Table 6 Priority Ratings for the Merits: Benefits, Costs, Opportunities, and Risks

Intensities: Very High (0.42), High (0.26), Medium (0.16), Low (0.1), Very Low (0.06)

		Benefits	Opportunities	Costs	Risks
Economic (0.56)	Growth (0.19)	High	Medium	Very Low	Very Low
	Equity (0.37)	Medium	Low	High	Low
Security (0.32)	Regional (0.03)	Low	Medium	Medium	High
	Non-Proliferation (0.08)	Medium	High	Medium	High
	Threat to US (0.21)	High	High	Very High	Very High
Political (0.12)	Constituencies (0.1)	High	Medium	Very High	High
	American Values (0.02)	Very Low	Low	Low	Medium
Priorities		0.25	0.20	0.31	0.24

We are now able to obtain the overall priorities of the three major decision alternatives listed earlier, given as columns in the table below which gives three ways of synthesize for the ideal mode, we see in bold that PNTR is the dominant alternative any way we synthesize as in the last two columns of Table 7.

Table 7 Two Methods of Synthesizing BOCR Using the Ideal Mode

Alternatives	Benefits	Opportunities	Costs	Risks	BO/CR	bB + oO - cC - rR
	(0.25)	(0.20)	(0.31)	(0.24)		
PNTR	1	1	0.31	0.54	**5.97**	**0.22**
Amend NTR	0.51	0.43	0.50	0.53	0.83	-0.07
Annual Exten.	0.21	0.13	0.87	0.58	0.05	-0.33

Network Validation Examples

Turn Around of the U.S Economy **(2001)**

Let us consider the problem of the turn-around of the US economy and introduce 3, 6, 12, 24 month time periods at the bottom of Figure 5 [9]. Decomposing the problem hierarchically, the top level consists of the primary factors that represent the forces or major influences driving the economy: "Aggregate Demand" factors, "Aggregate Supply" factors, and "Geopolitical Context." Each of these primary categories was then decomposed into subfactors represented in the second level. Under Aggregate Demand, we identified consumer spending, exports, business capital investment, shifts in consumer and business investment confidence, fiscal policy, monetary policy, and expectations with regard to such questions as the future course of inflation, monetary policy and fiscal policy. (We make a distinction between consumer and business investment confidence shifts and the formation of expectations regarding future economic developments.)

Under Aggregate Supply, we identified labor costs (driven by changes in such underlying factors as labor productivity and real wages), natural resource costs (e.g., energy costs), and expectations regarding such costs in the future. With regard to Geopolitical Context, we identified the likelihood of changes in major international political relationships and major international economic relationships as the principal subfactors. With regard to the subfactors under Aggregate Demand and Aggregate Supply, we recognized that they are, in some instances, interdependent. For example, a lowering of interest rates as the result of a monetary policy decision by the Federal Reserve should induce portfolio rebalancing throughout the economy. In turn, this should reduce the cost of capital to firms and stimulate investment, and simultaneously reduce financial costs to households and increase their disposable incomes. Any resulting increase in disposable income stimulates consumption and, at the margin, has a positive impact on employment and GNP. This assumes that the linkages of the economy are in place and are well understood. This is what the conventional macroeconomic conceptual models are designed to convey.

The third level of the hierarchy consists of the alternate time periods in which the resurgence might occur as of April 7, 2001: within three months, within six months, within twelve months, and within twenty-four months. Because the primary factors and associated subfactors are time-dependent, their relative importance had to be established in terms of each of the four alternative time periods. Thus, instead of establishing a single goal as one does for a conventional hierarchy, we used the bottom level time periods to compare the two factors at the top. This entailed creation of a feedback hierarchy known as a "holarchy" in which the priorities of the elements at the top level are determined in terms of the elements at the bottom level, thus creating an interactive loop. Figure 5 provides a schematic representation of the hierarchy we used to forecast the timing of the economic resurgence.

To obtain our forecast, we subsequently multiplied each priority by the midpoint of its corresponding time interval and added the results (as one does when evaluating expected values) as in Table 8.

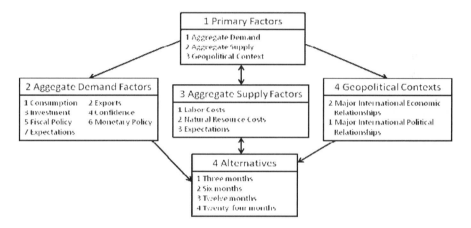

Figure 5 Overall View of the "2001" Model

Table 8 Summary of Results of the Forecast

Time Period	Midpoint of Time Period	Priority of Time Period	Midpoint x Priority
	(Expressed in months from present, with the current month as 0.)		
Three months	0 + (3 − 0)/2 = 1.5	0.30581	0.45871
Six months	3 + (6 − 3)/2 = 4.5	0.20583	0.92623
Twelve months	6 + (12 − 6)/2 = 9.0	0.18181	1.63629
Twenty-four months	12 + (24 − 12)/2 = 18.0	0.30656	5.51808
TOTAL			**8.53932**

We interpret this to mean that the recovery would occur 8.54 months from the time of the forecasting exercise, or in the fall. The Wall Street Journal of July 18, 2003, more than two year after the exercise had the following to say about the turnaround date:

The Wall Street Journal
Friday, July 18, 2003

Despite Job Losses, the Recession Is Finally Declared Officially Over

JON E. HILSENRATH

The National Bureau of Economic Research said the U.S. economic recession that began in March 2001 ended eight months later, not long after the Sept. 11 terrorist attacks.

Most economists concluded more than a year ago that the recession ended in late 2001. But yesterday's declaration by the NBER-a private, nonprofit economic research group that is considered the official arbiter of recession timing-came after a lengthy internal debate over whether there can be an economic recovery if the labor market continues to contract. The bureau's answer: a decisive yes.

When calling the end to a recession, the NBER focuses heavily on two economic indicators: the level of employment and gross domestic product, or the total value of the nation's goods and services. Since the fourth quarter of 2001, GDP has expanded slowly but consistently-rising 4 % through March of 2003.

Employers, however, have eliminated 938,000 payroll jobs since November 2001. In addition, 150,000 people have dropped out of the labor force because they are discouraged about their job prospects, according to the government.

Market Shares for the Cereal Industry (2002)

The following is one of numerous validation examples done by my graduate students in business most of whom work at some company. Many of the examples are done in class in about one hour and without access to data. The answer is only found later on the Internet. The example below was developed by Stephanie Gier and Florian John in March 2002. They write: To become familiar with the Super Decision software we have chosen to estimate the market shares for the Ready-to-Eat breakfast cereal industry. This idea was born after and delicious breakfast with Post's OREO O's. To see how good our assumptions were, we compare our calculated results with the market shares of 2001. First we created the model. We identified 6 major competitors in the ready to eat cereal market, Kellogg, General Mills, Post, Quaker, Nabisco and Ralston as our alternatives. There were more companies in this market having an actual cumulative market share of roughly about 6% that it turned out later that we had left out. Since we were only concerned with deriving relative values, the relative shares of other residual companies do not matter.

Major impacts on the companies' market shares are:

- Price of the products offered (named cost for the consumer)
- Advertising / Sales Ratio (how much money is spend for advertising)
- Shelf Space (places where the products are located in the stores)
- Tools (Selling Tools used to increase sales and market shares)
- Distribution / Availability (major distribution channels used to sell the product)

These five major impacts (clusters) are further divided in the following nodes:

Tools: (Coupons, trade dealing, in-pack premiums, vitamin fortifications)
Distribution: (Supermarket Chains, Food Stores, Mass Merchandiser)
Shelf Space: (Premium Space, Normal Space, Bad Space)
Cost: (Expensive, Normal, Cheap)
Advertising: (<15%,<14%,<13%,<12%,<11%,<5%)

Their interactions are depicted in Figure 6. Second comparisons were made along with calculations to obtain the final result in Table 9 which compares the outcome with the normalized actual values. Third we compared our calculated market shares with the real market shares for 2001. The table that follows lists estimated market share values and the actual ones taken from the website of the International Data Corporation.

The compatibility index value of 1.01403 (very good) is obtained by multiplying element-wise the matrix of ratios of one set of data, by the transpose of the matrix of ratios of the other set, adding all the resulting entries and dividing by n^2 and requiring that this ratio not be more than 1.1.

Let us describe the calculations needed to derive the result in the "Estimated" column of the table. From the pairwise comparison judgments we constructed a super matrix, done automatically by the software Super Decisions. Then we weighed blocks of the supermatrix by the corresponding entries from the matrix of priority vectors of paired comparisons of the influence of all the clusters on each cluster with respect to market share whose derived priorities for each matrix are represented in a column of Table 10. This yielded the weighted supermatrix that is now stochastic as its columns add to one. We raised this matrix to limiting powers to obtain the overall priorities of all the elements in Figure 6.

Table 9 Overall Results, Estimated and Actual

Alternatives	Kellogg	General Mills	Post	Quaker	Nabisco	Ralston
Estimated	0.324	0.255	0.147	0.116	0.071	0.087
Actual	0.342	0.253	0.154	0.121	0.057	0.073

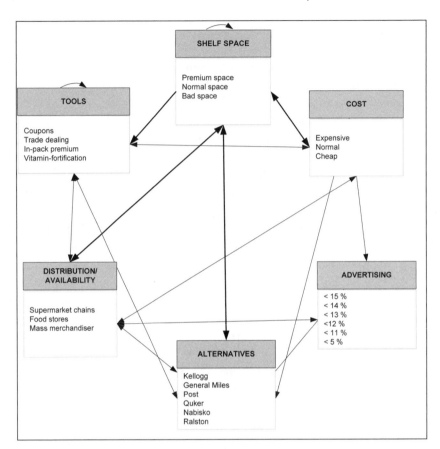

Figure 6 Cereal Industry Market Share

Table 10 Cluster Priority Matrix

	Advertising	Alternatives	Cost	Distrib./ Availability	Shelf Space	Tools
Advertising	0.000	0.184	0.451	0.459	0.000	0.000
Alternatives	0.000	0.000	0.052	0.241	0.192	0.302
Cost	0.000	0.575	0.000	0.064	0.044	0.445
Distribution / Availability	0.000	0.107	0.089	0.000	0.364	0.159
Shelf Space	0.000	0.071	0.107	0.084	0.297	0.000
Tools	0.000	0.062	0.302	0.152	0.103	0.095

Market Shares for the Airline Industry (2001)

James Nagy did the following study of the market share of eight US airlines. Nowhere did he use numerical data, but only his knowledge of the airlines and how good each is relative to the others on the factors mentioned below. Note that in three of the clusters there is an inner dependence loop that indicates that the elements in that cluster depend on each other with respect to market share. Table 11 gives the final estimated and the actual relative values that are again very close. Figure 7 shows the network model of clusters and their inner and outer dependence connections that produced these results. Nagy writes: "I initially chose the airline industry for the assignment because I was a frequent traveler. My study group at Katz helped me make the comparisons between airlines that I did not have first-hand experience as a passenger. Otherwise, I used my personal experience and perception of consumer sentiment towards the airlines to make the comparison. I was equally surprised at the results. In fact, I initially questioned how they could be so close. I would like to see the results of a study using today's consumer perception. A lot has changed in the industry since the 9/11 tragedy in the year 2001. You could divide the class up into 4 to 5 small groups and let them do the comparisons as individual groups and compare the results."

Table 11 Market Share of Airlines, Actual and Predicted

	Actual (yr 2000)	Model Estimate
American	23.9	24.0
United	18.7	19.7
Delta	18.0	18.0
Northwest	11.4	12.4
Continental	9.3	10.0
US Airways	7.5	7.1
Southwest	5.9	6.4
American West	4.4	2.9

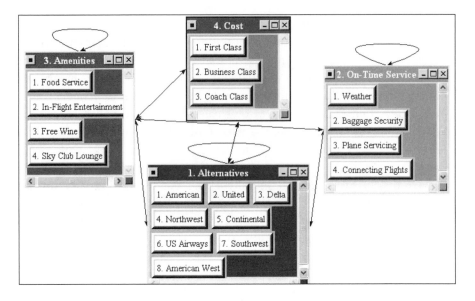

Figure 7 Airline Model From the ANP Super Decisions Software

Relationship Between the Supermatrix and the ANP and Input-Output Econometric Analysis

The following proof of the relationship between the supermatrix and Leontieff's Input-Output Model is given by Saaty and Vargas [10]. Figure 8 below depicts interdependence in economic input-output models.

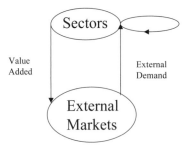

Figure 8 Input-Output Network

Let **A** be the matrix of relative input-output coefficients. Let v and d be the relative value added and the relative final demand vectors. Let x_{ij} the amount of resource that sector j receives from sector i. Let v_j be the value added corresponding to sector j and let d_i be the final demand of sector i. The value added of a sector includes wages and salaries, profit-type income, interest, dividends, rents, royalties, capital consumption allowances and taxes. The final demand of a sector includes imports, exports, government purchases, changes in inventory, private investment and sometimes, household purchases. Thus, the input-output matrix is given by:

$$
\begin{array}{c}
Sectors \\
S_1 \\
S_2 \\
\vdots \\
S_n
\end{array}
\quad
\begin{array}{cccc}
S_1 & S_2 & \cdots & S_n \\
\end{array}
\left(
\begin{array}{cccc|c}
x_{11} & x_{12} & \cdots & x_{1n} & d_1 \\
x_{21} & x_{22} & \cdots & x_{2n} & d_2 \\
\vdots & \vdots & \ddots & \vdots & \vdots \\
x_{n1} & x_{n2} & \cdots & x_{nn} & d_n \\
v_1 & v_2 & \cdots & v_n & 0
\end{array}
\right)
$$

Let $I_1, I_2, \ldots, I_n$ be the total input to the sectors and let $O_1, O_2, \ldots O_n$ be the total output of the sectors, i.e., $\sum_{j=1}^{n} x_{ij} + d_i = O_i$ and $\sum_{i=1}^{n} x_{ij} + v_j = I_j$.

Let the relative input-output coefficients be given by $a_{ij} \equiv \dfrac{x_{ij}}{I_j}$.

The relative final demand of a sector with respect to the other sectors is given by $a_{i,n+1} \equiv \dfrac{d_i}{\sum_{h=1}^{n} d_h}$. On the other hand, the relative value added is given

by $a_{n+1,1} \equiv \dfrac{v_j}{I_j}$. Thus, the matrix of interactions represented by the network in

Figure 8 is give by:

$$
W = \left(
\begin{array}{c|c}
\mathbf{A} & \overline{a}_{\bullet,n+1} \\
\hline
\overline{a}_{n+1,\bullet} & 0
\end{array}
\right)
=
\left(
\begin{array}{cccc|c}
a_{11} & a_{12} & \cdots & a_{1n} & a_{1,n+1} \\
a_{21} & a_{22} & \cdots & a_{2n} & a_{2,n+1} \\
\vdots & \vdots & \ddots & \vdots & \vdots \\
a_{n1} & a_{n2} & \cdots & a_{nn} & a_{n,n+1} \\
\hline
a_{n+1,1} & a_{n+1,2} & \cdots & a_{n+1,n} & 0
\end{array}
\right)
$$

Because W is a stochastic irreducible matrix, $\lim\limits_{k \to \infty} W^k$ is given by $\overline{w}e^T$ where $\overline{w}$ is a $(n+1) \times 1$ vector that is the principal right eigenvector of W, and $e^T = (1, 1, \ldots, 1)$ is the $1 \times (n+1)$ unit vector. Thus, we have $W\overline{w} = \overline{w}$ or

$$\sum_{j=1}^{n} a_{ij} w_j + w_{n+1} a_{i,n+1} = w_i, \quad i = 1, 2, \ldots, n$$

$$\sum_{j=1}^{n} a_{n+1,j} w_j = w_{n+1}$$

In matrix notation we have:

$$(I - A)\overline{w}_n = w_{n+1} \overline{a}_{\bullet, n+1}$$

$$a_{n+1,\bullet} \overline{w}_n = w_{n+1}$$

where $\overline{w}_n = (w_1, \ldots, w_n)^T$. Thus, we have $\overline{w}_n = w_{n+1}(I - A)^{-1} \overline{a}_{\bullet, n+1}$ and hence, we can write

$$\lim_{k \to \infty} W^k = \begin{pmatrix} w_{n+1}(I - A)^{-1} \overline{a}_{\bullet, n+1} \\ w_{n+1} \end{pmatrix} e^T .$$

Note that $\overline{w}_n = w_{n+1}(I - A)^{-1} \overline{a}_{\bullet, n+1}$ is the relative output of the economy as given by Leontieff's model.

Example of an Input-Output Matrix

Consider the following input-output matrix shown in Table 12.

Table 12 Input-Output Matrix

	Agriculture	Manufacturing	Services	Other	Final Demand	Total Output
Agriculture	10	65	10	5	10	100
Manufacturing	40	25	35	75	25	200
Services	15	5	5	5	90	120
Other	15	10	50	50	100	225
Value Added	20	95	20	90	0	
Total Input	100	200	120	90	225	645

The supermatrix corresponding to this input-output model is given in Table 13.

Table 13 The Supermatrix for the Input-Output Matrix

$$W = \begin{pmatrix} 0.100 & 0.325 & 0.083 & 0.022 & 0.044 \\ 0.400 & 0.125 & 0.292 & 0.333 & 0.111 \\ 0.150 & 0.025 & 0.042 & 0.022 & 0.400 \\ 0.150 & 0.050 & 0.417 & 0.222 & 0.444 \\ 0.200 & 0.475 & 0.167 & 0.400 & 0 \end{pmatrix}$$

and the limiting matrix $\lim_{k \to \infty} W^k$ is given in Table 14.

Table 14 Limiting Supermatrix of the Input-Output Table

$\lim_{k \to \infty} W^k$					
	0.115	0.115	0.115	0.115	0.115
	0.230	0.230	0.230	0.230	0.230
	0.138	0.138	0.138	0.138	0.138
	0.259	0.259	0.259	0.259	0.259
	0.259	0.259	0.259	0.259	0.259

$$\overline{w}_n = \begin{pmatrix} 0.114942529 \\ 0.229885057 \\ 0.137931034 \\ 0.25862069 \end{pmatrix}$$ and by normalizing to unity we can see that

$$\overline{w}_n (1 - w_{n+1})^{-1} = \begin{pmatrix} 0.15503876 \\ 0.310077519 \\ 0.186046512 \\ 0.348837209 \end{pmatrix} = \frac{1}{645} \begin{pmatrix} 100 \\ 200 \\ 120 \\ 225 \end{pmatrix}$$

which coincides with the normalized values of the total output of the economy.

Table 15 Input-Output Table of the Sudanese Economy (1976) by the Wharton Forecasting Associates

	Agriculture	Public Utilities	Manufacturing and Mining	Transportation and Distribution	Construction	Services
Agriculture	.0079 (.00737)	0 (0)	.2331 (.21953)	.0008 (.00042)	.0699 (.06721)	0 (0)
Public Utilities	.0009 (.00024)	0 (0)	.0130 (.01159)	.0075 (.00618)	0 (0)	.0033 (.00283)
Manufacturing and Mining	.0041 (.00393)	0 (0)	0 (0)	.0089 (.00857)	.0379 (.04216)	.0037 (.00322)
Transportation and Distribution	.0691 (.06993)	.1694 (.145360	.1281 (.12574)	0 (0)	.1115 (.09879)	.0153 (.00641)
Construction	0 (0)	0 (0)	0 (0)	0 (0)	0 (0)	.0546 (.05402)
Services	0 (0)	.0117 (.01030)	.0224 (.02549)	.0224 (.02422)	.0039 (.00520)	.0004 (.000210)

The input-output table (supermatrix) of the Sudan economy (1976) with eigenvector values as the estimates and the actual values in parentheses was computed by the Nobel Laureate Lawrence Klein who participated in the study with his Wharton Forecasting Associates. The results of this fairly complex exercise using paired comparison judgments are generally close to those of the econometric forecasting model.

Desirability of Drilling for Oil in Alaska – the ANWR Model

In late 2002 a study was done [11] to find out whether drilling for oil should be allowed in the Artic National Wildlife Reserve (ANWR) in northern Alaska. Environmentalists, mostly living in the lower 48 US states have been blocking drilling in the region. In the ANWR study the alternatives were: Do Drill, Do Not Drill. And the study results were compared against a poll of Alaskan residents asking the question: "Do you think we should drill, or not drill in ANWR?"

ANWR-Arctic National Wildlife Refuge covers 19 million acres on the Northern coast of Alaska north of the Arctic Circle and 1,300 miles south of the North Pole. The consensus of the geologic community is that the Coastal Plain of ANWR represents the highest petroleum potential onshore area yet to be explored in North America. If explored, it is estimated that it will take 15 years or more before oil and gas will reach the market. Legislation was passed in the 1980's that created a majority of the National Parks in Alaska and expanded ANWR to its current size. The Reagan Administration was ready to drill but was derailed by the Exxon Valdez catastrophe. The first Bush Administration likewise wanted to drill, but was unsuccessful. The Clinton Administration designated it as a protected area and it has been that way ever since then. The second Bush Administration, in response to ongoing Middle East violence and the 9/11 terrorist attacks, sees drilling in ANWR as vital not only for economic but national security reasons. Several environmental groups consider ANWR a great American natural treasure and one of the last places on the earth where an intact expanse of arctic and sub-arctic lands remain protected. They feel the habitat, the wildlife, and the culture need to be protected from the exploration of gas and oil. The top-level main network is shown in Figure 9.

Connected to each of the BOCR merit nodes is the subnet for Benefits that contains a hierarchy of control criteria: Economic, Political, Social. The control criteria in Figure 10 were pairwise compared for importance and their values derived.

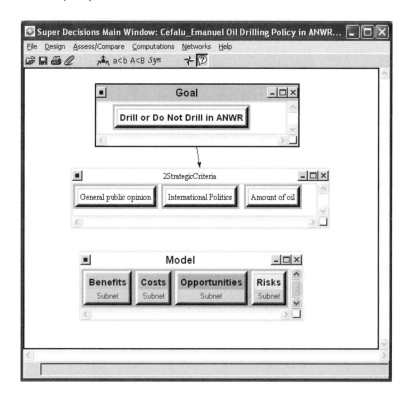

Figure 9 The Main Network of the ANWR Decision Model

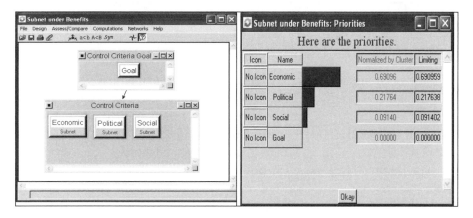

Figure 10 Subnet Containing Control Criteria Under Benefits

The subnet for Benefits containing a hierarchy of control criteria is shown in Figure 11. Connected to each control criterion node under benefits is a decision network containing the alternatives of the problem. The decision subnet for the economic control criterion under benefits is shown below in the figure. The final results are shown in the Figure 13 where the results from the subnets are combined in the main network using the prediction formula Bb + Oo + (1-C)c + (1- R)r where b, o, c, and r are the values for the decision alternatives from the control subnets, and B, O, C, and R are the priorities of the BOCR as determined by rating them under the strategic criteria.

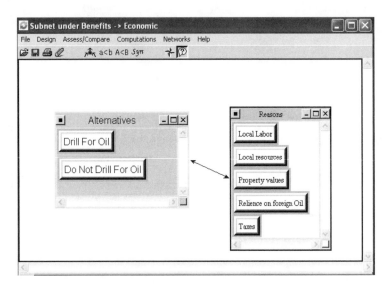

Figure 11 The Decision Subnet Under Economic Benefits

The strategic criteria here are General Public Opinion, International Politics, and Amount of Oil. They are first pairwise compared for importance, then used to rate the importance of the top rated alternative for each of the Benefits, Opportunities, Costs and Risks, called the merits of the decision, as shown in the table. The ratings categories themselves are pairwise compared to establish priorities for High, Medium and Low. To select the appropriate rating, one must keep in mind the highest priority alternative under the merit being evaluated. For example under risks: Do Not Drill is the highest priority alternative meaning that it is the most risky. One has to keep in mind for example, that the Risk merit under General Public Opinion is evaluated as low. The results of rating the merits are shown in Figure 12 in which the priority of the Benefits is .407, closely followed by Opportunities at .364. In this decision, Costs are found to be unimportant, and Risks are nearly half as important as Benefits or Opportunities. These values for the merits nodes are used to weight the values for the alternatives as determined in the subnets they control to give the overall results for the alternatives shown in Figure 13.

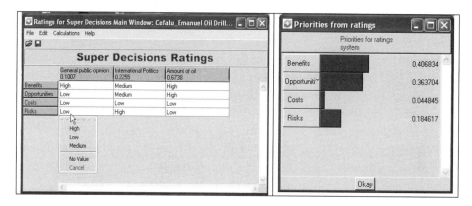

Figure 12 Using the Strategic Criteria to Evaluate the Top Alternative for Each of the BOCR Merits

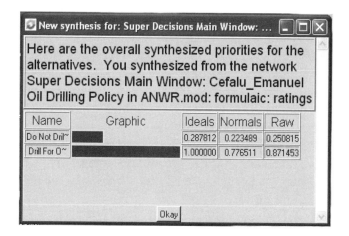

Figure 13 Final Results of ANWR Study

A recent poll (2002) conducted among native Alaskans found that they supported opening ANWR to oil and gas exploration 75% to 19% with 6% undecided. The question asked was "Do you believe oil and gas exploration should or should not be allowed within the ANWR Coastal

Plain?" Assigning the 6% equally yields 78% to 22%, the results of the poll are very close to the results of the model.

Conclusions

The examples shown above are a few chosen for their relative simplicity and importance from among numerous others developed by different people. It goes without saying that not everyone who uses the process without adequate knowledge and understanding would be able to get a good answer that can be validated in practice. Again the reason is that descriptive applications need a modicum of informed knowledge about the world that may not be available to satisfy the need to compare all the elements included in the model with sufficient accuracy. That is why group decision making tends to give better results because of the broader knowledge and also because of the possibility of debate that may change people's understanding-an important aspect for improving the validity of decisions.

References

1. Leshan, L. and H. Margenau (1982), *Einstein's Space and Van Gogh's Sky: Physical Reality and Beyond*, Macmillan 1st Collier Books
2. Buede, D. and D.T. Maxwell (1995), Rank Disagreement: A comparison of multi-criteria methodologies. *Journal of Multi-Criteria Decision Analysis* 4:1-21
3. Saaty T.L. and M.W. Khouja (1976), A Measure of World Influence, *Journal of Peace Science*, Spring
4. Saaty, T.L. and L.G. Vargas (1980), Hierarchical analysis of behavior in competition: prediction in chess, *Behavioral Sciences*, May
5. Saaty, T.L. and L.G. Vargas (1991), *Prediction, Projection and Forecasting*, Kluwer Academic, Boston
6. Blair, A., R. Nachtmann, J. Olson and T. Saaty (1987), Forecasting foreign exchange rates: an expert judgement approach, *Socio-Economic Planning Sciences*, Vol. 21, No. 6, pp. 363-369
7. Saaty, T.L. and M. Wong (1983), Projecting average family size in rural India by the Analytic Hierarchy Process, *Journal of Mathematical Sociology*, Vol. 9, pp. 181-209

8. Saaty, T.L. and Y. Cho (2001), The decision by the US Congress on China's trade status: a multicriteria analysis, *Socio-Economic Planning Sciences*, 35, pp. 243-252

9. Blair A.R., R. Nachtmann, T.L. Saaty and R. Whitaker (2001), Forecasting the resurgence of the US Economy in 2001: an expert judgment approach, *Socio-Economic Planning Sciences*, 36(2002) pp. 77-91

10. Saaty, T.L. and L.G. Vargas (1979), Estimating technological coefficients by the Analytic Hierarchy Process, *Socio-Economic Planning Sciences*, Vol. 13, pp. 333-336

11. Emanuel J. and P. Cefalu, (2002), *Drilling for Oil in the Arctic National Wildlife Refuge*, project in a graduate class: Decision Making in Complex Environments, Katz Graduate School of Business, University of Pittsburgh

Chapter 9

Resource Allocation with the AHP/ANP

In this chapter we deal with some illustrative examples in which the AHP is used frequently to prioritize people and to allocate limited resources to many projects. Because the AHP/ANP derives priorities from judgments according to the goals being served, it is used widely in business and government to allocate resource using these priorities, often with the help of linear programming.

Introduction to Resource Allocation

The Analytic Hierarchy Process (AHP) provides a way to rank the alternatives of a problem by deriving priorities. A question that occurs in practice is: what is the best combination of alternatives that has the largest sum of priorities and satisfies given constraints? This leads one to consider the interface between the AHP and the combinatorial approach inherent in Linear Programming (LP) briefly mentioned in Chapter 4. The priorities of the alternatives often serve as coefficients of the objective function of an LP problem. The constraints are determined from existing measurements such as the range for the number of employees needed and the salaries required for various jobs. Another way to use the AHP might be to determine the coefficients of the constraints. This chapter addresses the first half of the problem. Through various examples, we show how to apply the absolute measurement mode of the AHP together with LP to optimize human resource allocation problems. For example, one can determine which positions to fill or which mix of candidates to hire. We also give an example of how to allocate resources to maximize the returns to a corporation of its training programs. Finally we show that the combined AHP and LP model is capable of solving hiring problems involving synergy, such as when two persons with different complementary skills work as a team.

One often wonders why more people in organizations do not rush today to use a formal decision-making approach to make their complex decisions. A strange thing about people is that they value money and other valuable resources over their own loosely defined and not well-organized subjective value system. In addition, money is something they have learned to count and do other operations on - such as using it for barter, making exchanges or putting in and taking out of a bank. They feel sophisticated as they do it, and they feel comfortable with what they are doing. People seem know more about the value of money than about their inner selves. Because they exert effort to earn money, they feel compelled to distribute and use their money in a somewhat rational way. To them the effort spent to allocate money to projects and other things needs some justification. This is probably why prioritization in resource allocation is popular, particularly in business and government. Another area in resource allocation is to optimize the return on investments made in hiring people. Because considerable subjectivity involved in hiring people, it is helpful to have prioritization technique to deal with intangibles and make the process more objective, Saaty [1], and as in Chapter 4, Saaty, Vargas and Dellmann [2] .

This is simplified exposition about the uses of multi-criteria prioritization in resource allocation, and in particular the use of absolute measurement in the optimal assignment of human resources. This chapter places special emphasis on the measurement of intangible criteria and on their incorporation into the allocation process by combining the Analytic Hierarchy Process (AHP) and Linear Programming (LP) to rate and derive the best combination of people assigned to jobs. Use of the AHP enables us to address the issue of synergy between people that affects their qualification and whether they are selected singly or as a group. In a comprehensive review of Human Resource Planning, James A. Craft [3] speaks of Human Resource Planning as a process of moving an organization to its desired position with the right kind of people in the right job at the right time to maximize value creating activity to help employers effectively meet human resource requirements. To do this one needs to consider an organization's goals and objectives along with its various resource constraints.

Much of the literature in Human Resource Planning deals with future thinking by placing emphasis on forecasting needs [4,5,6,7,8]. The problem is how to implement the plan to satisfy the needs. One key implementation is that of staffing the organization through selection and allocation when forecast needs have been established. How can this be done in an optimal manner with consistency in achieving the organizational goals? The AHP offers new possibilities for tackling this problem because it is a multi-criteria methodology that deals with both tangibles and intangibles in an integrated and comprehensive manner within a hierarchic structure that relates people to the criteria and to the goals of the organization. As a mathematical procedure, it uses both available quantitative data along with the judgments of decision makers and experts to arrive at an overall optimum answer. Through the prioritization process of the AHP, one is able to determine the relative contribution of each alternative to the goal of the organization, whether that alternative is a job position or a particular individual with his or her qualifications. However, when a combination of positions or of individuals that best satisfies the goal subject to resource constraints is required, one needs to use an optimization procedure like LP. Our purpose here is to illustrate the use of absolute measurement in the AHP along with LP to obtain optimum human resource allocation. LP is widely used in the literature and is more of a technical subject. The problem is how to use the measurement derived from the AHP to formulate an LP model which is then solved using a standard software program like LINDO or EXCEL's Solver routine. In the following two sections we present practical examples to illustrate the proposed approach.

Solving Human Resource Requirement Problems

Human resource recruiting at BDS [9]

Biological Detection Systems (BDS), a small biotech start-up firm located north of Pittsburgh, Pennsylvania, is attempting to position itself for future growth by expanding its employee base. It has identified areas in Marketing, Manufacturing, and Research and Development which need increased manpower. BDS has $520,000 to invest in new employees. Therefore it wants to select those applicants which will provide the most benefits to the organization. For proprietary reasons, we do not provide a detailed description of the company's operation. The company's customer base was expanded from 75 users in its first year to over 500 through the third quarter of its third year, and BDS needed a way to prioritize the job positions to be filled as the rapid pace continued through the next two years. The positions to be filled are listed and briefly described in Table 1.

The object of this example is to determine the optimal number of positions required to be filled by the company, and to select the most qualified applicants for each position, who together would contribute the most to the achievement of the following organizational objectives:

- to increase its marketing effort in the clinical market areas
- to satisfy future demand for its product
- to better insure product quality
- to develop new products
- to manage/supervise employees

Table 1 Personnel Requirements

Position	Variable	Salary & Benefits in $ (000)	Personnel Required	Department	Description
V.P. of Marketing	y_1	120	1	Marketing	Take BDS products into use in the clinical or "real world" applications
Marketing Assistant	y_2	50	1	Marketing	Maintain customer database, organize mailing pieces and advertisements.
Customer Service Rep.	y_3	40	1-3	Marketing	Take orders, answer phones, first line of customer support.
Shipping Clerk	y_4	40	0-1	Marketing	Package and ship products to customers.
Lab Technician	y_5	40	2-5	R&D	Carry out experiments as specified by the lab supervisor.
Chemists	y_6	50	0-1	Manufact.	Manufacture dyes.
Biologists	y_7	45	1-2	Manufact.	Puts dyes on the biologicals.
Quality Specialists	y_8	70	0-1	Manufact.	Make sure products meet government regulations. Calibrate equipment.
Operations Supervisor	y_9	90	1	Manufact.	Schedule the production of reagents according to customer needs. Oversee operations.

The Evaluation Hierarchy

When evaluating candidates, BDS is confronted with a large number of tradeoffs over a diverse set of criteria. All the applicants for a single position will be rated and evaluated based on the same set of criteria for that position and priorities derived for each individual. Figure 1 shows the AHP hierarchy for BDS personnel selection problem. The goal of the hierarchy is to allocate the most qualified candidates to the various departments. The second level represents the five objectives of the company, followed by the three departments for which applicants will be hired in the third level. Level four identifies the positions that need to be filled within each department. The criteria for evaluating the candidates for each position are located in the fifth level. For example, VP of Marketing will be evaluated based on experience, contacts, synergy, education, and leadership. Experience will be measured in the number of years of industry experience the person has; contacts is used to evaluate the number of contacts the candidate has in the clinical health care industry; synergy attempts to determine how well the individual will fit within the organization; education is used to evaluate the candidates' formal education; and leadership attempts to measure a candidate's general leadership skills.

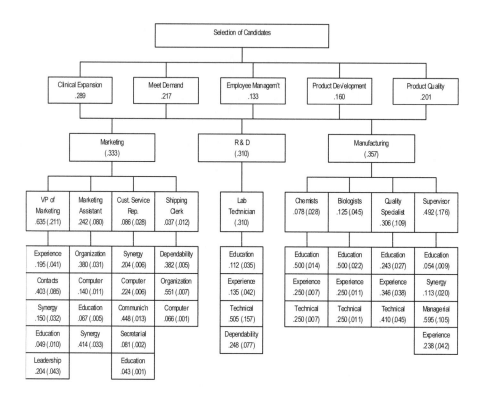

Figure 1 Selection Hierarchy for BDS with Local (Global) Priorities

To implement the AHP's absolute measurement in AHP, each criterion is divided into several intensity ranges to differentiate the qualification of the candidates with respect to that criterion. These intensities should be located in level six of Figure 1, and part of them can be found in Table 2. For example, the evaluation criteria for VP Marketing has the following intensities: (i) experience is divided into years and quality and years includes three intensities of high (corresponds to 15+ years of experience), medium (6 to 15 years), and low (5 years or less); (ii) quality, contacts and leadership are also divided into high, medium, and low; (iii) synergy into extreme, high, medium, and low with extreme rating awarded to individuals who are judged to be a perfect fit with BDS; and finally (iv) education is divided into

PhD, master, bachelor, and secondary. The complete selection criteria and their intensities for each job together with their relative importance are listed in Table 3.

Table 2 Rating Applicants for Each Position on the Criteria

	VP Marketing					
	Experience		Contacts	Synergy	Education	Leadership
	Years	Quality				
Applicants	.0174	.0239	.0852	.0316	.0103	.0431
James Plowski (x₁)	High	High	High	Medium	BS	Medium
Marsha Macon (x₂)	High	Low	Medium	High	PhD	High
Nancy Billings (x₃)	Low	High	Medium	Low	MS/MBA	Medium
Stanley Kent (x₄)	Medium	Medium	Low	Extreme	MS/MBA	Medium

	Lab Technician			
	Education	Experience	Technical	Dependability
Applicants	.0348	.0418	.1566	.0770
Melvin Harper (x₁₄)	High	Medium	Medium	High
Elizabeth Ott (x₁₅)	Medium	High	Medium	Medium
Heather Fink (x₁₆)	High	Medium	Medium	Low
Synder Smith (x₁₇)	Medium	Low	High	Medium
Symore Drone (x₁₈)	Medium	Low	Low	High
Raymond Garner (x₁₉)	Low	High	Low	Low
Mary Cunningham (x₂₀)	High	High	Medium	Medium

	Quality Specialists		
	Education	Experience	Technical
Applicants	.0265	.0378	.0448
Sammy Morgan (x₂₈)	BS	Medium	Medium
Prashant Gupta (x₂₉)	Masters	Medium	High

Intensities, Criteria Weights, and the Composite Scores

The nine positions are prioritized in terms of their contribution to the organizational objectives; four under marketing, four under manufacturing and one under R&D. The priorities of each are multiplied by the relative number of positions in its group to the total of 9 and the result is then normalized. The criteria for evaluation are then prioritized with respect to each of the positions, and the criteria intensities (not shown in the hierarchy) are prioritized with respect to their corresponding criterion. The applicants are then evaluated by assigning the appropriate intensity according to their qualifications. Since each applicant will be evaluated for a single position only, he or she will be rated according to the criteria for that position. His or her rating for the criteria for the other positions will be zero.

Table 3 Ideal Priorities of the Intensities Used for Rating Alternatives

Criteria by Job (global priority)	Intensities
VP of Marketing	
Experience (.041)	
Years (.0174)	HIGH (1) MEDIUM (.55) LOW (.101)[*]
Quality (.0239)	HIGH (1) MEDIUM (.382) LOW (.145)
Contacts (.0852)	HIGH (1) MEDIUM (.315) LOW (.099)
Synergy (.0316)	EXTREME (1) HIGH (.561) MEDIUM (.219) LOW (.092)
Education (.0103)	PHD (1) MASTERS (.912) BS (.647) SECOND (.288)
Leadership (.0431)	HIGH (1) MEDIUM (.315) LOW (.099)
Marketing Assistant	
Organization (.0305)	HIGH (1) MEDIUM (.315) LOW (.099)
Computer (.0113)	HIGH (1) MEDIUM (.315) LOW (.099)
Education (.0054)	MASTERS (.25) BS (1) SECOND (.501)
Synergy (.0333)	EXTREME (1) HIGH (.561) MEDIUM (.219) LOW (.092)
Customer Service	
Representative	EXTREME (1) HIGH (.561) MEDIUM (.219) LOW (.092)
Synergy (.0058)	HIGH (1) MEDIUM (.315) LOW (.099)
Computer (.0064)	HIGH (1) MEDIUM (.315) LOW (.099)
Communication (.0127)	HIGH (1) MEDIUM (.315) LOW (.099)
Secretarial (.0023)	MASTERS (.381) BS (1) SECOND (.876)
Education (.0012)	
Shipping Clerk	
Dependability (.0048)	HIGH (1) MEDIUM (.315) LOW (.099)
Organization (.0069)	HIGH (1) MEDIUM (.315) LOW (.099)
Computer (.0008)	HIGH (1) MEDIUM (.315) LOW (.099)
Lab Technician	
Education (.0348)	HIGH (1) MEDIUM (.315) LOW (.099)
Experience (.0418)	HIGH (1) MEDIUM (.315) LOW (.099)
Technical (.1566)	HIGH (1) MEDIUM (.315) LOW (.099)
Dependability (.0770)	HIGH (1) MEDIUM (.315) LOW (.099)
Chemists	
Education (.0139)	PHD (.19) MASTERS (.252) BS (1) SECOND (.171)
Experience (.0069)	HIGH (1) MEDIUM (.315) LOW (.099)
Technical (.0069)	HIGH (1) MEDIUM (.315) LOW (.099)
Biologists	
Education (.0223)	PHD (.19) MASTERS (.252) BS (1) SECOND (.171)
Experience (.0111)	HIGH (1) MEDIUM (.315) LOW (.099)
Technical (.0111)	HIGH (1) MEDIUM (.315) LOW (.099)
Quality Specialists	
Education (.0265)	PHD (.251) MASTERS (1) BS (.653) SECOND (.15)
Experience (.0378)	HIGH (1) MEDIUM (.315) LOW (.099)
Technical (.0448)	HIGH (1) MEDIUM (.315) LOW (.099)
Supervisor	
Education (.0094)	PHD (1) MASTERS (.389) BS (.189) SECOND (.062)
Synergy (.0198)	EXTREME (1) HIGH (.561) MEDIUM (.219) LOW (.092)
Managerial (.1046)	HIGH (1) MEDIUM (.315) LOW (.099)
Experience (.0418)	HIGH (1) MEDIUM (.315) LOW (.099)

* Intensity priorities are derived by pairwise comparison and idealized.

Each applicant collects a rating score which is the total of the global weights of the corresponding intensities (obtained by multiplying the priority of each intensity by the global priority of its corresponding criterion) assigned to him or her for each of the criteria. The higher the score, the more qualified the applicant is for the job. Table 4 shows the rank of the applicants according to their scores.

Table 4 Applicants Ranked by AHP Score

Name	Position	Score
James Plowski (x_1)	VP of Marketing	0.0684
Marsha Macon (x_2)	VP of Marketing	0.0489
Nancy Billings (x_3)	VP of Marketing	0.0440
Hana Coors (x_{31})	Operations Supervisor	0.0436
Prashant Gupta (x_{29})	Quality Specialist	0.0369
Stanley Kent (x_4)	VP of Marketing	0.0360
Henry Presley (x_{30})	Operations Supervisor	0.0271
Synder Smith (x_{17})	Lab Technician	0.0218
Tom Storey (x_6)	Marketing Assistant	0.0200
Jane Capelli (x_5)	Marketing Assistant	0.0196
Melvin Harper (x_{14})	Lab Technician	0.0193
Sammy Morgan (x_{28})	Quality Specialist	0.0191
Mary Cunningham (x_{20})	Lab Technician	0.0167
Kim McDonald (x_{27})	Biologist	0.0164
Elizabeth Ott (x_{15})	Lab Technician	0.0140
Megan Rice (x_{26})	Biologist	0.0129
Karen Kerns (x_{25})	Biologist	0.0120
Symore Drone (x_{18})	Lab Technician	0.0120
Heather Fink (x_{16})	Lab Technician	0.0117
Beth Foster (x_{23})	Chemist	0.0102
Tony Austin (x_{10})	Customer Service Rep	0.0084
Raymond Garner (x_{19})	Lab Technician	0.0076
Ed Flanders (x_8)	Customer Service Rep	0.0067
Willie Whiteshoe (x_{22})	Chemist	0.0058
Jim Bostead (x_9)	Shipping Clerk	0.0053
Terri Moore (x_{13})	Customer Service Rep	0.0053
John Jones (x_7)	Customer Service Rep	0.0049
Brian Buzelli (x_{21})	Biologist	0.0044
Teddy Star (x_{24})	Chemist	0.0044
Charles Young (x_{11})	Customer Service Rep	0.0040
Biff Van Swan (x_{12})	Shipping Clerk	0.0031

Each employee's total value in Table 4 has been adjusted to account for differences in the number of elements in the departments. Note that there is only one position for R&D Department and four positions for Marketing and Manufacturing Departments. To account for this the lab technicians final rating was multiplied by 1/9, and the other three positions by 4/9.

Manpower Allocation for BDS

In the following, we present two different but comparable linear programming models to help make the best human resource allocation decisions for BDS.

Model 1: Optimizing the individual applicants
The coefficients of the objective function below are the priorities of the individuals given in Table 4. The decision variables are $(0,1)$ subject to a salary constraint, upper and lower bound constraints on the number of people and the salary constraint given in Table 1. The binary integer LP is formulated as follows.

Maximize
$.0684x_1 + .0489x_2 + .0440x_3 + .0360x_4 + .0196x_5 + .0200x_6 + .0049x_7 + .0067x_8 + .0053x_9 + .0084x_{10} + .0040x_{11} + .0031x_{12} + .0053x_{13} + .0193x_{14} + .0140x_{15} + .0117x_{16} + .0218x_{17} + .0120x_{18} + .0076x_{19} + .0167x_{20} + .0044x_{21} + .0058x_{22} + .0102x_{23} + .0044x_{24} + .0120x_{25} + .0129x_{26} + .0164x_{27} + .0191x_{28} + .0369x_{29} + .0271x_{30} + .0436x_{31}$

Subject to the salary constraint:
$120x_1 + 120x_2 + 120x_3 + 120x_4 + 50x_5 + 50x_6 + 40x_7 + 40x_8 + 40x_9 + 40x_{10} + 40x_{11} + 40x_{12} + 40x_{13} + 40x_{14} + 40x_{15} + 40x_{16} + 40x_{17} + 40x_{18} + 40x_{19} + 40x_{20} + 50x_{21} + 50x_{22} + 50x_{23} + 45x_{24} + 45x_{25} + 45x_{26} + 45x_{27} + 70x_{28} + 70x_{29} + 90x_{30} + 90x_{31} \leq 520.$

The constraints on the number of people in each position are:

$x_1 + x_2 + x_3 + x_4 = 1$	Vice President of Marketing
$x_5 + x_6 = 1$	Marketing Assistant
$1 \leq x_7 + \ldots + x_{11} \leq 3$	Customer Service Representative
$0 \leq x_{12} + x_{13} \leq 1$	Shipping Clerk
$2 \leq x_{14} + \ldots + x_{20} \leq 5$	Lab Technician
$0 \leq x_{21} + x_{22} + x_{23} \leq 1$	Chemists
$1 \leq x_{24} + \ldots + x_{27} \leq 2$	Biologists
$0 \leq x_{28} + x_{29} \leq 1$	Quality Specialists
$x_{30} + x_{31} = 1$	Operations Supervisor

Model 1 is solved using Solver in Excel and the names of the employees that are to be hired to maximize BDS' goals are given in Table 5.

Table 5 The Optimal Solution of Model 1

Name	Position	Salary
James Plowski (x_1)	VP Marketing	$ 120,000
Tom Storey (x_6)	Marketing Assistant	$ 50,000
Tony Austin (x_{10})	Customer Service Rep.	$ 40,000
Melvin Harper (x_{14})	Lab Technician	$ 40,000
Synder Smith (x_{17})	Lab Technician	$ 40,000
Kim McDonald (x_{27})	Biologist	$ 45,000
Prashant Gupta (x_{29})	Quality Specialist	$ 70,000
Hana Coors (x_{31})	Operations Supervisor	$ 90,000
Total Salary		$ 495,000

Model 2: Optimizing the positions

In the second approach, we use an objective function whose coefficients are the priorities of the nine positions given in the fourth level of the hierarchy of Figure 1. The positions are denoted as Y1 to Y9 whose variables y1 to y9 are integers representing the number of jobs. This model determines the optimal number of jobs and then selects the best applicants for those positions. The previous model simply did the selection based on the rating of the applicants, taking the relative importance of the positions into consideration. The salary constraint and the upper and lower bounds on personnel requirements are the same as before. When the exercise is completed, applicants with the highest scores in their category are chosen. We have:

Maximize:
$.2822y_1 + .1076y_2 + .0382y_3 + .0000y_4 + .0689y_5 + .0000y_6 + .0556y_7 + .1360y_8 + .2187y_9$

The coefficients are obtained from the fourth level of the hierarchy (Figure 1) adjusted by multiplying the Marketing positions by 4/9, the R&D position by 1/9, the Manufacturing positions by 4/9, and then the results are normalized.

We have the salary constraint:
$120y_1 + 50y_2 + 40y_3 + 40y_4 + 40y_5 + 50y_6 + 45y_7 + 70y_8 + 90y_9 \leq 520.$

The departmental constraints are:
$y_1 = 1, y_2 = 1, \quad 1 \leq y_3 \leq 3, 0 \leq y_4 \leq 1, 2 \leq y_5 \leq 5, \qquad 0 \leq y_6 \leq 1$
$1 \leq y_7 \leq 2, 0 \leq y_8 \leq 1, y_9 = 1$
y_i are integers, and i=1 to 9.

The second approach produces the following LP solution that is consistent with that of the first approach in terms of the number of positions filled. The solutions are given below.

Note that optimization using LP is needed in this problem because BDS has allotted only $520,000 to spend on salary and benefits for additional employees, while to fill all the positions would require $830,000.

Table 6 The Optimal Solution of the Model 2 LP

Position	Selection	Position Salary	Total Salary
VP Marketing (y_1)	1	$ 120,000	$ 120,000
Marketing Assistant (y_2)	1	$ 50,000	$ 50,000
Customer Service Rep. (y_3)	1	$ 40,000	$ 40,000
Shipping Clerk (y_4)	0	$ 40,000	$ 0
Lab Technician (y_5)	2	$ 40,000	$ 80,000
Chemists (y_6)	0	$ 50,000	$ 0
Biologists (y_7)	1	$ 45,000	$ 45,000
Quality Specialists (y_8)	1	$ 70,000	$ 70,000
Operations Supervisor (y_9)	1	$ 90,000	$ 90,000
		Total Salary	$ 495,000

CNPITC Employee Training Program [10]

China National Publishing Industry Trading Corporation (CNPITC) is a diversified state-owned multi-billion-Chinese-Yuan trading company located in Beijing. The Department of Publications in charge of the most important and the most profitable business activity of the company has clients in Taiwan, Hong Kong, Singapore, Japan and other Asian countries. However, the business has not been growing for the last few years because of internal competition, saturated market, termination of funding, and lack of flexibility in human resource hiring, firing, and compensating. The department foresees a potential market in western countries, but it is not well-known internationally and only a few of its employees have been exposed to western culture or speak their languages. Only twenty out of its 90 full-time employees are college graduates, and most of them are new employees.

The department decided to carry out extensive training programs. There are 7 alternative training programs that can be considered for each trainee:

1. An overseas 11 month MBA program with an estimated cost of $40,000 per trainee.

2. An in-house training program, which costs little and would have a considerable impact, but lacks exposure to an international environment.
3. College program in Beijing, which costs only about $1,500 per student but the quality of its business program is not as good as an overseas MBA program.
4. Recruiting specialists, which cost about $10,000 per person.
5. Combine programs 2 and 3: in-house training and college program.
6. Combine programs 2 and 4: Recruiting specialists and providing them with in-house training.
7. Combine programs 3 and 4: Recruiting specialists and providing them with college education.

The question is, what programs to choose, and how many people for each program? The training programs are evaluated using absolute measurement, based on their benefits (Figure 2) and costs (Figure 3) for the organization as a whole. The analyses give the following result:

Table 7 The Benefits/Costs ratios as the Objective Function's Coefficients

Variables	Alternatives	$ Amount Needed	Benefits Score(B)	Costs (C)	B/C
x_1	Overseas training (1)	$40,000	0.402	0.674	0.60
x_2	In-house training (2)	$0	0.385	0.144	2.67
x_3	College program (3)	$1,500	0.224	0.273	0.82
x_4	Recruit specialist (4)	$10,000	0.278	0.156	1.78
x_5	(2) + (3)	$1,500	0.446	0.283	1.58
x_6	(2) + (4)	$10,000	0.635	0.308	2.06
x_7	(3) + (4)	$11,500	0.299	0.305	0.98

The B/C ratios are used as the coefficients in the LP objective function. The constraints must satisfy the following assumptions:

a. The department cannot have more than 40 employees in training in the same year.
b. The total funds available are $180,000 per year. The overseas training program must not cost more than $160,000 per year. The cost for the in-house training program is assumed to be negligible.
c. In-house training programs must have more than 10 and less than 30 participants.
d. At least two but no more than 16 trainees attend college education. At least 2 people are chosen for each basic program. At least two trainees are sent to overseas training, and no more than 10 specialists are hired.

e.   A trainee in the overseas training program cannot participate in another
     program, and no trainee can take more than two courses of training in the
     same year.

The sets of criteria in Figure 2 are as follows:
- The Criteria 1 elements include *Culture, Productivity, International
  Contact, Domestic Contact, Quality,* and *Knowledge.*
- The Criteria 2 elements include all those in Criteria 1 plus *Personal
  Gains*
- The Criteria 3 elements includes all those in Criteria 1 plus *contacts*
  (both *International* and *Domestic*)

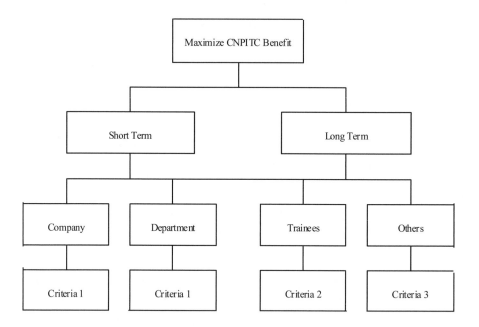

Figure 2 The Benefits Hierarchy

The LP formulation is as follows:

Maximize $.60x_1 + 2.67x_2 + .82''x''_3 + 1.78x_4 + 1.58x_5 + 2.06x_6 + .98x_7$

Subject to:

$$40,000x_1 + 1,500\,x_3 + 10,000\,x_4 + 1,500\,x_5 + 10,000x_6 + 11,500x_7 \leq 180,000$$
$$x_1 + x_2 + x_3 + x_4 + x_5 + x_6 + x_7 \leq 40$$

$x_1 \geq 2$, $x_1 \leq 4$, $2 \leq x_4 + x_6 + x_7 \geq 10$, $10 \leq x_2 + x_5 + x_6 \leq 30$, $2 \leq x_3 + x_5 + x_7 \leq 16$

The solution is:

x_1 Overseas training program	2
x_2 In-house training program	30
x_3 College program	0
x_4 Specialists recruited (do not take any other program)	6
x_5 In-house and College programs	0
x_6 Specialists recruited and taking in-house training program	0
x_7 Specialists recruited and taking college program	2

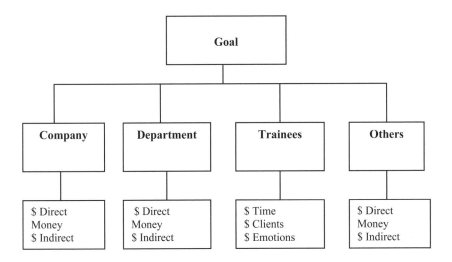

Figure 3 The Costs Hierarchy

Solving Problems with Synergy Conditions Using Combined AHP and LP

There are situations where interaction among cooperative individuals actually contributes more (or less) than the sum of what several members do independently. A very simple and important human cooperation example is men and women taken as couples in raising a family. In business, teamwork of employees with different organizational and technical skills is often required. In the political arena, a common reason why politicians cooperate is that it brings synergy. For example, suppose that political candidates X and Y can each win 10 million votes. Now X and Y agree to team up as president and vice-president, and the result is that together they win 25 million votes. Their synergy would have produced five million votes.

Synergy arises when two persons with different complementary skills cooperate. Positive human resource synergy takes the form of (1+1)>>2.

In the following numerical examples, the coefficients of the objective function can be derived by the AHP to include all the intangibles (and tangibles when desired): benefits, and sometimes the ratio of the benefits to the costs. In the following examples, tangibles costs in dollars are included as constraints in the optimization problem.

Negative Synergy

Negative synergy occurs when the sum of effects of the collaboration is less than that of the individual components of the mix. It can be called the (1+1)<2 effect. Individuals operating alone may each produce two units of output. However, with negative synergy, the combination of efforts results in less output than what would be achieved if individuals work alone. Negative synergy can result from inefficient committee makeups, lacking strategic fit among groups, and poorly coordinated joint efforts. In the following examples, Pi denotes the ith person or group.

An Example of Negative Synergy:

	P_1 x_1	P_2 x_2	P_3 x_3	P_1+P_2 x_4	Restriction
Benefits	.5	.3	.2	.6	Normalized if desired
Costs	3	2	3	5	6

Problem:

Maximize $\quad .5x_1 + .3x_2 + .2x_3 + .6x_4$

subject to $\quad 3x_1 + 2x_2 + 3x_3 + 5x_4 \leq 6$

Mutually exclusive Constraints

$x_1 + x_4 \leq 1, x_2 + x_4 \leq 1$

Preventing double counting

$x_1 + x_2 \leq 1$

$x_1, x_2, x_3, x_4 \in \{0,1\}$

We cannot have x_1 and x_2 together because the combined effect is replaced by x_4. Similarly, choosing x_4 would naturally exclude the choice of either x_1 or x_2, since x_4 includes both x_1 and x_2. The maximum value of the objective function is equal to 0.7, with $x_1=1$ and $x_3=1$.

Positive Synergy

In human resource management, synergy requires tapping into the human potential at its deepest level, and an essential precondition is a deep commitment to cooperation and integration. Positive synergy is an expected feature of cooperating groups and is a negotiating point between the acquirer and the acquired entities.

An Example of Positive Synergy:

	P_1 x_1	P_2 x_2	P_3 x_3	P_1+P_2 x_4	Restriction
Benefits	.5	.3	.3	.9	Normalized if desired
Costs	3	2	2	5	6

Problem:

Maximize $.5x_1 + .3x_2 + .3x_3 + .9x_4$

Subject to $3x_1 + 2x_2 + 2x_3 + 5x_4 \le 6$

Mutually Exclusive Constraints

$x_1 + x_4 \le 1, x_2 + x_4 \le 1$

Preventing double counting

$x_1 + x_2 \le 1$

$x_1, x_2, x_3, x_4 \ldots\ldots$

The maximum value of the objective function is equal to 0.9, with $x_4 = 1$.

Multiple Synergy/Restrictions

In the following example, there are positive and negative synergies, indicating that an organization may benefit from some specific employees' teamwork, or may be penalized by putting wrong workers in the same group.

An Example of Mixed Synergy:

	P_1 x_1	P_2 x_2	P_3 x_3	P_4 x_4	P_5 x_5	P_1+P_2 x_6	P_2+P_3 x_7	$P_1+P_2+P_3$ x_8	Restriction
Benefits	.1	.2	.3	.4	.5	.5	.7	.8	Normalized if desired
Cost 1	2	4	6	8	10	6	10	12	25
Cost 2	10	3	8	7	6	19	17	27	35

In the following X_6 and X_7 contain positive synergy, while X_8 gives negative synergy. The problem can be solved with the linear programming model shown below.

Problem: Maximize $.1x_1+.2x_2+.3x_3+.4x_4+.5x_5+.5x_6+.7x_7+.8x_8$

Subject to $2x_1+4x_2+6x_3+8x_4+10x_5+6x_6+10x_7+12x_8 \leq 25$

$10x_1+3x_2+8x_3+7x_4+6x_5+19x_6+17x_7+27x_8 \leq 35$

Mutually Exclusive Constraints

$x_1+x_6+x_8 \leq 1$, $x_2+x_6+x_7+x_8 \leq 1$, $x_3+x_7+x_8 \leq 1$

Preventing double counting

$x_1+x_2 \leq 1$, $x_2+x_3 \leq 1$, $x_1+x_2+x_3 \leq 1$, $x_6+x_8 \leq 1$, $x_7+x_8 \leq 1$

and $x_i \in \{0,1\}$ for $i=1$ to 7

The maximum value of the objective function is equal to 1.4, with. $x_4=1$, $x_5=1$, and $x_6=1$.

In this section, we have shown how negative, positive, and multiple synergy problems can be solved with LP model. Coefficients of costs and/or benefits can be derived using AHP. The combined AHP and LP approach discussed above can be easily modified to solve problems where people applying for a job are evaluated by including such criteria as flexibility, growth, challenge, independence, and productivity.

Conclusion

Linear programming is a useful optimization technique for solving allocation problems by taking tangible measurements into consideration. However, many real world problems cannot be readily solved by LP since they usually contain intangible variables that cannot be quantified. Because AHP is a model for measuring intangibles, combining the two makes it possible to deal with all optimization problems whether tangible or intangible. This subject is investigated in details in [2].

In one example we showed how to apply absolute measurement of the AHP together with LP to determine which positions to fill and which candidates to hire to satisfy salary and employee number requirement for each position. We then illustrated how the AHP enables one to include synergy in its prioritization to determine the best combination of people to hire. In this chapter we have shown that the combined AHP and LP model provides an effective tool for resolving human resource allocation problems with their many subjective and objective resource constraints, and a formal optimization technique is the best way to derive maximal benefits from organizations' investments.

References

1. Saaty, T. L. (1996), *Decision Making with Dependence and Feedback: the Analytic Hierarchy Process*, RWS Publication, Pittsburgh PA
2. Saaty, T.L., L.G. Vargas and K. Dellmann (2003), The Allocation of Intangible Resources: the Analytic Hierarchy Process and Linear Programming, *Socio-Economic Planning Sciences*, 37, pp. 169-184
3. Craft, J.A. (1995), *Human Resource Planning: Its Roots and Development in Management Thought*, Working Paper, Katz Graduate School of Business, University of Pittsburgh, Pittsburgh
4. Fisher, C.D. et al. (1993), *Human Resource Management*, Houghton Mifflin Company, Boston
5. Mathis, R.L. and J.H. Jackson (1991), *Human Resource Management*, West Publishing Corp., Minneapolis/St. Paul
6. Milovich, G.T. and J.W. Boudreau (1991), *Human Resource Management*, Irwin Publishers
7. Noe, R.A. et al. (1994), *Human Resource Management: Gaining a Competitive Advantage*, Austen Press, Burr Ridge, IL
8. Shuler, R.S. and V.L. Huber (1993), *Personnel and Human Resource Management*, West Publishing Corp., New York
9. Gabler, C. and D. Prado (1994), *A Manpower Allocation Model for Biological Detection Systems*, BQOM 2410 Class Project, University of Pittsburgh
10. Peng, Yuqing and Yun-Kwan Huang, 1994, *Choosing the Best Employee Training Programs*, BQOM 2410 Class Project, University of Pittsburgh

Chapter 10

Conflict and Conflict Resolution with the AHP/ANP

Applications of the AHP/ANP in conflict resolution have been applied to several conflicts two of which have been significant, and had their effect on the outcome: South Africa and Northern Ireland. A good source for such applications has been the book coauthored with Dr. Joyce Alexander [1].

Introduction

Where there are people with different objectives that cannot coexist, there is potential for conflict; if individuals or groups attempt to satisfy their own objectives, conflict in some form will occur. As Quincy Wright noted in his monumental work, A Study of War: "Conflict may properly designate a duel, a household brawl, a strife between political factions, a fight between street urchins, a suppression of rebellion, or a war between nations. Observations of any of these forms of conflict may throw light on the others."

Most discussions on conflict start with the premise that there will always be winners and losers in any situation where people have opposing desires. Some-times this is true; however, it is often possible to find a compromise that will work, if only in the short run; in the long run, of course, it is usually necessary to remove the underlying source of the conflict, if that is possible.

Conflict resolution has frequently been defined as the search for an outcome that, at a minimum, represents for some participants an improvement from, and for no participants a worsening of, their present situation. If there are such outcomes, we want to find them; we then need to see which of them is in some sense "best." To the Olympian observer, this is obviously the way to go.

However, in a conflict the participants will, in general, have conflicting objectives and desires and the so-called best outcome will almost certainly fall short of each party's desired outcome, in the view of that party. How can we persuade each party to cease pursuing its own goals to the limit and to accept the compromise solution?

The most distinctive attribute of humans is their ability to reason and analyze. It is particularly necessary that people in conflict should use reason, since there may be many interests at stake; to hold one's ground without the use of reason is to inhibit progress. We need to introduce more reason and less intransigence into our methods of conflict management.

However, reason alone does not lead directly to agreement. The initial step is often the acceptance of a broader framework for the conflict; such a framework should show some possible benefits to the parties. In other words, we often need to take time to engage in foreplay before we can embark on the resolution of a conflict.

Our attitudes about conflict have marked variability. At one extreme there are those who take immediate personal umbrage and who tend to react by improvising ways to wipe out the opponent lock, stock, and barrel,' forever. They are those who, after banishing everybody from the picture, would find themselves lonely and miserable and willing to start all over again, perhaps not completely reformed, but more penitent and ready to give and take.

At the other extreme there are those who appear to be cool, calm and calculating. They say, "Will it matter tomorrow, in a year, in ten or a hundred years?" Some even go farther than that. "I read somewhere," a baseball player said, "that our sun will burn out in 50 billion years, and when that happens the earth will go through space like a giant frozen snowball... Well the day that happens who is going to give a ---- if this pitch gives the other team a home run or not." To be sure, this is a comforting thought. But people cannot be as detached as that when their own security, and particularly of their loved ones, is threatened.

Most of us are more involved in daily living than is indicated by cosmic views of our role. We think that it makes a difference what we do and whether we do it or not. We like to see results. Obviously, our approach has to be a compromise between the extremes. The best motto may be ' 'Cool it. You win some, you lose some."

Innocent pursuit can often lead to conflict. Many people have developed the habit of maximizing their values. Most of the time they intend others no harm; they take from them simply to further their interests. When the taking becomes uncomfortable from whom they are taking, they need to be told, "This far and no farther." Without such constraints they may succeed in taking what they want little by little, like slicing small pieces of delicious salami without giving real cause for objection at any one slice. No single piece does harm, but together the slices take up the whole salami. The danger here is that if the constraints are not established at an early stage, putting them up later may invite aggression by little, apparently harmless, slices.

The conflict deepens when the optimizers think they are entitled to what they are taking. Hostilities develop when it belongs to someone else. Thus, in human relations boundaries are necessary, and becoming used to setting and accepting constraints is a part of living.

Two parties in real or potential conflict may hate each other in a variety of ways, not all of which are extreme. In fact, they may even like each other in some ways, or they may learn to like each other; this may help them to reach tradeoffs. It is often easier to do this with intangibles; this may then make it simpler to deal with the more concrete aspects of the conflict.

In practice, as a part of the negotiating tactic, parties do not like to sit facing each other, often from a fear that they might reveal something that gives the other side an advantage. This, of course, need not be so for representatives of nations in conflict, as their decisions can be vetoed by their leaders back home. More importantly, mediators and arbitrators are used as buffers who can convey a most agreeable attitude in explaining the tough line or opening position of each party. Most conflicts are greatly helped by the presence of a third party or organization called in to assist. The mediators' concern of balancing and creating a fair result should outweigh their strict concern for impartiality; the mediators must be careful that their impartiality would not lead them to play into the hands of the stronger party.

Of course, not all conflict is bad. In business, for example, competition, which is a form of conflict, often stimulates participants to work harder and to produce more or to carry out a project more efficiently or more imaginatively.

Not all conflicts need resolution. The human conflict for survival needs to be resolved, but there is no single formula for universal application. Much is left to intuition and experience. In personal relationships, conflict, provided it is not destructive, creates tension that stimulates creativity to find new ways to deal with problems.

Most conflicts impede progress, and ways must be found to manage or resolve them to enable people to continue their normal daily lives. In general one cannot expect the participants to give a full and fair picture of the situation, for they are more likely to emphasize their own concerns and views. Thus a third party is necessary. The question now is, how can this third party represent the conflict in a way that takes into account the interests and grievances of both parties. This creates the need for a framework or a model of the conflict.

There are certain preliminary steps to be taken in order to understand the nature of a particular conflict: 1. Identification of the parties to the conflict. 2. Identification of the objectives, needs, and desires of each of the parties. 3. Identification of possible outcomes of the conflict or of possible "solutions." 4. Assumptions about the way in which each party views its objectives and, in particular, its view of the relative importance of these objectives. 5. Assumptions about the way in which each party would view the outcomes and the way in which a given outcome might meet the objectives.

This seemingly simple set of steps presents many difficulties, since the perceptions of different individuals may differ sharply. "One of the very interesting problems in the study of the image and one which is still largely unsolved is of the conditions under which images of different individuals converge under the impact of symbolic communication and the conditions under which they diverge" (Boulding, The Image, 1956).

In consequence, the analyst who desires to model a current conflict and who seeks information from concerned parties runs the risk of allowing his or her formulation to be biased by their understanding of the situation. Even apparently unbiased observers tend to have a slanted view. One of my objectives in this work is to show how these differing perspectives can be of practical value in modeling the conflict.

One needs to recognize that developing a good model for a problem, and then using the model to analyze the problem, is not the same as finding a solution. However, a good model lays bare the structure of the problem and shows where there is room for constructive change and where there is room for compromise.

Our basic argument here is that it is first of all essential for all concerned parties to understand the nature and structure of the conflict. Such an understanding must draw on both objective and subjective interpretations of one s own motives and of the motives of others, together with a consideration of tangible and intangible factors in the conflict.

Therefore, an effective model of a conflict must include both the emotional and irrational in people along with the rational; this would enable them to make assumptions and manipulate ideas logically so that they can reach the emotional part of the problem and can achieve a catharsis by bringing the emotions to consciousness and affording them expression. This may be the only way for people to cooperate in venting their strongly held claims and beliefs. There is no guarantee that someone else's logical solution, disseminated persuasively at a certain moment of rational dialogue, would persist. As the parties walk out of the room, their negative emotions, now habituated to the conflict, would erupt anew to undo what may have been agreed.

Binding arbitration is a way to circumvent this; people accept some form of punishment if they do not agree, so they have to work on themselves by telling themselves that this is the best way to proceed and that, as this may not be the best of all possible worlds, a compromise may be all that can be hoped for. Otherwise there may be additional punishment.

It is then necessary for the parties to see the probable results of their actions taken in conjunction with the actions of others in the conflict. If all like what they see even though it does not provide everything that they want, well and good. If not, the parties may look at possible changes in their own behavior to see what effect such changes might have on the overall situation. It may be that they can effect improvements; it may be that they realize that they would be wise to settle for some compromise outcome.

Conflict is intimately tied to value and value satisfaction. Value is associated with importance and importance implies priority. Priority is an ordering of values on a cardinal scale because one can order a set of values none of which is important. Thus it appears that the study of priority is intrinsic to conflict management and resolution. Values differ among people and the problem is to reconcile different orderings by different parties so in the end they are all agreeable to the compromises made to change their order to obtain a shared and acceptable order.

Importance implies influence which we take as a primitive concept. Order according to importance means order according to influence. There are all kinds of influence and they need to be prioritized and synthesized in terms of higher values to obtain an overall influence and its corresponding outcome. In the end resolving conflict depends on the strength of influence actual or threatened. It is thus inevitable that in conflict resolution one needs to consider all potential influences and the outcome that is their consequence. But one does not have to guess what the outcome of influence may be because one can perform sensitivity analysis to surmise the most likely outcome and how stable it is to perturbations in the diverse influences.

The loving kindness principle (compassion): Do unto others as you *would* have them do unto you.

Do not do unto others as you would they should do unto you. Their tastes may not be the same.   ~George Bernard Shaw

The eye for an eye principle (retaliation): Do unto other what they *do* unto you; a perpetual cycle of violence.

The conditioning principle (natural instincts): Do unto others that which third others have *done* unto you.

Life is short. Love others more than you love yourself. Can you imagine doing that; it is a challenge.

Love yourself and hate others as potential enemies or hate yourself and love others. Hate everyone, yourself and others.

Conflict is 1) disagreement, opposition and collision between people due to difference in wants, ideas, beliefs, and values; 2) struggle to bring about change in ideas or in behavior towards people; 3) differences about the right to acquire land or property and who should have land or property.

There are four ways used in resolving a conflict to turn disagreement to agreement: 1) By working together and sharing ideas and values, 2) By working separately and using mediation to obtain a fair resolution through compromise, 3) By working separately and using intimidation, force and retribution to weaken the resolve of the opposition to achieve a desired goal, and 4) By dictating a solution from the outside with the threat of use of force in case of violation. We call the first kind *harmonious* conflict resolution. Because of their knowledge, experience and conditioning, people are likely to disagree, and it is a good thing that they do because they can learn, grow and change to improve and they need to get together for better understanding. The second kind of conflict in which the parties are willing to allow a third party to evaluate and prioritize their needs capabilities and rights we call *mediated* conflicts. The third kind of conflict in which the parties inflict pain on each other we call *retributive* (an eye for an eye) conflicts. The fourth kind we call *pseudo-rational* because of its reliance on punishment to get the parties to comply with the agreement. Research interest should be directed towards making resolution of all four kinds of conflict *rational* and subject to reason and thought.

All four methods of resolution require not only identifying all the issues involved down to the last detail and relating them in the way they happen in the world, but also need the idea of value and tradeoff. Without this knowledge it has been the custom for one to seek equilibrium solutions by using the assumed payoffs largely expressed in terms of ordinal numbers. With such knowledge, one seeks to equalize the outcomes for the parties within their respective value systems with payoffs expressed in terms of absolute numbers derived from paired comparisons. To make it possible to analyze conflict in a rational way we need accurate judgments that precede satisfying people's values and goals. These judgments would be provided by the parties themselves or by appropriate surrogates. There is less guessing than there is with the assignment of ordinals usually by a third party who wishes to analyze the conflict in search of equilibrium. Accuracy is obtained through measurement, and measurement involves both tangible and intangible factors. At bottom conflict resolution needs a way to lay out the issues in an agreed upon systematic framework that makes it meaningful to quantify and make tradeoffs. Such a framework also needed to identify the areas of disagreement and how crucial they are through prioritization. The framework would be expanded in the process of conflict resolution as needed to bring about agreement. It should be possible to combine different points of view in a large structure or structures that include all the issues and factors and other considerations of coalitions by the parties. It should be possible to prioritize the parties on the different issues according to need and claim and whatever is needed to make the parties feel that every point is included in the framework along with its priority.

It is not true that every conflict can be resolved in a fair and satisfactory way. By fair we mean that each party gets its share as determined by an impartial judge who can take all the necessary factors into consideration. There are insufficient resources to satisfy everyone's wants or needs. In case a conflict is about belief it can sometimes be smoothed over with words and promises. Conflicts about urgent physical needs involving people materials and territory may not be available to give no matter how much people want them. What kinds of conflict can be resolved fairly? They are the kind that involves more resources than is needed to satisfy the existing needs and possibly some of the desires and ambitions of some of the parties who may have much more than others and do not want to share or to give and often have the power to prevent others with an urgent need from taking some.

A person experienced in conflict resolution who also has all the necessary tools to study conflicts and suggest ways to resolve them should, on ethical grounds, be able and willing to use the ideas, he/she recommends for use by others, in their own personal conflicts. That also includes the ability to negotiate offering and accepting concessions. The workability of ideas is even more important than their content.

Descriptive and Normative Conflict Resolution

A descriptive or positive statement is a statement about *what is* that contains no indication of approval or disapproval (e.g., this paper is white; cows eat vegetables). It is clear that a positive statement can be wrong. A normative, or prescriptive "what ought to be" statement tells us how things should be (e.g., people *ought* to be honest). There is no way of disproving this statement. If one disagrees with it, he has no sure way of convincing someone who believes the statement that he is wrong unless one goes out to take samples of what is actually happening and show that the assertions made do not conform to reality. Religion is normative (categorical) about what should be, science is descriptive about what is.

Values

We use values to relate and interpret everything else that we experience and learn. It is the focus of our being. Value is an anchor that binds our energies, our thoughts, and our actions. In a sense, our values are we. They are not something abstract and eternal. Despite some overlap, the values of a tree or those of a bee differ in meaning and substance from our human values. That does not mean that our values are important for the tree; in fact, while the trees and their values are important to us, we and our values are not important to the trees unless we take care of them or want to destroy them.

Our values help us identify different properties and measure intensities within each property. Our human limitations do not allow an infinitely wide range of intensities. The range of certain measurements in science varies widely over the magnitude of objects and phenomena (from the size of atoms to the size of galaxies). However, the range of human values and feelings is very limited and varies over a few orders of magnitude. For example, our personal values are at their highest in representing our survival and physical needs, to a lesser degree they represent our needs for safety and security, for love and belonging, and for esteem and psychological and social self-realization (in the sense of Abraham Maslow); and at the lower end of the scale they represent our need to know and understand, and finally our aesthetic needs. As members of a group we are concerned about the survival of others, and as part of the environment we are concerned with preserving that environment. There are also group values to which we subscribe that are less instinctive than our personal values and that we learn from experience. Here is a list of some group values to which we subscribe:

Physical:	Health, Exercise, Sports,
Educational:	Learning, Communication, Information,
Economic:	Money, Property, Manufacturing, Agriculture,
Social:	Welfare, Cooperation, Organization,
Political:	Power, Influence,
Moral:	Order, Honesty, Trust,
Ideological:	Religion, Common Belief, Fervor,
Technological:	Innovation, Change, Problem Solving,
Military:	Security, Force, Defense, Territory,
Aesthetic:	Art, Music, Theater,
Competition:	Advertising, Quality, Improvement, Reasonable Pricing,
Negotiation:	Take and Give,
Conflict Resolution:	Reconciliation.

The science of decision-making is concerned with the relation between alternative actions or choices that need to be made and our system of values. That is why hierarchic and network structures are of essence in this undertaking.

Decision-making is a process that leads one to:
- Structure a problem as a hierarchy or as a network with dependence loops.
- Elicit judgments that reflect ideas, feelings, and emotions,
- Represent those judgments with meaningful numbers,
- Synthesize results,
- Analyze sensitivity to change in judgment.

The Theory of Games; A Normative Theory of Conflict Resolution

The major normative, *what-should-be* theory that deals with a formalization of the resolution of conflicts is the theory of games. It offers solutions that are thought to be mathematically best in some sense without asking the people involved what they think and how they feel about a prescribed solution! It is concerned with games of strategy, a well-known rational way to deal with only certain kinds of conflict. Not all conflicts can be formalized as games of strategy and resolved normatively. Its approach requires that strategies be identified in order to think about how to resolve conflicts.

Game theory studies conflict and cooperation by considering the number of players, their strategies and payoffs. Games have been classified as cooperative and non-cooperative and analyzed according to the degree of information available to the players. A game is played with pure and with randomized strategies. The players seek to maximize the expected value of their payoffs. For non-cooperative games there is the von Neumann minimax theorem for two-person zero-sum games proving that every finite zero-sum two-person game has a solution in mixed strategies. In 1950 John F. Nash extended this theorem to the existence of a solution of an n-person constant sum game in mixed strategies as a Nash Equilibrium solution. The Prisoner's Dilemma and Chicken are two non-cooperative games that do not yield satisfactory equilibrium solutions, and thus more than the existing concepts of equilibrium is still needed to obtain a good solution for them.

For cooperative games, von Neumann and Morgenstern introduced the idea of a characteristic function of a game and of the worth achievable by a coalition of some of the players independently of the remaining players. A solution is called a stable set with which is associated a core. The core may not always exist. But when it does, it can have a nucleolus, all of which contain the idea of solution to the cooperative game. Many alternative solution concepts have been proposed to deal with coalitions. The Shapely value is another approach to solving a cooperative game. This value sometimes belongs to the core of the game. How to calculate an equilibrium solution can involve nonlinear techniques that may be approximate.

Payoff and expected payoff are central concepts in game theory. But payoff is measured according to what values and whose values? How values are obtained, and are they unique or are there other measures of payoff and do they all yield the same solution? Is it possible to resolve conflicts by other theoretical means that do not parallel the game theoretic approach?

Game theory is an analytically interesting normative mathematical theory for the analysis of conflict. A once for all solution is not always the best way to resolve value disputes. Practice in small steps can be more effective. Game theory offers what looks best in some framework to a limited number of interested mathematicians, and this framework is relative to the numbers and measurements used. If the nature of measurement changes the method may also change. No one goes to a game theorist for counseling. One goes to a psychologist, a psychiatrist or a priest. Mathematicians themselves along with game theorists have personal problems when they want things to come out the way they think, which is precisely what conflict resolution is about. But game theorists are not particularly known to be the most satisfied and happy people and that is not because they have forces opposing them and stifling their rationality. We need to air out the issues within the framework of a structure and express judgments and preferences and synthesize them in a way that the parties agree on.

I have been a strong advocate and expositor of game theory in the past. I helped spend large sums of government money to use game theory in arms control negotiations to little advantage. It is too normative and theoretical and tied to the mind of its developers to make it useful to practitioners involved in negotiations. Mathematicians have been known to advise a judge willing to listen as to how best to arbitrate a conflict between two parties with ideas from game theory. Such a solution may or may not have been satisfactory to either party, but they had to abide by it for fear of the law and its use of force. We know of no example where a conflict was resolved by game theory and accepted by the parties rationally, but there may be some. The question is whether any party in a conflict can understand and subscribe to reasoning involved in game theoretic language to accept its prescription for the answer.

An intriguing problem in game theory is the assumption that it is possible to estimate payoffs for strategies in a game before the strategies of one player have been matched against those of the opponent in actual competition. Except for the simplest and most transparent situations it is impossible to spell out all the moves and tactics of a real-life strategy to really get a good idea of how well it would fare in competition. Some broad qualities of a strategy may be known, but exact prescriptions of its effectiveness may encounter such unanticipated problems in practice that it may be difficult to get a "good" estimate of its worth when compared with other strategies. According to our long use of game theory in problems of arms control and disarmament, we always felt that the numbers used in game theory are artificial at best and the resulting analyses did not take into consideration sufficient detail because of the problem of how to get numbers for intangibles and how to combine these numbers in a legitimate way. Equilibrium analysis has not been a major instrument in resolving actual conflicts. It is the tradeoffs that have to be made on many intangible issues that need to be considered and these cannot be done without legitimate quantification. It calls for the use of the AHP/ANP in conflict analysis and resolution. The mathematician George Polya writes on the side of creativity and action that if a method tried for long does not work it should be abandoned for another. That is less likely to happen if there is no other way. Hopefully people would consider another way if there is one and we believe that there is and we offer some aspects of its potential use below. Our development may not be complete because it has not yet been researched for half a century or more as game theory has by numerous people to develop all its potentials. However, it has been tried in a number of situations where opposing parties sat down to discuss and understand their differences. A number of decisions have been made using it in both the cooperative case as in group decision making where individuals work together to obtain an overall solution and in the non-cooperative case where interests are opposed as for example in the Israeli-Palestinian conflict.

A Descriptive Theory of Conflict Resolution

Conflict resolution is a multiparty, muticriteria and multiperiod decision-making process that involves use of prioritization in the context of benefits, opportunities, costs and risks. From the field of behavioral economics that imports insights from psychology into economics, one learns that conflict resolution is also an evolutionary process of learning to enrich the structure of factors included in the framework of analysis and the interaction and influence of these factors on the outcome with the passing of time. There are many conflict situations in which the grievance that a party has against another party or parties cannot be described in terms of strategies and in terms of responses to these strategies. A helpless person may have many creative and rational complaints against society but has no meaningful strategy to act on his/her grievances if indeed he/she who may also be crippled and inarticulate can. In other words not every wrong in the world can be formed as a game of strategy. Thus conflicts that can be formalized in terms of opposing strategies are a special case of conflicts in general. It is known that non-cooperative games do not always have an equilibrium solution for all the parties involved and these are the most intractable and pressing kinds of conflict including terrorism as a special case. The question is whether there is a way to formalize conflicts rationally in order that one may consider their solution without recourse to the idea of strategy where there may be none, or when there is to examine strategy as a particular case of a more general concept? It is easy to give examples of conflicts where no solution is possible. In a hungry society with little food to go around, the hungry would be opposed to the well fed for the threat of their survival. With increasing population and despite creativity and progress, it may be that the world would reach a point where not all essential amenities would be potentially available to everyone.

New light may often be shed on a conflict. Experience has shown that a conflict may be alleviated by the use of a mediator who introduces "bargaining chips" into the negotiations. In a retributive non-cooperative conflict, if A and B are the parties to the conflict, A will evaluate not only the incremental benefits to be received but also the cost to the opponent B of providing a concession: The greater each value, the greater the gain. Thus A's gain for a given item or concession may be described as the product of A's benefits and B's costs (as A perceives them). We have the following ratios for the two parties A and B.

$$\text{(as perceived by A)}$$

$$A\text{'s ratio} \quad \frac{\text{gain to A}}{A\text{'s perception of gain to B}} = \frac{\sum A\text{'s benefits X B's costs}}{\sum B\text{'s benefits X A's costs}} = \frac{\text{gain to A}}{\text{loss to A}}$$

where $\sum$ is the sum taken over all concessions by B in the numerator and by A in the denominator. A's *perceived ratio* for B is the reciprocal of the above.

$$\text{(as perceived by B)}$$

$$B\text{'s ratio} \quad \frac{\text{gain to B}}{B\text{'s perception of gain to A}} = \frac{\sum B\text{'s benefits X A's costs}}{\sum A\text{'s benefits X B's costs}} = \frac{\text{gain to B}}{\text{loss to B}}$$

where Σ is the sum taken over all concessions by A in the numerator and by B in the denominator. A's *perceived ratio* for A is the reciprocal of the above. If both A and B's perceive benefits and costs in the same way, these ratios would be reciprocals of each other. This almost never happens, however.

Obviously, each party would like its ratio to be as high as possible. If A's ratio for some package is less than 1, then A will perceive B's ratio as being greater than 1 and will feel that it has not been treated fairly. The aim must be to find single concessions and groups of concessions where each party perceives its own ratio to be greater than 1. This requires skilled mediation [1].

As just explained, each party calculates its gain as the product of its benefits and its perceived value of the costs to the opponent and its loss as the product of its costs and its perceived value of the benefits to the opponent. Thus, in a conflict resolution scenario, wherein each party has a set of concessions to make, party A, for example, calculates the benefits it will accrue from B's concessions to B, and its perception of the benefits from B from these concessions.

Thus, there will ordinarily be four such calculations for each party and many more for a mediator, for example, who would use the judgments the parties give him and would compare them with his own perceptions; the mediator would then attempt to alter their perceptions or convince them that certain concessions are more to their advantage and advise them of the order in which such concessions should be made.

We have applied this kind of analysis to the conflict in South Africa and to the Free-trade discussions between Canada and the United States in great detail in the referenced book. They were made before the settlement in South Africa, asked for, paid for and communicated to the South African government at the time and the second discussed publicly at a large meeting for the purpose in Vancouver where the ideas were discussed before the agreements were made.

A Case Towards a Consensus Agreement for a Middle East Conflict Resolution

Frustrated with the current state of the Middle East but encouraged by earlier attempts at modeling complex problems, the authors [6] participated in a panel discussion assembled to address the conflict and propose a possible road-map to peace, and this effort continues with substantial financial support by a well-known foundation. The participants in this project did not come to a single course of action that will result in peace in the Middle East but did reach a consensus agreement about a resolution that needs to be managed. This part of the chapter explores the process, the outcome and the factors that influence the decision as well as potential pitfalls. The Analytic Network Process (ANP), is used in this analysis. It provides a framework for synthesizing judgments on the diverse aspects of the problem represented in the structure of the decision. It pieces together these judgments in a holistic and logical way.

The Middle East conflict is not a series of wars tending toward peace, but a state of continued belligerency interrupted by war. It is not a single isolated problem to be solved but a system of people with conflicting aspirations. Physically, the problem is geographic with two parties desiring the same piece of land, but its origins are deeply rooted in people's beliefs and in their attachments to a land consecrated by their great religions. There are claims made by these people of rights to live in the land and to have a state to maintain an identity. The problem is greatly compounded by widespread activities in the area, to include arms supply, cause support and the development of vested interests, thereby placing the problem in a complex global framework. Although one might expect that the global framework might accelerate a solution, in fact it complicates it due to the diversity of each participant's interests. Hence, a solution has eluded the global community. The Israeli-Palestinian conflict continues to plague the Middle East and threaten stability, not just regionally, but also globally by inciting some terrorist claims. Despite the best efforts of diplomats and world leaders, a satisfactory resolution has not emerged. Hence, it is with some degree of hubris that we present a solution that we expect will outperform other efforts. What we suggest is a holistic model that explores feedback from various criteria and input from key constituents. The Wall Street Journal of November1, 2007 reports that "Karen Hughes, who led efforts to improve the U.S. image abroad and was one of President Bush's last remaining advisors from the close circle of Texas aides said the Iraq war was usually the second issue that Muslims and Arabs raised with her, after the longstanding conflict between Israel and the Palestinians. Ms. Hughes said she advised Mr. Bush and Ms. Rice two years before that U.S. help in ending the six-decade-old fight over Israel would probably do more than anything else to improve the U.S. standing world-wide."

A major problem in analyzing conflicts in quantitative terms is how to deal with the measurement of intangible factors that arise in order to make tradeoffs with the other tangible factors when benefits and potential benefits, costs and potential costs are involved. Our goal is to show how to use ANP in benefits, opportunities, costs and risks (BOCR) framework to develop and project the most likely best solution that takes into consideration the interests and influences of all the parties involved in the ongoing conflict in the Middle East. It is the overall influences that determine what would be best that is not subject to change or caprice.

We need a practical quantitative approach that enables one to synthesize payoffs on different criteria. It delves in greater depth into the fine structures of strategies according to their merits and weaknesses when confronted with those of the opponent than does a game theoretic approach.

It makes it possible for the parties to recognize and account for the strengths and weaknesses (political, military, social and so on) of their strategies against those of the opposition. The parties can work together through their representatives (perhaps often through the UN and in the presence of other parties to mitigate exaggerations and excessive claims) or do the analysis on their own with their own judgments partly imputed to what they think the opposition desires. In the absence of one party the judgments are surmised by the analyst from publicly declared positions and subjected to sensitivity analysis in case of uncertainties. In this manner one can evaluate the strategies of each party according to its merits against the strategies of the opponent(s) to improve the parties' understanding of the conflict in which they are involved. This type of analysis involves multi-criteria decisions with intangible payoffs derived from paired comparisons of the relative merits of the strategies against each of the opponent's strategies and then synthesizing the outcome across all merits and weaknesses, analyzed in short, medium and long range time frames.

Background

Peace is almost always secured through accommodation, bargaining, and compromise – even after an overwhelming victory is obtained by one side. Our approach utilizes the Analytic Network Process, because it fits the realism in eliciting and capturing the intensity of judgments regarding the dominance of some factors over other factors, the synthesis of group judgments, and the performance of sensitivity analysis for the stability of the outcome. The study involved a mixed group of Palestinians, knowledgeable pro-Israeli experts, and others from the outside, like China, Saudi Arabia, Turkey, and the US.

Over a three day period, the panel structured the problem, defined the constituents and developed several potential alternatives. The process was not without conflict and negotiation of its own. At times, the panel differed on various definitions, on the structure of the model, and on the potential solutions. However, there was nearly always unanimous agreement on the nature of the conflict, with little debate within either side about the underlying concerns or where the power and influence belonged that could bring about termination of he then 58 year old confrontation. Similarly, there was practically no problem in identifying the key constituents. However, since the beginning of the conflict, leaders and others have proposed many alternatives solutions. These influenced the perception of the participants in regard to potential alternatives. In fact, one person suggested that the participants could have difficulty "thinking outside the box." He thought that the group was so influenced by previous attempts that they experienced difficulty in conceptualizing 'creative' alternatives that had not been proposed previously.

With the help of intelligent informed people we felt that we could identify the major influences operating in the Middle East Conflict, prioritize them and find the most likely outcome. We had some objectivity because we had participants to represent the viewpoint of the Palestinians, the Israelis and the Americans, the major parties that will have to be involved in any solution. So we had sufficient information to represent the different interests and did not necessarily have to have the actual leaders and politicians. We were fairly aware what the extremist positions are and what they could do and we included that in the model's structure and the judgments we gave. In the end sensitivity analysis determined the stability of our recommended solution in view of all sorts of variations produced by different interests whether moderate or extremist. Unlike the use of statistics it is not always necessary in the analysis of complex problems to involve a large sample of diverse people who may or may not have the complete understanding needed to resolve a problem.

What follows is a brief account of the method employed, the model, the structure of the problem as a decision with benefits, opportunities, costs and risks and how comparisons were made in the analysis of the outcomes, recommendations for implementation, summary, and recommendations for getting others to look at the problem in this integrated and comprehensive framework.

The ANP frees us from the burden of ordering the components in the form of a directed chain as in a hierarchy. We can represent any decision as a directed network. While the AHP has a visibly better structure that derives from a strict understanding of the flow of influence, the ANP allows the structure to develop more naturally, and therefore is a better way to describe faithfully what can happen in the real world. These observations lead us to conclude that hierarchic decisions, because of imposed structure are likely to be more subjective, dependent on expert knowledge and predetermined. Further, by including dependence and feedback and by cycling their influence with the supermatrix, the ANP is more objective and more likely to capture what happens in the real world. It does things that the mind cannot do in a precise and thorough way. Putting the two observations together, the ANP is likely to be a strongly more effective decision-making tool in practice than the AHP.

The ANP has a four phase structure of complex decisions: (1) *the hierarchies or networks of influences* and "objective" facts that make one alternative of the decision more desirable than another for each of the control criteria under the BOCR merits; (2) *pairwise comparisons* of the elements in each component according to inner or outer influences and derivation of the priorities of the elements and then also of the component of these elements according to their influence on each components to make the supermatrices of priority vectors stochastic and raise it to limiting powers; (3) *a relatively subjective value system for evaluating whether or not to make a decision and if it is made what the different priorities of each of the BOCR merits are* used to combine the four outcomes and obtain an overall ranking of the alternatives; and (4) *sensitivity analysis* to determine the stability of the best outcome subject to perturbations in judgments . In each of these phases there are major concerns that are subdivided into less major ones and these in turn into still smaller ones. Knowledge about the level of subjective values where one must use the absolute mode of measurement of the AHP can be enriched by information from what goes before it, but does not depend on them for its priorities. It provides the intensities on which the BOCR merits are rated one at a time and then normalized. This level cannot be conveniently integrated into a single structure with the other two that precede it, and thus it appears that most decisions, despite their use of a network structure due to the subjective thinking involved, are embedded in a higher order hierarchic structure. A decision may involve three or four adjacent ranges of homogeneous elements in each to represent personal values (Maslow put them into seven groups). Roughly speaking, we have lumped them in decreasing order of importance: 1) Survival, health, security, family, friends and basic religious beliefs some people were known to die for; 2) Career, education, productivity and lifestyle; 3) Political and social beliefs and activities; 4) Philosophical thoughts and ideas and things that are changeable, and it does not matter exactly how one advocates or uses them. There are similar values for a group, a corporation, a country and for the entire world as represented for example by the United Nations.

In sum, the ANP provides:

1) A methodical approach that is useful for making it possible for different individuals and groups to provide and combine their judgments according to their own importance, which is included in the judgments. Although both theory and software can do it, in this exercise consensus was used to record each pairwise comparison judgment;

2) A structure to represent all the elements of the problem proposed by anyone present or known from other sources so that nothing is left out because of complexity. The comprehensive structure puts people at ease that nothing is hidden or left out. It facilitates agreement on the judgments used to derive the best alternative outcome;

3) The stability of the outcome to possible changes or future threats.

Structuring the ANP Model for the Middle East Conflict Resolution

We defined the problem as an attempt to understand what forces and influences, because of their relative importance, would implicitly drive the outcome towards a consensus peace accord for the conflict between Israel and the Palestinians. To accomplish this task, a panel of 8 individuals was assembled to represent a cross section of people: international thinking representatives (3), Israeli thinking representatives (2), a Palestinian (1) and Muslim thinking representatives (3). In most cases, the individuals crossed the various categories and interests and did not fall into discrete separate groups. It was recognized that the panel did not represent a valid cross-sample or that the size of the panel was adequate to represent the different population sizes involved. It was agreed that the work is exploratory in nature, intended to demonstrate how the method can be used over a short period of time to arrive at a reasonable solution that is not outlandish to any of the sides.

It was agreed by all participants that no part of the decision would be done without consensus agreement whether it is what to add or delete from the model or to make or not make comparison judgments on low priority criteria in order to save time to arrive at an answer in three days. It was justified to do that because it was clear that such factors and their contributing judgments were not worth the effort. It was the role of the moderator to facilitate the process and ensure that all parties agreed before moving on to the next step in the process. However, the moderator made no contribution to the agreement but facilitated mutual understanding among the participants. Since pairwise comparisons are made in the prioritization stage of the ANP, it is critical that all parties understand the definitions of the terms used. Moreover, as illustrated later in the chapter, many questions about what dominated what with respect to a certain factor and how strongly it dominated it was often difficult to understand and even more difficult to conceptualize in practice. Hence, many of the questions were developed at length and repeatedly until they were well understood by all.

This underscores the specific nature of the Middle East conflict and the necessity for consensus. Language and understanding matter!

To ensure mutual understanding, the moderator needed to track the events on a screen projected for the participants and to use an additional measure to track the questions that were currently under consideration. In addition, the moderator maintained on the first screen the following items:

1) The software used for the ANP model;
2) Documentation of the definitions, terms and criteria agreed upon;
3) Notes on the 'process' and the steps taken to reach consensus;
4) Agenda.

Although the level of detail and effort taken to document the process seemed excessive at first, it was clear from the start that not only were the initial steps taken helpful but they had to be augmented further. The augmentation included the use of other visualization tools in order to gain consensus. Hence, the steps taken to document the panel's efforts are a nontrivial event. In fact, the use of the various 'tools' were necessary on multiple occasions to overcome objections. We believe that without these various tools, the group would have experienced greater hardships in reaching consensus.

As mentioned above, at no point in the development and evaluation of the problem was the process easy and we caution against the belief that this was anyone's intention. In fact, the "purpose" of the exercise was not easily agreed upon and on several occasions in the three days over which the panel met, the question about the purpose of the exercise was repeatedly readdressed. The panel agreed that its goal was to move toward a consensus agreement for what outcome is the best resolution of the Middle East Conflict. The group looked at the purpose of the project from various perspectives. First, the panel suggested that potential definitions for the panel's purpose could include:

- Peace in the region;
- Impact on global peace;
- Recognition of defined borders;
- Long-term future stability.

It was also recognized that there is an equally legitimate claim to view the problem from the vantage point of a more extremist Palestinian whose goals might include:

- Let them return (the Israelis) to where they came from;
- Right to return that creates a Palestinian majority;
- Allocation of natural resources including land;
- Infiltration of patriots - 'terrorists';
- Elimination of Israeli nuclear threat.

Finally, one might take the position of more extremist Israeli views whose goals might include:

- Status quo; Palestinians remain squeezed into small territories with restricted movement;
- Deport all Palestinians;
- Continued control of all resources;
- NO pro-Palestinian country should be able neutralize Israel's nuclear power.

After considerable discussion and we overly compress the process here, the panel agreed that any resolution is a process that requires consensus (of process but not of judgments) and it is consensus "buy-in" that encourages participation of all constituents.

Agreement on the 'purpose' of the panel was not the only portion of the model that needed some dialogue. In fact, every step in the 'process' required negotiation and consensus. Several ways were proposed within the panel about how to construct the model and develop the issues. It was agreed that any solution would have benefits, opportunities, costs and risks (BOCR). However, it was not as easy for the panel to agree on the strategic criteria in terms of which they would evaluate and synthesize.

The Strategic Criteria used to evaluate the BOCR are representative of the impact that a selected alternative would have on Global Peace, Long-Term Stability, Peace in the Region, and Recognition of Defined Boundaries. Although the panel selected the four strategic criteria in Figure 1, they agreed later that Global Peace should be removed from the comparisons since stability and regional peace are believed to be strongly correlated with Global Peace.

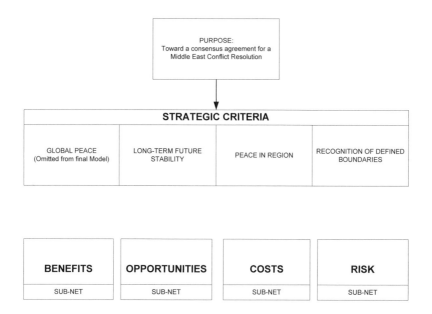

Figure 2 The ANP Main Top-level Structure for the Middle East Conflict Resolution Model

While the strategic criteria and their meanings were still fresh and prior to moving into the development of the BOCR sub-networks (subnets), the panel evaluated the Strategic Criteria with respect to the purpose of the undertaking. The results of the comparisons are shown in the section below on Prioritization. However, we believe that it is useful to detail the nature of the comparison for the Strategic Criteria at this point in order to mirror the efforts and document the methodology that we used in this case. The panel was presented with the pairwise comparisons of the four Strategic Criteria with the following questions involving pairs of criteria: "Which factors contribute more strongly and how much more strongly to resolving the conflict in the Middle East according to the desire of all the parties for 1) Global Peace or for Long-Term Future Stability in the Region, 2) Global peace or Peace in Region, 3) Global Peace or Recognition of Defined Boundaries, 4) Long-Term Future Stability or Peace in Region, 5) Long-Term Future Stability or Recognition of Defined Boundaries and finally 6) Peace in Region or Recognition of Defined Boundaries? Because Global Peace was eliminated, only the last three comparisons were made. Now we consider what numbers to use to express the judgments about dominance. Physics depends on measurements and on experts to interpret the meanings of those measurements. The ANP depends on individuals in each decision problem to represent what they think the people involved prefer or think is more important in that decision.

Table 1 gives the pairwise comparisons of the strategic criteria.

Table 1 Strategic Criteria Judgments

	Long-term future stability	Peace in region	Recognition of Defined Borders
Long-term future stability	1	1/4	1
Peace in region	4	1	3
Recognition of Defined Borders	1	1/3	1

Merits

Returning to our conflict problem, the top-level structure has the four Benefits/Opportunities/Costs/Risks (BOCR) merits and their sub criteria shown in Figure 1 which represents the total initial model. Some of the nodes in both the Strategic Criteria and the subordinate networks of the BOCR were eliminated after the initial ratings due to the level of insignificant contributions that they added to the overall result because of their low priorities as compared with the other factors. The subnets under each of the four BOCR merits were developed independently. The benefits and costs were conceptualized as the short-term or internal aspects of the alternative evaluation while the opportunities and risks were thought of as those elements that have long-term influences.

a. **The Benefits Subnet**: benefits are defined as the short-term gains that any group might experience given the criteria below.
   ▪ *Economic Status* in this network is defined as the short-term potential gains that might be realized given the implementation of one of the alternatives.
   ▪ *Human Rights* are defined as the short-term improvements in how the United Nations state what constitutes basic human liberties / freedoms.
   ▪ *Safeguard the oil supply* is defined as the incremental stability to the consistent delivery of oil; i.e. limited disruption to oil production.
   ▪ *Saves Lives* is defined as the reduction in the loss of lives.
   ▪ *Standard of Living* is defined as the incremental improvement for overall living conditions.

In the initial phases of developing the model, the panel faced the challenge to build a 'robust' model that includes all the criteria that they felt were important to accurately reflect those elements that would be important to reach a resolution. With respect to the short-term gains that might be realized by the constituents, the foregoing five criteria are the full set of short-term benefits necessary to realize a full benefits model. As the panel developed the connections among the various nodes in the cluster, they reached a consensus that not all five of the nodes were essential. *Economic Status* and *Human Rights* were retained, but it was believed that *Saves Lives* and *Standard of Living* were subsumed under them. *Safeguarding the oil supply* was not a valid criterion for the benefits network. In addition, the model provided legitimacy for what the members of the panel felt intuitively; the two excluded criteria were not significant to the model. In fact at first the two deleted criteria were included and were omitted after their priorities turned out to be very low in relation to the other three criteria.

The Benefits subnet is shown in Figure 2 as a sample of what the subnets under the BOCR model look like. The circular arrow shown in Figure 2 represents the fact that the "Constituents" cluster has feedback within the cluster. The implication of feedback within the alternative cluster is that each of the various constituents within this cluster influences the others within the cluster. For instance, a decision made by one party in the cluster influences the other parties in that cluster so that a movement toward peace by the Israelis and the Palestinians for example would have positive implications for both the United States and 'Others'. More detail about the implications of feedback and dependency will be discussed as findings.

b. **The Costs Subnet** represents the short-term expenses and pains incurred by the constituents.

   - *Arms industry* includes those costs that would be experienced by the arms industries through either loss of income or additional limitations to trade / sale placed on suppliers.
   - *Internal chaos in Israel* is the attempt to capture the 'price' paid for disruption to lives that may be realized through the selection of any resolution alternative.
   - *Making sacrifices* identifies the real expense incurred through both monetary and non-monetary forfeitures that may be incurred through any one of the various alternatives.
   - *Relocation / dislocation* node represents the real expense of dislocation caused by the option of any one of the alternatives.

- *Reparations* are the price that would need to be paid for conciliatory actions.

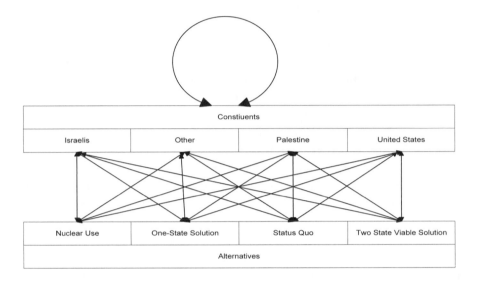

Figure 2 Benefits Subnetwork

The panel used the same process for the Costs subnets that they used for the Benefits subnet. Once the initial comparisons were made, the *Arms Industry* and *Relocation / Dislocation* were omitted since these two criteria accounted for insignificant priorities. The two omissions are not surprising since *Relocation* was captured by the *Reparations* criteria and the costs to the *Arms industry* are significantly outweighed by the potential costs of the other criteria.

c.   **The Opportunities Subnet is** the long-term positive potentials that exist for the constituents.
   - *Global Stability* is the opportunity for greater stability throughout the world in order to foster a secure environment.
   - *Regional Stability* focuses on the regional stability surrounding the immediate parties to the conflict.
   - *Return 'home'* represents the right of return for all displaced parties.
   - *Safeguard the oil supply* refers to the long-term safety to the global distribution of oil.

The panel went through similar efforts in the Opportunities subnet as they did with the Benefits subnet. In the initial development of this subnet, four criteria were included as given above; the final model only contained *Regional Stability* and *Return 'home'*. Once again, *Safeguard the oil supply* was not deemed appropriate for the final consideration due to its low priority.

d. The Risk Subnet

- *'Wrong' people return* is the risk that the people who would return under the right to return option will be subversive types looking to incite further disruption instead of the type who want to foster a *sensus communitas*.

- *Further increase in radicalism* is the risk that selection of any one of the alternatives would lead to an increase in radical activities.

- *Further instability in region* is the potential of an alternative to lead to increased instability via continued fighting.

- *Limited longevity that promotes return to conflict* refers to the fact that an alternative, if opted for, may not be viable for long-term. Hence, the probability that it returns to a state of conflict may increase the problem since it may be seen as a continued failures of the leadership to implement a resolution.

Under the Risk subnet, only *'Wrong' people return* had sufficiently low priority to delete it from the model; the remaining criteria were maintained throughout the analysis.

Figure 3 summarizes the BOCR merits networks. In other words, it highlights both the short-term and long-term aspects of the model as well as the gains and losses that impact the alternatives.

Each of the criteria in Figure 3 under the BOCR merits model was evaluated with respect to the various constituents that influence the outcome of the model. Figure 4 illustrates the network of the various constituents. The constituent network captures the feedback and interdependence among the various parties. Although it may appear intuitive that choices made by Israel impact the Palestinians, the nature of the feedback and dependence involving the other parties (the U.S., Arabs, Muslims and the rest of the world) was not adequately understood until implemented in the model. The outcome of the dynamics between the various constituents is further explored below.

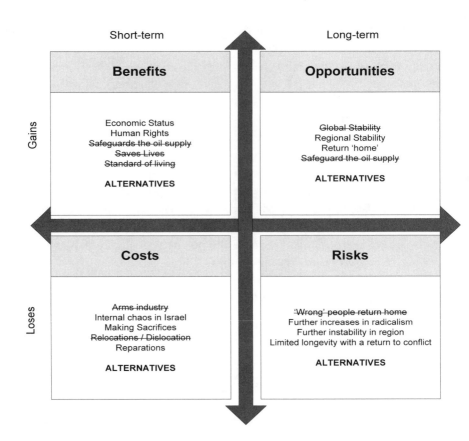

Figure 3 Summary of the Merits Networks

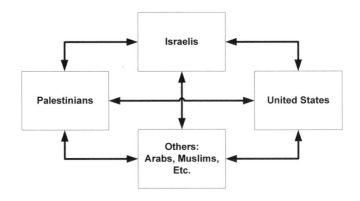

Figure 4 Constituent Network

<u>**Alternatives**</u>

The panel had to consider not only those initiatives that are 'popular' but also to develop 'creative' alternatives that may not have been explored or even present novel approaches. Furthermore, the group was instructed to think of alternatives as if there were no limits or boundaries. However, it was not easy to develop novel alternatives because of the enduring nature of the conflict and because of the scope of alternatives that have been developed thus far.

The full list of alternatives considered is as follows:

- Status Quo
- Two-viable-state solution
- Nuclear use
- One-state solution
- Legal solution enforced by the U.N.
- Two-viable-state solution (Positive initiative by Israel, economic contribution, etc…)
- Two-viable-state solution (Change in U.S. policy)
- Two-viable-state solution (Saudi initiative (2002) / Beirut Declaration).
- United Nations partition (1947)
- Jewish state

We consider the four highlighted bullets above as the final alternatives to determine which has the greatest likelihood of long term success according to the projected ability of the parties to exert the influences needed to bring them about. The most significant part of the 'process' to note is that reducing the list to a select few options was the result of the group negotiating an agreement. The panel came to a consensus that the various two-viable-state solutions could be captured under one alternative with the understanding that the details of implementation would be worked out as part of the long-term process. The Two-viable-State Solution captures the various forms that include the Bush Model, or the Saudi Initiative. This model recognizes the various independent states as autonomous.

The threat of Nuclear Use captures the potential of a party in the conflict using a nuclear device to influence the outcome. The threat of use means Israel's possession of nuclear weapons as a deterrent for other groups to use but it also captures a potential radical group's ability to obtain and utilize nuclear weapons. Of all of the alternatives, this was the most difficult one to conceptualize when assessing the priorities in the evaluation process. In general, the group agreed that this was the least likely alternative but that it was necessary to include in the model since the threat exists and remains an option.

One-state solution combines both the Palestinians and the Israelis into a single unified state that recognizes all individuals as politically and socially equal as in a democracy. Status Quo is a continued condition that has periodic rises in hostility and warfare. To make this alternative sound plausible, one of the Palestinian participants humorously suggested that the most rapid way to resolve the conflict is for all Palestinians to convert to Judaism; he was told by an Israeli friend that many Russians had been brought into Israel and later converted to Judaism.

Prioritization

Strategic Criteria and Their Priorities

As explained above, the three strategic criteria were evaluated and their priorities shown below were used as the guiding factors of the BOCR merits. A sample of the questionnaire that uses the fundamental scale of absolute numbers and questions is shown in Table 1 and the results of those comparisons are shown in Figure 5 and explained below.

Long-Term Future Stability captures the belief of the panel that any alternative that does not address and promote continuous stability in the region may contribute more harm than benefit. Additionally, the panel's consensus is that economic, political, and social developments in the region are dependent upon the 'stability' of the environment.

Peace in Region identifies the panel's conviction that economic, social, and political growth depend on long-term peace. Hence, any alternative must be evaluated against the potential of the choice to promote regional peace.

Recognition of Defined Boundaries was identified by the panel as a strategic criterion because agreed upon boundaries are a necessary component in selecting a resolution alternative.

Among the three strategic criteria to evaluate the BOCR merits, Peace in the Region has the highest priority (0.634) in contrast with Recognition of Defined Borders (0.192) and Long-Term Future Stability of (0.174). Therefore, we can qualify these priorities with the observation that any alternative selected must contribute to the long-term future stability of the region. The significant difference in the priorities underscores the overall importance that the panel placed on long-term stability, because economic, social, and political development in the region depend on stability.

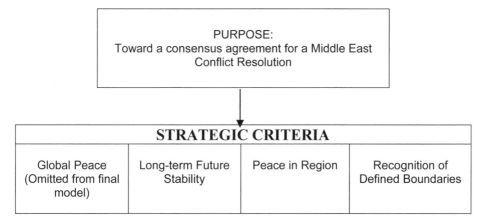

Figure 5 Hierarchy for Rating the BOCR Merits

BOCR Merits and Their Priorities
        The importance of the four BOCR merits with respect to the strategic criteria is determined by prioritizing them according to the following five intensities and their priorities derived through pairwise comparisons:

Intensities	Very High	High	Medium	Low	Very Low
	0.42	0.26	0.16	0.10	0.06

along with their priorities that are obtained at the outset and shown in figure 5.
        The rating outcome and final weights for each of the four merits are summarized in Table 2. These values are used as default values in an additive formula in developing the ANP model later on. For example, we asked the question for each of the merits: "what is the 'merit' of the top alternative under Benefits with respect to each of the Strategic Criteria?" This process was carried out in a similar way for Opportunities, Costs, and finally Risks. For instance, it was observed that there is a very high potential Benefit with respect to the first strategic criterion, i.e., Long-Term Future Stability. Once consensus was reached on the ratings for each of the merits, the resultant weights of the merits were derived as given in column 6 of Table 2.

Table 2 Priority Ratings for the Merits: Benefits, Opportunities, Costs and
Risks with respect to the Strategic Criteria

Merits	Long-Term Future Stability 0.174	Peace in Region 0.634	Recognition of Defined Boundaries 0.192	Sum of Weighted Values	Normalized
B	Very High	High	Medium	0.64	0.20
O	High	High	High	0.61	0.19
C	Very High	Very High	Very High	1	0.31
R	Very High	Very High	Very High	1	0.31

Decision Networks

Considerable time was invested in defining terms, constructing the
model, and reaching agreement on various aspects of the pairwise
comparisons made in the evaluation of the BOCR merits. Substantial use of
the various media was made during this portion of the evaluation in order to
reach consensus. Table 3 shows a sample of the ratings that the panel used to
reach a consensus. Note that each of the numbers entered into the
comparison sheet was agreed on by the group. At times, the discussion that
ensued from the nature of the question was lengthy. Conversely, there were
some questions on which the group was able to reach immediate agreement.

Table 3 Sample Fundamental Scale of Absolute Numbers Questionnaire for
BOCR Merit

	Israelis	Palestinians	U.S.	Other
Israelis	1	1/4	1/3	2
Palestinians	4	1	2	6
U.S.	3	1/2	1	3
Other	1/2	1/6	1/3	1

Ten decision networks were created, one for each of the surviving
BOCR criteria. As explained earlier each decision network contains the
cluster of alternatives in addition to a cluster of the constituents. Table 4
shows each of a total 10 ratings for the BOCR constituents prioritized by
pairwise comparisons and its corresponding value in relation to the criteria
whose priorities were also obtained through pairwise comparisons. Both the
local and global priorities are shown with respect to the various merits in the
model. The values of global priorities were obtained as the product of BOCR
rating (Table 2) times the corresponding local priority times the priority of its
constituent:

Table 4 Criteria and Their Priorities

Merits	Criteria	Constituents	Local Priorities	Global Priorities
Benefits	Human Rights 0.90	Israelis Palestinians United States Others	0.141 0.340 0.300 0.218	0.025 0.061 0.054 0.039
	Economic Status 0.10	Israelis Palestinians United States Others	0.154 0.274 0.310 0.263	0.003 0.005 0.006 0.005
Opportunities	Regional Stability 0.50	Israelis Palestinians United States Others	0.340 0.232 0.268 0.159	0.032 0.022 0.025 0.015
	Return Home 0.50	Israelis Palestinians United States Others	0.141 0.507 0.112 0.240	0.013 0.048 0.011 0.023
Costs	Internal Chaos In Israel 0.12	Israelis Palestinians United States Others	0.460 0.397 0.058 0.084	0.017 0.015 0.002 0.003
	Making Sacrifices 0.74	Israelis Palestinians United States Others	0.395 0.392 0.099 0.114	0.091 0.090 0.023 0.026
	Reparations / Relocations 0.15	Israelis Palestinians United States Others	0.253 0.336 0.201 0.210	0.012 0.016 0.009 0.010
Risks	Further Increase in Radicalism 0.46	Israelis Palestinians United States Others	0.421 0.332 0.125 0.122	0.058 0.046 0.017 0.017
	Further Instability in Region 0.34	Israelis Palestinians United States Others	0.277 0.330 0.110 0.282	0.028 0.024 0.011 0.029
	Limited Longevity that Promotes Return to Conflict 0.21	Israelis Palestinians United States Others	0.493 0.318 0.079 0.111	0.031 0.020 0.005 0.007

a) Benefits

Among the two benefits criteria, the human rights criterion has the highest priority of 0.9 as compared with the economic benefits criterion of 0.1. Among the benefits criteria, the highest priority given by those representing the Palestinians with respect to human rights is (0.340). Interpretation of the priorities suggests that with respect to benefits, the Palestinians have the most to gain in the short run due to immediate improvement in human rights.

Although the United States has the next highest priority under economic benefits in Table 5, it also had the next highest priority for human rights since under the benefits node, human rights has the highest priority and the global rating for the United States is higher under this cluster. We interpret the United State's high rating under the benefits cluster to be indicative of public perception and political motivation. The overall results of the Benefits subnets are given in Table 5.

b) Opportunities

Within the opportunities cluster, both criteria had the same weighting which demonstrates that both regional stability and the right to return home have equal weights (0.50). However, it is interesting to note that within the regional criterion, the Israelis have the greatest weight (.340) while in returning home (0.507), the Palestinians have the greatest weight. In the long run, the Israelis perceive the greatest opportunity in the region's stability whereas the Palestinians believe that they have the greatest opportunity with the right to return home. Further, given that the Palestinians have the greatest global weight (0.048), suggests that overall the Palestinians' right to return home has the greatest global opportunity within the model. Table 6 presents the overall ranking of the alternatives with respect to opportunities.

c) Costs

Among the three costs criteria, the Making Sacrifices costs criterion has the highest priority of 0.74 compared with the Reparations / Relocations costs criterion of 0.15 and the internal chaos costs criterion of 0.12. Among the costs constituents, the highest priority emerged from the rather evident conviction that both the Palestinians (0.392) and the Israelis (0.395) would have to make many sacrifices in the short run. Given that the global ratings of the other constituents on the other cost criteria are relatively low, we believe that implementation of a best alternative to a peace agreement will need to pay attention to the short term sacrifices that both groups will have to make. Table 7 shows the overall results of the alternatives with respect to the costs.

Table 5 Benefits' Overall Results

Criteria Alternatives	Economic Status 0.10	Human Rights 0.90	Final Outcome
Nuclear Use	0.113	0.111	0.111
One-state Solution	0.944	0.960	0.959
Status Quo	0.633	0.588	0.592
Two-viable-state Solution	1	1	1

Table 6 Opportunities' Overall Results

Criteria Alternatives	Regional Stability 0.5	Return Home 0.5	Final Outcome
Nuclear Use	0.32	0.13	0.23
One-state Solution	0.96	0.55	0.76
Status Quo	0.54	0.16	0.35
Two-viable-state Solution	1	1	1

Table 7 Costs' Overall Results

Criteria Alternatives	Internal Chaos in Israel 0.12	Making Sacrifices 0.74	Preparations/ Relocations 0.15	Final Outcome
Nuclear Use	1	1	1	1
One-state Solution	0.38	0.38	0.26	0.36
Status Quo	0.56	0.71	0.16	0.61
Two-viable-state Solution	0.30	0.31	0.44	0.32

d) Risks

Among the three risk criteria, the criterion Further Increase in Radicalism has the highest priority of 0.46 compared with Further Instability in the Region (0.34) and with Limited Longevity with a Return to Instability

(0.21). Interpretation of the results given in the risks merit is that the greatest long-term risk is that a selected alternative might result in an increase in radicalism that would further promote conflict in the region. This is followed by the risk that there might be an increase in instability due to implementation of one of the alternatives. Among the risks constituents, the highest priority is Israel's for both Increase in Radicalism (0.421) and for Limited Longevity with a Return to Instability (0.493). The findings presented here suggest that the Israelis are most concerned with the long-term risk of violence in the region (0.058). Similarly, with respect to the global priorities, we see that the Palestinians are also concerned with Long-Term Violence in the region (0.046). The final outcome for risks is given in Table 8.

From a conflict resolution management perspective, it is worth noting that the local and global priorities are significant. These outcomes provide leaders with information important to overcoming obstacles toward a consensus agreement for a Middle East Conflict Resolution. For instance, the panel's evaluation under Benefits indicates that Human Rights have the higher of the two priorities. Furthermore, the Local Priorities under Human Rights suggests that both the Palestinians and the United States are fairly equal. Therefore, those leaders managing the process will know that with respect to Benefits (i.e. short-term gains); one ought to focus on the two groups with the highest ratings in order to ensure success. The remaining entries in Table 5 may be used similarly.

Table 8 Risks' Overall Results

Criteria \ Alternatives	Further Increase in Radicalism 0.46	Further Instability in Region 0.34	Limited Longevity with Return to Conflict 0.21	Final Outcome
Nuclear Use	0.60	1	1	1
One-state Solution	0.40	0.24	0.43	0.43
Status Quo	1	0.55	0.76	0.98
Two-viable-state Solution	0.35	0.17	0.37	0.36

Synthesis of the BOCR Merits

Until about the year 1999, many examples of the ANP used the BO/CR ratio to evaluate the alternatives in the final decision. This "marginal" ratio assumes that all four merits are equally important which of course need not be the case. Even if not equally important and therefore weighted by the priorities of the BOCR merits, it would be multiplied by a positive constant that is greater or less than one indicating overall gain or loss over the short term. In 1999, this author developed a way to derive priorities for each of the four merits B, O, C, R, through ratings with respect to strategic criteria and use them to compose the weights of the alternatives by multiplying them by the corresponding priority of their merit adding the results for benefits and opportunities and subtracting from that the results for the costs and risks. This method gives the correct outcome when for example dollars are used. The priorities of the BOCR are rated with respect to strategic criteria that are used when there are many decisions to be taken to decide which one to take first and which second and so on. It is what individuals do in a day or over a period of time to prioritize all the decisions they face, or governments to allocate resources to their many decisions over a period of time. Instead of multicriteria decision making, it is a multi-decisions problem.

The results obtained from the rating system (Table 2) and the overall results of the BOCR Merits are normalized and synthesized in order to capture the final outcome of the entire process. For our purpose, we used the multiplicative power weighted formula which is expressed as ((bB)(oO))/((cC)(rR))and referred to as Multiplicative or Marginal Synthesis. For the Additive or Total Synthesis, we used the additive formulation expressed as ((bB)+(oO))-((cC)-(rR)). Multiplicative Synthesis illustrates which of the alternatives is preferable in the short term given all of the criteria under consideration; Additive Synthesis illustrates the alternative that is preferable in the long term [3]. We see that under both short and the long term the Two-State option is the best alternative.

After three days of discussion, analysis and evaluation, it turned out that the best alternative is a Two-state Solution and this was neither voiced nor explicitly subscribed to in advance. Recall that the group defined the Two-state solution to include the various forms suggested through the years which includes for example the rather well-known Bush Model, or the Saudi Initiative which also recognizes two independent autonomous states. The priorities also highlight points to keep in mind in the process of reaching agreement on a solution to resolve the Middle East Conflict where 'trouble' might arise and give leaders prior indication in order to avoid those pitfalls.

The results shown in Table 9 suggest also that the One-state Solution may be a viable option but with nearly half the priority of the best alternative. Recall that the One-state Solution was defined by the panel as the commingling of both the Palestinians and the Israelis under one unified state structure that recognizes all individuals as politically and socially equal under the generally understood notion of democracy. Given the relative nearness of the outcomes, leaders will need to monitor the process to gain insight into which direction seems more likely to succeed.

Table 9 Synthesis of the Alternatives (Overall Results)

Alternatives	Benefits 0.196	Opportunities 0.190	Costs 0.307	Risks 0.307	Multiplicative Synthesis	Additive Synthesis
Nuclear Use	0.11	0.23	1.00	0.82	0.00	(0.49)
One-state Solution	0.96	0.76	0.36	0.35	0.34	0.11
Status Quo	0.59	0.35	0.61	0.80	0.26	(0.25)
Two-viable-state Solution	1.00	1.00	0.32	0.29	0.62	0.20

It is the Two-state-viable solution that comes out as the best alternative under all situations. Table 9 demonstrates that under both the multiplicative and the additive forms of synthesis, the Two-state solution is the best alternative.

There are far reaching implications for both the decision and implementation of the alternative derived in the model. Given that the Status Quo and the Nuclear Use options come out as clear negatives in the long run, we conclude that under no circumstance should either option be considered. This seems intuitive for the nuclear use option but may not have appeared so for the status quo. However, it is not difficult to determine that the current situation is not working given the periodic unrest in the Middle East and hence a negative outcome arises in the model that the panel put together.

Interpretation of the difference between the one-state solution and the two-state solution needs further elaboration. In Table 9, we see that there is a sizable difference between the one-state and the two-state solutions. One might expect that the one-state solution is a more viable option given the efficiencies that might arise from the two peoples coming together and in the integration of the land. However, given the BOCR results above, we see that there is greater B and O and less C and R in the two-state solution then there is in the one-state solution; this provides some insight into where our investigation into the management of resolving the conflict ought to begin.

For instance, Table 4 shows that the Israelis could have the greatest 'risk' of increased radicalism and limited longevity whereas for the Palestinians the greatest risk is that there will be greater instability in the region. When we consider it along with the results presented in Table 8 Risks' Overall Results), we conclude that for the panel the concern was that the One-state solution poses the greatest risk for an increase in radicalism and limited longevity for the Israelis whereas for the Palestinians there is a concern that this solution will promote an increase in regional instability.

The major difficulty that we experience when we attempt to reach a conflict resolution roadmap in a conventional way is that it is difficult to keep all of the alternatives in mind at once in order to evaluate them. It is even more difficult to maintain cognitive attention of all of our judgments simultaneously in order to measure the importance of the alternatives with respect to the criteria that one puts forth. The outcome would be a matter of which of the highly respected or dominant participants puts forth the best argument that captures the minds of the others. The result of dominance over rational participation as described in this chapter is that one of the parties does not have a buy-in to the solution. A program such as the Analytic Network Process facilitates the cognitive mapping, simultaneous prioritization, and participation that make 'buy-in' possible. Further, what was once viewed as an esoteric prioritization process of the decision makers is now reduced to codified decisions by all the parties. The result of the codification process is joint-agreement and documentation for future review and follow-up.

Incidentally, BOCR to an economist is concerned with short and long term influences including all objects and factors in the problem, whereas SWOT (strengths, weaknesses, opportunities and threats) to a planner or manager are concerned with internal and external factors at a single instant but repeat for different periods of time. SWOT assigns ordinal numbers to the factors' importances without making comparisons and also assign probabilities to their occurrence, multiply the probabilities by the importances and calculate overall strengths, weaknesses etc. and then take the difference S-W and O-T obtaining two numbers as coordinates of a point on two axes, whose positive variable parts are S and O and negative part W and T. Then they develop managerial instructions for what to do if the point lies in the four different quadrants. An expert in strategic planning pointed out to us that most people use SWOT analysis qualitatively, not quantitatively and it always precedes the decision on what actions to take in the process of planning.

Sensitivity Analysis

An interesting aspect of the model is that no matter how the criteria are adjusted or perturbed, the outcome remains stable. Figure 6 is a sample sensitivity analysis that is indicative of all of those produced in this model. The sensitivity results from this model suggest that the model is extremely insensitive implying that if the decision-makers focus on the simple outcomes suggested in this model a long-term solution may be reached.

Conclusions

The final outcome suggests that the best policy to resolve the Middle East Conflict is to establish a two state solution. Since there is more than one proposal on the details of such a solution, it is equally important to develop each proposed model in ways that address a given set of criteria that would guarantee the long term stability and peace in the region. Then another ANP model must be developed to evaluate each proposal against its criteria to select the most viable one that will serve the ultimate goal of this project. The authors agree that this work should be expanded to explore the opinions of those who are living in the region, regardless of their ethnic background or religion. An ANP based questionnaire might have an interesting result for academia and politicians as well. Such investigation should cover this phase of the research and the second one regarding the best outcome.

The model and the results given in this chapter suggest a variety of ways to manage the conflict resolution process and the implementation. The work presented here provides the reader with areas of potential concern for the leaders that must address the concerns of the various constituents and the people who must live in the environment. The most significant results of the model do not come from the numbers that are generated from the process, but rather the efforts and road-map that are generated. The results suggest that in order for any solution to work, the Israelis must recognize the Palestinians and their cause as an independent people with certain rights and concerns and the Palestinians will need to recognize Israel as an independent people with certain rights and concerns. The priorities generated reinforce the need for both parties (Israelis and Palestinians) to embrace the Middle East resolution as the leaders of the process in order to facilitate the development of *communitas* toward the resolution.

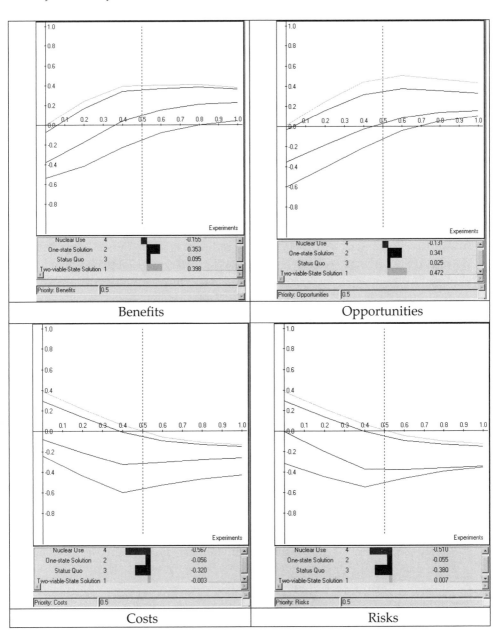

Figure 6 Sample Sensitivity Analysis

Finally, the reader might question why one should accept the judgments of the particular set of judges? Would different experts produce a different result? We believe that the structure of the problem is sufficiently general that people are not likely to differ on what factors to include. Let us consider the judgments. Had the audience included radical thinkers such for example as those Palestinians who are very angry and do not wish Israel well, or Israelis who wish the Palestinians would simply go away and disappear, the outcome could have been different. There are people in Israel who look at things in the long term and would like to keep the land a hostage in the hope that time would be on their side, but it is certain that the majority of people in Israel would like to live in peace with the Palestinians but do not know exactly how to bring that about because of a great feeling of insecurity. Reluctantly, we believe that radicals tend to move away from rationality due to their excessive passion. What we have established here is a compelling framework for radicals to consider. To solve a difficult problem such as this, one brings to the table people who are willing to compromise and not extremists. Had a different rational group done the exercise we feel certain that their answer would have been similar. The way to test the stability of this outcome, which we also did, is through sensitivity analysis. Doing that by varying the emphases provides considerable reassurance that the outcome is stable to variations in the judgments when they are not too intractable on important items.

This effort is continuing with a larger number of Israelis and Palestinians. It will focus on details of water resources, Jerusalem as joint capital, removing the settlement and defining territories.

References

1. Saaty, T.L. and J. Alexander (1989), *Conflict Resolution: The Analytic Hierarchy Process*, Praeger, New York
2. Saaty, T.L. and L. Vargas (2006), *Decision Making with The Analytic Network Process, Economics, Political, Social and Technological Applications with Benefits, Opportunities, Costs, and Risks*, Springer
3. Saaty, T.L. (2005) *Theory and Applications of The Analytic Network Process*, RWS Publications, Pittsburgh, PA
4. Saaty, T.L. (2001), *The Analytic Network Process*, 2nd edition, RWS Publications, Pittsburgh, PA

5. Saaty, T.L. (1999), *Decision Making for Leaders*, 2nd edition, RWS Publications, Pittsburgh, PA
6. Zoffer, H., A. Bahurmoz, M. Hamid, M. Minutolo and T. Saaty (2008), Synthesis of Criteria Decision Making: A Case Towards a Consensus Agreement for a Middle East Conflict Resolution, *Group Decision and Negotiation*, 17, pp. 363-385

Additional Readings

1. Rapoport, A. (1960), *Fights, Games and Debates*, University of Michigan Press
2. Von Neumann, J. and O. Morgenstern (1944), Theory of Games and Economic Behavior, Princeton University Press
3. Barash, D.P. (2003), *The Survival Game: How Game Theory Explains the Biology of Cooperation and Competition*, Owl Books
4. Myerson, R. B. (1991), *Game Theory: Analysis of Conflict*, Harvard University Press
5. Axelrod, R. (1984), *The Evolution of Cooperation*, Basic Books
6. MacKay, A.F. (1980), *Arrow's Theorem: The Paradox of Social Choice - A Case Study in the Philosophy of Economics*, New Haven and London: Yale University Press
7. Luce, R.D., and H. Raiffa (1957), *Games and Decisions: Introduction and Critical Survey*, Wiley
8. Isaacs, R. (1999), *Differential Games a Mathematical Theory with Applications to Warfare and Pursuit, Control and Optimization*, Dover Publications
9. Weibull, J.W. (1995), *Evolutionary Game Theory*, MIT Press
10. Brams, S. J. (1994), *Theory of Moves*, Cambridge University
11. Ritzberger, K. (2002), *Foundations of Non-Cooperative Game Theory*, Oxford University Press
12. Fudenberg D., and D.K. Levine (1998), *The Theory of Learning in Games*, The MIT Press
13. Elster, J. (1990), *Solomonic Judgements: Studies in the Limitations of Rationality*, Cambridge University
14. Kremenyuk V. A. (ed.) (2001), *International Negotiation*, Jossey-Bass
15. Moffit M.L. and R.C. Bordone (eds.) (2005), *The Handbook of Dispute Resolution*, Jossey-Bass
16. Raiffa H. (2000), *The Art and Science of Negotiation*, Harvard University Press
17. Susskind L. (1996), *Dealing With an Angry Public*, Free Press
18. Ury W. (1993), *Getting Past No*, Bantam Books

Chapter 11

Multi-Decisions Decision-Making: In Addition to Wheeling and Dealing, Our National Political Bodies Need a Formal Approach for Prioritization

This chapter deals with the following ideas:
- There are numerous situations in which we must prioritize many decisions in order to allocate effort and resources. How to do that by using yet higher form criteria?
- What values to use as enduring guides for establishing priorities for activities to enable us to best apply our mental and physical resources to obtain the greatest overall benefit from these decisions.
- How Congress does it.
- Group and party effect.
- Bills before Congress in 2005 and their priorities derived by us.

Introduction

Individuals, corporations and governments constantly face the extremely complex problem of ordering and prioritizing their numerous decisions according to urgency and importance. They need to sequence expenditures and allocate scarce resources to optimize the returns on their investments over time. Prioritization requires general and diverse economic, social, political, environmental, cultural and other criteria that reach beyond the familiar process of deciding on the best alternative in making a single decision. Decisions about decisions are more difficult as the best choice for each particular decision is often unknown requiring a large amount of time and resources to determine. There are three cases to consider: 1) The best alternative in each decision is known, 2) The best alternative in each decision is unknown, and 3) A combination of these two cases. What are the values and criteria that we need to use to prioritize the decisions themselves as the alternatives of a more general decision process? Decision-making often involves, among other things, generating alternatives, setting priorities, choosing a best alternative, allocating resources, determining requirements, predicting outcomes, designing systems, optimizing performance, insuring the stability of a system, planning, and resolving conflicts. Government decisions are even more complex than those of corporations: corporations do not have the issues with pressure from all sides that governments have, nor do they involve as much politics. And they are much more resource oriented than governments that tend to make their decisions easier with narrower constraints.

In practice, it often happens that which decision is chosen first for implementation depends more on the politics of what other decisions need to be made than on the merits of that particular decision. Decision making is a complex subject whose ideas and principles apparently are not well understood or practiced with convincing logic. We plan to tackle the subject in some variety and depth in the hope that through better understanding we can also develop ways to quantify it as we do in the example at the end of this exposition. I call this subject Multi-Decisions Decision-Making (MDDM). Unlike Multi-Criteria Decision-Making (MCDM), the broader advocacy by the diverse people affected by the decisions, the politics involved, the timing, sequencing and scheduling all need to be part of our considerations in MDDM.

The ways we do MCDM are inadequate for dealing with MDDM. In MDDM the problems are more general and vastly more complex. The messy and very down-to-earth approach politicians take daily requires a different approach from the academic approach one takes in MCDM. Their work has to do with making a multiplicity of decisions each of which may or may not have been worked out or has yet identified a best alternative. The decisions need to be ordered and implemented to satisfy further criteria. Such decisions usually influence each other and have interdependencies that are related to the criteria used to make these decisions. The multi-decisions problem touches on the more general subject of human values and their priorities and the contribution that each decision makes to these values. Solution of this problem belongs to the domain of dynamic optimization subject to uncertainty in which need, urgency and the overall merits of benefits (B), opportunities (O), costs (C) and risks (R) play a significant role in organizing decisions in a sequence for implementation. The merits need to be prioritized with respect to general strategic criteria. That is why the subject of criteria as related to values takes on particular significance when choosing among decisions to implement. The greatest challenge is that the future will present new uncertainties and new concerns that create new decisions, and we need to know how to make such decisions in the face of uncertainty. Scenario-building is a useful tool for dealing with such future oriented dynamics.

In an article in the Wall Street Journal, Saturday-Sunday, Jan 28-29, 2006, Gerald Seib said, "The administration tried to make a decision on how to straighten out Social Security last year and discovered that, while a president may get to choose how to tackle any given problem, he doesn't always get to choose which problems to address. In 2005, the country decided Social Security wasn't a big enough problem – yet. The president's annual State of the Union address recognizes this reality. What's in the address this year will be health care, energy and Iran. What's out will be Social Security, tax-code overhaul and new tax cuts."

MDDM problems bring us head-on to the question of how to address and order our values. Their differing orders of importance point to the need for hierarchic structures of influence. Our purpose here is to determine how to develop priorities for all the elements we consider in making all sorts of decisions. In our structure of the most general decision process we need to first consider important ideas in the constitution and the bill of rights, for example the priority of duty and of happiness in a particular decision. Such considerations suggest values to pursue in terms of which we should prioritize our needs.

There are two aspects to modeling a problem quantitatively. The first is to create a structure that represents the different parts of the problem and their interconnections according to the flow of influence among them. The second is to study the intensity and stability of flows within the structure. In science, the second is done quantitatively by solving equations and inequalities. The first is done creatively through identification, enumeration and order relations among the elements by arranging the elements in a hierarchy or a network. How to structure our problems and piece together the different ideas about what must be done is a highly demanding process of creative thinking and understanding and is at least as important as (and can be far more complex than) performing the operations within a structure. We tend to think of structures as physical objects forced on us, but most structures are built in our minds for our own convenience to understand occurrences around us that are both physical and mental. Fundamentally structures are no less mathematical in nature than are operations and transformations that take place within them. But as yet we are not as sophisticated in dealing with them.

All meaning we assign to things depends on our system of values both concrete and abstract. While single decisions are evaluated in terms of local criteria like a locally Euclidean (flat) coordinate system on a manifold that cannot be used to study the entire manifold holistically, multiple decisions are evaluated in terms of global criteria or values that relate to what is more or less widely accepted as good and bad that are like general coordinates on a manifold that cannot be used to study local properties as do the Euclidean coordinates. These are two very different ways to look at decision making and value systems. However, most values are adopted relative to other people and to circumstances, by looking at alternative assumptions and attitudes. The concept of attitude arises from attempts to account for observed regularities in the behavior of individual persons. One tends to group others around him into common classes; he may assign people who are illegal immigrants to a single class and behave similarly toward all of them. In such a case he is said to hold an attitude specific to that group. In addition there are perceptual, emotional, and motivational attributes. In business, corporate values may be not just to make a profit but to reflect the drive to serve customers with integrity and concern.

We have to answer questions like: How did the need arise to decide on what to do? What causes are involved and who and how many are affected by it? How do we define the actions to be taken to satisfy that need? How well can those actions be implemented and how soon? What is the decision? When analyzing a decision one asks: What are the values that affect this decision? What must be done to best realize them? What position do I want to take or can't take? What role or roles am I expected to play? And so on.

There are at least six orders of complexity for those having the problem of ordering many decisions: single individuals, groups, corporations, governments, and many governments working cooperatively as within the United Nations, or working collectively through coalitions. We shall treat only a small part of this formalization of the problem, using the U.S. Congress as an illustration.

Decision Making in a Political Environment

Society has a myriad of needs and these needs are variable and dynamic in the degree to which they must be satisfied. So long as there are people in this world, and their number is on the increase, needs for their satisfaction will constantly increase. These needs relate to individuals, families and groups of individuals, nations and the environment that is used to satisfy the needs.

We attempt to satisfy such collective, broad, and widespread needs and regulate the way these needs are satisfied by organizing governments and electing representatives to do the job. One of the most important needs for the officials involved is the need to get re-elected and keep their jobs. To satisfy this need, these officials often do not act objectively, but pursue their own self-interest in retaining power by getting re-elected. To implement their decisions they need the co-operation of other politicians. They also need to persuade their constituents to both re-elect them and to pay taxes to make it possible for them to take the necessary actions to satisfy the people's needs. By paying taxes, most people's ability to provide for their own personal needs is diminished so there is a trade-off politicians must make between people's personal good and the public good. Politics is important for the survival and success of any society. How can our knowledge about decision-making help officials to make better decisions?

It is a law of nature that people act in their self-interest. Does this self interest guarantee that society's needs can be satisfied in an optimal way? Not necessarily. An official may be elected on a popular issue, but then his ideas and ambitions on other needs may not serve society well. That may be one reason why the scientist whose work requires objectivity does not see politics as a good and useful way of doing things because by its very nature it does not optimize, due to the need of the politician to retain power to continue making decisions being so high on the list. In politics, people must make tradeoffs and accept less. This is a process of sub-optimizing, and it is here to stay.

A useful idea for generating resources as a base for taxes to help solve other problems in a free society is to allow enterprises to flourish so that more people can be employed and more resources created, not only to serve people's needs directly by the people themselves, but through the resources provided to the government to satisfy the broader needs of society. How important the various needs are depends on the values we attach to things and on the priorities of these values. The case of the US Congress is an excellent example of a government in a free society attempting to encourage enterprises to create resources and to satisfy the needs of the people. Politicians are essential for helping enterprises flourish to create resources to allocate for the benefit of hopefully the largest number of people in society.

To identify needs, the government has different cabinet departments and agencies which survey the situation and make a thorough study of the needs in a particular area, estimate the amount of resources needed, how they would be used and how to get them. This is a reasonably good entry into the problem of prioritization.

Decision Making in Politics - How Congress Does It

Decision-making in politics is very different from decision making in a business that is primarily concerned with its own survival and profitability. First, it is important to distinguish between a description of how Congress makes its decisions and how it can make these decisions to better advantage. One can develop different sets of criteria for ranking decisions. The most relevant criteria that determine if and when Congress will act are the following, in no particular order: (1) the nature of the need to be satisfied; (2) the demand for congressional action, which stems from public opinion or the pressure of interest groups that may not arouse much public attention; (3) the complexity of the issue, in political and public-policy terms that can affect Congress' ability to get consensus for action; and (4) the costs (does Congress have the money or other wherewithal to do it?). Jonathan Moon [1] has studied the issue with regard to legislative proposals in the US Senate. Here is a summary of some of his findings.

Since there are many potential issues that can be addressed, a fundamental aspect of lawmaking involves the choice of which issues to pursue and how strongly to pursue them. At the early stage of legislative production, policy alternatives are shaped through the efforts – intensive activities of legislators – to gather information, draft bills, build coalitions and keep pace with the activities of various interest groups. The decisions most constantly on a Senator's mind are not how to vote, but what to do with his time, how to allocate his resources of time and influence, and where to put his energy. *Costs and benefits are important considerations.* Legislators are policy motivated and their preferences are defined by policy outcomes. Aside from the premise that committee assignments and committee leadership lower the marginal costs of legislative attention, it may also be true that these factors raise the benefits of attention because they indicate better access to and influence over the legislative agenda. There are four basic sets of factors that affect a legislator's issue attention decisions: *preferences, national conditions, committee* and *party*. The question is to what extent each factor influences issue attention. Three types of preference subfactors are *constituency, ideological* and *partisan interests*. Constituency induces preferences through re-election, ideology means beliefs about what constitutes good public policy from personal convictions or induced by constituents' beliefs. Party means that the voters and the electorate associate different political parties with the successful handling of different issues.

National conditions indicate whether there are opportunities for policy change based on deficiencies in law and policy.

Majority party status involves two factors: the majority party's control of institutional resources determines issue attention. They introduce more bills than the minority party for all issues. Second they give more attention to issues that the majority party owns. There is one committee with primary jurisdiction over each issue except health, which comes under the jurisdiction of transportation. There is little support for the hypothesis that partisan differences influence attention independent of constituency economic interest and ideology. The hypothesis that the majority party control of resources and the agenda allow it to subsidize the attention costs of its members is soundly rejected. The central finding of the analysis is that committee membership is the dominant influence on senators' attention to issues. They give more attention to issues under their jurisdiction than nonmembers. The effects of constituency, ideology and party are significant to a lesser extent. *A bold conclusion that might be drawn from the results is that senators stumble upon issues more often than they actively seek them out. They pursue issues within the set of opportunities provided by their committee assignments.* Other sources indicate that many issues are brought before Congress by the President or by Secretaries of different departments in the Executive Branch.

We may divide decisions into different categories to get a better handle on them. So far, multi-criteria decision-making has focused on homogeneous decisions that can be described sufficiently to model them. Heterogeneous decisions are diverse and intractable because they can be subject to chance and to the vagaries of human society, like the terrorist acts of 9/11. The occurrence of the decisions themselves is a dynamic process whereby the arrival of an urgent decision may set aside work on an existing one, something like preemptive queuing phenomena.

MCDM methods can be appropriately used to help committees use judgments and understanding to decide on the priorities of the issues they consider because they know their criteria best for those kinds of special issues. Further and at least as important is to help the leadership in Congress to prioritize the bills brought forth by the many committees and urgent bills brought from other sources so they can be submitted for a vote before the senate or house. In addition, MCDM methods can be used by the members of Congress themselves so they can vote for or against a bill or, when the process becomes more entrenched and sophisticated, use intensity of preference instead of yes-no to determine the outcome of a bill. Finally, the president, whose influence is very great in determining the bills considered by the committees and by Congress, needs to use a process of prioritization of national interests to decide whether to sign or veto a bill.

When we think of the nature of various decisions we realize that they do not all have the same need and urgency for implementation nor is there the possibility to implement them all. Some decisions are long term and need to be started immediately at a low threshold to make possible subsequent stages of implementation. Among the criteria that one needs to consider are both positive and negative ones. Noteworthy is the need, the **urgency** of implementation (sometimes we may wish to implement the less important decisions to get them out of the way), the **timing** of implementation, the **availability of resources** that are on hand and other resources that need to be gradually secured through other means, the **benefits, opportunities, costs** and **risks** involved in each decision, the fact that new decisions will be arriving that may change the priority of implementing others, the contributions of these decisions to the welfare and happiness of people, to alleviating suffering and pain, to society, politics, technology and the like. During the past elections, candidates in the U.S. have had to make promises on decisions ranging from the economy, taxation, and unemployment, to health benefits, to the benefits and harms of outsourcing to the wars in Iraq and in Afghanistan and to terrorism. These are decisions of different kinds and implementing one decision has an effect on implementing others. They each have their own benefits, opportunities, costs and risks. They all deserve consideration but not to the same degree of urgency and requirement for resources. How do we combine these considerations to help us obtain an overall priority list for all the decisions we must make?

Many decisions by Congress have to do with providing economic support and levying taxes. But there are also legal, political and social decisions that legislate on certain prohibitions like drugs and abortion and going to war, or the status of illegal immigrants. Some of the legislation is proactive but much of it is reactive to things that have happened or have become problematic. In society the decisions made have to do with how many resources there are to implement decisions ranging from economic to human; what people and how many need that kind of assistance, what support and lobbies there are in favor or against and what sort of pressures they can bring about; how the issue affects the image, standing and the chance for reelection of the officials who make the decisions; the short and long term impact of a decision and its domestic and international economic, political and social repercussions.

In government often the negotiability of an issue is important. If there is early agreement on a decision, the positive attitude may carry over to other issues and conversely. Sometimes by putting forward the most divisive issue, it is hoped that afterward people will rally together to agree on subsequent ones.

A major distinction must be made between the desirability of a decision and the short and long run consequences of taking that decision. There are preferences about the actions to take and other preferences for the consequences of these actions. To include such preferences for consequences one must examine influences about what the results of decisions can be.

Due to the high volume and complexity of its work, Congress divides its tasks among approximately 250 committees and sub committees. The House and Senate each have their own committee system, which are similar. Within chamber guidelines, however, each committee adopts its own rules; thus, there is considerable variation among panels. The following will give an idea of how Congress is organized.

The Senate Committees
Standing Committees:
Agriculture, Nutrition, and Forestry, Appropriations, Armed Services, Banking, Housing, and Urban Affairs, Budget , Commerce, Science, and Transportation, Energy and Natural Resources, Environment and Public Works, Finance, Foreign Relations, Health, Education, Labor, and Pensions, Homeland Security and Governmental Affairs, Judiciary, Rules and Administration, Small Business and Entrepreneurship, Veterans Affairs

Special, Select, and Other Committees:
Indian Affaires, Select Committee on Ethics, Select Committee on Intelligence, Special Committee on Aging

Joint Committees:
Joint Committee on Printing, Joint Committee on Taxation, Joint Committee on the Library, Joint Economic Committee

The House Committees:
Agriculture, Appropriations, Armed Services, Budget, Education & the Workforce, Energy and Commerce, Financial Services, Government Reform, Homeland Security, House Administration, International Relations, Judiciary, Resources, Rules, Science, Small Business, Standards of Official Conduct, Transportation & Infrastructure, Veterans Affairs, Ways & Means, Joint Economic, Joint Printing, Joint Taxation, House Permanent Select Committee on Intelligence

Bills before Congress (Early 2005)

Abortion, prohibit taking minors across state lines to circumvent parental notification; Abortion, require informing women who seek one about pain to unborn child; Arctic National Wildlife Refuge, designate a portion as wilderness; Bankruptcy reform; Schumer amendment to prevent anti-abortion protesters from using bankruptcy to avoid fines or judgments; Class action lawsuits, assure fairness; Clear Skies Act (emissions control for power plants); Congressional Gold Medals, provide reasonable standards for; Constitutional amendments; Continuity of Congress (special elections/appointments in national emergencies); Death gratuity for military, improve; Estate tax, make repeal permanent; Farm subsidies, limit federal farm payments; FCC indecency, penalties, increase; Flag desecration, constitutional amendment prohibiting; Genetic information, prohibit employers and health insurers from discriminating on the basis of; Gun liability bill, Immigrants, establish driver's license regulations and ID security standards for; Incapacitated Persons Legal Protection Act (provide habeas corpus protections); Insurance, increase coverage of Service members' Group Life program; Insurance, prevent sales of abusive policies to military personnel; Marriage, defined as between a man and a woman only, amendment to the Constitution; Minimum wage, increase; Same-sex marriage, constitutional amendment prohibiting; Senate committee organizing resolutions; Social security numbers, enhance privacy protections and prevent fraudulent misuse; Social security overhaul, including creation of personal accounts; Spyware, protect Internet users from unknowing transmission of personal data; Stem cell research, allow human embryonic; Tax cuts, make permanent; Terri Schiavo bill; Transportation (TEA-21), reauthorization of surface transportation programs; Tsunami relief, accelerate tax benefits for charitable cash contributions; Welfare bill (TANF)

Strategic Decision Making

Decision-making provides the interface between science and philosophy and in particular the theory of value. When one has a single decision to make one answers the question: which of these alternatives is the best one. When one has many decisions to make, one answers the question: "Which of these best alternative decisions should we choose first?" The answer to the first decision is determined in terms of the characteristics of a particular decision; that to the second in terms of the characteristics of many decisions which means the criteria people use to decide or not to decide. I call these *strategic criteria*. They are economic, physical, social, political, legal, technological, ideological, and others. Their priorities are set in terms of the higher goals of well being, survival, peace, and beliefs about the future. In considering multiple decision problems, it is inevitable that one becomes philosophical about the essential meaning of value. Although it is difficult to be exhaustive we can list a variety of values that people use. It is fair to assume that not all values are known and well defined. There is synergy in all that we do that creates value and the values of today are not the values of yesterday. Still, our desire for survival, well-being and peace are permanent values.

There are different levels of urgency in making decisions: different ability to pay, different importance assigned in terms of tactics and strategy, short and long term. How many people are affected, how lasting is the effect of that decision and what happens to the environment. An individual, a group, a company, or a government can organize their areas of concern, the urgency and the magnitude of influence with which they are needed so that caprice in decision making will gradually diminish and disappear and coping with life will become more systematic from the specific to the most general. We would then have more time to focus on expanding our horizons for the future and choosing the most appropriate ones that integrate well with what we know. What we need to do is to identify and classify our values and our decisions to make a science of it. The most urgent decisions have to do with conflict resolution so that the decisions we make are built upon and not cancelled or destroyed by conflict. Implementing decisions depends on resources and how much we have of them and how much we need. Resources are an essential part of decision making. When two parties in a conflict encounter a seemingly impossible impasse, it is important to explore the objectives and values underlying each party's problem and initial proposed solution. After the discussion has progressed from a story about a problem to a description of a desired objective the key questions to ask on which there are numerous variations are:

What is the advantage you seek in getting your objective? What benefits would come to you from having X, your stated goal? How would you gain from getting that for yourself? If you got X, how would that help you?

These questions direct the listeners' attention to their deeper objectives and the values that would be fulfilled if their objectives were achieved.

Axiology – the Study of Values

No philosopher has been more intensely concerned with questions of value than Nietzsche was. His early works dealt mainly with such questions. His masterpiece, *Thus Spoke Zarathustra*, revolves around evaluation concerns, as do most of his later works. He says, "All the scientists have to do from now on is to prepare the way for the future task of philosophers. This task is the solution of the problem of value, the *determination of the order of rank among values.*" (From "The Giants of Philosophy", Knowledge Products, Nashville, TN.)

Multi-decisions problems bring us head on to the question of ordering our values. *Values are enduring guides for establishing priorities for activities to enable us to best apply our mental and physical resources to obtain the greatest overall benefit.* We use values to relate and interpret everything else that we learn and experience. They are the focus around which our thinking revolves. Value is an anchor that binds our energies, our thoughts, and our actions. In a sense, our values are us. They are not something abstract and eternal. Despite some overlap, we can imagine that the unspoken and unexamined values of a tree and other plants on which we depend for survival, or the values of a bee differ in meaning and substance from our human values. That does not mean that our values are important for the tree; in fact, while the trees and their values are often important to us, we and our values are not important to the trees unless we want to destroy them. At the outset we must establish the fact that no matter how scarce or rare a thing may be, if no one desires it, it will have no value, power or influence. In addition no matter how valuable a thing may be if everyone has all they want of it, no one will pay a price to get more of it. The value of something is its capacity to satisfy some human need. Value represents the object's utility.

The value of a thing is a social property expressing the social nature of the labor of that thing. Only objects that have use also have value.

There is a near infinity of values attached to everything and every idea we have like religion and magic. Many people believe that value theory that is so fundamental to decision-making is the most important area in philosophy. All religions and most philosophical movements have been concerned with it to some degree. In philosophy, value theory, or axiology, concerns itself with the notion of goodness. It divides into ethics, concerning the morally good and aesthetics, concerning the artistically good, or the beautiful. It also concerns social goodness, and considerations relating to economics and political science. Value defines "good" and "bad" for a community or society. It affects everyone's life – maybe all life forms and not just people. What kinds of things are good? What is "good"? What is "bad"? What is important about our needs and wants? What is the ultimate reference for value, God, evolution and change, law and order?

People who have thought about the subject of value are divided as to how value or values are to be regarded. To some economists such as Ludwig von Mises "value" always has a subjective quality. The basic idea is that there is no implicit value in objects or things and that value derives from the psychology of market participants. Subjective value theory says that things have no inherent value but have value only insofar as people desire them. A piece of candy has value to us when we are hungry. If we eat a big dinner instead of the candy, that candy has no value to us at that time. The value of the candy changed according to our desire. In economic value theory, the value of the candy is the amount of labor that goes into making it. It would still cost the same at the store whether we are hungry or not. On the other hand, ethics and aesthetics commonly consider intrinsic goodness, and these lead to very different kinds of considerations about value. In this case value has a universal importance beyond the time dependent preference of individuals. Values change over time, in space, and from young to old. The concept of the spirit of the times (*Zeitgeist*) was introduced by Friedrich Hegel (1770-1831). The Zeitgeist values of our times are not easy to enumerate. They vary with the fashions.

There are six value-spheres about which it might be possible to reach consensus. They are the pursuit of *wealth, order, truth,* the *sacred, virtue,* and *beauty*. These have been called the *cardinal values*. They are all products of society. The cardinal values are embedded in the major institutional realms, i.e., the economy, politics, science, religion, ethics, and the arts. The ideal of contemporary American and European society is an all-round society that affords people the opportunity to freely pursue the cardinal values. The importance of free enterprise, civic liberties, academic freedom, artistic freedom, and freedom of religion are examples.

Examples of Values:
Personal Values: For most people the order of their personal values may be something like the following:
Physical Values of Health, Comfort & Hygiene
Ethical & Religious Values -Life & Death
Family Values - Love, Caring & Nurturing
Knowledge, Facts & Information Values
National Values – Party Commitments & Political leanings
Global Values - What to do about international issues

A single decision involving the selection of a best alternative requires knowledge of objectives and criteria to evaluate the alternatives of that particular decision. A multi decision ordering of several diverse best alternatives requires knowledge of values served by all the alternatives. Each alternative serves some objective or objectives that may differ from those served by the other alternatives. The objectives themselves are part of higher-level objectives needed to determine the contributions of the different decisions.

An objective of a decision is defined by values and their priorities. It appears that the objectives of decisions can be varied and numerous because the values are numerous. For example, the objective of a car is to transport people, the objective of food is nourishment and these two objectives are substantially different. However, all objectives serve direct needs of people or of the environment that can affect people indirectly. Thus the higher order values have to do with people or with the environment (both physical and biological) which also relate to animals and plants. As a result we can say there are three kinds of high order values: those that deal strictly with people, those that deal strictly with the environment, and those that deal with people and the environment in an interdependent way. We need to do three things.

1. Identify these different higher order values,
2. Prioritize them
3. Use them to prioritize the contributions of best outcomes of decisions according to BOCR (benefits, opportunities, costs and risks).

The decisions may be interdependent and deriving their priorities requires use of the Analytic Network Process (ANP).

One would expect the highest level values to have more stable priorities in practice than lower level ones, with stability gradually decreasing as one descends to the lowest level. This tells us that it is important to derive priorities for values or strategic criteria at the highest levels irrespective of the decisions in which they are used. Given the priorities of outcomes, we need another set of factors that have to do with the decision to sequence and implement the different decisions. Among them are knowledge, urgency, cost, effectiveness, implementation, knowledge, preparation, and so on. Here is a list used in a real life corporate decision.

Examples of objectives that satisfy certain values:
Expense Reduction
> Reduce Personnel Costs, Reduce Operating Costs, Reduce Systems Costs
Improve Productivity
> Reduce Time on Work Performed, Reduce Throughput
Revenue Generation
> New Sales, Customer Retention
Key Business Drivers
> Increased Profits from Expense Savings, Improved Customer Retention, Comply with Government Regulations, Minimize Product Defects
Minimize Risk
> Schedule Risk, Cost Risk, Performance Risk

Abraham Maslow [2] classified seven basic needs in order of importance from the most basic to the least basic need: I. Homeostatic Needs (Physiological), II. Safety and Security Needs, III. Love and Belonging Needs, IV. Esteem Needs, V. Self-Actualization Needs, VI. To Know and Understand Needs, and VII. Aesthetic Needs

There is overlap from need to adjacent need. Each successive need emerges little by little as the previous need is partially satisfied. A need may be satisfied 25 percent when the next one will be felt. If the previous need is satisfied a following need may emerge.

A Philosophy of Science Perspective on Values

Nicholas Rescher's Introduction to Value Theory [3] classifies values. *A person's values are clues to guide deliberations to arrive at decisions and to explain actions.* A thing has value when it is the object of interest—any interest. Values are related to actions in categorically different ways: *A motive, habit or disposition for action* (bravery, generosity); *A physical state* (health, good looks); *A capability, skill or talent* (agility, endurance); *A state of mind or attitude* (indifference to money, patriotism); *A character trait* (resoluteness); *A state of affairs* (privacy, economic justice).

 K.Baier and N. Rescher [4] provide a comprehensive list of values.

A Tentative Register of American Values
NOTE: We deal here with overtly espoused and publicly appealed to values to the exclusion of (i) unconscious motives (e.g., conformist culture insecurity vis-a-vis Europeans) and (ii) traits of national character (e.g., love of novelty). The factors included in the register are such that explicit or overt appeal to them can well be expected from publicly recognized spokesmen for values: newspaper editorialists, graduation exercise speakers, religion-moral sermonizers, and political orators. Such values can be extracted by "content analysis" of the pronouncements of such sources. The values now at issue are those generally acknowledged and widely diffused throughout the society and not those specific to some group (physicians, Catholics, Chinese-Americans, Westerners). Moreover they are all socially general values in that those who espouse them do so as to value them not only personally (for themselves) but societally (for people in general). In short we are concerned to list genuine values adherence and dedication to which is at this writing widely diffused throughout virtually all sectors of American society. The scheme of classification turns on the issue of the setting at issue in the maintenance of the value (oneself, one's group, the society, the nation, all of mankind, the environment).

I. Self-oriented values:
1. Personal "material" welfare (the right to life and the pursuit of happiness):
 a. Health (physical and mental well-being),
 b. Economic security and well-being ("materialism" and the American way of life)
 c. Personal security (stability of the conditions of life)

2. Self-respect (the right to be treated as a person and as a member in good standing of the community; honor, honorableness)
3. Self-reliance (self-sufficiency; rugged individualism and the pioneer tradition)
4. Personal liberty (the right to endeavor to "shape one's own life," to work out major facets of one's own destiny and to go one's own way)
5. Self-advancement ("success," ambition, diligence)
6. Self-fulfillment (and "the pursuit of happiness")
7. Skill and prowess
   a. The intellectual virtues (intelligence, education, know-how, realism, practicality, versatility, etc.)
   b. The physical virtues (strength, dexterity, endurance, good appearance, cleanliness, etc.)
   c. The virtues of the will (strengths of character):
      1) Readiness for hard work (industriousness)
      2) Toughness (fortitude, endurance, bravery, courage)
      3) Initiative and activism (the "go getter" 'approach)
      4) Self-control (temperateness, sobriety)
      5) Perseverance and steadfastness
   d. Competence (pride of workmanship)
   e. Inventiveness and innovativeness
   f. Initiative (the "self-starter")
   g. Well-informedness (access to information, being "in the know")
   h. Faith ("believing in something" including "having a sense of values")
   i. Appreciation and appreciativeness (of "the good things of life").

II. Group-oriented values:

1. Respectability (group acceptance, avoidance of reproach, good repute, conformity, the "done thing" and the "herd instinct")
2. Rectitude and personal morality (honesty, fairness, probity, reliability,
3. Reasonableness and rationality (objectivity)
4. The domestic virtues (love, pride in family role, providence, simplicity, thrift, prudence, etc.)
5. The civic virtues (involvement, good citizenship, law-abidance, civic pride—the "greatest little town" syndrome)
6. Conscientiousness:
   a. Devotion to family, duty
   b. Personal responsibility and accountability

    c. Devotion to principle (especially of one's religion—"the god-fearing man")

7. Friendship and friendliness:
    a. Friendship proper
    b. Loyalty (to friends, associates)
    c. Friendliness, kindliness, helpfulness, cooperativeness, and courteousness (the good scout; "getting along with people")
    d. Fellow-feeling (compassion, sympathy, and "love of one's fellows"
    e. Gregariousness
    f. Receptivity (openness, patience, "the good listener")
    g. Personal tolerance ("live and let live," "getting along with people
    h. Patience

8. Service (devotion to the well-being of others)
9. Generosity (charity, openhandedness)
10. Idealism (hopefulness in human solutions to human problems)
11. Recognition (getting due public credit for the good points scored in the game of life; success and status)
12. Forthrightness (frankness, openness, sincerity, genuineness; keeping things "above board," the fair deal)
13. Fair play (the "good sport")

III. Society-oriented values:

1. Social welfare (indeed "social consciousness" as such)
2. Equality:
    a. Tolerance
    b. "Fair play," fairness
    c. Civil rights
3. Justice (including legality, proper procedure, recourse)
4. Liberty (the "open society"; the various "freedoms")
5. Order (public order, "law and order")
6. Opportunity ("land of opportunity" concept; the square deal for all)
7. Charity (help for the "underdog")
8. Progressivism optimism (faith in the society's ability to solve its problem
9. Pride in "our culture" and "our way of life"

IV. Nation-oriented values:

1. The patriotic virtues (love of country, devotion to country, nation pride):
    a. National freedom and independence
    b. National prosperity and national achievement generally

    c. Patriotism and national pride
    d. Concern for the national welfare
    e. Loyalty (to country)
    f. Chauvinism (nationalism, pride in national power and preeminence)
2. Democracy and "the American way"
3. "Public service" in the sense of service of country (the nation)

V. Mankind-oriented values:
1. The "welfare of mankind"
    a. Peace
    b. Material achievement and progress
    c. Cultural and intellectual achievement and progress
2. Humanitarianism and the "brotherhood of man"
3. Internationalism
4. Pride in the achievements of "the human community"
5. Reverence for life
6. Human dignity and the "worth of the individual"

VI. Environment-oriented values:
1. Aesthetic values (environmental beauty)
2. Novelty

Prioritization

There are critical decisions, essential decisions, average everyday decisions, whimsical decisions, and not-so-important decisions. Looking at them in this light, importance (how many people they affect), party position, past history, urgency, resources, timing and impacts are decisive factors.

    Judgments expressed in the form of comparisons are fundamental in our cognitive makeup. The Analytic Hierarchy Process (AHP) and its generalization to dependence and feedback, the Analytic Network Process (ANP) are theories about how to measure alternatives or courses of action under both tangible and intangible criteria, then synthesize these measures to make a decision. Real life decisions involve benefits, costs, opportunities and risks and how to combine them and allocate resources subject to constraints.

    Granted that politicians and business people are influenced to vote for many reasons and interests, what are the criteria that they consider while voting? In general terms they would be interested in the benefits, the opportunities, the costs and the risks that are associated with the issues that they vote on. What are the criteria involved in each of these four BOCR merits? Although our list is incomplete, it is worthwhile to identify these values.

Here are some influences that act on a politician's mind:

Political (constituency votes, party loyalty, owing favors)

Economic (amount of resources involved, gains to be made, taxes and other money collection)

Social (kind of people affected, equality,...)

Legal (race, gender and other equality issues, what to legitimize and what to ban like drugs, gay marriage and so on, national holidays)

Military (defense and size of forces and kind and number of weapons

Environmental (diverse pollution like mercury and other health hazards, oil exploration, national parks)

Technological (earth, material and space exploration -NASA-)

Health (standards, foods, drinks, tobacco, exercise, medical practices, air and water quality)

International (relations with other countries, passing on what countries should join the WTO, United Nations, country by country relations)

Ideological (investigating communism in the old days, some religious practices like removing the 10 commandments from buildings and no prayer in public)

Residual other (incidental factors like honoring people with citizenship, congressional medal of honor)

Congressional Committee Concerns

On a more general level, Congressional committees can be seen to have the following concerns:

Chronological (urgency, disaster oriented, human suffering and survival)

Physical (health, Exercise, and Sports)

Educational (learning, communication, and information)

Economic (money, property, business, manufacturing, and agriculture)

Social (welfare, cooperation, and organization)

Political (power, influence, party, and election)

Environmental (using and protecting the physical and biological environment)

Legal (need for laws and enforcement of compliance)

Moral (order, honesty, and trust)

Ideological (religion, common belief, and fervor)

Technological (innovation, change, problem solving)
Military (security, force, defense, and territory)
Aesthetic (art, music, and theater)
Competition (advertising, quality, improvement, Fair Trade, reasonable
    pricing)
Negotiation and Conflict Resolution (take and give, reconciliation)

This list may be combined into a shorter list: Economic, Political
(both national and international), Physical, Social, Legal, Techno-
environmental, Ideological and Military. These in turn may be combined
into three overriding factors: Economic, Political, and Legal as in the
Legislative, the Executive, and the Legal branches of government.

Were we to organize a large set of decisions according to priority of
implementation we would first rate these decisions one at time with respect
to the categories and subcategories described above after developing a set of
priorities for them, and then we would develop a set of different order of
magnitude intensity levels to use in rating the decisions. The system can be
further refined by comparing groups of decisions according to their standing
in the ratings. As new decisions are added they take their place in the ratings
system.

Group and Party Effects – What Congress Should Do

One might perceive rightly or wrongly that Congress has been using the
buckshot approach in making its decisions that cover the needs of the nation.
What else can they do? Can their process of decision making be organized in
some way that would not put off the politicians but strengthen their resolve
and reward their pride even more in the breadth and depth of their
accomplishments? We think so. Let us see how.

The AHP/ANP approach is a very general way to structure a
problem holistically as part of a system and relate its parts according to
influence. We have chosen the simplest and most direct route to prioritizing
most of the bills that have been before Congress recently.

The decision criteria were established through in-depth reviews of
the functions of the U.S. government as well as some interviews with experts
in governmental affairs. We reviewed the committees in the Senate
including: the Standing; Special; Select and Joint committees. Additionally
we reviewed the committees in the House as well as the Bills before
Congress to gain as much insight as possible into its activities. Our goal with

the decision criteria was to focus on the highest level and next lower level of purposes of the Government rather than break out every single low level function. The analysis is targeted at providing a coherent and justifiable framework for assisting key senior decision makers in the U.S. Government with prioritizing the issues they should address in 2005 based on their importance in serving the American people. The example is an illustration of what and how one can use comparisons to create priorities in an accurate and justifiable way. One needs to seek further agreement from many more people in government to fine tune the results obtained here.

Decision Goal: To Prioritize Congressional Decisions to be Made
Transportation and Communication
International Relations
Justice and Regulation
Health
Learning and Knowledge
Science
Education
Technology
Security
Armed Services and Veterans Affairs
Homeland Security
Intelligence
Economic Prosperity
Availability of Resources
Appropriations
Taxation
Business
Agriculture/Environment and Resource Management
International Trade
Labor
Social Services
Social Security
Welfare
Indian Affairs

Figure 1 Criteria To Prioritize Decisions for Immediacy of Congressional Action

An essential consideration in using the judgment process to prioritize decisions is the power to be accorded to each of the different contributors to the judgment process. Voting according to party position is different than voting alone or with another group. The judgments on each matter may not be equally important and thus the AHP method of synthesizing judgments would be applied to raise that judgment to the power of its source. The numerical value of the power is obtained from an appropriate hierarchy for the importance of the different parties. It is followed by taking the geometric mean of all the judgments raised to the powers to obtain the single judgment and the process is repeated for all the judgments. The criteria priorities are determined here by comparing them with respect to the goal to determine which is more important. But it would be better to derive their priorities by comparing them using the ANP [5] with respect to some select very important decisions at least to get a rough idea as to their importance in the real situation when decisions are made under pressure to decide on what is more important and how much more important it is. The alternatives were rated with respect to the subcriteria using scale intensities shown above the table used for rating them. One can allocate resources to projects proportionately to their ratings in a dynamic way as more money and more bills and projects are added. The priorities serve as a measure of performance to determine how much money to allocate to cover the costs of those decisions that are funded completely (zero-one allocation), or in part by specifying levels such as 20%, 40%, and so on.

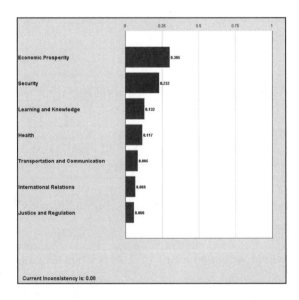

Figure 2 Priorities of the Major Areas of Government
(Most criteria have subcriteria with priorities)

Bill	Score	Transportation and Communication (0.085)	International Relations (0.07)	Justice and Regulations (0.06)	Health (0.118)	Science (0.034)	Education (0.067)	Technology (0.034)	Services and Veterans Affairs (0.105)	Homeland and Security (0.053)	Homeland Security (0.053)	Intelligence (0.075)	Appropriations (0.013)
Class action lawsuits, assure fairness	0.391	0.000	0.000	0.800	1.000	0.250	0.250	0.250	0.250	0.000	0.000	0.000	0.250
Allow human embryonic stem cell research	0.299	0.000	0.250	0.800	1.000	1.000	0.800	0.800	0.000	0.000	0.000	0.000	0.250
Continuity of Congress (special elections/appointments in national emergencies)	0.274	0.250	0.250	0.250	0.000	0.000	0.000	0.000	0.500	1.000	1.000	0.500	0.250
Minimum wage increase	0.253	0.000	0.250	0.250	0.000	0.000	0.000	0.000	0.000	0.000	0.000	0.000	0.800
Drivers licenses and security for immigrants	0.245	0.000	0.500	0.250	0.000	0.000	0.000	0.000	0.000	1.000	1.000	0.500	0.250
Social Security overhaul including personal savings accounts	0.243	0.000	0.000	0.250	0.250	0.000	0.000	0.000	0.250	0.000	0.000	0.000	1.000
Make tax cuts permanent	0.238	0.000	0.000	0.000	0.000	0.000	0.250	0.250	0.000	0.000	0.000	0.000	0.800
Protect internet users from unknown transmission of personal data	0.237	0.800	0.000	0.800	0.000	0.250	0.000	0.500	0.000	0.000	0.000	0.000	0.000
Farm Subsidies- Limit Federal Farm Payments	0.236	0.000	0.250	0.000	0.000	0.000	0.000	0.000	0.000	0.000	0.000	0.000	1.000
Clear Skies Act (emissions control for power plants)	0.215	0.000	0.000	0.250	0.500	0.250	0.250	0.250	0.000	0.000	0.000	0.000	0.250
Transportation (TEA-21), Re-authorization of surface transportation programs	0.202	1.000	0.000	0.000	0.000	0.000	0.000	0.000	0.000	0.000	0.000	0.000	0.800
Prohibit descrimination based on genetic health info	0.185	0.000	0.000	0.500	0.250	0.500	0.000	0.250	0.000	0.000	0.000	0.000	0.250
Increase coverage of service members life insurance	0.178	0.000	0.000	0.250	0.000	0.000	0.000	0.000	1.000	0.000	0.000	0.000	0.500
Death gratuity for military, improve	0.177	0.000	0.000	0.250	0.250	0.000	0.000	0.000	0.800	0.000	0.000	0.000	0.500
Improve Death Gratuity for Military	0.175	0.000	0.000	0.250	0.000	0.000	0.000	0.000	1.000	0.000	0.000	0.000	0.500
Senate committee organizing resolutions	0.165	0.000	0.000	0.250	0.250	0.250	0.250	0.250	0.250	0.250	0.250	0.250	0.250
Estate tax, make repeal permanent	0.161	0.000	0.000	0.250	0.000	0.000	0.000	0.000	0.000	0.000	0.000	0.000	0.800
Provide standards for Congressional Gold Medals	0.157	0.000	0.000	0.250	0.000	0.000	0.000	0.000	1.000	0.250	0.250	0.250	0.000
Repeal Estate Tax	0.151	0.000	0.000	0.250	0.000	0.000	0.000	0.000	0.000	0.000	0.000	0.000	0.250
Incapacitated Persons Protection Act	0.149	0.000	0.000	0.800	0.000	0.000	0.000	0.000	0.000	0.000	0.000	0.000	0.250
Enhance privacy of social security numbers	0.136	0.000	0.000	0.250	0.250	0.000	0.000	0.000	0.000	0.500	0.500	0.000	0.250
Amend to marraige between only man and woman	0.134	0.000	0.000	0.800	0.250	0.000	0.500	0.000	0.000	0.000	0.000	0.000	0.250
Prohibit minors having abortions across state lines	0.128	0.000	0.000	0.800	0.250	0.000	0.000	0.000	0.000	0.000	0.000	0.000	0.250
Terry Schiavo bill	0.118	0.000	0.000	1.000	0.500	0.000	0.000	0.000	0.000	0.000	0.000	0.000	0.000
Tsunami Relief, accelerate tax benefits for charitable contributions	0.112	0.000	1.000	0.000	0.250	0.000	0.000	0.000	0.000	0.000	0.000	0.000	0.250
Prohibit same sex marraige	0.104	0.000	0.000	1.000	0.000	0.000	0.000	0.000	0.000	0.000	0.000	0.000	0.000
Prevent sales of abusive life policies to military service members	0.103	0.000	0.000	0.500	0.000	0.000	0.000	0.000	0.500	0.250	0.250	0.250	0.250
Increase FCC indecency penalties	0.069	0.000	0.000	0.800	0.000	0.000	0.000	0.000	0.000	0.000	0.000	0.000	0.000
Gun Liability Bill	0.054	0.000	0.000	0.500	0.000	0.000	0.500	0.000	0.000	0.000	0.000	0.000	0.250
Amendment Prohibiting Flag Desecration	0.015	0.000	0.000	0.250	0.000	0.000	0.000	0.000	0.000	0.000	0.000	0.000	0.000

Note: Excellent 1.000, Very Good 0.800, Good 0.500, Marginal 0.200, No Contribution 0.000

Table 1 Priorities of the Bills According to the Criteria

One way to deal with urgency is to include a special criterion called "urgency" and assign it a priority alongside the other factors and prioritize all the bills past and present with respect to it over regular time horizons and note the change in overall priorities of all the bills. One can then also periodically reassign resources for their implementation.

In Table 1 we give the bills and their priorities according to the foregoing criteria.

Conclusion

We have seen that the matter of voting on bills in government is a very complicated process that involves national objectives, constituency interests and commitments to party and to other senators or representatives each time an official has to vote. We have sketched a way for dealing with multiple decisions and indicated that the objectives and values needed must be so general as to include all decisions. We've also sketched a list of such broad criteria and developed tables for their priorities and those of the bills before Congress in 2005 evaluated in terms of these criteria by way of an example. It is still possible to vote yes or no on a low priority bill, or to change the priority of a bill according to how it stands with respect to additional criteria not on the list in case it encounter insurmountable obstacles to get a high priority [6]. We hope that in this preliminary chapter we have provided ideas to ordinary people and to corporations to use criteria similar to those discussed here and illustrated in the example to prioritize their many decisions to determine which decision they should focus on first. Strategic criteria are used in every application we have made in the past several years by applying the AHP/ANP to all decisions in the context of BOCR. This provides a natural link between making single decisions and making multiple decisions.

References

1. Moon, J. (2004), *Issue Attention and Legislative Proposals in the US Senate*, Graduate School of Business, Stanford University
2. Maslow, A. (1954), *Motivation and Personality*, New York: Harper & Row, Publishers, Inc.
3. Rescher, N. (1969), *Introduction to Value Theory*, New Jersey: Prentice-Hall, Inc.

4. Baier K. and N. Rescher eds. (1969), *Values and the Future*, New York, The Free Press

5. Saaty, T.L. (2005), *Theory and Applications of the Analytic Network Process*, RWS Publications, Pittsburgh, PA

6. Saaty, T.L. and J.S. Shang (2007), Group Decision Making Through Voting: Head-Count versus Intensity of Preference, *Socio-Economic Planning Sciences* 41(1), pp. 22-37

Part V

Uncertainty and Time Dependence of Judgments and Replies to Criticisms of the AHP

Chapters 12, 13, and 14 deal with topics mentioned in the title of this part.

Chapter 12

The Unknown in Decision Making
What to Do About It

This chapter deals with the following ideas:

- Augmenting a hierarchic or network structure of a decision at different levels and several times as the need may be with a hypothetical element or criterion called "other" to help the expert who may be unsure of his structure to attribute influence to what may have been left out of the model that is unknown
- Illustrating and testing the stability of a decision with respect to the "other"

Introduction

The unknown or "other" that affects our lives is what we usually very much want to know about to cope with uncertainty. We often suspect that it affects us with partial and indefinite evidence that it exists but we only have uncertain feelings about it. Even when we do not know what it is we would like to allow for its influence in our explaining the outcome of a decision. One way to deal with the many factors of a decision is to include the unknown as one of them and then determine its priority of influence on the outcome by comparing it with other factors. We are able to do that to the extent that we are sure of what we know and of the residual that remains outside our understanding that may also have some effect on what we do. Confidence from good understanding and past success are what we need in order to judge the potential significance of what we don't know on the outcome. We can then perform sensitivity analysis to see how much effect unknown factors can have on the stability of the choice we make. Pairwise comparisons make it possible to tackle this idea explicitly and rather simply. This note illustrates how to prioritize and test the effect of the unknown alongside the known.

To deal with complexity our mind must model it by creating a structure and providing observations, measurements, judgments and of course hopefully rigorous analysis to study the influences of the various factors included in the model. How well the model works out depends on several factors having to do with its **structure** whose meaning and purpose are identified and described with language and words and the **flows** within the structure to serve the goals and purpose of the model for computing the relative dominance of the influences involved. In general the structure is fixed for a given analysis. However, the flows are dynamic and are mostly studied with logic and mathematics. Smets [1] very aptly addresses issues having to do with the goodness of the logical and mathematical aspect of our models in terms of three forms of ignorance: incompleteness, imprecision and uncertainty. There is concern in the literature about all three of these forms of ignorance. Although he does not decompose his discussion about ignorance by making a distinction between structure and flow, we believe that his scheme is useful for that purpose. With imprecision we associate the fact that we cannot pinpoint exactly the names and identity of the criteria and alternatives or the precise values of variables that in the case of decision-making take the form of numerical judgments. With uncertainty we associate probabilities with the different factors used in the model and with the likelihood that the judgments are what we think they are.

To reduce computational effort where the number of decision functions can be very large, Moskowitz and Wallenius [2] augmented an algorithm by Moskowitz by allowing the decision maker to interactively express strong binary preferences for partial decision functions at each stage of the recursion. From each revealed preference, an imprecise probability or utility function is imputed. It is then used to prune statistically dominated decision functions to smaller but relevant subsets of such functions, which converge to an optimal solution. Takeda [3] proposed a new procedure for treating what he calls pseudo-criteria based on the Analytic Hierarchy Process (AHP). This procedure differs from how other people may do it and requires only incomplete information on the weights but not the precise weights themselves. Deng [4] provided a fuzzy approach for tackling qualitative multicriteria analysis problems. We and others have had difficulty in justifying the fuzzy approach applied in the context of the AHP because its use of simulations to crank out a large number of estimates can be shown by many examples not to improve the final priorties obtained by the AHP.

Many studies are concerned with uncertainty, which is studied by using the concept of probability [5]. Beynon [6] introduced DS/AHP that incorporates Dempster-Shafer theory of evidence within the framework of the AHP. It provides a measure of uncertainty in the final results based on a functional form of the preference weightings that makes it possible to understand the appropriateness of the rating scale values used in the DS/AHP method, by evaluating the range of uncertainty expressed by the decision maker. Reuven [7] considered that the rank order of decision alternatives depends on two types of uncertainties: (1) the future characteristics of the decision making environment described by a set of scenarios, and (2) the decision making judgments regarding each pairwise comparison. He describes a simulation approach for handling both types of uncertainties in the AHP.

Paulson [8] described a methodology for the propagation of uncertainty in the AHP. The sole source of the uncertainty is assumed to lie in the entries of the preference matrices. He studied uncertainty in the rankings of the decision alternatives and in the probability of rank reversals as functions of the number of alternatives and of the depth of the hierarchy. Ranking uncertainty is found to decrease as the number of alternatives or the depth of the hierarchy is increased. Zahir [9] developed an algorithm to incorporate uncertainties within the framework of the AHP. He showed how to compute uncertainties in the relative priorities of a decision and provided an algorithm with computational procedures for doing it.

Yu [10] uses combined Goal Programming (GP) and AHP approaches to consider uncertainty. Since pairwise comparison values are the judgments obtained from an appropriate semantic scale, in practice the decision maker(s) usually gives some or all pairwise comparison values with a degree of uncertainty rather than precisely. By employing goal programming to treat a fuzzy AHP problem, Yu incorporated an absolute term linearization technique and a fuzzy rating expression into a GP-AHP model for solving group decision making fuzzy AHP problems.

Sugihara et al [11] proposed an interval preference relation. Since a pairwise comparison matrix in the AHP is based on human intuition, the given matrix will often include inconsistent elements that violate transitivity. Interval judgment data are used to express uncertainty in human pairwise comparison judgments from which interval weights are obtained that represent inconsistency in the judgment data.

O'Connor et al [12] described problems in maintenance arising from not having clear criteria and not having robust decisions with which to maintain failing equipment. The object of this work was to develop a dynamic and adaptive maintenance decision-making system using the AHP that utilizes existing data and supports decisions accordingly. Faults identified as others or unknown were approximately 30 percent of the total faults. The maintenance tradesmen decided to examine the faults in greater detail and classify them. In the end unidentified faults became less than 5 percent of the total faults for any machine. It is this concern with identifying the unknown and its effects that concerns us here.

Here we show how to include unknown influences as an intangible whose effect is determined through relative measurement. Instead of assigning (guessing) probabilities to the unknown, we derive priorities by performing the more general operation of paired comparisons. This involves systematic and reasoned redundancies in all the judgments about the likelihood of influence which then helps improve the validity of the numbers assigned. The unknown is simply a measure of the confidence an expert has about covering all the important criteria that influence the outcome of the decision. This enables one to capture the relative effect of what one "feels" the unknown to have on the outcome of the decision as one of the factors. The process itself diminishes uncertainty about the values of these probabilities. This says nothing about the naiveté and ignorance of the judge. It simply provides a means to remove doubt about the factors and their influence on the decision. With the unknown included as a criterion, the decision maker should no longer have any doubt about the factors included. They are all there. One caveat is that the unknown cannot be too important in priority for then one would be making a decision based on ignorance about other important criteria that should be involved. The main advantage of including a factor called "other" or the "unknown" is that it makes it possible for the decision maker to do sensitivity analysis to test the potential stability of the outcome with respect to the "unknown" according to his belief. It is an alternative that involves the use of uncertain knowledge instead of statistical methods of projection to determine the degree of confidence in the outcome of a decision under uncertainty. It is likely to be of value to an expert known for his care and accuracy in making decisions.

There are two kinds of "other" we can think of. One is to think of "other" as miscellaneous diverse criteria not considered in the decision. Such criteria we believe can and should be included as subcriteria of a parent criterion designated as for example "miscellaneous". But that is not what we have in mind. We are thinking of *residual* criteria that one may suspect are there but cannot articulate them explicitly. Residual does not mean central in the sense that they would serve as an alibi for ignorance. Their relative priorities must be commensurate with those of the criteria that are known.

Further Elaboration on the Unknown as the Criterion "Other"

The unknown is usually considered as an intangible and thus its *relative importance* with respect to other known criteria has so far eluded serious consideration even when probabilities could be assigned to the occurrence of the alternatives with respect to it. In using paired comparisons as a way to derive relative measurement, we can determine the perceived relative importance of the factor about which we are uncertain. It is precisely the multicriteria nature of this idea that attracted our attention to how to consider such a factor in decision-making. We can, in a constructive fashion, illustrate how to represent the unknown and determine how sensitive the final outcome is with respect to it as a reflection of our knowledge and confidence.

There are two types of unknown effects in decision-making. The first is the existence of criteria that are unknown but can affect the outcome of that decision. It is felt that there is something else out there that can influence the outcome, but it is not known exactly what it is. If the importance of such a criterion is thought to be significantly larger than the importance of the known factors as reflected by their priorities obtained through paired comparisons with the other criteria, then one cannot reliably say that one knows enough to make a decision. This observation equally applies if the unknown criteria can be attributed with more than about 10% of the overall influence. The unknown needs to fall on the lower side of the scale of priorities but still be comparable in relative terms with what is known. Sensitivity analysis would later show whether the best alternative is insensitive to the unknown factor. One would then adopt the best alternative for the decision. If it is sensitive to the unknown factor, then a second alternative may be sufficiently close to the first in priority and at the same time insensitive to the unknown factor in which case it may be more desirable to adopt for the decision than the highest ranked alternative.

The second type of unknown effect in a decision involves criteria that are known but there is incomplete information about how the alternatives rank with respect to these criteria. In this case one needs to look for the relevant information to enable examine the alternatives carefully with respect to each of these criteria. This takes both effort and time. We know of an example where it took months to perform experiments at very high cost to clarify the behavior of the alternatives with respect to a certain important criterion.

What is important to note here is that depending on the experience, intelligence and alertness of the decision maker this "other" factor can be very important, in which case it is futile to make a decision because the unknown dominates the known. Only when the priority of other is not too large relative to the other factors can one decide through sensitivity analysis whether or not to adopt the decision. We now illustrate with examples.

Examples

This section gives examples in which *"Other"* as an important factor can change the outcome of the decision problems.

Selecting a Pipeline Route in South America

Executives of a South American oil company (example due to the first author's colleague Ernest Forman) must choose among three locations to construct an oil pipeline. The alternatives are a northern route to Covenas, a southern route to Orito, and a western route to Bahia. The southern and western routes terminate on the west side of the Panama Canal and the northern route terminates on the east side; selecting the western route would result in a $1 per barrel increase in profit due to saving in transportation. While this is a factor affecting NPV (Net Present Value), management has to balance its profit motive with concerns for the environment and for managerial control. So, in the end the cost savings due to transportation are insufficient to make the western route best.

During the decision session, discussion among vice presidents, engineers, and operating managers of the company was instructive as each group member learned from the others' information and insights.

The problem of choosing the best route for the pipeline is shown in Figure 1. Notice that some criteria have sub-criteria – for example, Environment is broken down into Social and Physical. The alternatives are evaluated directly for the criterion Net Present Value, but they are evaluated for each of the subcriteria under Environment for example. ECP refers to equal capital partners.

The next step is to make comparison judgments. The decision-making group from the oil company assessed the relative importance of all possible pairs of criteria with respect to the overall goal *Select Best Pipeline Route*, coming to a consensus judgment on each pair. The question to ask when comparing two criteria is: which is more important and how much more important is it with respect to selecting the best pipeline route?

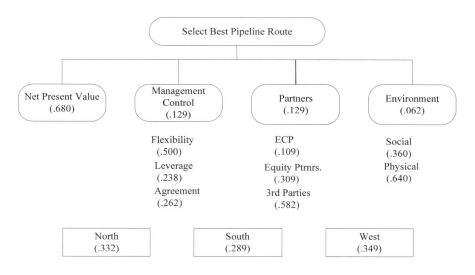

Figure 1 The Pipeline Decision Model

The matrix of pairwise comparison judgments for the criteria determined by the decision-makers in this case is shown in Table 2. Beynon [14] investigated using the Parzen Window method what he considered acceptable comparison matrices and their resultant priority values for a number of alternative 9-unit scales and the AHP's 1-9 scale. The number of acceptable combinations of pairwise comparisons subject to different consistency levels (20%, 10%, 8% and 5%) for the 1-9 scale and the four alternative scale units are given. To enable an analysis of the spread of priority values it is necessary to produce an estimated distribution. He showed that each one of the scales offers a varying number of acceptable comparison matrices for the different consistency levels.

Webber [15] also reported on results of three experiments about whether differences in the scale used or the format order of paired comparisons yields significant differences in AHP models. He used alternative scales, alternative random versus nonrandom formats, and alternative top-down versus bottom-up ordering. Students enrolled in an introductory management course in the College of Business at a large, urban university participated in this study. Over 340 students joined in laboratory groups of no more than 15 students at a time. Overall, for the survey research instrument, no strong, consistent differences were found in the responses associated with Scale, Format, or Order.

The priorities are obtained by raising the matrix to large powers to capture all the interactions (transitivities), summing the entries in each row, and dividing by the total sum of the rows. We are permitted to use decimal values between the integers, such as 2.6, if desired. It is mathematically demonstrated by using the logarithmic law of stimulus-response that it is necessary to use this fundamental scale to obtain meaningful results in practice. It represents the normal range of human sensitivity to phenomena that are homogeneous.

In Table 1 below, when comparing NPV on the left with Environment on top, it is thought that NPV is between strongly and very strongly more important, and the value six is entered in the (NPV, Environment) position, and automatically a 1/6 is entered in the (Environment, NPV) position. Similarly, in comparing Partners with NPV, it is thought that Partners is not more important than NPV, but the opposite, NPV is very strongly more important. Thus, 1/7 is entered in the (Partners, NPV) position and a 7 is entered in the (NPV, Partners) position and so on. We always compare the criterion on the left as to how much more dominant it is than the criterion at the top. If it is not, the reciprocal value is used.

First the criteria are compared for their importance with respect to the goal as shown in Table 1 below:

Table 1 Comparing the Criteria for Importance with Respect to the Goal

	Net Present Value (NPV)	Management Control	Partners	Environment	Priorities
NPV	1	7	7	6	.680
Mgt. Control	1/7	1	1	3	.129
Partners	1/7	1	1	3	.129
Environment	1/6	1/3	1/3	1	.062

Then the subcriteria are compared with respect to their importance to the criterion they fall under. For an example of comparing the subcriteria beneath the criterion Partners, see Table 2. Finally the alternatives are compared with respect to each of the criteria or subcriteria above them as in Table 3.

The priorities for each set of judgments for the alternatives are shown in Table 4. They are combined by multiplying the values for North, South and West under each criterion or subcriterion directly linked to the routes, by the weighted value shown for the criterion or subcriterion and adding. The priorities of the criteria and subcriteria (called covering criteria of the alternatives) sum to 1.000. The best overall choice is seen to be the Western route.

Table 2 Judgments Under the Criterion Partners

Partners	ECP	Equity	3rd Parties	Priorities
ECP	1	1/3	1/5	.109
Equity	3	1	1/2	.309
3rd Party	5	2	1	.582

Table 3 Judgments for Alternatives Under the Subcriterion Physical

Physical	North	South	West	Priorities
North	1	1/3	1/2	.163
South	3	1	2	.540
West	2	½	1	.297

Table 4 Synthesis for Final Answer

	NPV .680	Flexibl .064	Lever .031	Agree .034	ECP .014	Equity .040	3rd Pty .075	Social .023	Phys .039	Overall Priority
North	.312	.726	.182	.182	.122	.093	.669	.190	.163	.332
South	.304	.172	.273	.273	.230	.167	.243	.547	.540	.289
West	.384	.102	.545	.545	.648	.740	.088	.263	.297	**.349**

Now we introduce the unknown criterion "other", first in Figure 2, and then in Table 5 for comparison.

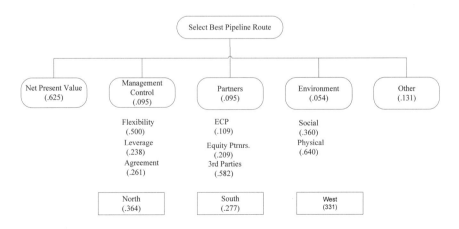

Figure 2 The Pipeline Decision Model

Table 5 Comparing the Criteria for Importance with Respect to the Goal

	Net Present Value (NPV)	Management Control	Partners	Environ.	Other	Priorities
NPV	1	7	7	6	6	.625
Mgt. Control	1/7	1	1	3	1/3	.095
Partners	1/7	1	1	3	1/5	.095
Environment	1/6	1/3	1/3	1	1/3	.054
Other	1/6	3	5	3	1	.131

The new priorities for each set of judgments are shown in Table 6 below together with the final outcome. The best overall choice is now seen to be the Northern route. It illustrates that "Other", which represents unknown risks for this problem, is an important factor to include in the model.

Table 6 Synthesis for Final Answer

	NPV .625	Flexibl. .047	Lever .023	Agree .025	ECP .010	Equity .029	3rd Pty .055	Social .019	Phys .034	Other .131	Overall Priority
North	0,312	0,726	0,182	0,182	0,122	0,093	0,669	0,190	0,163	0.624	**.364**
South	0,304	0,172	0,273	0,273	0,230	0,167	0,243	0,547	0,540	0.182	.276
West	0,384	0,102	0,545	0,545	0,648	0,740	0,088	0,263	0,297	0.194	.330

Sensitivity Analysis

Without "other" the model gives **West** as the best alternative. But if the priority of NPV which is the most important criterion for the problem decreases from 0.680 to 0.526, then North becomes the best alternative. On adding "other" as a criterion with priority 0.13, the best alternative is changed from West to **North**. If the priority of "other" is decreased from 0.13 to 0.074 or if the priority of NPV is increased from 0.624 to 0.730, West turns out to be the best among the three alternatives. Thus we see that "other" with a small priority of 0.13 can change the best alternative from West to North. This is an example where concern with what may not be identified as a criterion whose priority is low (0.074) can give a significantly different answer.

Market Share of Wall Mart, K-Mart and Target
    This is a simple network model to estimate the current relative market share of Walmart, Kmart and Target. Figures 3 and 4 give the criteria

without and with" other" followed by Table 7 with the outcomes that are compared with the actual market share relative values.

Figure 3 The Criteria for Market Share of Wall Mart, K Mart and Target – Without Other–

Figure 4 The Criteria for Market Share of Wall Mart, K Mart and Target – With Other–

Other: Customer awareness, family, teenagers.

Table 7 Estimated and Actual Market Shares

Alternatives	Without Other	With Other	Actual Market Shares
K-Mart	0.235	0.223	0.259
Target	0.143	0.205	0.193
Wall-Mart	0.622	0.572	0.548
Hadamard Index	1.0309	1.0101	

To get an index of how close the result is to actual market share, we used the Hadamard product (element-wise rather than the usual row x column multiply and add process) on the product of the matrix of ratios from the actual market share vector and the transpose matrix of ratios of the estimated market share vector. The compatibility should be less than 1.1 to decide that the solution is acceptable. We calculated this index for both models without and with "other". The results are 1.0309 and 1.0101, respectively, the compatibility of the second being better than that of the first.

Pizza Market

Figure 5 The Criteria for Market Share of Pizza Companies
–without Other–

Figure 6 The Criteria for Market Share of Dell, Compaq and Gateway
–with Other–

Other: Company's location, management and so on.

Table 8 shows estimated and the actual market share values.

Table 8 Estimated and Actual Market Shares

Alternatives	Without Other	With Other	Actual Market Shares
Domino	0.284	0.279	0.249
Little Cesar	0.134	0.129	0.164
Papa John	0.137	0.130	0.115
Pizza Hut	0.445	0.462	0.472
Hadamard Index	1.0232	1.0218	

Our conclusion is that using "other" can enrich our approach to decision making and appears to improve the accuracy of the outcome of a decision.

Selecting a National Health Plan

While national health plans vary, they all focus on decreasing costs. Currently, approximately 37 million Americans are uninsured and millions more are vastly underinsured. The U.S. has easily the most expensive health care system in the world. Despite the allocation of such large sums of money to health care, the U.S. ranks in the lower middle third in the quality of care among industrialized nations. The goal of this model is to choose a national health plan for the United States focusing on the effects of nationalized health care, health care costs, quality of care, probability of acceptance, and the overall benefits to society. Four types of health care systems are considered:

National Health System (NHS): Both the financing and distribution of health care services are the responsibility of the federal government. All health care is owned and provided by the government, and physicians are employees of the government. The benefits are: complete health insurance coverage for everyone, and relatively low overall health care costs. Low efficiency is a common criticism of NHS.

National Health Insurance (NHI): The concept of NHI is very similar to that of NHS; the government is responsible for financing health care services only, the distribution is provided by the market. NHI plans seem to decrease health care costs in general while simultaneously providing health insurance coverage for everyone. The rationing of health care is prevalent because the government has a restricted budget.

Employer Health Insurance (EHI): EHI calls for mandatory employer provision of health insurance for employees and their families.

School District Health Insurance (SDHI): This is a private sector approach aimed at extending coverage to the uninsured and underinsured by calling for health insurance based public school enrollment. By combining the children in public school and their families into one large statewide group, the plan greatly increases the purchasing power of each individual family, without changing the basic structure of the current health care system.

Table 9 gives the results with and without the criterion "Other". Without "Other", the model gives SDHI as the best alternative. On adding "Other" as a criterion with priority 0.109, the best alternative is changed from SDHI to EHI.

Principia Mathematica Decernendi

Table 9 Synthesis for Final Answer

	Criteria					Alternatives			
	Health Care Costs	Quality of Care	Probability of Acceptance	Overall Benefits to Society	Other	NHS	NHI	EHI	SDHI
Without Other	0.081	0.522	0.049	0.348		0.128	0.188	0.321	**0.363**
With Other	0.068	0.474	0.042	0.307	0.109	0.130	0.182	**0.345**	0.343

Sensitivity analysis has shown that if the priority of "Other" is increased from 0.109 to 0.162 in the new model, EHI remains the best but with priority 0.360.

Our conclusion is that using "Other" can enrich our approach to decision making and appears to improve the accuracy of the outcome of a decision. We are unable to say exactly when "Other" would be good to consider in a decision and when not if we do not have some data to check against.

Conclusions

People who have clear and definite choices to make are often less likely to be concerned about other factors that might influence their choice than people who must decide from among closely related alternatives. For the latter, hidden factors can influence the outcome and must be searched for, identified and used.

There are occasions when even if an alternative has a high priority relative to other alternatives that priority is questionable because there may be other criteria that need to be identified and used that can change the ranks obtained for the alternatives. In that case "other" would not be of help. One needs to be fairly sure that all the important criteria have been used and the priorities of the alternatives are close, in which case "other" would be useful to determine the stability of the best alternative.

References

1. Smets, P. (1991), Varieties of Ignorance and the Need for Well-Founded Theories, *Information Sciences*, 57-58, pp. 135-144
2. Moskowitz, H. and J. Wallenius (1990), Preference-Order Recursion for Finding Relevant Pure, Admissible and Optimal Statistical Decision Functions, *Decision Sciences* 21, pp. 521-532
3. Takeda, E. (2001), A Method for Multiple Pseudo-Criteria Decision Problems, *Computers and Operations Research*, 28(14) pp. 1427-1439
4. Deng, H. (1999), Multicriteria Analysis with Fuzzy Pairwise Comparison, *International Journal of Approximate Reasoning* 21(3), pp. 215-231
5. Marshall, K.T. and R.M. Oliver (1995), *Decision Making and Forecasting: with Emphasis on Model Building and Policy Analysis*, McGraw Hill, California
6. Beynon, M. (2002), DS/AHP Method: A Mathematical Analysis, Including an Understanding of Uncertainty, *European Journal of Operational Research* 140 (1), pp. 148-164
7. Reuven, R.L. and K. Wan (1998), A Simulation Approach for Handling Uncertainty in the AHP, *European Journal of Operational Research* 106(1), pp. 1116-1122
8. Paulson, D. and S. Zahir (1995), Consequences of Uncertainty in the AHP, *European Journal of Operational Research* 87(1), pp. 45-56
9. Zahir M.S. (1996), Incorporating the Uncertainty of Decision Judgments in the Analytic Hierarchy Process, *European Journal of Operational Research*, 53(2), pp. 206-216
10. Yu, C. (2002), A GP-AHP Method for Solving Group Decision Making Fuzzy AHP Problems, *Computers and Operations Research*, 29(14), pp. 1969-2001
11. Sugihara, K. and H. Ranaka (2001), Interval Evaluations in the Analytic Hierarchy Process by Possibility Analysis, *Computational Intelligence*, 17 (3), pp. 567-579
12. O'Connor, R.F., G.B. Williams and A.W. Labib (1998), An Effective Maintenance System Using Analytic Hierarchy Process, *Integrated Manufacturing Systems*, 9/2, pp. 87-98
13. Saaty, T.L. (2000), *Fundamentals of Decision Making and Priority Theory with the Analytic Hierarchy Process*, Vol.VI of the AHP Series, RWS Publications, Pittsburgh, PA

14. Beynon, M. (2002), An Analysis of Distributions of Priority Values from Alternative Comparison Scales within AHP, *European Journal of Operational Research*, 140(1), pp. 104-117

15. Webber, S.A., B. Apostolou and J.M. Hassell (1996), The Sensitivity of the Analytic Hierarchy Process to Alternative Scale and Cue Presentation, *European Journal of Operational Research*, 96(2), pp. 351-362

Chapter 13

Time Dependent Decision Making; Dynamic Priorities in the AHP/ANP

This chapter deals with the following ideas:
- How do we deal formally with time dependent judgments?
- Is it better to use variations in the structure of a decision to allow for variations in time or is it better to use functions and other analytical ways to express judgments over time?

Introduction

Sound decision making not only requires that we look ahead as a process of thinking and planning, but also that our structures be flexible to include change so that we can constantly revise our decision because the system itself is in imbalance resulting in a non-stationary optimum. Thus optimizing inefficiently by selecting a best decision at a given time can only be a sub-optimum over a long range time horizon because of the fundamental influence of change in any survivable system. There are three ways to cope with this problem. The first is to make the best choice according to short, mid and long term merits with a feedback loop or a holarchy used to prioritize them according to their benefits, opportunities, costs and risks evaluated in terms of strategic criteria used in general to guide all our decisions [1]. The other is to make the judgments mathematically depend on time and express them as functions, discussed in this chapter. The third and less practical way is to revise a decision every once in a while. Although many decisions can be tested in advance through sensitivity analysis to determine their long term stability, revision after implementation can be both controversial and costly. One may have to abandon an already finished resource intensive alternative for another such costly alternative. In politics, we circumvent doing it by electing new leaders with the perspective we want, so they can focus on making better decisions for pressing needs in society.

So far most of us have had no way to combine dollars with yards or pounds to trade them off. We would be truly multi-dimensional if we could combine the different dimensions into a single dimension that represents our priority of importance. That is precisely what the AHP and ANP help us do in a more or less precise way, depending on the level of experience that we bring to bear on a decision problem. Until recently, the AHP and ANP have been **static** in that they have used numbers and derived numbers to represent priorities. What we need is to make them dynamic by using numbers or functions and then deriving either numbers that represent functions like expected values, or deriving functions directly to represent priorities over time. My aim here is to extend the AHP/ANP to deal with time dependent priorities; we may refer to them as DHP/DNP (Dynamic Hierarchy Process/Dynamic Network Process). At this point we may not know enough to develop the necessary fundamental scale of functions to use in making paired comparisons of intangibles. But if nothing else DHP and DNP work with tangibles now and we need to weight and trade off tangibles as functions of time.

Time dependent decision-making that we call dynamic decision-making is a subject that we need today. So far we have thought of our decisions as known alternatives to choose from. But these alternatives may evolve over time along with our preferences for them like stocks in the stock market whose prices constantly change over time. Our actions need to vary over time like a medicine capsule that releases different amounts of chemical at different times. Time dependent decisions are a reality and not a complicated idea that we can ignore. At a minimum they are needed in technical design problems in which the influences of several tangible design factors change over time and tradeoffs must be made among them to enable the system to respond differently and continuously over the time of its operation. But the power and potential of the subject lie in its use of judgment to make comparisons to derive relative real valued functions for intangibles from paired comparisons. Because we can do that for real numbers we can also do it for complex numbers. They have a modulus (magnitude) and an argument (direction), each of which is real. That is where we need to go later to derive relative complex functions from paired comparison expert judgments. The modulus is estimated in the usual way of comparing magnitudes and the argument or angle is estimated along the lines of rate of change comparison given below. In this way the two parts of a complex number are derived from paired comparisons.

There is a caveat to the foregoing observations. There was a time when I, as a mathematician, taking space and time as major building blocks of all scientific thinking, wanted to generalize the discrete approach to decision making to continuous judgments somewhat overlooking the fact that people are constantly changing their judgments about influences in a fast-changing world and I did considerable work to implement such thinking as can be seen in this chapter. However, now I believe that such decisions may only be useful for robots or physical things because the outcome of influences is in constant flux and emergent properties like water from hydrogen and oxygen make it impossible to think that one can be in sufficient control to anticipate all likely outcomes in the face of completely new properties whose influences are not really known or understood well and whose consequences may not be durable. This limits the judgment process to what is known in the near present. Dynamic priorities are most likely to be unstable, cannot be made at one time about how they would be preferred at another distant time, but only near the time at which the judgments are made. This is a major observation. Priorities inevitably change over time because people learn new things and themselves change their judgments.

There are essentially two analytic ways to study dynamic decisions: structural, by including scenarios and time periods as elements in the structure that represents a decision, and functional by explicitly involving time in the judgment process. A possible third way would be a hybrid of these two.

The **structural** method is most familiar today and it involves using scenarios or time periods as factors in the hierarchic or network structure of a decision, and then making appropriate judgments. Generally contrast scenarios such as optimistic, status quo and pessimistic, or more specific ones such as different values for the economy or the stock market are put near or at the top of a hierarchy. The likelihood of the scenarios is first determined in terms of higher level criteria under the goal such as economic, political, social and technological, that are themselves prioritized according to their prevailing influences over a certain time horizon. Judgments are provided for the behavior of the alternatives with respect to the factors encountered under each scenario [2]. Synthesis reveals the best alternative to follow in view of the mix of potential scenarios. For more detail about this method see [3] where contrast scenarios are discussed. The other structural method is to put actual time periods at the "bottom" of the structure, prioritize them and finally combine their priorities by, for example, using the idea of expected value. This method was used in estimating when the US economy would recover and is illustrated in the next section.

The second approach where the judgments themselves change with time is **functional** in the literal sense. Whatever the structure may be, time dependent judgments are provided using functions from which priorities are then obtained and synthesized as one generally does with the AHP/ANP. We have two problems to solve when using dynamic judgments in the AHP/ANP. The first is what scale to use to represent dynamic judgments and how in this case it can be made to satisfy the axiom of homogeneity. The second is how to generate close form expression for the principal eigenvector of a matrix whose order is more than four. Because seven is an upper bound on producing results with reliable consistency, it is sufficient to find ways to derive the principal eigenvector of a matrix of order seven or less. This task can also be done in two ways, analytically and numerically. This chapter is about both these ways but particularly about the mathematics of the functional way. In making pairwise comparisons we estimate how many times one element is more important than another with respect to a common property by forming their ratios if we know their measurements and get an expert to tell us when we do not have their exact measurements. Each judgment is expressed with a number.

Suppose now that the measurements are a function of time. If we know the functions, we can form their ratios, but if we do not, what kind of typical functions can we use to represent ratios in a standard way just as we use numbers in a standard way. If humans have an intrinsic ability to look at the future of two stocks whose values appreciate over time and can say that on the whole one would be a better investment than the other, then one would like to capture this intuitive understanding by some standard functions to apply in all situations where we have to deal with intangibles over time. We have to do this kind of thinking even if we do not know much about the exact future. Like the US building a 60 billion dollar anti-missile system based on imagined threats over a future time horizon that may not materialize. The decision would be a function of time going forward or pulling back as the need may be. What are typical functions to use in describing in an uncertain way the ratio of anticipated variations of two functions over time? I will discuss and illustrate my proposed approach to this problem.

A Structural Dynamics Example

Let us consider the problem of predicting the data of turn-around of the US economy in the crisis that began in December 2007. The model and judgments were made in March 2009 by my long time friend Indonesia's great economist and Cornell University Professor Iwan Azis. We only present the network and outcome that is a synthesis from numerous pairwise comparison matrices.

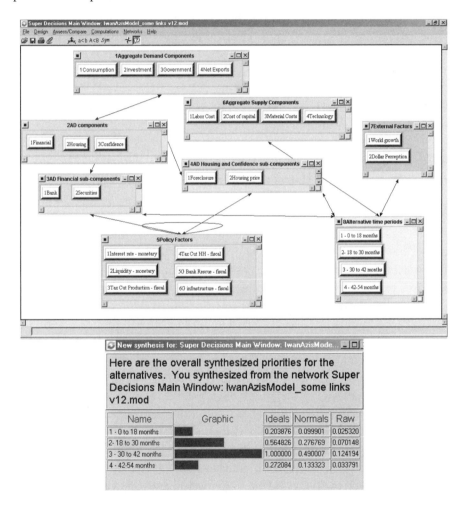

Figure 1 Network and Outcome for Predicting Turnaround Date of the U.S. Economy

The expected value calculations are shown below:

Name	Normals	Midpts	Normals multiplied by Midpts
1 - 0 to 18 months	0.099901	9	0.899109
2- 18 to 30 months	0.276769	24	6.642456
3 - 30 to 42 months	0.490007	36	17.64025
4 - 42-54 months	0.133323	48	6.399504

The sum of the entries in the last column 31.58132 is the expected number of months (from December, 2007 to about July, 2010) which is the length of the turnaround time. Note that December 2007 was the official date of the beginning of recession as determined by the National Bureau of Economic Research (NBER).

The measure against which the predictions of the model will be validated will be the time determined by the National Bureau of Economic Research (NBER) which will probably not make its judgment until a year or more after the turnaround occurs.

Functional Dynamics: Numerical Solution of the Principal Eigenvalue Problem by Raising the Matrix to Powers – A Basic 3 x 3 Example

Because priorities are obtained in the form of the principal eigenvector and because this vector is obtained by raising the paired comparisons matrix to powers, particularly in this case, we do not need to solve equations. We are fortunate in this special and rare case to do that. In the AHP one simply composes by multiplying and adding functions. So, in principle, there is no major theoretical difficulty in making decisions with dynamic judgments. In the ANP the problem is to obtain the limiting result of powers of the supermatrix with dynamic priorities. Because of its size, for the foreseeable future, the supermatrix would have to be solved numerically. It may even turn out in the long run that this is the more efficient way to obtain priorities from the supermatrix even when we have analytic expressions to represent priorities introduced in the usual way in the supermatrix to raise it to powers to obtain its limit for various values of time.

We remind the reader that if one has the principal eigenvector of a matrix, to test for consistency one obtains its principal eigenvalue by forming the scalar product of the principal eigenvector and the vector of column sums of the matrix. Generally, given an eigenvector, this is also the way to obtain its corresponding eigenvalue.

The typical form of a judgment matrix in dynamic form is:

$$A(t) = \begin{bmatrix} a_{11}(t) & a_{12}(t) & \cdots & a_{1n}(t) \\ a_{21}(t) & a_{22}(t) & \cdots & a_{2n}(t) \\ \vdots & \vdots & \vdots & \vdots \\ a_{n1}(t) & a_{n2}(t) & \cdots & a_{nn}(t) \end{bmatrix}$$

$a_{ij} > 0, a_{ji}(t) = a_{ij}^{-1}(t)$. As in the discrete case, when $A(t)$ is consistent, we have $a_{ij}(t) = w_i(t)/w_j(t)$.

The basic idea with the numerical approach is to obtain the time dependent principassl eigenvector by simulation. One expresses the judgments functionally but then derives the eigenvector from the judgments for a fixed instant of time, substitutes the numerical values of the eigenvectors obtained for that instant in a supermatrix, solves the supermatrix problem and derives the priorities for the alternatives. Repeating the process for different values of time one generates a curve for the priorities of the alternatives and then approximates these values by curves with a functional form for each component of the eigenvector. It is sufficient to illustrate this entire procedure for one matrix.

Let us consider the 3 by 3 matrix with dynamic coefficients shown below. The rows of the two tables below the matrix give the principal eigenvector for the indicated values of t. They are then plotted in the diagram below that and an algorithm is used to find the analytic expressions for the best fitting curves for the three components of the eigenvector. This entire process can be made automatic in software for dynamic judgments.

$$A(t) = \begin{bmatrix} 1 & a(t) & b(t) \\ 1/a(t) & 1 & c(t) \\ 1/b(t) & 1/c(t) & 1 \end{bmatrix} \quad \begin{array}{l} a(t) = 0.1 + t^3 \\ b(t) = 1 + 2t^2 \\ c(t) = 1 + \frac{1}{2}e^t \end{array}$$

The following expressions are best least-squares fits in some technical sense of each set of numerical data for the components shown in Table 1 and plotted in Figure 3

$$w_1(t) \approx \frac{1}{\sqrt{2\pi}} \int_{-\infty}^{-0.053+1.151\ln t} e^{-\frac{z^2}{2}} dz, \quad t > 0.4$$

$$w_2(t) \approx \frac{1}{\sqrt{2\pi}} \int_{-\infty}^{-0.344-0.905\ln t} e^{-\frac{z^2}{2}} dz, \quad t > 0.4$$

$$w_3(t) \approx e^{-0.956-0.979t}, \quad t > 0.4$$

Table 1 Eigenvectors for Different Values of Time for Matrix Above

t	a(t)	b(t)	c(t)	t	w1	w2	w3
0	0.1	1	1.5	0	0.12202	0.648329	0.229651
0.05	0.100125	1.005	1.525636	0.05	0.122032	0.650441	0.227527
0.1	0.101	1.02	1.552585	0.1	0.122939	0.65207	0.224991
0.15	0.103375	1.045	1.580917	0.15	0.125189	0.652457	0.222354
0.2	0.108	1.08	1.610701	0.2	0.129205	0.650917	0.219878
0.25	0.115625	1.125	1.642013	0.25	0.135356	0.646922	0.217721
0.3	0.127	1.18	1.674929	0.3	0.143922	0.640169	0.215909
0.35	0.142875	1.245	1.709534	0.35	0.155057	0.630604	0.214339
0.4	0.164	1.32	1.745912	0.4	0.168789	0.618394	0.212817
0.45	0.191125	1.405	1.784156	0.45	0.185024	0.603858	0.211119
0.5	0.225	1.5	1.824361	0.5	0.203569	0.587395	0.209036
0.55	0.266375	1.605	1.866627	0.55	0.224166	0.569422	0.206412
0.6	0.316	1.72	1.911059	0.6	0.246511	0.550334	0.203156
0.65	0.374625	1.845	1.95777	0.65	0.270281	0.530484	0.199235
0.7	0.443	1.98	2.006876	0.7	0.29515	0.510183	0.194667
0.75	0.521875	2.125	2.0585	0.75	0.320802	0.489692	0.189507
0.8	0.612	2.28	2.11277	0.8	0.346935	0.469231	0.183833
0.85	0.714125	2.445	2.169823	0.85	0.373278	0.448984	0.177738
0.9	0.829	2.62	2.229802	0.9	0.399583	0.4291	0.171317
0.95	0.957375	2.805	2.292855	0.95	0.425637	0.4097	0.164664
1	1.1	3	2.359141	1	0.451256	0.390876	0.157868

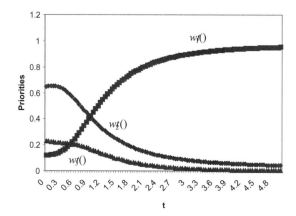

Figure 3 A Plot of the Numerical Estimate of the Components of the
Principal Right Eigenvector

Functional Dynamics: Analytic Solution of the Principal Eigenvalue Problem by Solving Algebraic Equations of Degree n

Because we need to solve for the principal eigenvector, Perron theory gives us a way to obtain it more simply than by solving a high order algebraic equation or even by raising the matrix to arbitrarily large powers. On p. 20 of

Horn and Johnson's "Matrix Analysis" [4] there is a brief discussion of the classical adjoint. Let $M = A - \lambda_{max}(T) \, I$ be an n by n matrix, where A is the pairwise comparisons matrix and I is the identity matrix. What we now show is only useful when we know $\lambda_{max}(T)$. Let M' be the matrix whose entry in the ith row and j^{th} column is $(-1)^{i+j}$ times the (n-1 by n-1) determinant of the matrix obtained by removing the ith column and j^{th} row of M. Note the row/column transposition. Then $M \, M' = \det (M) \, I$. Now M has rank n-1. We note that in our situation, because its characteristic polynomial is of degree n and vanishes at $\lambda_{max}(T)$, the rank of M cannot be more than n-1. By Perron, $\lambda_{max}(T)$ is unique and cannot again be the root of a determinant of an n-1 minor of M and the rank of M is precisely n-1. Thus $MM' = 0$ and every column of M' is an eigenvector of M (belongs to the kernel of M). Since the kernel of M is one-dimensional, all of the columns of M' must be proportional. They are also nonzero vectors because the rank of M is n-1 that is "some" n-1 by n-1 minor is nonsingular. This gives us another way of getting the principal right eigenvector of A when we know $\lambda_{max}(T)$. But for the supermatrix we already know that $\lambda_{max}(T) = 1$ which follows from:

$$\max \sum_{j=1}^{n} a_{ij} \geq \sum_{j=1}^{n} a_{ij} \frac{w_j}{w_i} = \lambda_{max} \text{ for max } w_i$$

$$\min \sum_{j=1}^{n} a_{ij} \leq \sum_{j=1}^{n} a_{ij} \frac{w_j}{w_i} = \lambda_{max} \text{ for min } w_i$$

Thus for a row stochastic matrix we have

$$1 = \min \sum_{j=1}^{n} a_{ij} \leq \lambda_{max} \leq \max \sum_{j=1}^{n} a_{ij} = 1, \text{ thus } \lambda_{max} = 1.$$

The same type of argument applies when a matrix is column stochastic.

Here is an example of the foregoing ideas. The matrix A, its principal right eigenvector and its eigenvalues are:

$$
\begin{bmatrix}
1 & 2 & 3 & 4 & 5 \\
\frac{1}{2} & 1 & 2 & 3 & 4 \\
\frac{1}{3} & \frac{1}{2} & 1 & 2 & 3 \\
\frac{1}{4} & \frac{1}{3} & \frac{1}{2} & 1 & 2 \\
\frac{1}{5} & \frac{1}{4} & \frac{1}{3} & \frac{1}{2} & 1
\end{bmatrix}
\begin{pmatrix}
0.418539 \\
0.262518 \\
0.159923 \\
0.097253 \\
0.061767
\end{pmatrix}
\left\{
\begin{array}{c}
5.06808 \\
0.00498879+0.582755i \\
0.00498879-0.582755i \\
-0.0390289+0.068286i \\
-0.0390289-0.068286i
\end{array}
\right\}
$$

$\lambda_{max}(A) = 5.06808.$

The matrix $M=A-\lambda_{max}(A)\,I$ is given by:

$$
\begin{bmatrix}
-4.06808 & 2 & 3 & 4 & 5 \\
\frac{1}{2} & -4.06808 & 2 & 3 & 4 \\
\frac{1}{3} & \frac{1}{2} & -4.06808 & 2 & 3 \\
\frac{1}{4} & \frac{1}{3} & \frac{1}{2} & -4.06808 & 2 \\
\frac{1}{5} & \frac{1}{4} & \frac{1}{3} & \frac{1}{2} & -4.06808
\end{bmatrix}
$$

Its adjoint matrix M' is:

$$
\begin{bmatrix}
136.49 & 214.908 & 353.393 & 580.105 & 924.877 \\
85.6099 & 134.796 & 221.657 & 363.855 & 580.105 \\
52.1526 & 82.116 & 135.031 & 221.657 & 353.393 \\
31.7155 & 49.9371 & 82.116 & 134.796 & 214.908 \\
20.1428 & 31.7155 & 52.1526 & 85.6099 & 136.49
\end{bmatrix}
$$

Note that MM' = 0 =

$$
\begin{bmatrix}
-3.62\times10^{-12} & 8.35\times10^{-14} & 4.35\times10^{-14} & 3.83\times10^{-13} & 1.63\times10^{-13} \\
1.96\times10^{-14} & -3.61\times10^{-12} & 2.97\times10^{-14} & 1.20\times10^{-14} & 1.98\times10^{-14} \\
2.10\times10^{-14} & -2.05\times10^{-14} & -3.69\times10^{-12} & -9.44\times10^{-14} & 1.09\times10^{-13} \\
-2.64\times10^{-14} & -2.58\times10^{-14} & 1.58\times10^{-14} & -3.69\times10^{-12} & 4.67\times10^{-14} \\
1.36\times10^{-14} & 2.35\times10^{-14} & 3.04\times10^{-14} & 2.93\times10^{-14} & -3.66\times10^{-12}
\end{bmatrix}
$$

Any column of M' such as the first gives principal right eigenvector given above in normalized form.

In this chapter we give the analytic solution for deriving the eigenvector for up to a 4x4 matrices and also give the solution of the quintic equation for the eigenvalues in closed form. The reader interested in this problem can contact this author for more general information on the solution of the quintic, sextic and septic equations. A technical problem that arises in this approach is that because of the time dependence of the coefficients of the matrix, it is difficult to generate the eigenvector of priorities in symbolic form if the order of the matrix is more than four. The reason is that in these cases one must solve a polynomial equation to obtain the principal eigenvalue and derive the corresponding principal eigenvector and we have expressions given below for both of these for $n \leq 4$. But for $n > 4$ the story is complicated and has a long history in our time. *Mathematica* is a good program for providing the eigenvalues and the eigenvectors of matrices of large order. It would also be useful if one were to use it for time dependent judgments by taking different times, entering these numerical values of time, solving an entire decision problem numerically, and repeating the process. In the end the several decision-outcome values can be approximated by time dependent curves.

Quadratic Case

To obtain the eigenvalue and eigenvectors of a 2 by 2 matrix, we must solve the problem

$$\begin{bmatrix} 1 & a(t) \\ 1/a(t) & 1 \end{bmatrix} \begin{bmatrix} w_1(t) \\ w_2(t) \end{bmatrix} = \lambda_{max} \begin{bmatrix} w_1(t) \\ w_2(t) \end{bmatrix}$$

for which we know because the matrix is consistent that $\lambda_{max}(t)=2$. For the eigenvector we need to solve the system of equations:

$$w_1(t) + a(t)w_2(t) = 2w_1(t)$$
$$w_1(t)/a(t) + w_2(t) = 2w_2(t)$$

The first equation yields $w_1(t)=a(t)w_2(t)$, and because $w_1(t)+w_2(t)=1$, we have for our solution $w_1(t)=a(t)/[1+a(t)]$, $w_2(t)=1/[1+a(t)]$.

Cubic Case

We suppress the use of the parameter t in what follows. We have : $\lambda_{max}=(a_{13}/a_{12}a_{23})^{1/3}+(a_{12}a_{23}/a_{13})^{1/3}+1$. If we define $\Delta=a_{12}a_{23}+a_{13}(\lambda_{max}-1)$ and $D=a_{12}a_{23}+a_{13}(\lambda_{max}-1)+(\lambda_{max}-1)a_{23}+(a_{13}/a_{12})-1+(1-\lambda_{max})^2$, we have

$$w_1 = \frac{\Delta}{D}$$

$$w_2 = \frac{(\lambda_{max}-1)a_{23}+(a_{13}/a_{12})}{D}$$

$$w_3 = \frac{-1+(1-\lambda_{max})^2}{D}$$

Quartic Case

If we define

$$B = \left(\frac{a_{23}a_{34}}{a_{24}} + \frac{a_{24}}{a_{23}a_{34}} \right) + \left(\frac{a_{12}a_{24}}{a_{14}} + \frac{a_{14}}{a_{12}a_{24}} \right) + \left(\frac{a_{12}a_{23}}{a_{13}} + \frac{a_{13}}{a_{12}a_{23}} \right) + \left(\frac{a_{13}a_{34}}{a_{14}} + \frac{a_{14}}{a_{13}a_{34}} \right)$$

$$C = 3 - \left(\frac{a_{12}a_{23}a_{34}}{a_{14}} + \frac{a_{14}}{a_{12}a_{23}a_{34}} \right) - \left(\frac{a_{12}a_{24}}{a_{13}a_{34}} + \frac{a_{13}a_{34}}{a_{12}a_{24}} \right) - \left(\frac{a_{14}a_{23}}{a_{13}a_{24}} + \frac{a_{13}a_{24}}{a_{14}a_{23}} \right)$$

Then

$$\lambda_{max} = \left[-8 + \frac{B^2}{2} + 8C + \sqrt{\left[-\frac{4}{3}(C+3) \right]^3 + (8 - \frac{B^2}{2} - 8C)^2} \right]^{1/3}$$

$$+ \left[-8 + \frac{B^2}{2} + 8C - \sqrt{\left[-\frac{4}{3}(C+3) \right]^3 + (8 - \frac{B^2}{2} - 8C)^2} \right]^{1/3}$$

and

$$w_1 = \frac{\overline{w_1}}{Q}, w_2 = \frac{\overline{w_2}}{Q}, w_3 = \frac{\overline{w_3}}{Q}, w_4 = \frac{\overline{w_4}}{Q}$$

where

$$Q = (\lambda_{max} - 1)^3 + (a_{14} + a_{34} + a_{24})(\lambda - 1)^2$$

$$+ \left[(a_{12}a_{24} - 3) + (a_{13} + a_{23})a_{34} + \left(\frac{1}{a_{12}} + \frac{1}{a_{13}} \right)a_{14} + \frac{a_{24}}{a_{23}} \right](\lambda_{max} - 1)$$

$$+ \left[(a_{12}a_{23}a_{34} - a_{12} - a_{14} - a_{24} - a_{34}) + \left(\frac{a_{13}a_{24}}{a_{23}} + \frac{a_{13}a_{34}}{a_{12}} \right) \right.$$

$$+ \left. \frac{a_{14}a_{32} + a_{12}a_{24}}{a_{13}} + \frac{a_{14} - a_{13}}{a_{12}a_{23}} \right]$$

$$\overline{w_1} = a_{14}(\lambda_{max} - 1)^2 + (a_{12}a_{24} + a_{13}a_{34})(\lambda_{max} - 1) + (a_{12}a_{23}a_{34} + \frac{a_{13}a_{24}}{a_{23}} - a_{14})$$

$$\overline{w_2} = a_{24}(\lambda_{max} - 1)^2 + (a_{23}a_{34} + \frac{a_{14}}{a_{12}})(\lambda_{max} - 1) + (\frac{a_{13}a_{34}}{a_{12}} + \frac{a_{14}a_{23}}{a_{13}} - a_{24})$$

$$\overline{w_3} = a_{34}(\lambda_{max} - 1)^2 + (\frac{a_{24}}{a_{23}} + \frac{a_{14}}{a_{13}})(\lambda_{max} - 1) + (\frac{a_{14}}{a_{12}a_{23}} + \frac{a_{12}a_{24}}{a_{13}} - a_{34})$$

$$\overline{w_4} = (\lambda_{max} - 1)^3 - 3(\lambda_{max} - 1) - (\frac{a_{12}a_{23}}{a_{13}} + \frac{a_{13}}{a_{12}a_{23}})$$

REMARK It is easy to see from this solution that if any coefficient is increased (decreased) in a given row of the pairwise comparison matrix the value of the eigenvector component corresponding to that row is increased (decreased) relative to the remaining components. This property holds for a reciprocal matrix.

The Quintic and Higher Order Cases

Algebraic Equations by Theta Constants, in Tata Lectures on Theta II [5], do not require the use of Tschirnhausen transformations. Let $f(x) = a_0 x^n + a_1 x^{n-1} + \ldots + a_n = 0$, $a_0 \neq 0$ be an algebraic equation irreducible over a subfield of the complex numbers. A root of this equation can be expressed in terms of theta functions of zero argument involving the period matrix derived from one of two types of hyper-elliptic integrals.

Bernd Sturmfels [6] gives the solution of the quintic equation in term using the finest of the 2^{n-1} triangulations of the hypergeometric differential equations and corresponding 2^{n-1} series solutions. The roots of the quintic $a_5x^5+a_4x^4+a_3x^3+a_2x^2+a_1x+a_0=0$ one of which is the principal eigenvalue that may also be obtained in other ways are given by an infinite series and the question about such expansions is whether the series always converge. We have:

$$X_{1,-1} = -\left[\frac{a_0}{a_1}\right], X_{2,-1} = -\left[\frac{a_1}{a_2}\right]+\left[\frac{a_0}{a_1}\right], X_{3,-1} = -\left[\frac{a_2}{a_3}\right]+\left[\frac{a_1}{a_2}\right],$$

$$X_{4,-1} = -\left[\frac{a_3}{a_4}\right]+\left[\frac{a_2}{a_3}\right], X_{5,-1} = -\left[\frac{a_4}{a_5}\right]+\left[\frac{a_3}{a_4}\right].$$

Each bracket represents a power series with a monomial in the bracket as its first term:

$$\left[\frac{a_0}{a_1}\right] = \frac{a_0}{a_1}+\frac{a_0^2 a_2}{a_1^3}-\frac{a_0^3 a_3}{a_1^4}+2\frac{a_0^3 a_2^2}{a_1^5}+\frac{a_0^4 a_4}{a_1^5}-5\frac{a_0^4 a_2 a_3}{a_1^6}-\frac{a_0^5 a_5}{a_1^6}+\ldots$$

$$\left[\frac{a_1}{a_2}\right] = \frac{a_1}{a_2}+\frac{a_1^2 a_3}{a_2^3}-\frac{a_1^3 a_4}{a_2^4}-3\frac{a_0 a_1^2 a_5}{a_2^4}+2\frac{a_1^3 a_3^2}{a_2^5}+\frac{a_1^4 a_5}{a_2^5}-5\frac{a_1^4 a_3 a_4}{a_2^6}+\ldots$$

$$\left[\frac{a_2}{a_3}\right] = \frac{a_2}{a_3}-\frac{a_0 a_5}{a_3^2}-\frac{a_1 a_4}{a_3^2}+2\frac{a_1 a_2 a_5}{a_3^3}+\frac{a_2^2 a_4}{a_3^3}-\frac{a_2^3 a_5}{a_3^4}+2\frac{a_2^3 a_4^2}{a_3^5}+\ldots$$

$$\left[\frac{a_3}{a_4}\right] = \frac{a_3}{a_4}-\frac{a_2 a_5}{a_4^2}+\frac{a_3^2 a_5}{a_4^3}+\frac{a_1 a_5^2}{a_4^3}-3\frac{a_2 a_3 a_5^2}{a_4^4}-\frac{a_0 a_5^3}{a_4^4}+4\frac{a_1 a_3 a_5^3}{a_4^5}+\ldots$$

$$\left[\frac{a_4}{a_5}\right] = \frac{a_4}{a_5}.$$

Value of Pairwise Comparisons - An Example

The following example shows that by making pairwise comparisons we learn much more about the detail of a dynamic priority function than if we were to simply guess at each component of the eigenvector components individually.

Family Spending Time at Home

Let us consider the simple case of a family with a father, a mother, and a child. Obviously the amount of time the child spends at home will depend on his age. An infant will spend the same amount of time at home as the mother and then, as he grows older, he will spend progressively less time at home compared to the mother. We assume that the mother does not go out to work.

If we were to compare the length of time spent at home by mother and child and plot this relation as a function of time (i.e., as the child grows older), we would get the type of curve shown in Figure 4.

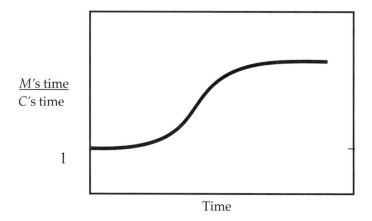

$\underline{M's\ time}$
$C's\ time$

1

Time

Figure 4 Relative Time at Home – Mother to Child

Thus the curve begins with the home maker mother and child spending the same amount of time, then the ratio of mother's to child's time increases until it levels off by the time the child is in her/his mid-teens. Comparison of father to child times yields a relationship that is a mirror image of the above -reflected about a horizontal axis halfway up the curve. This is illustrated in Figure 5. The relative length of time spent by father and mother would not vary too much and could be expected to be fairly constant.

If we were to make a pairwise comparison of the different lengths of time spent at home by the different members of the family, we would get a sequence of comparison matrices each corresponding to a particular period of time.

Consider the time period corresponding to the child's age 0-4 years. If we were to exclude, say, eight hours of the night, we would expect the mother and child to spend about two to three times the length of time the father spends at home. The mother and child would of course spend the same amount of time.

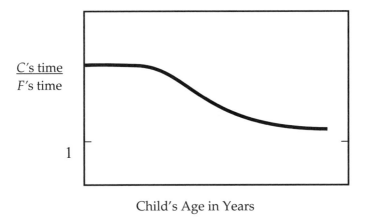

C's time / F's time

1

Child's Age in Years

Figure 5 Relative Time at Home – Child to Father

This would give rise to the following matrix:

$$
\begin{array}{c c}
 & \begin{array}{ccc} F & M & C \end{array} \\
\begin{array}{c} F \\ M \\ C \end{array} &
\left[\begin{array}{ccc}
1 & 1/2.5 & 1/2.5 \\
2.5 & 1 & 1 \\
2.5 & 1 & 1
\end{array} \right]
\end{array}
$$

$\lambda_{max} = 3.0$, C.I. = 0.0, C.R. = 0.0

This yields the following eigenvector for their relative times at home:

$F : 0.167$
$M: 0.417$
$C : 0.417$

That would seem to be a reasonable estimate of the proportions of time each spends at home. Around the age of four the child begins school, so there is a sudden change in the relative proportions of time spent at home by mother and child and by father and child.

Moving to the time dependent situation, we can express the varying proportions in a single matrix whose entries where developed using Table 2 below:

$$
\begin{array}{c@{}c}
 & \begin{array}{ccc} F & \quad M & \qquad\quad C \end{array} \\
\begin{array}{c} F \\ M \\ C \end{array} &
\left[\begin{array}{ccc}
1 & 1/2 & 1/(3\text{-ln } t/2) \\
2 & 1 & 0.4+\text{ln } t/2 \\
3\text{-ln } t/2 & 1/(0.4+\text{ln } t/2) & 1
\end{array} \right]
\end{array}
$$

The variable t denotes the child's age ranging between 4 and 16 years. This matrix, along with the previous one, gives rise to the curves in Figure 6, Figure 7 and Figure 8 that depict the corresponding pairwise comparisons as time varies from zero to 16 years.

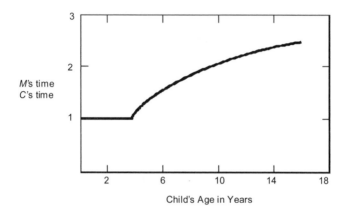

Figure 6 Mother to Child: age 0-16 years

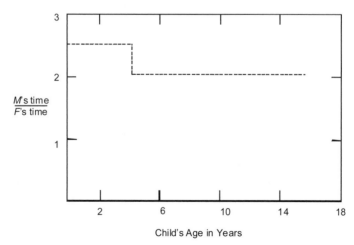

Figure 7 Mother to Father: Age 0-16 years

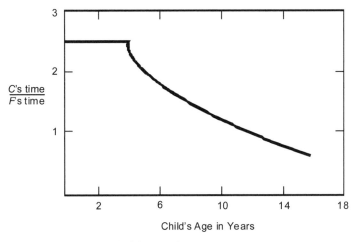

C's time
F's time

Child's Age in Years

Figure 8 Child to Father: Age 0-16 Years

The solution of the maximum eigenvalue problem corresponding to these pairwise comparison curves for $(4 \le t \le 16)$ is

$$\lambda_{max} = 1 + \left[\frac{2}{(3 - \ln t / 2)(0.4 + \ln t / 2)} \right]^{1/3} + \left[\frac{(3 - \ln t / 2)(0.4 + \ln t / 2)}{2} \right]^{1/3}$$

The corresponding eigenvector is given by

$$w_1 = \Delta / D; w_2 = \left[(\lambda_{max} - 1)(0.4 + \ln t / 2) + \frac{2}{3 - \ln t / 2} \right] / D; w_3 = \left[-1 + (-2)^2 \right] / D$$

where

$$\Delta = 0.5(0.4 + \ln t / 2) + \frac{\lambda_{max} - 1}{3 - \ln t / 2}$$

$$D = (\lambda_{max} - 0.5)(0.4 + \ln t / 2) + \frac{\lambda_{max} + 1}{3 - \ln t / 2} - 1 + (1 - \lambda_{max})^2$$

As the child finishes school, he begins spending even less time at home than the father. The proportions once again become fairly constant and are reflected in the following (consistent) pairwise comparison matrix:

$$\begin{array}{cc} & \begin{array}{ccc} F & M & C \end{array} \\ \begin{array}{c} F \\ M \\ C \end{array} & \left[\begin{array}{ccc} 1 & 0.5 & 1.25 \\ 2 & 1 & 2.5 \\ 0.8 & 0.4 & 1 \end{array} \right] \end{array}$$

$\lambda_{max} = 3.0$, C.I. $= 0.0$, C.R. $= 0.0$

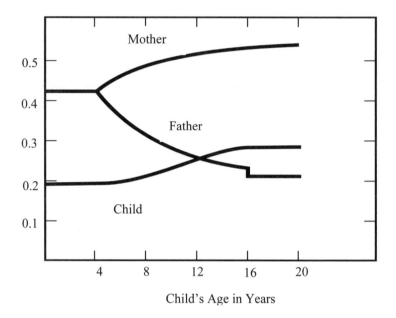

Child's Age in Years

Figure 9 Relative Proportion of Time Spent at Home

The eigenvector solution is given by:

F: 0.263
M: 0.526
C: 0.211

Plotting these results together for $0 \le t \le 4$, $4 \le t \le 16$, and $16 \le t$ gives a realistic representation of the relative time, with respect to all others, which each spends at home (see Figure 9).

Pairwise Comparison Judgments and Scale – General Discussion

Recall that in making paired comparisons of intangibles, we use the smaller or lesser element as a unity and estimate the larger one as a multiple of it. We can also do that in dynamic judgments by simply introducing a function to estimate how many times more is the larger element than the unit. In this case there may be a change of unit of the comparison if the larger element becomes the smaller and must serve as the unit. Just as we used absolute numbers to enter into the comparison matrix in the static case, we need to enter basic functions to represent judgments in the dynamic case. What typical functions can we use that would for example approximate well the functions of the family example above? I do not have a conclusive answer to that question, if indeed there is an answer to it. For the pairwise comparison judgments one may attempt to fit one of the functions given in Table 2 to the dynamic judgments. These functions have been left in parametric form so that the parameter may be set for the particular comparison, hopefully meeting the homogeneity requirement of the 1-9 scale used in the discrete case as a limit on the range of values. They, and combinations of them, reflect our intuitive feeling about relative change in trend: constant, linear, polynomial, logarithmic, exponential, oscillatory, and finally discrete that allows for sudden change like a Dirac delta function.

Table 2 This Author's Idea of A Mathematician's Formulation of a Dynamic Judgment Scale

Time-dependent importance intensity	Description	Explanation
a	Constant for all t, $1 \leq a \leq 9$ an integer	No change in relative standing
$a_1 t + a_2$	Linear relation in t, increasing or decreasing to a point and then a constant value thereafter. Note that the reciprocal is a hyperbola.	Steady increase in value of one activity over another
$b_1 \log (t+1) + b_2$	Logarithmic growth up to a certain point and constant thereafter	Rapid increase (decrease) followed by slow increase (decrease)
$c_1 e^{c_2 t} + c_3$	Exponential growth (or decay if c_2 is negative) to a certain point and constant thereafter (not reciprocal of case c_2 is negative is the logistic S-curve)	Slow increase (decrease) followed by rapid increase (decrease)
$d_1 t^2 + d_2 t + d_3$	A parabola giving a maximum or minimum (depending on d_1 being negative or positive) with a constant value thereafter. (May be modified for skewness to the right or left)	Increase (decrease) to maximum (minimum) and then decrease (increase)
$e_1 t^n \sin(t + e_2)$	Oscillatory	Oscillates depending on n, n > 0 ($n \leq 0$) with decreasing (increasing) amplitude
Catastrophes	Discontinuities indicated	Sudden changes in intensity
Polynomials are known in general to approximate to continuous functions on a closed interval arbitrarily closely.		

The following is an example given by Andreichicov and Andreichicova [7]. They assumed that the preferences for alternatives at the bottom with respect to the criteria in the fourth hierarchy level of Figure 10 would remain constant in the future. However, they assumed that preferences for the factors located at the second hierarchy level would vary.

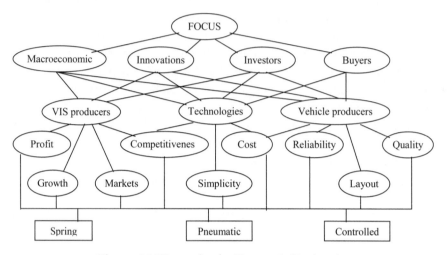

Figure 10 Hierarchy for Dynamic Evaluation

Table 3 Priority Vectors for Criteria in the Static Problem

	Macroeconomic	Innovations	Investments	Buyers
FOCUS	0.380	0.085	0.466	0.069
	VIS producers	Vehicles producers	Technologies	
Macroeconomic	0.109	0.582	0.309	
Innovations	0.105	0.258	0.637	
Investments	0.167	0.740	0.094	
Buyers		0.167	0.833	
	Profit	Growth	Competitiveness	Markets
VIS producers	0.532	0.097	0.186	0.186
	Quality	Cost	Reliability	Layout
Vehicles producers	0.143	0.402	0.054	0.402
	Competitiveness	Cost	Simplicity	
Technologies	0.333	0.333	0.333	

The relative importance of the criteria for each actor also would be subject to modification in the future. The filling of pairwise comparison matrices as the dynamic task was made as follows. There were (n-1) cells selected in a matrix which is the minimum connection to form a spanning tree and hence a consistent matrix, where the functions describing changes of appropriate preferences were made. The preferences at the time coincided with preferences in the static task. The values for the other (n^2-2n+1) preferences were calculated on the basis of the ($n-1$) functions given (*Auto*). Thus there was no problem of inconsistency during solution of the dynamic problem. Forming the functions was produced experimentally with the help of the software developed by the authors.

The dynamic paired comparison matrices were the following:

FOCUS	Macroeconomic	Innovations	Investments	Buyers
Macroeconomic	1	$1/0.25e^{0.6t}$	Auto	$1/(0.2-0.05t+0.08t^2)$
Innovations	$0.25e^{0.6t}$	1	$0.2-0.18t+0.15t^2$	Auto
Investments	auto	$1/(0.2-0.18t+0.15t^2)$	1	Auto
Buyers	$0.2-0.05t+0.08t^2$	Auto	Auto	1

VIS producers	Profit	Growth	Competitiveness	Markets
Profit	1	$1/(0.2+0.05t+0.025t^2)$	$1/0.333e^{0.43t}$	$1/0.333e^{0.43t}$
Growth	$0.2+0.05t+0.025t^2$	1	Auto	Auto
Competitiveness	$0.333e^{0.43t}$	Auto	1	Auto
Markets	$0.333e^{0.43t}$	Auto	Auto	1

Vehicles producers	Quality	Cost	Reliability	Layout
Quality	1	$0.333+0.4t+0.04t^2$	$3-1.15t+0.18t^2$	$0.333+0.15t$
Cost	$1/(0.333+0.4t+0.04t^2)$	1	Auto	Auto
Reliability	$1/(3-1.15t+0.18t^2)$	Auto	1	Auto
Layout	$1/(0.333+0.15t)$	Auto	Auto	1

Table 4 Priority Vectors for Alternatives in the Static Problem

	Coil Spring	Pneumatic	Controlled
Profit	0.648	0.230	0.122
Growth	0.143	0.429	0.429
Competitiveness	0.075	0.333	0.592
Markets	0.109	0.582	0.309
Quality	0.066	0.319	0.615
Cost	0.751	0.178	0.070
Reliability	0.637	0.105	0.258
Layout	0.105	0.258	0.637
Simplicity	0.751	0.178	0.070

The other paired comparison matrices were the same as in the static problem. The results are shown in Figure 11.

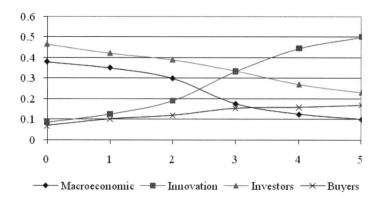

Figure 11 Change in Factor Priorities over Time

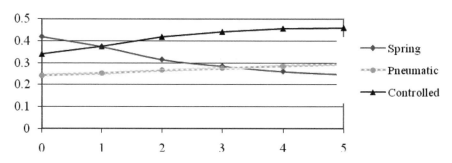

Figure 12 Change in Each Alternative's Priorities over Time

The priority of innovation is expected to increase in the future. The buyer's priority will also increase slightly. The investor's importance and macroeconomic influence will decrease. These modifications and the changes in the importance of the criteria for producers will result in a change in the order established for the alternatives. The spring coil, which is simple and cheap, moves from first place to last place. The best alternative in the future will be VIS controlled, which has high vibroisolation quality and high cost. The low priority of the pneumatic VIS in both cases might be explained by its relatively high cost and low reliability.

Fundamental Scale of Relative Change - On the Rate of Change of Intangibles

Let us now turn to a more practical way of creating a fundamental scale that is in harmony with any person's way of looking ahead to make comparisons. As in the discrete case, because we have intangibles we have no functions to describe their behavior absolutely, but we can compare them to derive scales of relative change over time. We have no problem to deal with tangibles whose behavior over time is known though a function-of-time expression for each.

The question is how to generalize this idea to the dynamic case. Two kinds of data need to be generated. One is the initial point $x(0)$ of the curve of relative change. Here we ask the same question as in the discrete case: which of the two dominates the other with regard to a common attribute they share? The other question has to do with their perceived relative change: which of the two is perceived to change more than the other with respect to a common attribute they share? This second question is answered with perhaps different estimates for different time periods.

As in the discrete case, an individual has the ability to recognize distinctions among high, medium and low and for each of these also three distinctions of high, medium and low. In the case of static judgments that deal with numbers we had the nine values of the fundamental scale 1-9. We assume for the moment that when we compare two (tangible) activities each described by a curve as a function of time that we can make these nine distinctions in their rates of change relative to one another. How can each of these curves vary so that we would be able to divide the relative variation between them into recognizable nine categories over time? We note that in the simplest case where both functions are linear in time and their relative variation expressed by their ratio is a hyperbola over time. A hyperbola has a simple but rather sophisticated interpretation. What are different possible interpretations of variations (ratios) between two functions? To deal with such concepts effectively we need to think of time in two ways, the hard way as a tangible measured on a clock and make judgments over known perhaps uniform time intervals, or the soft way as an intangible divided according to our feelings about it such as short term, mid term and long term. This author's idea of a practical-minded person's representation of a dynamic judgment scale of relative changes is shown in Table 5. The slopes of lines in the table are the tangents of increasing angles in degrees from 0 to 30 to 45 to 60 to 90.

Table 5 Formulation of a Dynamic Judgment Scale Using Slope

Comparison of A over B
Extreme Increase $\nearrow$ Very Strong Increase: x(t) = 2.414t $\nearrow$ Strong Increase: x(t) = t $\nearrow$ Moderate Increase ; x(t) = 0.414t $\nearrow$ Equal; x(t) = 1 $\rightarrow$ Moderate Decrease: x (t)=-0.414t $\searrow$ Strong Decrease: x (t)=-t $\searrow$ Very Strong Decrease: x (t)=-2.414t $\searrow$ Extreme Decrease $\downarrow$

Comparison of A over B	Slope of Line $(0 \leq \theta \leq 90°)$	Slope of Line $(0 \leq \theta \leq 45°)$	Slope of Line $(0 \leq \theta \leq 22.5°)$
Extreme Increase	∞	1	0.414
Very Strong Increase	2.414	0.668	0.303
Strong Increase	1	0.414	0.199
Moderate Increase	0.414	0.199	0.098
Equal	0	0	0
Moderate Decrease	-0.414	-0.199	-0.098
Strong Decrease	-1	-0.414	-0.199
Very Strong Decrease	-2.414	-0.668	-0.303
Extreme Decrease	$-\infty$	-1	-0.414

An application of it over time is shown in Table 6.

As in the 1-9 scale, time horizons may be divided into 9 periods starting with the present time and relative increases and decreases further refined. Here a function representing judgments may descend below $x(t) = 1$ and thus the coefficient may include a description of both dominance and being dominated. Its transpose is the reciprocal function. Because we do not wish to use upward or downward arrows for an entire judgment over a time horizon interval, we can replace such a "Dirac" type function by a curve that rises or falls sharply and continuously over the interval. Examples are $(t-a)^{-1}$, $|t-a|^{-1}$ and $(t-a)^{-2}$. Homogeneity needs to be maintained not only for magnitudes but also for the angle of relative change. The angle span for homogeneity may be less than 90 degrees. Perhaps it should be closer to a radian $360/2\pi=57.296°$ and its division into ranges of just noticeable increases in slope or angle. There needs to be a theoretical way to justify the bound on the homogeneity of relative change. When exceeded, one may have to use clustering as in the comparison of different magnitudes.

Table 6 Different Possible Formulations and Variations using the Basic Scale in Table 5

Time Horizons	Short-term	Mid-term	Long-term	Combined Over the Three Horizons	Functional Form
Comparison of A over B	→	↗	↓	→↗↘	$a_{12}(t) = \begin{cases} x_1(0) & 0 \le t \le t_1 \\ x_1(0) + 0.414(t - t_1) & t_1 < t \le t_2 \\ x_1(0) + 0.414(t_2 - t_1) & t_2 < t \le t_3 \\ -2.414(t - t_2) \end{cases}$
Comparison of A over C	↘	↓	↗	↘↘↗	$a_{13}(t) = \begin{cases} x_2(0) - t & 0 \le t \le t_1 \\ x_2(0) + 1.414t_1 - 2.414t & t_1 < t \le t_2 \\ x_2(0) + 1.414t_1 - 4.828t_2 + 2.414t & t_2 < t \le t_3 \end{cases}$
Comparison of B over C	↓ →	↑	↓→↑		$a_{23}(t) = \begin{cases} x_3(0)t_1(t_1 + t)^{-1} & 0 \le t \le t_1 \\ \frac{1}{2}x_3(0) & t_1 < t \le t_2 \\ \frac{1}{2}x_3(0)\dfrac{t_3 + t}{t_3 + t_2} & t_2 < t \le t_3 \end{cases}$

Note that because the time horizons are not well specified over time, instead of connecting their end points to make a continuous curve, one may select the mid-point of a time horizon to draw each line segment and take their points of intersection as the positions where the composite curve connects. A better alternative is to divide each of short, midterm and long-term into three intervals sand provide judgments of relative change by the above scale for each. This is time consuming but more accurate even if one were to repeat the same judgments over success intervals.

We now show by an example that real life situations reveal themselves along similar lines to the line segments we combined to put together decisions made over short, medium and long term time horizons. The example has to deal with the earnings and projected electricity use by the three companies involved (taken from the internet) as shown in Figure 13.

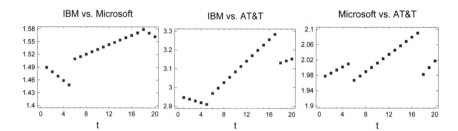

Figure 13 Relative Earnings of Software Companies

Judgments fitted with linear approximations:

$$
\begin{array}{c}
\begin{array}{cccc}
\textit{Short Term} & \textit{IBM} & \textit{MSFT} & \textit{AT \& T}
\end{array} \\
\begin{array}{c}
\textit{IBM} \\
\textit{MSFT} \\
\textit{AT \& T}
\end{array}
\begin{bmatrix}
1 & 1.499 - 0.0103t & 2.955 - 0.0089t \\
 & 1 & 1.969 + 0.0079t \\
 & & 1
\end{bmatrix}
\end{array}
$$

$$
\begin{array}{c}
\begin{array}{cccc}
\textit{Medium Term} & \textit{IBM} & \textit{MSFT} & \textit{AT \& T}
\end{array} \\
\begin{array}{c}
\textit{IBM} \\
\textit{MSFT} \\
\textit{AT \& T}
\end{array}
\begin{bmatrix}
1 & 1.476 + 0.0056t & 2.797 + 0.089t \\
 & 1 & 1.899 + 0.1125t \\
 & & 1
\end{bmatrix}
\end{array}
$$

$$
\begin{array}{c}
\begin{array}{cccc}
\textit{Long Term} & \textit{IBM} & \textit{MSFT} & \textit{AT \& T}
\end{array} \\
\begin{array}{c}
\textit{IBM} \\
\textit{MSFT} \\
\textit{AT \& T}
\end{array}
\begin{bmatrix}
1 & 1.733 - 0.089t & 2.943 + 0.0104t \\
 & 1 & 1.668 + 0.0175t \\
 & & 1
\end{bmatrix} S
\end{array}
$$

Plots of estimated dynamic priorities versus actual are shown in Figure 14.

It may be possible to aggregate a judgment function into a number by assuming that each discrete judgment on a curve arises from different observations about a future determined not by a point but by an interval of time. In that case one uses the geometric mean of all these judgments leading to a product integral. As in the discrete case where we have for the product of the judgments $x_1, x_2, ..., x_p$:

$$
x_1 \, x_2 \cdots x_p = e^{\log x_1 x_2 \cdots x_p} = \prod_{i=1}^{p} e^{\log x_i} = e^{\sum_{i=1}^{p} \log x_i} \longrightarrow e^{\int \log x(\alpha) d\alpha}
$$

This product reduces to a product integral yielding a single number for an answer, for our case we replace α by t and $x(\alpha)$ by $x(t)$ in the integral above to obtain a number for each judgment.

Finally, one can use the criterion $a_{ij}w_j/w_i \gg 1$ of the AHP or the gradient approach (more complex in the dynamic case) to improve overall consistency. One would possibly be dealing with nonlinear inequalities.

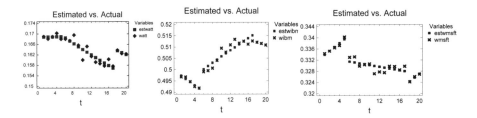

Figure 14 Estimated versus Actual Relative Values for the Three Companies

A Complete Example with Paired Comparisons

Let us consider the case of tangibles. We have two people, the first is a years older than the second, where $a = 30$. As seen in Figure 15 as time lapses the difference between their ages remains constant. However, the ratio of their ages in the (1,2) position in the paired comparison matrix below is a hyperbola given by $(a+t)/t=1+a/t$ as shown in Figure 16. Initially the ratio is infinite when $t = 0$. As time lapses this ratio converges asymptotically to the line $x(t)=1$. The pairwise comparison matrix formed by taking the ratios of the functions of age of the two people is given by:

$$\begin{bmatrix} 1 & (a+t)/t \\ t/(a+t) & 1 \end{bmatrix}$$

which has the normalized principal right eigenvector:

$$w_1(t) = (a+t)/(a+2t), w_2(t) = t/(a+2t).$$

The ideal mode solution is 1, $t/t+a$, $t>0$, $a \geq 0$, with a graph comprised of a horizontal line and a curve as shown in Figure 17 is a plot of the normalized eigenvector components.

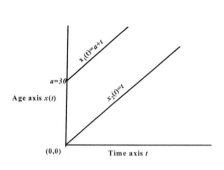

Figure 15 Age as a Function of Time   **Figure 16** Hyperbola; $x_1(t)/x_2(t)=1+30/t$

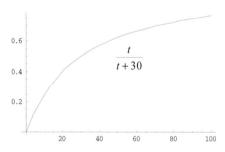
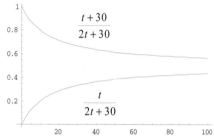

Figure 17 Graph of the Ratio of the   **Figure 18** Graph of Normalized
Functions $x_2(t)/x_1(t)=t/(t+30)$ Dependent Eigenvector $w_1(t)$,
                                            $w_2(t)$ with $a=30$

We continue our illustration of a multicriteria problem by considering another attribute besides age that is measurable over time, and that is strength. Let us assume that strength increases to a certain value ≤ 1 and then decreases with age eventually to zero at death as in Figure 19. Assume that Figure 19 describes the strengths of the two individuals and that the corresponding equations are:

$$y_1(t) = 1 - \frac{1}{2500}(t-20)^2, \, y_2(t) = 1 - \frac{1}{2500}(t-50)^2$$

Forming the ratios of the functions that represent the relative strengths of the individuals we have the paired comparison matrix below:

$$\begin{bmatrix} 1 & \dfrac{y_1(t)}{y_2(t)} \\ \dfrac{y_2(t)}{y_1(t)} & 1 \end{bmatrix}$$

The above matrix has a normalized eigenvector of [$y_1(t)$, $y_2(t)$] which gives the solution vector [$u_1(t), u_2(t)$] with:

$$u_1(t) = 1 - \frac{1}{2500}(t-20)^2 / [1 - \frac{1}{2500}(t-20)^2 + 1 - \frac{1}{2500}(t-50)^2],$$

$$u_2(t) = 1 - \frac{1}{2500}(t-50)^2 / [1 - \frac{1}{2500}(t-20)^2 + 1 - \frac{1}{2500}(t-50)^2]$$

The graph of this time dependent eigenvector solution of strength is shown in Figure 20.

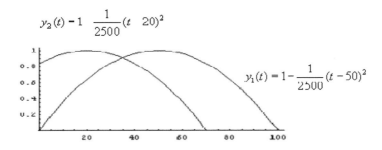

Figure 19 Graph of the Two Strength Functions [$y_1(t)$, $y_2(t)$]

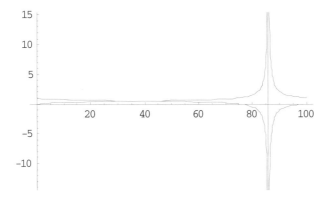

Figure 20 Time Dependent Eigenvector Solution of Strength Graph [$u_1(t)$, $u_2(t)$]

We obtain the composite vector of the two alternatives, age and strength, by combining the two vectors obtained for age and strength.

Finally let us assume that the two criteria age and strength are equally important so we can weight and add the two vectors $w_1(t)$, $w_2(t)$ with $a=30$ and $[u_1(t), u_2(t)]$. We might also have given the criteria time dependent weights to do the weighting and adding. We have the following solution for our final composite vector $[z_1(t), z_2(t)]$. Its graph is shown in Figure 21.

$$z_1(t) = [\frac{1}{2}(30+t)/(30+2t)] + \frac{1}{2}[1 - \frac{1}{2500}(t-20)^2]/[1 - \frac{1}{2500}(t-20)^2 + 1 - \frac{1}{2500}(t-50)^2],$$

$$z_2(t) = [\frac{1}{2}t/(30+2t)] + \frac{1}{2}[1 - \frac{1}{2500}(t-50)^2]/[1 - \frac{1}{2500}(t-20)^2 + 1 - \frac{1}{2500}(t-50)^2].$$

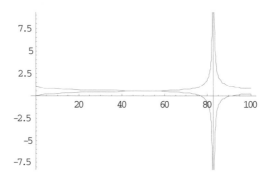

Figure 21 Graph of Synthesized Solution $[z_1(t), z_2(t)]$

Historical Background

Solution of the cubic and the quartic became common knowledge through the publication of the *Ars Magna* of Geronimo Cardano (1501-1576). But Cardano was not the original discoverer of the solution of either the cubic or the quartic. Generally the solution of the cubic is attributed to the Italian professor Scipione del Ferro (1465-1526), from Bologna, one of the oldest of the medieval universities and a school with a strong mathematical tradition.

The solution of the quartic is attributed to Ludovico Ferrari (1522-1565). The names of Niccolo Fontana (1500-1557) the stammerer (Tartaglia) is also associated with the solution of the cubic because he elaborated on Del Ferro's solution and became addicted to solving cubic equations. It was from Ferrari in 1547-48 that the history of this spectacular discovery became public knowledge. Ferrari reduced the solution of the general bi-quadratic equation to that of a cubic equation. It was Cardano who considered negative numbers and called them "fictitious".

Nearly 250 years later it became known from the works of Abel and Ruffini and from Galois theory that a quatric is the largest degree equation for which one can obtain the roots (eigenvalues in our problem) in the form of radicals. This means that the roots can be expressed as a finite formula involving only the four arithmetic operations and the extraction of roots. We have already given symbolic expressions for the principal eigenvalue and eigenvector in symbolic form for $n \leq 4$ in my first book on the AHP [10]. Still even in these cases, it is a relatively complicated process to weight and synthesize time dependent priorities for the alternatives. Once we have the outcome, we can analyze its rate of change with respect to time by taking its derivative.

The mathematics to do this in general symbolic form is not here yet, nor is PC computer technology necessarily up to the task. To solve a quintic equation in symbolic form in order to get the principal eigenvalue we are told by the chart distributed in 1994 by Wolfram Research on the quintic equation that it requires a trillion bytes, or one gigabyte of storage. One wonders what solving higher order equations would require. The upshot is that we can do time dependent AHP/ANP numerically by simulation. One would express the judgments functionally but then derive the eigenvector from the judgments for a fixed moment of time, put the outcome in a supermatrix, solve the problem and derive the outcome for the alternatives. Repeating the process for different values of time generates a curve for the priorities. One then approximates these values by curves with a functional form for each coefficient.

The Quintic and Higher Order Cases

The poster distributed by Wolfram Research in 1994 gives a nice introduction to the classical methods for symbolic computation of the roots of an algebraic equation. All algebraic equations of degree 4 and less can be solved using only square and cubic roots. Solutions of algebraic equations using radicals are called radical solutions. Abel (1802-1829) proved that the general equation of degree higher than four could not be solved using radicals. Galois (1811-1832) provided a method to characterize equations that are solvable by radicals. His method involved the development of group theory to determine the effect of permuting the roots of the equation on functions of the roots. The solution of the quartic equation can be related to the 4! = 24 symmetries of the tetrahedron, and those of the quintic equation to the 5! = 120 symmetries of the icosahedron. The general quintic equation can be solved by Kiepert's algorithm [12] using theta series (see below; power series, sometimes also called Taylor series have the form, $\sum_{n=0}^{\infty} c_n t^n$,Laurent series the form $\sum_{n=-\infty}^{\infty} c_n t^n$, and Puiseux series often encountered in this connection the form $\sum_{n=-\infty}^{\infty} c_n t^{n/k} k$, a fixed natural number).

The fact that radicals cannot be used in all cases of the quintic and higher order equations leads to the question as to what type of functions are needed to solve equations of higher degree than 4. Hyperradicals is the term used for such functions. Hermite, for example, showed that elliptic modular functions provide solutions to the quintic equation. Tschirnhausen transformations are often used to simplify the form of an algebraic equation, solve it in the reduced form and then apply the inverse transformation to obtain the solution of the general equation. Actually, the equation $a_0 x^n + a_1 x^{n-1} + \ldots + a_{n-1} x + a_n = 0$, $a_0 \neq 0$ is reduced to $z^n + b_1 z^{n-4} + \ldots + b_{n-1} x + b_n = 0$ with three fewer terms, and thus the quintic equation takes the form $z^5 + b_4 z + b_5 = 0$. Theta functions are periodic functions that can be represented by series whose convergence is extraordinarily rapid. Jacobi and Abel in 1827 studied these functions for the first time. We have,

$$\theta_2(z,q) = 2 \sum_{n=0}^{\infty} q^{(n+1/2)^2} \cos(2n+1)z$$

$$\theta_3(z,q) = 1 + 2 \sum_{n=0}^{\infty} q^{n^2} \cos 2nz$$

The elliptic modular function $\varphi(z)$ is given by:

$$\varphi(z) = \sqrt[8]{\frac{\theta_2(0,z)^4}{\theta_3(0,z)^4}}$$

Camille Jordan proved in 1870 that an algebraic equation of any degree can be solved in terms of modular functions. The following theorem of H. Umemura [5] does not require the use of Tschirnhausen transformations. Let $f(x) = a_0 x^n + a_1 x^{n-1} + \ldots + a_n = 0$, $a_0 \neq 0$ be an algebraic equation irreducible over a subfield of the complex numbers. A root of this equation can be expressed in terms of theta functions of zero argument involving period matrix derived from one of two types of hyperelliptic integrals.

Conclusions

It appears that independently from whether people like to do or can do dynamic comparisons, there would always be technological problems with mathematical engineering design that require the use of AHP/ANP in dynamic form. The first applications may not be taxing to our ingenuity to deal with functions instead of numbers, but it is certain that soon after they will and I expect that extensions of this chapter will make that appear even more plausible.

Perhaps one of the advantages of dynamic judgments may be that the requirement of homogeneity is given up to the mathematics of the functions one uses. It seems to me that while this may be reasonable for technical but not behavioral problems. One may be able to compare the relation between two machines constructed in a systematic way so that their relative behavior is predetermined. In that case homogeneity is not needed as a requirement on the fundamental scale.

One thing we have to learn to do is to create a scale that is truly associated with our intuition so that we can use it in the natural and spontaneous way people have learned to use the scale 1-9 that is associated with verbally expressed judgments. Intuitively I think this is a considerable worthy challenge of our effort to extend the AHP/ANP.

References

1. Blair, A.R., R. Nachtmann, T.L. Saaty and R. Whitaker (2002), "Forecasting the Resurgence of the U.S. Economy in 2001:An Expert Judgment Approach", *Socio-Economic Planning Sciences*, 36, 77-91
2. Wind, Y. and T.L. Saaty (1980), "Marketing Applications of the Analytic Hierarchy Process," *Management Science*, 26 (7)
3. Saaty, T.L., and K. Kearns (1991), *Analytical Planning*, RWS Publications, Pittsburgh, PA
4. Horn, R.A, and C.R. Johnson (1985), *Matrix Analysis*, Cambridge University Press
5. Mumford, D. (1984), *Tata Lectures on Theta II*, vol. 43 of Progress in Mathematics, Birkhaüser, Boston, MA
6. Sturmfels, B. (2000), "Solving algebraic equations in terms of A-hypergeometric series." *Discrete Math*, 210, No. 1-3, pp. 171-181

7. Andreichicov, A. and O. Andreichicova (2001), "A Choice of a Perspective System for Vibration Isolation in Conditions of Varying Environment," pp. 13-24, *ISAHP Proceedings 2001*, Bern, Switzerland

8. Kuffler, S. and J.G. Nichols (1976), *From Neuron to Brain*, Sunderland, MA, USA: Sinauer Associates

9. Saaty, T.L. (1999), *The Brain: Unraveling the Mystery of How it Works, The Neural Network Process*, RWS Publications, Pittsburgh, PA

10. Saaty, T.L. (1980), *The Analytic Hierarchy Process*, McGraw Hill International, New York. Translated to Russian, Portuguese, and Chinese. Revised edition published in paperback (1990, 1996), RWS Publications, Pittsburgh, PA

11. King, R.B. (1996) *Beyond the Quartic Equation.* Basel, Switzerland: Birkhäuser

12. Kiepert, L. (1878), Auflösung der Gleichungen vom Fünften Grades, *J. für Math.*, 87, pp. 114-133

Chapter 14

Addressing with Brevity Criticisms of the Analytic Hierarchy Process

A new scientific truth does not triumph by convincing its opponents and making them see the light, but rather because its opponents eventually die, and a new generation grows up that is familiar with it.

Max Planck

This chapter deals with the following ideas:
- What have been the main criticisms of the AHP and are they a result of understanding the AHP as a new paradigm or attempting to force it to behave according to traditional ways of measurement and ranking?
- The chapter provides an overview that covers the main criticisms of the AHP and our replies to them.
- Because of many papers written by people on the subject, we have classified them and replied to them briefly in each category without giving lengthy repetitions of what is already known in the literature.

Introduction

In this chapter we address five types of criticisms of the AHP. They seem to all arise from the fact that people derive their understanding from the use of measurement scales with arbitrary units to measure things one at a time, and from the absence of understanding that criteria themselves are intangible and to assign them priorities that differ from application to application we need to compare them in a valid and sound way. One noisy criticism from numerous sources (but much less if ever now mainly due to better understanding at last) has been the concern with illegitimate changes in the ranks of the alternatives, called rank reversal, upon changing the structure of the decision. It was believed that rank reversal is legitimate only when criteria or priorities of criteria or changes in judgments are made. Rank reversals were shown by critics to occur when using comparisons and relative measurement that is *essential* in prioritizing criteria and also alternatives on intangible criteria in two ways: First, when new alternatives are added or old ones deleted; and second, when new criteria are added or old ones deleted with the caveat that the priorities of the alternatives would be tied under these criteria and hence argued that the criteria should be irrelevant when ranking the alternatives. Rank reversals that followed such structural changes were attributed to the use of relative measurement and normalization. Rating alternatives one at a time with respect to the criteria using the ideal mode, always preserves rank. Also, the ideal mode is used with paired comparisons to preserve rank. But rank can and should reverse under more general conditions than had previously been recognized as in introducing copies or near copies of alternatives and criteria turn out not to always be so strictly independent among themselves and from the alternatives. The second concern is about inconsistent judgments and their effect on aggregating such judgments or on deriving priorities from them. A modicum of intransitivity and numerical inconsistency, usually not considered or thought to be permissible in other theories, is permissible in the AHP so that decisions can be treated realistically rather than axiomatically truncated. A condition that may not hold with inconsistent judgments is Pareto optimality. Pareto optimality is an ordinal relation which demands of a method used to aggregate judgments of individuals in a group to a representative collective judgment for that group that when all individuals in the group prefer A to B then the group judgment must prefer A to B. Because in the AHP judgments are not ordinal, it is possible to aggregate the individual judgments into a representative group judgment with or without Pareto optimality. Another condition also inherited from expected utility theory has to do with a relation called Condition of Order Preservation (COP): For all alternatives x_1, x_2, x_3, x_4, such that x_1 dominates x_2 and x_3 dominates x_4, if the evaluator's judgments indicate the extent to which x_1 dominates x_2 is greater than the extent to which x_3 dominates x_4, then the vector of priorities w should be such that, not only $w(x_1) > w(x_2)$ and $w(x_3) > w(x_4)$ (preservation of order of preference) but also that $\dfrac{w(x_1)}{w(x_2)} > \dfrac{w(x_3)}{w(x_4)}$ (preservation of order of intensity of preference). This condition holds when judgments are consistent but may or may not hold when they are inconsistent. It is axiomatically imposed, sacrificing the original intent of the AHP process to derive priorities that match the reality represented by the judgments without forcing consistency. The third criticism has to do with attempts to preserve rank from irrelevant alternatives by combining the comparison judgments of a single individual using the geometric mean (logarithmic least squares) to derive priorities and also combining the derived priorities on different criteria by using multiplicative weighting synthesis. The fourth criticism has to do with people trying to change the fundamental scale despite the fact that it is theoretically derived and tested by comparing it with numerous other scales on a multiplicity of examples for which the answer was known. The fifth and final criticism has to do with whether or not the pairwise comparisons axioms are behavioral and spontaneous in nature to provide judgments.

Interestingly, the AHP/ANP provides a way to make complex decisions in the most general structures encountered in real life. It makes it possible to derive priorities for all the factors in such structures and synthesize them for an overall outcome, as no other method can because one can build scales for tangibles and intangibles, yet we know little about criticisms of framing and validating problems within such a wide perspective that includes structures, not only for dependence and feedback, but also for benefits, opportunities, costs and risks analyzed separately and then synthesized for the final outcome or in conflict resolution with or without a moderating negotiator.

We give an overview that covers the main criticisms and our replies to them. Because we and others have written numerous chapters in reply to criticisms, we have opted to classify them briefly in each category without giving lengthy repetitions of what is already known in the literature.

Rank Reversal

Change in Structure by Adding/Deleting Alternatives

In relative measurement, unlike measurement on a scale with an arbitrary unit where alternatives are assigned a value independently of other alternatives, when alternatives are compared on several criteria and their weight aggregated, their ranks can change when alternatives are added or deleted [1, 2, 3, 4]. The AHP with its ideal mode preserves rank in rating alternatives [5]. This is equivalent to measuring alternatives one at a time. Adding or deleting alternatives can have no effect on the value and rank of any other alternative. All known software programs that people use implement the ideal mode. In addition when paired comparisons are used, again the ideal mode is often used to preserve rank by idealizing only the first set of alternatives but not after. Thereafter, any new alternative is only compared with the ideal and its priority value is allowed to exceed one before weighting and adding and normalizing. This way the rank of the existing alternatives is always preserved. It is interesting to point out that the distributive mode of the AHP (uniqueness is important), the ideal mode of the AHP (uniqueness is not important), and utility functions (use of interval scales for the ideal), yield the same ranking of alternatives with surprisingly high frequency, except for the case of copies or near copies of an alternative in which the distributive mode always reverses rank, which is legitimate when the uniqueness of the most preferred alternative is important [6].

Here is an illustration of rank reversal due to Corbin and Marley [7]. It concerns a lady in a small town, who wishes to buy a hat. She enters the only store in town, and finds two hats, a and b, that she likes equally well although she leans toward a. However, suppose that the sales clerk discovers a third hat, a_1 identically to a. Then the lady may well choose hat b for sure (rather than risk the possibility of seeing someone wearing a hat just like hers), *a result that contradicts regularity.*

Luce and Raiffa [8], wrote in their book Games and Decisions, four variations on the axiom about whether rank should or should not be preserved with *counterexamples* in each case and without concluding that it always should and why.

They write:

"Adding new acts to a decision problem under uncertainty, each of which is weakly dominated by or is equivalent to some old act, has no effect on the optimality or non-optimality of an old act.

and elaborate it with

If an act is non optimal for a decision problem under uncertainty, it cannot be made optimal by adding new acts to the problem.

and press it further to

The addition of new acts does not transform an old, originally non-optimal act into an optimal one, and it can change an old, originally optimal act into a non-optimal one only if at least one of the new acts is optimal.

and even go to the extreme with:

The addition of new acts to a decision problem under uncertainty never changes old, originally non-optimal acts into optimal ones.

and finally conclude with:

The all-or-none feature of the last form may seem a bit too stringent ... a severe criticism is that it yields unreasonable results."

The question is not whether rank should be preserved, because it is widely believed that it cannot and should not always be preserved [9], but it is whether or not the assumption of independence applies, an assumption used by most multi-criteria methods. Adding copies or near copies of an alternative until the universe is full of them can depreciate the value and also the rank of that alternative and, as a counter example, negates the possibility of proving a theorem that the rank of independent alternatives must always be preserved when the judgments remain the same and no criteria are added or deleted or their weights changed. A criterion such as "manyness" that represents the number of alternatives cannot be used in the ranking because it forces the dependence of the ranking of each alternative on the existence of every other alternative thus contradicting the assumption of independence. It is illogical (or we might also add incorrect) for a multicriteria method that uses the rating of alternatives one at a time not to take this into account. Utilitarian philosophers of the 18th century believed that people ought to desire those things that will maximize their utility. However, this utilitarian viewpoint was abandoned because it was deemed that utility was impossible to measure. Instead, structural accounts of rationality and formal definitions of utility such as rational choice theory were favored. In rational choice theory, the criteria are assumed utility independent and the condition empirically tested. But because the criteria cannot be separated from the alternatives, the resulting weights are not really importance weights but scaling constants. Consequently, according to strong advocates of this theory, independence of the criteria among themselves must be assumed [10, 11]. Contrary to this assumption, in the AHP/ANP everything can depend on everything else including itself! In the AHP/ANP rank is always allowed to change. It is preserved only when the criteria are conditions imposed on the alternatives and possibly attributes that have had long standing and acquired an importance of their own apart from any particular alternative [12]. For example, we all have the habit of ascribing human kind of rationality to how the universe operates and assign rationality high priority. It is not the way some dervishes and ascetics and certainly not the way plants and animals feel about it.

Change in Structure by Adding/Deleting Criteria

In general, it is known in decision making that if one alters criteria or criteria weights then the outcome of a decision will change possibly leading to rank reversal. This is precisely what some authors use to criticize the AHP. There are two situations. The first is called "wash criteria" which involves the deletion of criteria that are assumed irrelevant because the alternatives have equal or nearly equal priorities under them [13]. The second is called "indifferent criteria" which involves the addition of criteria again assumed irrelevant for the same reason as "wash criteria" [14]. In the first case the authors made the error of renormalizing the weights of the remaining criteria that then gave rise to rank reversal because the weights of the criteria were changed [15]. In the second case the addition of a new criterion that was irrelevant also led to rank reversal for exactly the same reason of changing the weights of the criteria. It is surprising that anyone would want to add irrelevant criteria and use it to make an important decision. This approach treats the weights of the criteria not as representative of their importance but as scaling constants like in Multi-Attribute Utility Theory [10].

The correct approach to deal with wash and indifferent criteria is not to delete them or add them but simply to in the former case assign zero priorities to the alternatives and keep that criterion, and in the latter case not to add them or if added to consider this a new decision respecting the influence of added criteria on the final outcome which, as we said above, could lead to different priorities and ranks.

Consistency, Pareto Optimality and Order Preservation

As we said before, Pareto optimality in ordinal preference settings is a condition imposed on preferences which says that if every member of a group prefers A to B then the group must also prefer A to B. This condition is also known as unanimity. Underlying this condition is the hidden assumption of the transitivity of preferences. In the AHP with its reciprocal condition on the judgments, the geometric mean has been shown to be the unique way to derive a group judgment from the individual judgments under fairly general conditions. Note that Pareto optimality as used in economic and social practice applies to a final ordering of each individual of all the alternatives and not to judgments that obtain that order. In the AHP because preference order is indicated by priorities rather than by an ordinal statement of preference, Pareto optimality always holds when the stated condition is satisfied, and there is no problem with Pareto optimality.

When Pareto optimality is applied to judgments, there two possibilities: The first is when all judgments in a pairwise comparison matrix $A=(a_{ij})$ are consistent (i.e., $a_{ij}a_{jk}=a_{ik}$, $\forall i,j,k$ and a_{ij} have the form $a_{ij}=w_i/w_j$ where the w_i's are the priorities), in which case one has transitivity and also Pareto optimality. The second is when the judgments are inconsistent. In this case Pareto optimality holds under restrictive conditions like row dominance for each individual, i.e., there is an ordering of the rows and corresponding judgments in each row.

One may ask: Why should Pareto optimality be imposed on a method that uses cardinal preferences when it already has a process for aggregating individual judgments, along with the importance of the individuals involved, into a group judgment? If the members of the group are agreeable to using the geometric mean to combine their judgments, even if Pareto optimality is not satisfied, why should their combined judgment be any less valid than any other procedure that satisfies Pareto optimality?

Finally, Pareto optimality is not universally regarded as a desired condition in all decisions. A common criticism of a state of Pareto efficiency is that it does not necessarily result in a socially desirable distribution of resources, as it may lead to unjust and inefficient inequities [16, 17].

A condition that mirrors preferences expressed with interval scale value functions is the Condition of Order Preservation (COP) [18]. In interval scale value theory, a value function v must satisfy the condition that if a consequence i is preferred to a consequence j more than a consequence h is preferred to a consequence k then v(i)-v(j)>v(h)-v(k). Note that preferences are ordinal and hence no intensity of preference or judgment is involved. On the other hand, an individual imposing COP assigns judgments to the preferences. Thus, if a_{ij}>a_{hk} then $\dfrac{w_i}{w_j} > \dfrac{w_h}{w_k}$. This condition is always satisfied if the judgments are consistent because all logical methods of deriving priorities yield the same priorities. When the judgments are inconsistent, only the eigenvector obtains priorities that capture the transitivity of dominance reflected in the judgments. A major property of consistent judgments arranged in a matrix $A=(a_{ij})$ is that it satisfies the condition $A^k=n^{k-1}A$, where n is the order of A, so all powers of A are essentially equal to A. Now dominance of an inconsistent matrix no longer satisfies this condition and one must consider priorities derived from direct dominance as in the matrix itself, second order dominance obtained from the square of the matrix and so on. The total dominance of each element is obtained as the normalized sum of its rows. The result is an infinite number of priority vectors each representing a different order of dominance. The Cesaro sum of these vectors is equal to the priority vector obtained from the limiting powers of the matrix. Thus, only the eigenvector gives the correct ordering and priority values. COP imposes a condition on the priorities based solely on the original preferences without regard to dominance of higher order, and it thus likely to lead to the wrong priorities and order. In fact, we know of the existence of examples to support this statement [19]. COP was devised for use in a method known as MACBETH [20]. However, the value functions derived are interval scales so COP is expressed as ratios of differences. Finding the value function that satisfies COP in MACBETH involves an optimization technique that yields a non-unique solution.

To summarize, COP forces the condition that $a_{ij}>1$ should imply $w_i>w_j$, which is not always true when the judgments are inconsistent; violates the integrity of the eigenvector as the way to derive priorities capturing higher order interactions among the judgments; artificially forces adjustment of the judgments without asking the decision maker if the altered value is acceptable in his framework of understanding; and yields invalid results for single matrices with known measurements.

Priority Derivation and Synthesis with the Geometric Mean

A number of people concerned with always preserving rank look for schemes to synthesize inconsistent judgments and also priorities [21]. The only other method that has been proposed and pursued in the literature has been the geometric mean for a single matrix [22], in which the elements in each row of the matrix are multiplied, the nth root taken and the resulting vector normalized. This process does not capture the effect of transitivity of dominance in the case of inconsistent judgments and hence, it can lead to wrong priorities and order [23].

Synthesizing priorities derived in any manner by raising them to the power of the priority of the corresponding criterion and then multiplying the outcome [24, 25] has the shortcoming that $0<x<y<1$ and $0<p<q \Rightarrow x^p>y^q$ for some p and q. This means that an alternative that has a smaller value under a less important criterion is considered to be more important than an alternative that has a larger value under a more important criterion, which is absurd.

One can also show the absurdity of this process of synthesis because it yields wrong known results. By considering alternatives with known measurements under two or more criteria which then inherit their importance from the measurements under them, normalizing these measurements, raising them to the power of the priority of their corresponding criterion and multiplying, one obtains a different outcome than simply adding the measurements and then normalizing them [26].

Altering the Fundamental Scale

A number of authors have proposed changes in the fundamental 1-9 scale of the AHP more as a passing suggesting without either a proof of the resulting improvement if any or validation examples to test their assertions [27, 28].

Are The Axioms About Comparisons Behaviorally Meaningful?

People who subscribe to expected utility theory claim (see for example, Dyer 1990 [4], p.251) "…each of these axioms has a clear and obvious meaning as a description of choice behavior. Therefore, each axiom can be debated on the basis of its appeal as a normative descriptor of rationality, and each axiom can also be subjected to empirical testing." This statement is the basis for the criticism of the fundamental scale in the AHP. Are paired comparisons behaviorally based or are they an invention of ours? In Chapter 1 we quoted the psychologist Arthur Blumenthal [29] who believes that there are two types of judgment: "*Comparative judgment* which is the identification of some relation between two stimuli both present to the observer, and *absolute judgment* which involves the relation between a single stimulus and some information held in short term memory about some former comparison stimuli or about some previously experienced measurement scale using which the observer rates the single stimulus." In the Analytic Hierarchy Process (AHP) we call the first *relative measurement* and the second *absolute measurement*. In relative measurement we compare each alternative with many other alternatives and in absolute measurement we compare each alternative with one ideal alternative we know of or can imagine, a process we call *rating alternatives*. The first is descriptive and is conditioned by our observational ability and experience and the second is normative, conditioned by what we know is best, which of course is relative. Comparisons must precede ratings because ideals can only be created through experience using comparisons to arrive at what seems best. It is interesting that in order to rate alternatives with respect to an ideal as if they are independent can only be done after having made comparisons that involve dependence to create the ideal or standard in the first place. Making comparisons is fundamental and intrinsic in us. They are not an intellectual invention nor are they something that can be ignored.

The need for quantifying the intensity of preferences is all around us. Donald J. Boudreaux [30] writes:

"My third reason for not voting is that voting registers only each voter's order of preferences and not that voter's intensity of preferences. Unlike in private markets where I can refuse to buy a good or service if I judge its price to be too high—and then decide to buy that same product if its price falls—in elections each voter merely gets to say which candidate he prefers above all who are on the ballot. If I vote for Smith rather than Jones, this means only that I prefer Smith to Jones. My vote for Smith reveals nothing about how much I prefer Smith to Jones."

Paired comparisons consist of two steps. First, as in utility theory, there is a binary comparison, for example, alternative A is preferred to alternative B. Second, we must decide with how much more intensity we prefer A to B. Because in expected utility theory preferences are built on lotteries, it is already assumed that intensity of preference is accounted for, even though utilities do not always represent intensity of preference [31]. Without the probability function one is left with ordinal utilities which yield only ranking. Probabilities play the role of the fundamental scale in the AHP. On the other hand, in the AHP articulates the intensity of pairwise comparison preferences using an instinctively built in absolute scale

Pareto (1848-1923) rejected altogether the idea that quantities of utility mattered. He observed that if we map preferences onto Edgeworth's indifference curves, we know everything necessary for economic analysis. To map these preferences, we make *pairwise comparisons* between possible consumption bundles. The agent will either be indifferent between each bundle, or else will prefer one to the other. By obtaining comparisons between all bundles, we can draw a complete map of an individual's utility. These comparisons were ordinal in nature and did not go far enough to represent intensity of preference.

General Observations

We gave the above arguments about the major issues. The references include many chapters we know about, our published responses to some and also references to chapters we wrote mostly on the subject of rank preservation and reversal.

The first chapter questioning some aspect of the AHP was that by Watson and Freeling [1]. The authors questioned the validity of the questioning process by means of which judgments are elicited [33]. Belton and Gear [2] built an example of a simple hierarchy with three criteria and 3 alternatives, and showed that adding a copy of an alternative made rank reversal was possible [34]. The same problem was reported in [3]. Later Dyer [4] used the same arguments to challenge the validity of the axioms and the principle of hierarchic composition, and provided his own solution which he considered to be consistent with expected utility theory! [35, 36]

Holder [21] criticized the eigenvector method by questioning the validity of the optics experiment and the principle of hierarchic composition, for the same reason which was rank reversal [23]. The same criticisms were voiced in [24, 28, 13, 37, 14]. All these authors criticize the principle of hierarchy composition. Salo and Hamalainen [28] also criticize the composition principle in the Analytic Network process.

Other authors have criticized the AHP on the grounds that the 1-9 scale is not appropriate [27, 24, 28].

In group decision making the geometric mean has been criticized because it violates Pareto optimality [24].

There have been people who expect to put their own default numbers in an AHP structure without input about the particular decision and get rational numerical outcomes. One such person that has published notes against the AHP and other decision methods with strongly made arguments, mostly published in unrefereed journals, is Jonathan Barzilai [38]. He has been promising for many years to provide the scientific community his own decision theory. Whitaker [39, 40] has shown in detail where his thinking is in error. One of his fundamental assumptions is that in order for paired comparisons to be valid the underlying scale must be a ratio scale. He totally ignores the fact that paired comparison judgments are represented by numbers from an absolute scale and that the derived priority scales are relative scales of absolute numbers with no zero and no unit. For attributes/properties for which a scale has not yet been developed he assumes that there cannot be information about them that can be measured and hence paired comparisons with respect to criteria are invalid. He announces by fiat and without proof that hierarchic composition is linear and that it generates nonequivalent value functions from equivalent decompositions. In fact both theory and many examples show that hierarchic composition is nonlinear and the value functions generated are valid when it is done correctly.

Replies to the issues in such chapters have been properly addressed in the literature and will not be repeated here.

Conclusions – Our Concern with Validation in Decision Making in General

It is considered scientifically justifiable to require some sort of objective validation of numbers derived as answers in decision making. People in the field of decision making, particularly the normative kind, seem to be oblivious to the issue of validation as if it is a requirement they do not have to heed. It is true that judgments and priorities are subjective, but this does not mean that what a decision maker obtains by following the number crunching dictates of some theory will be justifiable to use in practice. It may be that results from their theory appear reasonable to the creators of it who are conditioned by a few techniques they know well, but they may have no real credibility in practice. Nor is the consent of the decision maker proof of anything because he may not be sophisticated in demanding justification according to more rigid standards of knowledge and practice. Nor is it proof that the technique is right if the decision outcome worked out successfully one time or even a few times.

The AHP is a psychophysical theory that finds some of its validations in measurement itself. We have already dedicated chapter 8 by way of validating the AHP in practical examples where measurements are already known. Some are with single matrices, some with hierarchies and some even with networks [41]. Here is one more example recently done.

L.G. Vargas applied judgments to estimate the relative size of the populations of seven cities in Spain. The judgments and the close outcome to the actual relative values are shown in Table 1.

Table 1 Which city has the larger population?

	Madrid	Barcelona	Valencia	Sevilla	Zaragoza	Malaga	Bilbao	Priorities	Actual in millions	Relative actual
Madrid	1	2	5	5	6	6	9	0.429	3.400.000	0.434
Barcelona	1/2	1	2	2	3	3	4	0.197	1.500.000	0.192
Valencia	1/5	1/2	1	1	1	1.5	2	0.091	740.000	0.095
Sevilla	1/5	1/2	1	1	1	1	2	0.086	700.000	0.089
Zaragoza	1/6	1/3	1	1	1	1	2	0.079	600.000	0.077
Malaga	1/6	1/3	1/1.5	1	1	1	1	0.068	528.000	0.067
Bilbao	1/9	1/4	1/2	1/2	1/2	1	1	0.048	358.000	0.046

We recommend that multicriteria methods put greater emphasis on validation to acquire greater credibility in practice. Validation is much more difficult when all judgments depend on feelings alone without memory from the senses and when the criteria are all intangible. But there are other ways to improve the credibility of the outcome that have been discussed in the literature [41].

References

1. Watson, S.R. and A.N.S. Freeling (1982), Assessing Attribute Weights, *Omega* 10(6), pp. 582-583
2. Belton, V. and A.E. Gear (1983), On a Short-coming of Saaty's Method of Analytic Hierarchies, *Omega* 11(3), pp. 228-230
3. Dyer, J.S. and H.V. Ravinder (1983), *Irrelevant Alternatives and the Analytic Hierarchy Process*, Working Chapter, The University of Texas at Austin
4. Dyer, J. S. (1990), Remarks on The Analytic Hierarchy Process, *Management Science* 36(3), pp. 249-258
5. Millet, I. and T. L. Saaty (2000), On the relativity of relative measures – accommodating both rank preservation and rank reversals in the AHP, *European Journal of Operational Research* 121, pp. 205-212
6. Saaty, T. L. and L. G. Vargas (1993), Experiments on Rank Preservation and Reversal in Relative Measurement, *Mathematical and Computer Modeling* 17(4/5), pp. 13-18
7. Corbin, R. and A. A. J. Marley (1974), Random Utility Models with Equality: An Apparent, but not Actual, Generalization of Random Utility Models, *Journal of Mathematical Psychology* 11 pp. 274-293
8. Luce, R.D. and H. Raiffa (1957), *Games and Decisions: Introduction and Critical Survey*, Wiley, New York
9. Tversky, A., P. Slovic and D. Kahneman (1990), The Causes of Preference Reversal, *The American Economic Review* 80(1), pp. 204-215
10. Keeney, R.L. and H. Raiffa (1976), *Decisions with Multiple Objectives: Preferences and value Tradeoffs*, New York, John Wiley & Sons
11. Kamenetzky, R. D. (1982), The Relationship Between the Analytic Hierarchy Process and the Additive Value Function, *Decision Sciences* 13(4), pp. 702-713
12. Saaty, T.L. (1991), Rank and the Controversy About the Axioms of Utility Theory — A Comparison of AHP and MAUT, The 2nd International Symposium on The Analytic Hierarchy Process, Pittsburgh, PA
13. Finan, J.S. and W.J. Hurley (2002), The Analytic Hierarchy Process: Can Wash Criteria Be Ignored? *Computers and Operations Research* 29(8), pp. 1025-1030

14. Perez, J., J.L. Jimeno and E. Mokotoff (2006), Another Potential Shortcoming of AHP. *TOP* 14(1), pp. 99-111

15. Saaty, T.L. and L.G. Vargas (2006), The Analytic Hierarchy Process: wash criteria should not be ignored. *Int'l J'l of Management and Decision Making* 7(2/3), pp. 180-188

16. Sen, A. (1993), Markets and Freedom: Achievements and limitations of the market mechanism in promoting individual freedoms. *Oxford Economic Chapters* 45(4), pp. 519-541

17. Barr, N. (2004), *Economics of the Welfare State*. New York, Oxford University Press (USA)

18. Bana e Costa, C.A. and J.C. Vansnick (2008), A critical analysis of the eigenvalue method used to derive priorities in the AHP. *European Journal of Operational Research* 187(3), pp. 1422-1428

19. Salomon, V.A.O. (2008), An Example of the Unreliability of MACBETH Applications. 4th International Conference on Production Research, June, Sao Paulo, Brazil

20. Bana e Costa, C.A., J.M.D. Corte and J.C. Vansnick (2003), MACBETH, Working Chapter 03.56. London, London School of Economics

21. Holder, R.D. (1990), Some Comments on the Analytic Hierarchy Process, *Journal of the Operational Research Society* 41(11), pp. 1073-1076

22. Barzilai, J. (1997), Deriving weights from pairwise comparison matrices. *Journal of the Operational Research Society* 48(12). Pp. 1226-1232

23. Saaty, T.L. (1991), Response to Holder's Comments on the Analytic Hierarchy Process. *The Journal of the Operational Research Society* 42(10), pp. 909-914

24. Lootsma, F.A. (1993), Scale Sensitivity in the Multiplicative AHP and SMART, *Journal of Multi-Criteria Decision Analysis* 2, pp. 87-110

25. Barzilai, J. and F.A. Lootsma (1997), Power Relations and Group Aggregation in the Multiplicative AHP and SMART, *Journal of Multi-Criteria Decision Analysis* 6, pp. 155-165

26. Vargas, L.G. (1997), Why the Multiplicative AHP is Invalid: A practical counterexample. *Journal of Multi-Criteria Decision Analysis* 6, pp. 169-170

27. Ma, D. and X. Zheng (1991), 9/9-9/1 Scale Method of AHP. Proceedings of the 2nd Int.'l Symposium on the AHP, Pittsburgh, PA, University of Pittsburgh, 1, pp. 197-202

28. Salo, A.A. and R.P. Hamalainen (1997), On the Measurement of Preferences in the Analytic Hierarchy Process, *Journal of Multi-Criteria Decision Analysis* 6(6), pp. 309-319

29. Blumenthal, A. (1977), *The Process of Cognition*, Englewood Cliffs, New Jersey, Prentice-Hall, Inc.

30. Boudreaux, D.J. (2008), The Freeman: Ideas on Liberty, *Foundation for Economic Education* 58(3)

31. Sarin, R.K. (1982), Strength of Preference and Risky Choice, *Operations Research* 30(5), pp. 982-997

32. Dehaene, S. (1997), *The Number Sense*, Oxford University Press

33. Saaty, T.L., L.G. Vargas and R.E. Wendell (1983), Assessing Attribute Weights by Ratios, *Omega* 11(1), pp. 9-13.

34. Saaty, T.L. and L.G. Vargas (1984), The Legitimacy of Rank Reversal, *Omega* 12(5), pp. 513-516

35. Harker, P.T. and L.G. Vargas (1990), Reply to "Remarks on The Analytic Hierarchy Process" by J.S. Dyer. *Management Science* 36(3), pp. 269-273

36. Saaty, T.L. (1990), An Exposition of the AHP in Reply to the Chapter: Remarks on the Analytic Hierarchy Process, *Management Science* 36(3), pp. 259-268

37. Hurley, W.J. (2002), Letters to the Editor: Strategic Risk Assessment. *Canadian Military Journal* Summer 3-4

38. Barzilai, J. (1998), On the Decomposition of Value Functions. *Operations Research Letters* 22, pp. 159-170

39. Whitaker, R. (2004), Why Barzilai's Criticisms of the AHP are Incorrect. Int'l Meeting of the Multi-Criteria Decision Making Society, Whistler, Canada

40. Whitaker, R. (2007), Criticisms of the Analytic Hierarchy Process: Why they often make no sense. *Mathematical and Computer Modeling* 46(7/8), pp. 948-961

41. Whitaker, R. (2007), Validation Examples of the Analytic Hierarchy Process and Analytic Network Process. *Mathematical and Computer Modelling* 46(7/8), pp. 840-859

Part VI

Continuous Judgments

In this part we generalize the use of judgments from the discrete pairwise comparisons process in decision making to the case of continuous judgments and sensations in response to stimuli. The mathematics changes from the finite and discrete to the infinite and continuous using the ideas of the relatively new field being intensively developed in our time, functional equations.

There are two ways to generalize the mathematics of the eigenvalue problem of reciprocal pairwise comparisons matrices and of consistent matrices. In general, consistency appears to be a required condition because it generalizes to continuous form without complications and also because measure theory and Lebesgue integration allow for sets of measure zero where inconsistencies may occur.

The first way to make the generalization is formal and is simple as it generalizes the pairwise comparisons' discrete process used in reciprocal matrices to the continuous process of comparisons that uses a Fredholm integral equation of the second kind. What is new in this generalization turns out to be that it is necessary to obtain solutions of a functional equation that are consequently solutions of this Fredholm equation. In other words, unlike the discrete case in which each eigenvalue problem must be solved to obtain the priorities that correspond to the numerical judgments, in the continuous case we already have the general solution except for its two parameters whose values are not fixed and must be numerically determined in each application. For our purpose, the kind of solution obtained is very significant to characterize response to stimuli as the human senses and the human mind do. The solutions obtained belong to the real and complex domains as they apply to the workings of neurons with electric signals in creating sensations such as images with the eyes and sounds with the ears to respond to physical reality and with feelings and thoughts to respond to other feelings and thoughts and to make meaning of experience.

The second way to make the generalization is to create structure(s) like a network and its supermatrix which involves the interaction and impact of neurons on other neurons and involves a large number of clusters and sub-clusters, elements and sub-elements. In that case the entries which are neural firings are functions of time and each row and column of such a very large feedback matrix is a vector assumed to have an infinite number of entries to enable the generality of the mathematics. Thus instead of finite dimensional vector spaces, we would be dealing with elements in Hilbert space. One step further in the generalization takes us from a vector to a function and more generally to an operator on functions as the matrix itself operates on its judgment entries. The eventual outcome that characterizes neural firing as a decision process is described in terms of solutions of an operator equation describing complex responses to stimuli in order to capture their mental representations proportionately.

The universe is altogether known to us with our minds. Looking at galaxies and their black holes and their billions of stars, we see that influence and power in the universe are fragmented and do not belong to any single source. To learn about them as a whole we need to synthesize our understanding about them as cosmologists, astronomers and scientists have been doing. But what they do is very much related to how our brains are equipped to work and not in some metaphysically absolute preordained way. We are one kind of entities that respond to stimuli in certain ways that enhance its survival and not from pre-established objective ways from beyond this world.

It is becoming increasingly apparent that what is needed, in fact, is a method of "synthesis"—that is, forming a whole of the parts. The whole thus formed would hopefully permit evaluation of the primal impact of various solutions offered. It may be argued that analysis "from above", i.e., analysis from the whole to the part, as is described by Max Wertheimer in Gestalt Theory in 1925, will accomplish the same. It seems, however, that there is a basic difference of purpose between analysis, even "from above" and synthesis. Analysis aims to extend man's understanding while synthesis seeks to enable him to act.

Chapter 15

From The Discrete to the Continuous
Judgment as Response to Stimuli

Introduction

In this chapter we generalize further the mathematics of the fundamental idea of an infinite number, a continuum, of pairwise comparisons. This leads us from the solution of a finite system of homogeneous equations or alternatively, and according to the theory of Perron, to raising a positive reciprocal pairwise comparisons matrix to limiting powers to obtain its principal eigenvector, to the solution of a Fredholm equation of the second kind to obtain its principal eigenfunction. A necessary condition for the existence of this eigenfunction $w(s)$ is that it be the solution of the functional equation $w(as)=bw(s)$. Surprising and useful properties of this solution emerge and are related to how our brains respond to stimuli through the electrical firing of neurons and how bodies in the universe responding to each other's influence satisfy a near inverse square law discovered in physics - the principle that responding to influences in a manner that satisfies a natural law is an attribute of all things be they material or mental. We believe that this is the insight that drove Julian Huxley [1] to observe as said in Chapter 1 that something like the human mind might exist even in lifeless matter. It is the vital force called Chi that in Taoism and other Chinese thought is believed to be inherent in all things. The unimpeded circulation of Chi and a balance of its negative and positive forms in the body are held to be essential to good health in traditional Chinese medicine. Thus all things that exist respond to stimuli to a larger or smaller extent as our mind does.

Motivation

We can describe our responses to stimuli mathematically as follows. A stimulus S of magnitude s, is received as a similarity transformation as, where $a > 0$ is referred to as a dilation of s. The dilation is a *stretching* if $a > 1$, and a *contraction* if $a < 1$. Without such proportionality, it would be impossible to establish a meaningful relationship between the dimensions of the object in the mind as we conceptualize it and what its real dimensions are. An effective response $w(as)$ to a perturbed stimulus s must be faithful in capturing the magnitude of the stimulus after it is received and needs to be proportional to responding to that original stimulus without perturbation, namely $w(as) \propto w(s)$. It turns out that this functional equation is identical with the equation we obtain as a necessary and sufficient condition for the existence of a solution to the generalized formulation of the discrete eigenvalue problem to continuous paired comparisons.

Before we turn to that generalization we note that if there are several stimuli our overall response to them needs to also satisfy a proportionality relation. In that case the foregoing functional equation would take on the form:

$$w(a_1 s_1, ..., a_n s_n) = bw(s_1, ..., s_n)$$

It may be that the stimulus is an oscillatory electric signal that is better characterized by amplitude and angle. In that case instead of a real variable s the stimulus is better characterized by a complex variable z and the parameters a and b may themselves be complex numbers. In that case the solution would be a complex valued function.

Generalizing From Discrete to Continuous Judgments

There is a way to formulate the problem of automatic decisions that relates to the stimulus-response equation $w(as)=bw(s)$. It involves generalizing the discrete, eigenvalue-oriented decision-making of the AHP to the continuous case where Fredholm's equation is the continuous version of the discrete eigenvalue formulation. In that generalization it turns out that the functional equation $w(as)=bw(s)$ is a necessary condition for Fredholm's integral equation of the second kind to be solvable. Instead of finding the eigenvector of a pairwise comparison matrix one uses the kernel of an operator. Operations on the matrix translate to operations on the kernel. From the matrix formulation leading to the solution of a principal eigenvalue problem

$$\sum_{j=1}^{n} a_{ij} w_j = \lambda_{max} w_i, \sum_{i=1}^{n} w_i = 1$$

we have

$$\int_a^b K(s,t)\, w(t)\, dt = \lambda_{max}\, w(s) \text{ or } \lambda \int_a^b K(s,t) w(t) dt = w(s)$$

$\int_a^b w(s)ds = 1$ where the positive matrix A is replaced by a positive kernel

$K(s,t) > 0$, the continuous version of pairwise comparisons and the eigenvector w by the eigenfunction $w(s)$. Note that the entries in a matrix depend on the two variables i and j that assume discrete values. Thus the matrix itself depends on these discrete variables and its generalization, the kernel function, depends on two (continuous) variables. The reason for calling it a kernel is the role it plays in the integral, where without knowing it we cannot determine the exact form of the solution. The standard way in which the first equation is written is to move the eigenvalue to the left hand side which gives it the reciprocal form. In general, by abuse of notation, one continues to use the symbol λ to represent the reciprocal value and with it one includes the familiar condition of normalization $\int_a^b w(s)ds = 1$. Here also, the kernel $K(s,t)$ is said to be 1) consistent and therefore also reciprocal, if $K(s,t) K(t,u) = K(s,u)$, for all s, t and u, or 2) reciprocal, but perhaps not consistent, if $K(s,t) K(t,s) = 1$ for all s,t.

A value of λ for which Fredholm's equation has a nonzero solution $w(t)$ is called a characteristic value (or its reciprocal is called an eigenvalue) and the corresponding solution is called an eigenfunction. An eigenfunction is determined to within a multiplicative constant. If $w(t)$ is an eigenfunction corresponding to the characteristic value λ and if C is an arbitrary constant, we see by substituting in the equation that $Cw(t)$ is also an eigenfunction corresponding to the same λ. The value $\lambda=0$ is not a characteristic value because we have the corresponding solution $w(t) = 0$ for every value of t, which is the trivial case, excluded in our discussion. The material immediately below is also found with proofs in my book on the brain [2].

Theorem 1 *$K(s,t)$ is consistent if and only if it is separable of the form:*
$$K(s,t) = k(s)/k(t)$$

Proof (Necessity) $K(t, u_0) \neq 0$ for some $u_0 \in S$, otherwise $K(t, u_0) = 0$ for all u_0 would contradict $K(u_0, u_0) = 1$ for $t = u_0$. Using $K(s,t) K(t,u) = K(s,u)$, for all s, t and u, we obtain

$$K(s,t) K(t, u_0) = K(s, u_0)$$

$$K(s,t) = \frac{K(s,u_0)}{K(t,u_0)} = \frac{k(s)}{k(t)}$$

for all $u_0 \in S$ and the result follows.

(Sufficiency) If $K(s,t)=k(s)/k(t)$ holds, then it is clear that $K(s,t)$ is consistent.

We now prove that as in the discrete case of a consistent matrix, whereby the eigenvector is given by any normalized column of the matrix, that an analogous result obtains in the continuous case.

Theorem 2 *If $K(s,t)$ is consistent, the solution of $\lambda \int_a^b K(s,t)w(t)dt = w(s)$ is given by*

$$w(s) = \frac{k(s)}{\int_S k(s)ds}$$

Proof We replace $w(t)$ in $\lambda \int_a^b K(s,t)w(t)dt = w(s)$ by $\lambda \int_a^b K(s,u)w(u)du$ inside the integral and repeat the process n times. Passing to the limit we obtain:

$$w(s) = \lim_{n \to \infty} \lambda^n \int_S \int_S ... \int_S K(s,s_1)K(s_1,s_2)...K(s_{n-1},s_n)ds_1...ds_n$$

Since $K(s,t)$ is consistent, we have :

$$w(s) = \lim_{n \to \infty} \lambda^n \int_S \int_S ... \int_S K(s,s_n)ds_1...ds_n = \lim_{n \to \infty} \lambda^n \int_S K(s,s_n)ds_n$$

With $\int_S w(s)ds = 1$ we have

$$w(s) = \lim_{n \to \infty} \int_S K(s,s_n)ds_n / \int_S \lim_{n \to \infty} \int_S K(s,s_n)ds_n ds$$

$$= \lim_{n \to \infty} [\int_S K(s,s_n)ds_n / \int_S \int_S K(s,s_n)ds_n ds]$$

Also, because $K(s, s_n)$ is consistent we have $K(s, s_n)=k(s)/k(s_n)$ and

$$w(s) = \frac{k(s)}{\int_S k(s)ds} = \alpha k(s) \cdot$$

In the discrete case, the normalized eigenvector was independent of whether or not all the elements of the pairwise comparison matrix A are multiplied by the same constant a, and thus we can replace A by aA and obtain the same eigenvector. Generalizing this result to the continuous case we have:

$$K(as, at)=aK(s,t)=k(as)/k(at)=a\,k(s)/k(t)$$

This means that K is a homogeneous function of order one. Because K is a degenerate kernel, we can replace $k(s)$ above by $k(as)$ and obtain $w(as)$. To prove that $w(as) = bw(s)$, from $w(s) = \dfrac{k(s)}{\int k(s)ds}$ and $\dfrac{k(as)}{k(at)} = a\dfrac{k(s)}{k(t)}$, we first

show that $\dfrac{w(as)}{w(at)} = \dfrac{w(s)}{w(t)}$. Integrating both terms of $\dfrac{k(as)}{k(at)} = a\dfrac{k(s)}{k(t)}$ first over s,

we have $\dfrac{\int k(as)ds}{k(at)} = a\dfrac{\int k(s)ds}{k(t)}$. Next, rearranging the terms and integrating

over t, to obtain $\int k(as)ds \int k(t)dt = a \int k(s)ds \int k(at)dt$ which implies that

$a\dfrac{\int k(s)ds \int k(at)dt}{\int k(as)ds \int k(t)dt} = 1$. Thus,

$$\frac{w(as)}{w(at)} = \frac{k(as)/\int k(as)ds}{k(at)/\int k(at)dt} = a\frac{k(s)/\int k(s)ds}{k(t)/\int k(t)dt}\frac{\int k(at)dt}{\int k(as)ds}\frac{\int k(s)ds}{\int k(t)dt}$$

$$= \frac{k(s)/\int k(s)ds}{k(t)/\int k(t)dt} = \frac{w(s)}{w(t)}$$

Assuming that the domain of integration is bounded or at least measurable, by integrating $w(as) = \dfrac{w(s)}{w(t)}w(at)$ over t we have $w(as)\int_{\Omega} dt = w(s)\int_{\Omega}\dfrac{w(at)}{w(t)}dt$ and

writing $b = \dfrac{1}{\int_{\Omega} dt}\int_{\Omega}\dfrac{w(at)}{w(t)}dt$, we have $w(as)=bw(s)$.

We have proved:

Theorem 3 *A necessary and sufficient condition for $w(s)$ to be an eigenfunction solution of Fredholm's equation of the second kind, with a consistent kernel that is homogeneous of order one is that it satisfy the functional equation*
$$w(as)=bw(s)$$

Solutions of the Functional Equation $w(as)=bw(s)$ in the Domain of Reals

What we want in the continuous case is a general solution for all consistent kernels. With general integration inconsistency is not as important for our purpose. We know of no general (non-iterative) method for solving an integral equation in closed form in an unknown kernel, and our kernel here, although it is consistent, is unknown. Fortunately we can obtain the general solution in the real and then again in the complex domains by solving the functional equation $w(as)=bw(s)$ that is a necessary and sufficient condition for the solvability of Fredholm's equation. In both the real and the complex cases we have the general single-valued and also the general multi-valued solutions. In the single-valued cases we have, in particular, also the general continuous and the general differentiable solutions. In the case of complex valued functions of a complex variable we have the general everywhere analytic solutions (except perhaps at 0). The general solutions look essentially different according to whether $|a|\neq 1$ or $|a|=1$ (for positive real variables the case $a=1$ is trivial). Let us illustrate briefly how the real-valued solution is obtained. There is no room in this chapter to give all the details found in my book on the brain [2].

If we substitute $s=a^u$ in $w(as)=bw(s)$ we obtain

$$w(a^{u+1})-bw(a^u)=0.$$

Again if we write $w(a^u)=b^u p(u)$, we obtain:

$$p(u+1) - p(u)=0.$$

This is a periodic function of period one in the variable u (such as $\cos u/2\pi$). Note that if the parameters a and s are real, then so is u which may be negative even if a and s are both assumed to be positive. Finally we have

$$w(s) = b^{\log s/\log a}\, p(\frac{\log s}{\log a})$$

The right hand side of this equation is a damped periodic function.

By dividing its variable by its period, any periodic function can be reduced to a periodic function of period one. Thus, whatever is known about periodic functions applies to periodic functions of period one and conversely. If P is periodic of period T, i.e. $P(x+T)=P(x)$, then $p(x)=P(Tx)$ will be periodic of period 1:

$$p(x+1)=P(T(x+1))=P(Tx+T)=P(Tx)=p(x);$$

the converse operation is obvious.

If in the last equation $p(0)$ is not equal to 0, we can introduce $C=p(0)$ and $P(u)=p(u)/C$, we have for the general response function $w(s)$,

$$w(s) = Ce^{\log b\frac{\log s}{\log a}} P\left(\frac{\log s}{\log a}\right)$$

where P is also periodic of period 1 and $P(0)=1$. Note that $C > 0$ only if $p(0)$ is positive. Otherwise, if $p(0) < 0$, $C < 0$.

Analogously, the general complex solution of our functional equation is given by:

$$w(z) = Cb^{[\log |z| / \log |a|]} g(z)$$

where $C > 0$. The [ ] in the above expression denotes the "closest integer from below" function, and g is an arbitrary solution of $g(az)=g(z)$.

Our solution which represents response to a force, that serves as a stimulus, is general and has applicability to all phenomena whose measurement is based for example, on ratio scales as in physics. When we speak of response subject to ratio scales, it is not only response of the brain to a stimulus, but also the response of any object to a force or influence to which it is subject.

Pursuing our generalization of discrete comparisons, and adopting the paradigm that neurons are decision makers that perform reciprocal comparisons in milliseconds, how to synthesize the firings of many neurons requires that we adopt the geometric mean again as a generalization of the discrete case. Without going into the details of such synthesis, we note that outcome of products of functions of the form $w(s) = b^{\log s/\log a} p(\dfrac{\log s}{\log a})$ is again a function of the same form with different parameters a and b because the product of two periodic functions of period one is also a periodic function of period one. It is useful for explaining synthesis of electric signals as in the brain. A significant observation is that rather than adding signals, due to the reciprocal property they are multiplied, which is likely to be at odds with what people have been considering in the literature so far. The presence of synapses in the brain makes it possible to interpret the process of addition of neural firings.

For completeness it may be useful to give the solution to the equation $w(a_1s_1,\dots,a_ns_n)=bw(s_1,\dots,s_n)$ which involves proportionate response to multiple stimuli although as we shall see later each neuron in the brain specializes in a task involving a single variable. These single variables must somehow be combined to form a function of several variables.

We replace the variables s_i with the complex variables z_i so that the equation becomes $w(a_1z_1,\dots,a_nz_n)=bw(z_1,\dots z_n)$. The solution of this equation is given by

$$w(z_1,\dots,z_n) = b^{\sum_{k=1}^{n}(\log z_k / \log a_k)/n} P(\log z_1 / \log a_1,\dots,\log z_n / \log a_n)$$

where P is an arbitrary periodic function of period one in n variables:

$$P(u_1 +1,...,u_n +1) = P(u_1,...,u_n), u_i = \log z_i / \log a_i.$$

Solution of the last functional equation in the complex domain is due to Karol Baron [2]. It is given by

$$w(z_1,...,z_n) = z_1^{k_1} \cdots z_N^{k_N} \, G(|z_1|, ..., |z_M|, \frac{\log |z_{M+1}|}{\log |a_{M+1}|}, ..., \frac{\log |z_N|}{\log |a_N|}, \arg z_1, ..., \arg z_N)$$

where G is a doubly periodic with periods
$(0, \underset{M}{\ldots}, 0, 1, \underset{M-N}{\ldots}, 1, \arg a_1, ..., \arg a_N)$ and $(0, ..., 0, \underset{n+1}{2\pi}, 0, ..., 0)$ for $l \in \{1, ..., N\}$,
It is known that a single-valued analytic function cannot possess more than two linearly independent periods.

A Continuum Number of Stimuli

For a continuum number of stimuli let $K(\mathbf{X},\mathbf{Y})$ be a compact reciprocal kernel i.e. $K(x,y)K(y,x)=1$, for all $x \varepsilon \mathbf{X}$ and $y \varepsilon \mathbf{Y}$, where $\mathbf{X}$ and $\mathbf{Y}$ are compact subsets of the reals. We have the equation $w(\mathbf{X}) = \lambda \int_\Omega K(\mathbf{X};\mathbf{Y})w(\mathbf{Y})$. Formally, we write the general solution in the form

$$w(\mathbf{X}) = [\exp \int_\Omega (\log x / \log a)dx]P(\frac{\log \mathbf{X}}{\log a})$$

that is a product integral.

Table 1 provides a summary of the eigenvalue formulation of the paired comparisons process in both the discrete and continuous cases.

To keep the story of the continuous case together, we decided to repeat in about a page what we already shown before to justify the adoption of the Fundamental Scale of the AHP. It has to do with the fact that the well-known Weber-Fechner logarithmic law of response to stimuli can be obtained as a first order approximation to our eigenfunction solution through series expansions of the exponential and of a periodic function of period one (for example the cosine function $\cos u/2\pi$) for which we must have $P(0) = 1$ as:

$$v(u) = C_1 e^{-\beta u} P(u) \approx C_2 \log s + C_3$$

where $P(u)$ is periodic of period 1, $u = \log s / \log a$ and $\log ab \equiv -\beta$, $\beta > 0$.

The expression on the right is known as the Weber-Fechner law of logarithmic response $M = a \log s + b$, $a \neq 0$ to a stimulus of magnitude s.

Table 1 Mathematical Formulation and Solution of the Paired Comparisons Process

Discrete	Continuous
$A=(a_{ij})$, A consistent that is $a_{ij}a_{jk}=a_{ik}$, then $a_{ij}=w_i/w_j$ and $$\sum_{j=1}^{n} a_{ij}w_j = nw_i, \ i = 1,...,\ n, \sum_{i=1}^{n} w_i = 1$$	$K(s,t)$ consistent that is $K(s,t)K(t,u)=K(s,u)$ then $K(s,t)=K(s)/K(t)$ and $$\lambda\int_a^b K(s,t)w(t)dt = w(s), \ \int_a^b w(s)ds = 1$$
$A=(a_{ij})$, A reciprocal that is $a_{ji}=1/a_{ij}$ but not consistent, then $$\sum_{i=1}^{n} a_{ij}w_j = \lambda_{max}w_i, \sum_{i=1}^{n} w_i = 1$$	$K(s,t)$ reciprocal that is $K(s,t)K(t,s)=1$, but not consistent, then $$\lambda\int_a^b K(s,t)w(t)dt = w(s), \ \int_a^b w(s)ds = 1$$
Principal eigenvector solution of $Aw=\lambda_{max}w$	Eigenfunction solution also solution of functional equation $w(as)=bw(s)$; $w(s) = b^{\log s/\log a} p(\dfrac{\log s}{\log a})$ or more simply $w(u)=e^{au}p(u)$, $a=\log b$, $u=\log s / \log a$. In the complex domain a single valued solution of the functional equation: $w(az)=bw(z)$, is $w(z)=cb^{\log|z|/\log|a|}g(z)$ where $g(z)$ is an arbitrary solution of $g(az)=g(z)$.
Hierarchic Composition gives rise to multilinear forms $$w_i^h = \sum_{i_2,...,i_{h-1}=1}^{N_{h-1},...,N_1} w_{i_1 i_2}^{h-1}...w_{i_{h-2}i_{h-1}}^2 w_{i_{h-1}}^1 \ i_1 \equiv i$$	Hierarchic composition in the case of a finite number of criteria is a particular case of the multiple stimuli solution. It is a product integral in the case of a continuum number of criteria, as in the case of a continuum number of stimuli
Network composition also gives rise to convergent series of multilinear forms	Continuum composition- same as with hierarchic composition

The integer-valued scale of response in the form of paired comparison judgments in the AHP can be derived from this the logarithmic response function in the following way: For a given value of the stimulus, the magnitude of response remains the same until the value of the stimulus is increased sufficiently large in proportion to the value of the stimulus, thus preserving the proportionality of relative increase in stimulus for it to be detectable for a new response. This suggests the idea of just noticeable differences (jnd), well-known in psychology. Thus, starting with a stimulus s_0 successive magnitudes of the new stimuli take the form:

$$s_1 = s_0 + \Delta s_0 = s_0 + \frac{\Delta s_0}{s_0} s_0 = s_0(1+r)$$

$$s_2 = s_1 + \Delta s_1 = s_1(1+r) = s_0(1+r)^2 \equiv s_0\alpha^2$$

$$s_n = s_{n-1}\alpha = s_0\alpha^n \ (n = 0,1,2,...)$$

We consider the responses to these stimuli to be measured on a ratio scale ($b=0$). A typical response has the form $M_i = a \log \alpha^i$, $i = 1,...,n$, or one after another they have the form:

$$M_1 = a\log\alpha, M_2 = 2a\log\alpha,..., M_n = na\log\alpha$$

We take the ratios M_i/M_1, $i=1,...,n$ of these responses in which the first is the smallest and serves as the unit of comparison, thus obtaining the *integer* values 1, 2, ..., n of the fundamental scale of the AHP. It appears that numbers are intrinsic to our ability to make comparisons, and were not invented by our primitive ancestors. We must be grateful to them for the discovery of the symbolism.

Compatibility in the Continuous Case

We now derive a compatibility index in the continuous case along the lines discussed for the discrete case in Chapter 4. We consider the solution of the equation $w(as)=bw(s)$ given by $w(s) = b^{\log s/\log a} p\left(\dfrac{\log s}{\log a}\right)$ and rewrite it as

$w(s) = e^{\log b^{\log s/\log a}} p\left(\dfrac{\log s}{\log a}\right) = e^{\alpha u}p(u)$, $\alpha = \log b$, $u = \log s/\log a$ and our compatibility index is given by:

$$\frac{1}{T^2}\int_0^T\int_0^T \frac{e^{\alpha_1 u}p(u)/2\pi}{e^{\alpha_2 u}p(u)/2\pi}\frac{e^{\alpha_2 v}p(v)/2\pi}{e^{\alpha_1 v}p(v)/2\pi}dudv = \frac{1}{T^2}\frac{e^{(\alpha_1-\alpha_2)T}-1}{\alpha_1-\alpha_2}\frac{1-e^{-(\alpha_1-\alpha_2)T}}{\alpha_1-\alpha_2}$$

$$= \frac{1}{T^2}\frac{e^{(\alpha_1-\alpha_2)T}-1-1+e^{-(\alpha_1-\alpha_2)T}}{(\alpha_1+\alpha_2)^2} = \left(\frac{e^{(\alpha_1-\alpha_2)T/2}-e^{-(\alpha_1-\alpha_2)T/2}}{(\alpha_1+\alpha_2)T}\right)^2$$

$$= \frac{1}{4}\left(\frac{e^{(\alpha_1-\alpha_2)T/2}-e^{-(\alpha_1-\alpha_2)T/2}}{(\alpha_1+\alpha_2)T/2}\right)^2 = \frac{1}{4}\left(\frac{e^\gamma-e^{-\gamma}}{\gamma}\right)^2 \to 1 \text{ as } |\gamma|\to 0.$$

References

1. Huxley, J. (1953), *Man in the Modern World*, Mentor Books, New York
2. Saaty, T.L., (2000), *The Brain, Unraveling the Mystery of How it Works: The Neural Network Process*, RWS Publications, Pittsburgh, PA

Chapter 16

Proportionate Response to Natural Law
Inverse Squares True Only Approximately

This chapter deals with the following ideas:
- All natural laws are recognized by us as stimuli to which we respond with our bodies or by inference with our minds.
- That so far our mathematical formulations of natural laws due to gravity, light and others in physics have been conjectures validated through experiments but not derived from basic principles as we have done here with our proportionality equation.
- That it is not true that they take on the strict from of an inverse square law but a modified form of it that involves parameters whose values can change the outcome in extreme cosmic galactic levels and in nano levels exploration.

Introduction

All laws of nature are stimuli to be responded to in some proportionate way. Their influence is felt or noticed and responded to in appropriate ways which make it a law rather than a continuous but haphazard force to which there is no systematic way to respond. It would not be recognized as a law in that case. As a law it must be obeyed with uniformity and with appropriate regularity. It is true that in art, music and mathematics we can think of ideas that involve no proportionality, but that is not true when we need to understand the world well in order to act and react to it in effective ways. We now show what kind of response there can be when our assumption of proportionality is applicable.

All methods of decision-making must be justified on the basis of the validity of their assumptions and on their successful application in practice. The rationalist sees coherence and scope as the crucial requirements. The empiricist regards prediction and validation as the crucial step, making new predictions using the theory then comparing those predictions with the facts to confirm whether it worked. The constructivist says that the best test of a theory in science is the consistent and coherent, though diverse, framework it provides to deal with wide ranging situations. These are philosophies about scientific theories and their applications. They make fine distinctions between different aspects of a theory and its applications and where the emphasis should be placed to arrive at truth and validity.

The modern philosopher Paul Feyerabend objects to any single prescriptive scientific method on the grounds that any such method would limit the activities of scientists, and hence restrict scientific progress. He argues that the only approach that does not inhibit progress, whatever it may be, is "anything goes, which is the terrified exclamation of a rationalist who takes a closer look at history."

The AHP/ANP provide structures and a process that parallels to a considerable extent what people would do on their own in a more complicated and less orderly way, than what now they can do more simply and more faithfully using such a structured process to deal with complexity. The AHP/ANP include basic aspects of the four philosophies of science mentioned above. They have a fairly comprehensive mathematical foundation and have been used to address a vast breadth of problems and concerns of people regarding the benefits, opportunities, costs and risks of a decision and how to combine them. There have been many and varied applications involving predictions and validations, and other kinds of decision making such as planning and the resolution of conflicts. The AHP and ANP so far appear to be free of paradoxes and do not require strong assumptions. This makes them amenable to wide-ranging uses. They use a fundamental scale to make judgments that is natural and that people intuitively use every day so they do not have to be educated in mathematical complexities to associate numbers with preferences as they make decisions.

Inverse Square Laws in Physics

The solution of Fredholm's equation derived in the last chapter is defined in the frequency domain or transform domain in Fourier analysis as it is based on the flow of electric charge. We must now take its transform to derive the solution in the spatial or time domain. Thus our solution of Fredholm's equation here is given as the Fourier transform,

$$f(\omega) = \int_{-\infty}^{+\infty} F(x)\, e^{-2\pi i \omega x}\, dx = C e^{\beta \omega}\, P(\omega)$$

whose inverse transform is the inverse Fourier transform of a convolution of the two factors in the product. We have :

$$F(x) = \int_{-\infty}^{+\infty} f(\omega)\, e^{2\pi i \omega x}\, d\omega$$

which we now find.

Since our solution is a product of two factors, the inverse transform can be obtained as the convolution of two functions, the inverse Fourier transform of each of which corresponds to just one of the factors.

Now the inverse Fourier transform of $e^{-\beta u}$ is given by

$$\frac{\sqrt{(2/\pi)}\beta}{\beta^2 + \xi^2}$$

Also because a periodic function has Fourier series expansion we have

$$P(u) = \sum_{k=-\infty}^{\infty} \alpha_k\, e^{2\pi i k u}$$

whose inverse Fourier transform is:

$$\sum_{k=-\infty}^{\infty} \alpha_k \delta(\xi - 2\pi k)$$

Now the product of the transforms of the two functions is equal to the Fourier transform of the convolution of the two functions themselves which we just obtained by taking their individual inverse transforms. We have, to within a multiplicative constant:

$$\int_{-\infty}^{+\infty} \sum_{k=-\infty}^{\infty} \alpha_k\, \delta(\xi - 2\pi k)\, \frac{\beta}{\beta^2 + (x-\xi)^2}\, d\xi = \sum_{k=-\infty}^{\infty} \alpha_k \frac{\beta}{\beta^2 + (x - 2k\pi)^2}$$

We have already mentioned that this solution is general and is applicable to phenomena requiring relative measurement through ratio scales. Consider the case where

$$P(u) = \cos u/2\pi = (1/2)(e^{iu/2\pi} + e^{-iu/2\pi}).$$

Bruce W. Knight adopts the same kind of expression for finding the frequency response to a small fluctuation and more generally using $e^{iu/2\pi}$ instead. The inverse Fourier transform of $w(u) = C\, e^{-\beta u} \cos u/2\pi$, $\beta > 0$ is given by:

$$C \frac{\beta}{\sqrt{2\pi}} \left[\frac{1}{\beta^2 + \left(\dfrac{1}{2\pi} + \xi\right)^2} + \frac{1}{\beta^2 + \left(\dfrac{1}{2\pi} - \xi\right)^2} \right]$$

When the constants in the denominator are small relative to ξ we have C_1/ξ^2 which we believe is why optics, gravitation (Newton) and electric (Coulomb) forces act according to inverse square laws. This is the same law of nature in which an object responding to a force field must decide to follow that law by comparing infinitesimal successive states through which it passes. If the stimulus is constant, the exponential factor in the general response solution given in the last chapter is constant, and the solution in this particular case would be periodic of period one. When the distance ξ is very small, the result varies inversely with the parameter $\beta > 0$.

The simple and seemingly elegant formulations in science are not to be. LeShan and Margenau report on page 75 in their book "Einstein's Space to Van Gogh's Sky" Macmillan Publishing Co. Inc., New York 1982 that "Long after Newton proposed his inverse square law of gravitation, an irregularity in the motion of the planet Mercury was discovered. Because of a certain precession—i.e., its entire orbit seemed to revolve about one of its foci—it did not exactly satisfy Newton's law. A mathematician proposed, and showed, that if the exponent 2 in Newton's law were changed ever so slightly—to something like 2.003, the precession could be accounted for. But this suggestion fell upon deaf ears: No astronomer took seriously the possibility that a basic law of nature should lack the simplicity, the elegance, the integer 2 conveyed".

More importantly and very intriguing is the possibility that β may be very large and its effect balances off the effect of ξ. Since a stimulus often passes through a medium and arrives somewhat weaker at its response destination, the effect of the medium may be great and affects the response substantially. It seems that dark matter in space acts like such a gravitational influence medium, and moderates behavior. For example it is well-known that the outer stars of a galaxy would be driven much farther due to centrifugal force and the effect of distance, but the effect of dark matter serves to pull these stars inwards, diminishing the overall effect of the forces countering gravitation.

Discrete Judgments and the Inverse Square Law in Optics

Below is an experiment to validate the relationship between the pairwise judgment and the Inverse Square Law in optics. Four identical chairs were placed on a line from a light source at the distances of 9, 15, 21, and 28 yards. The purpose was to see if one could stand by the light and look at the chair and compare their relative brightness in pairs, fill in the judgment matrix and obtain a relationship between the chairs and their distance from the light source. This experiment was repeated twice with different judges whose judgment matrices are shown in Table 1.

Table 1 Pairwise Comparisons of the Four Chairs

Relative visual brightness
(1st Trial)

	C_1	C_2	C_3	C_4
C_1	1	5	6	7
C_2	1/5	1	4	6
C_3	1/6	1/4	1	4
C_4	1/7	1/6	1/4	1

Relative visual brightness
(2nd Trial)

	C_1	C_2	C_3	C_4
C_1	1	4	6	7
C_2	1/4	1	3	4
C_3	1/6	1/3	1	2
C_4	1/7	1/4	1/2	1

The judges of the first matrix were the author's young children, ages 5 and 7 at that time, who gave their judgments qualitatively. The judge of the second matrix was the author's wife, also a mathematician not present during the children's judgment process. In Table 2 we give the principal eigenvectors, eigenvalues, consistency indices and consistency ratios of the two matrices.

Table 2 Principal Eigenvectors and Corresponding Measures

Relative brightness eigenvector
(1st Trial)

Relative brightness eigenvector
(2nd Trial)

0.61	0.62
0.24	0.22
0.10	0.10
0.05	0.06

λ_{max} = 4.39, C.I. = 0.13, C.R.= 0.14 λ_{max} = 4.10, C.I. = 0.03, C.R.= 0.03

Table 3 Inverse Square Law of Optics

Distance	Normalized distance	Square of normalized distance	Reciprocal of previous column	Normalized reciprocal	Rounding off
9	0.123	0.015 129	66.098	0.607 9	0.61
15	0.205	0.042 025	23.79	0.218 8	0.22
21	0.288	0.082 944	12.05	0.110 8	0.11
28	0.384	0.147 456	6.78	0.062 3	0.06

First and second trial eigenvectors of Table 2 have been compared with the last column of Table 3 calculated from the inverse square law of optics. The root mean square deviations (RMS) and the median absolute deviation around the median (MAD) were computed and are both very small. It is interesting and important to observe that the judgments have captured a natural law here. It would seem that they could do the same in other areas of perception or thought, as we show in the next example.

Note the sensitivity of the results as the closest chair is moved even closer to the light source, for then it absorbs most of the value of the relative index and a small error in its distance from the source yields great error in the values. What is noteworthy from this sensory experiment is the observation or hypothesis that the observed intensity of illumination varies (approximately) inversely with the square of the distance. The more carefully designed the experiment, the better the results obtained from the visual observations.

We now discuss the idea that there is a close mathematical relationship between physics and the Analytic Hierarchy Process. We argue that numerical scales used in physics must be interpreted in terms which the scientist understands through experience and through theories advocated by experts in the field. In physics there are primary variables and secondary variables defined in terms of them, all measured on ratio scales. We show that hierarchic composition in the AHP works in a similar way to physics and we illustrate this with an example.

The Measure of all Things - Human Judgment

All measurement data, whether in physics, engineering or sociology must be interpreted to be understood. Such numbers describe the degree of a property an object or event possesses; how fast, how long, how poor. Numbers tell us how much more of the property an object has one day than another; or how much more it has than another object, or how much more or less than a certain standard. One needs to exercise caution about what these numbers mean.

In the Wall Street Journal of April 11, 2001, under Review and Outlook, an article about the meaning of scales appeared. It emphasized that units of measurement are fundamentally arbitrary and may make no sense to an individual and the individual must translate the meaning of a measurement to something that is more familiar and that is used more often. Scales have both an objective and a subjective aspect. They rely, not only on scientifically calibrated scales, but also on feel. It also argued that the Metric system, neat as it may be, has no organic roots. The meter is taken as one ten-millionth of the (inaccurately) measured distance between the poles. But a foot derives from the length of a foot, an inch from the first segment of the thumb and a cup from the amount of water a man can hold in both hands. What truly matters about units of measurement is that we understand the amounts and distances to which they correspond. If one has a good feel for the size of an ounce without doing any calculations, it does not matter that dividing a pint by 16 is inconvenient. The conclusion is that the impact of measurement on the mind and the corresponding judgment that counts and not the judgment itself. One can force new measurements onto packages, but one cannot force them into the way people think.

Our ability to assess the meaningfulness of measurement is limited. For example, beyond certain cold temperatures we observe in everyday experience, we have no idea how much colder -160°C is than -140°C. One is a greater or smaller amount than the other, but we have no feeling for it. On the other hand, a difference of 20°F in our range of sensation has much more meaning to us. The temperature reading of 50°F is more comfortable than 30°F, and 100°F is much less comfortable than 80°F. What a comfortable temperature is even depends on whether we are accustomed to the weather in New York, Siberia or Kenya. Understanding measurements depends on our experience and perception acquired through living, learning and training. The significance of measurements on different scales is a phenomenon cultivated in us through conditioning. A measurement has no significance in itself. Our conclusion is that we always interpret the meaning of data subjectively, as we interpret other stimuli with our senses—such as how bright light is to the eye or how soft velvet is to the touch. The basic problem is to create a scientific framework for interpreting data.

Knowledge is how the mind perceives the world. Change in relationships means change of perception; learning is the identification of things and of properties and relations among things and among properties of things and synthesis of these properties as they change over time. Some relations appear to change and others do not from which the concept of a fact or an unchanging relation is obtained. Mathematics abstracts this approach of identifying and defining things and analyzing relations among them in quantitative and abstract qualitative ways. Everything is a collection or a composite of properties or attributes and how they relate to the properties of other things and to the environment with its many things. Multi-criteria decision-making is concerned with the measurement and synthesis of properties of alternatives as they influence the outcome of a decision. Even though it is now in its infancy, it appears that the study of multi-criteria decision-making has great bearing on all other areas of knowledge and the synthesis of that knowledge into greater complexity. It should be noted that not all knowledge is of this kind. Optimization is a tool of the mind that has no immediate counterpart in reality. The mind is capable of thinking and doing things that transcend the real world of things and their properties. The AHP/ANP approach empowers the human mind to make explicit its essential ability to make paired comparisons using fairly good but not necessarily "perfect" judgments and helps to synthesize these judgments. It achieves its high precision by aggregating multiple trials of insightful human judgments from one or from several people.

The mathematics of decision-making is closely linked to how the brain works to make decisions. The workings of the brain depend on the decision of neurons to fire or not to fire. That in turn is related in some way to stimulus response theory. The question is whether it is possible to generalize the subject so that stimulus response relates to the laws of physics for example so that what we perceive or are able to perceive coincides with what physics tells us about the laws of nature. But the laws of nature to humans are precisely what they are able to detect with their minds and bodies and then interpret and connect these perceptions. It would seem that all the things we know about are a consequence of what our neurons are capable of registering and synthesizing.

If the parallel between neural response and what is known and perceived in the real world were to be carried to its logical limits, one may say that all our quests in mathematics should be traceable to what our neurons are capable of doing. Firing has intensity and frequency. Judgments and feelings require order and preference. Priorities have order. Synthesis has multilinear forms, commutativity and non-commutativity associativity and non-associativity. Arithmetic requires counting with absolute numbers. Physics requires measurement with ratio and interval scales. The complexity of the world that we perceive is based on these and on other related ideas. We only have a glimmering of how to make this entire connection work for us.

So much of modern applied mathematics is tied to the calculus and its generalizations so that the use of coordinate systems is thought to be mandatory and the only way to analyze problems. With the arrival of computers, numerical approaches to problem solving have become much easier to do. In fact the computer has been used to prove the four-color conjecture by exhausting the cases. Because human judgment is the final creator of what function to use to describe a problem and what differential equation to formulate and solve, one wonders whether it is ordained that this be the only way to do things. There is another alternative using relative measurement. With relative measurement one sometimes needs the ratio of two quantities and at other times the difference between them. Still another is to take the ratio of differences. Let us assume that the priorities of a set of alternatives have been derived and ordered in increasing fashion. Is there a way to deal with the idea of rate of change as in the calculus that is based on infinitesimals? We do not have infinitesimals in paired comparisons. What we can do is to take differences in priorities in successive order and divide them by other differences and speak of the ratio or relative change in the values. In the calculus one deals with relative change with respect to an independent variable that is assumed to change linearly. We do not have such a parallel concept but what we have is a ratio of pairs of differences in values analogous to finding out how much more a derivative changes at one point of a function as compared with its change at another point. This is likely to be a useful concept in decision-making.

Multidimensional and Unidimensional Scales

The AHP derives relative numbers from pairwise comparisons in the form of priorities. To go from actual numbers to priorities one normalizes and cannot go back to the original measurements without knowing how the two kinds of numbers correspond.

Among the many possible ways to combine measurements belonging to different ratio scales, two have relevance for this discussion. One way is to raise the measurements from a ratio scale to an appropriate power, and then multiply the results together thus obtaining a multidimensional scale. This is what is done in physics. For example in the formula $F = ma$ where force is a product of mass and acceleration, the measurement of force is obtained by directly multiplying the measurements of mass m which is a primary variable and acceleration whose units are expressed in a combination L/T^2 of distance (or length) and time, which are primary variables. Another example is $E = mc^2$ from the theory of relativity involving energy in terms of mass and the speed of light.

The other way of combining measurements first interprets the importance of the measurements in the context of their variables or criteria and then rescales the magnitudes of measurements according to priority or importance of each of the criteria, which in turn receive priorities with respect to a single overall goal. These priorities are then multiplied by the measurements with respect to the criteria. Finally, corresponding measurements with respect to each criterion are summed to obtain a unidimensional scale. This is what is done in the AHP approach to multicriteria decision-making.

Physics uses instruments to perform measurement. What the measurements signify must be interpreted according to a base of knowledge that has been agreed upon by experts. Decision theory also transforms information and data to judgments within a frame of reference, a hierarchy of criteria and goals, of an individual or a group. We will show that the two ways of combining measurements are related in both structure and numerical representation.

The AHP is based on a single fundamental scale of absolute numbers. It derives numbers that represent order that takes precedence over metric closeness (order topology). The AHP uses hierarchic and network structures to decompose the complexity of the elements involved and then synthesize its measurements. Physics scarcely uses formal structures to establish its measurements. These structures are very simple compared with what the AHP uses. The AHP is applied to each problem separately by relying on judgments. There is no law that governs all its observations of influences. Physics, on the other hand, has a few laws that are assumed to explain everything. The AHP relies on judgments and is therefore subjective because judgments can differ from one person to another. Physics assumes that measurement with scales is direct and objective as they should not be different if different people are doing it.

To combine different scales into a single scale in the AHP one must tradeoff a unit of one against a unit of another using the weights of the criteria, something impossible to do in physics because one does not trade off independent variables according to their importance. Moreover, combining measurements in the Analytic Hierarchy Process gives rise to multilinear forms and to tensors. They are the basic formal interface between hierarchic measurement and physics where tensors also play an important role in Maxwell's equations, in the General Theory of Relativity and in Differential Geometry. They are the abstract generalization of expressions which are obtained by multiplying and adding numbers from different scales in the process of synthesizing measurements.

Let us summarize some of the significant differences in measurement between the AHP and physics possibly repeating what we said before. The AHP deals with importance as does physics and is therefore descriptive, but it also deals with preference and likelihood where it is being used to predict. It can be normative (preference) or descriptive (importance and likelihood). Physics is only descriptive and predictive.

The AHP works in an intensity of dominance or frequency domain. Physics works in the space time domain the Fourier transform of what the AHP obtains in the continuous case. Physics uses a multiplicity of linear ratio scales with arbitrary units to measure different objects and phenomena. It combines its measurements into a single formula that represents multidimensional measurements. How far apart the measurements are is its main concern in interpreting the measurements (metric topology).

In the end an AHP analysis is complete and only needs to be subjected to sensitivity analysis to determine its stability. In physics the meaning of the measurements does not only depend on their accuracy but also on what the numbers obtained using a particular unit mean.

Physics is the study of influences and assumes they are the result of a few deterministic causes and effects. In quantum theory this idea moves into the realm of statistics because the uncertainty there means that measurements elude deterministic reasoning. Thus in AHP judgment is used in the form of probability to represent occurrences at a fairly macro level. Judgment would be difficult to use in quantum theory and thus one must make statistical assumptions about interactions among influences. In the AHP causes and effects are detailed in the structure developed for the particular problem under study and every item is included. In behavioral situations there can be many different causes that determine an outcome and these are not governed by a particular law. In the AHP there are no irreducible random events as all events are related. Representing influences in the AHP is assumed to depend on the knowledge and experience of people and varies from problem to problem whereas in non-quantum physics the influences are generally deterministic like gravitation and electromagnetism and there is proportionality of influence whose kind does not change in different situations. The AHP allows for dependence and feedback. In physics the different dimensions of measurement are independent. Mass does not depend on length for example.

The AHP has been applied to a few cases to derive priorities that are subject to the laws of physics where intensity of response is involved. Its generalization to the continuous case produces formulas that involve the inverse square law as a very general law in stimulus response. Many physics formulas in gravity, optics and electricity satisfy this kind of law. This should be looked into more closely.

Because the AHP combines the objective problem of measurement with the subjective problem of meaning, it has also developed a scientific process for combining group judgments to give greater objectivity to its findings. Priorities for the judges themselves can be included by raising the judgments to the power of their importance. It appears reasonable and likely to expect that physics which separates the problems of measurement from the problem of meaning has no way to deal with the second except by using the shared understanding of experts.

In principle the AHP can transmit the see and touch dimension of people to the quantum level by using an appropriate hierarchic structure to deal with meaning and dimension of going from the very large to the very small. Physics remains fragmented without a unifying single theory.

Physics has a few laws that are assumed to explain everything. The AHP is applied to each problem separately by relying on judgments. There is no single law that is assumed to govern all its observations about different influences and their effects.

The AHP deals with importance as in physics but also with preference and likelihood. Physics is descriptive and predictive.

Physics is metric and depends on the size of the measurements but not particularly on their order. The AHP is based on the idea of dominance and order for its measurements that are relative and represent priorities of importance.

Physics assumes that measurement with scales is direct and objective as it does not rely on people doing it. The AHP relies on judgments and is therefore subjective because judgments can differ from one person to another.

Physics uses a multiplicity of ratio scales with their arbitrarily chosen units to measure different attributes and phenomena like length, mass, and time. Physics combines its measurements into a single formula that represents multidimensional measurements. How close and accurate the measurements are is its main concern (metric topology). The different kinds of measurement in physics cannot be reduced to a single scale. To combine different scales into a single scale one must tradeoff a unit of one against a unit of another, something impossible to do in physics as it requires the ideas of importance and preference by making comparisons.

Our thinking has brought us two ways to look at the world, the hierarchic-network approach that enables us to deal both tangible and intangible measurements and the coordinate system of physics that can only deal with tangible measurements. Below we give a simple illustration, a very elementary one, of how the two ways of thinking may be related.

Formulas as in Physics Involve Identifying, Prioritizing and Synthesizing Primary Variables

The subject of how to use additive synthesis in the AHP in situations where we have mathematical formulas to obtain results particularly in physics is worth considering. In mathematics we use linear dimensions to study problems but curvilinear coordinates are also used and other kinds also. There may be a way to lay out the perceived structure of any problem so that its properties can be identified and aggregated in such a way that their relative influences can be captured by making comparisons. That appears to be a more promising approach than taking on different methods of composition for different structures. The danger of customizing the composition for each different structure is that we would have a fragmentary approach to the world and would still need a customized way to put together the fragments. Dimensionality is one way to simplify structures in physics, but psychological attributes do not seem to be amenable to such a simplified approach and they are often involved in problems.

An abstract hierarchy that corresponds to a physics problem consists of three levels. It is an incomplete hierarchy. The focus or goal is the new concept or composite variable defined by or decomposed into the second level elements. These are the secondary variables that are composites of primary variables. They are like the clusters or criteria of a decision hierarchy. Each secondary variable is defined in terms of either a primary variable or the reciprocal of a primary variable. In addition, a secondary variable can itself be a primary variable. The primary variables and their reciprocals are in the third level of the hierarchy.

The hierarchy would only show those primary variables needed to define the secondary variables in the second level. They are measured on an absolute scale that is homogeneous, usually extending from zero to infinity. Let us now consider how hierarchic composition gives the desired outcome. We must caution the reader that the hierarchical formulation will mimic physics knowledge. It cannot set down arbitrary judgments and magically lead to new physics formulas. We can also learn how to create structural links in domains whose relations and data are external to our feelings. Our purpose here is to illustrate the parallel in structure and calculation.

Since the power of a variable is a measure of the dominance of that variable with respect to other variables, we assume that it is meaningful to say that one variable is more important (has a higher priority) than another. The parallel between physics and the AHP suggests that such importance is reflected in the power of the primary variable.

The period of a pendulum is given by

$$t = 2\pi \sqrt{\frac{h}{g}}$$

Our object is to show that this relation can be derived hierarchically using knowledge from physics instead of subjective judgments. We first conjecture that t depends on the mass m of the bob of the pendulum, the height h of the pendulum, acceleration due to gravity g and the angle θ. This leads to the hierarchy in Figure 1.

The composite concept or goal is the period t. It needs to be expressed as a composite function of the primary variables and only after that, the primary variables are grouped as secondary variables. Hierarchically, we let a, b, c, and d be the normalized 'priorities' ($a+b+c+d=1$) of the secondary variables, mass m, gravity g, height h, and angle θ. They give rise to the consistent matrix of paired comparisons, shown in Table 4.

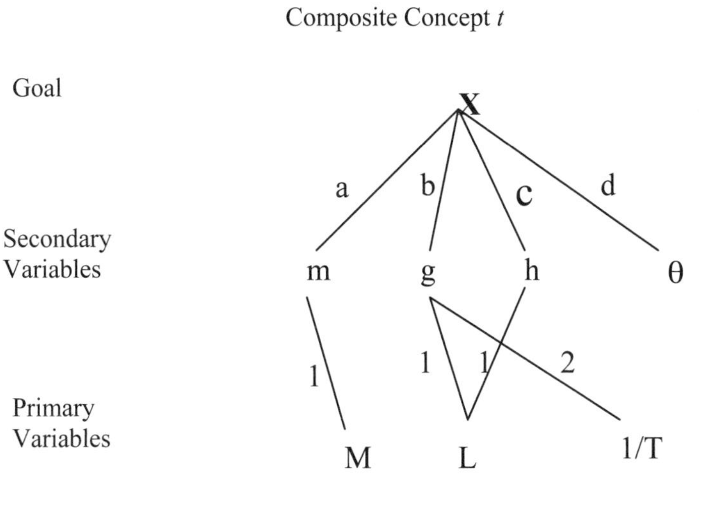

Composite Concept t

Figure 1 Hierarchy of Physics Variables

Table 4 Comparison of Powers of Primary Variables

t	m	g	h	θ
m	a/a	a/b	a/c	a/d
h	b/a	b/b	b/c	b/d
g	c/a	c/b	c/c	c/d
θ	d/a	d/b	d/c	d/d

What does it mean to compare mass versus gravity for importance as we are asked to do in an AHP formulation? We believe it means this: Which is more important in determining the period (or time) of a pendulum, gravity or mass? And what does 'more important' imply? If, for example, a 20% increase in mass affects t more than a 20% increase in gravity, then mass is a more important factor.

Because the matrix of paired comparisons is consistent, any column of this matrix gives the relative weights. Let us use the first column. If we divide each entry in a column by the sum of the column, we have for the relative values a, b, c, d.

Next we determine the priorities of the primary variables in the third level under each secondary variable. These are absolute numbers known from the *definition* in physics of each secondary variable and are shown in Figure 1. To clarify the ideas we list in a table all primary variables and their reciprocals and assign to each secondary variable the priority of its corresponding primary variables. For example, by definition, $g=L/T^2$ and in Table 5, we enter under g, 1 in the L row as L appears to the first power and 2 in the $1/T$ row which appears to the second power and 0 elsewhere.

Table 5 Primary Variables and their Reciprocals and Secondary Variables

t	m	g	h	θ
M	1	0	0	0
$1/M$	0	0	0	0
L	0	1	1	0
$1/L$	0	0	0	0
T	0	0	0	0
$1/T$	0	2	0	0

On noting that $1/x = x^{-1}$, we can reduce this array to one involving the primary variables by using negative numbers as in Table 6.

Table 6 Aggregated Primary Variables and Secondary Variables

	t	m	g	h	θ
M	1	0	0	0
L	0	1	1	0
T	0	-2	0	0

According to Fechner's formula we perceive the intensities of M, L, and T, as logarithms of the actual values. We now apply the composition principle of the AHP to these perceived values of the absolute measurements of M, L, and T. We have, as one can surmise from Figure 1,

$$a \cdot 1 \cdot \log M + b \cdot 1 \cdot \log L + c \cdot 1 \cdot \log L + b \cdot -2 \cdot \log T = \log M^a L^{(b+c)} T^{-2b}.$$

To recover the actual measurement period t we take the exponential of this result. However, because the actual measurement of t belongs to a ratio scale, we multiply by a constant K and write the following equality:

$$t = K M^a L^{(b+c)} T^{-2b}$$

which is the most important result of this analysis. Here the parameters a, b, and c are still unknown and must be determined. We do not involve the intensities of M, L, and T in that process since their priority is defined by their power that is what we must find. We use knowledge from physics to equate powers of primary variables. We write

$$\begin{pmatrix} 0 \\ 0 \\ 1 \end{pmatrix} = \begin{pmatrix} 1 & 0 & 0 & 0 \\ 0 & 1 & 1 & 0 \\ 0 & -2 & 0 & 0 \end{pmatrix} \begin{pmatrix} a \\ b \\ c \\ d \end{pmatrix}$$

We have on the left the dimensions of the period of the pendulum that are simply time. On the right we have the hierarchic composition of the priorities in the third and second levels, respectively. Dimensional equivalence (which in AHP jargon we call priority equivalence) of the two sides for each primary variable leads to the three equations

$$a = 0, \quad b + c = 0, \quad -2b = 1,$$

and their solution is $b = -1/2$ and $c = 1/2$. In dimensional terms, $d = 0$ since the angle θ is the ratio of the radius to the circumference and thus it is dimensionless.

Having obtained the powers of the secondary variables, we can use them to relate the basic concept that is the period t of the pendulum to the product of the secondary variables because of the logarithmic relation. The final result is $t = K\sqrt{h/g}$. The value K is determined experimentally. Our final expression is $t = 2\pi\sqrt{h/g}$.

This approach gives us an idea of what we may have to do to derive formulas involving behavioral variables.

Chapter 17

Response to Stimuli Received in the Brain is Impulsive

"The nervous system appears constructed as if each neuron had built into it an awareness of its proper place in the system."

-Kuffler and Nicholls

Introduction

Our concern in this chapter continues what went before in the last chapter: what is the requirement on the forces and influences of nature so that they would preserve order through proportionality? We need proportionality to understand order in a consistent way of thinking. When things and events are not proportionate in their structures and intensity of occurrence, whether regular or irregular, we may remember them but would be unable to relate them. Proportionality is the essence of creating connections, bridging gaps to improve understanding and bring things together. Chaos is an absence of proportion. All forms of order depend on proportionality of which symmetry is but one of the basic governing attributes. From loose and unorganized proportionality to tight and very organized symmetry. Symmetry has been studied scientifically with mathematics and applied among others, in physics and conservation laws. Proportionality has been examined as an aesthetic attribute like in the Golden Mean but not in sufficient depth to understand its role in the general scheme of things particularly as it relates to human thinking understanding and creativity in connecting things but more importantly in maintaining consistency. In fact all order involves some degree of proportionality. This is what we want to examine.

  Until today, philosophers, mathematicians and scientists have, only loosely or not at all, come to recognize the fact that our brain and nervous system, by their very functions and responsibilities by responding to stimuli, are mathematical in nature. They synthesize simple electric signals with fragmentary information into complex images, sounds, tastes, smells, hot and cold and all sorts of feelings. These feelings are quantitative according to intensity and kind of firings. All qualities out there become quantitative electricity and all our feelings are also quantitative electricity. All objects soft or hard, sharp or smooth along with biology and life itself are known, understood and felt electrically. Our brains are mathematical through and through. They don't only perceive physical happenings from the outside, but also respond to internal messages from memory to which they respond with action or with story-telling and history building. How do they do it?

Our mind is the child of our brain which is made up of tens of billions of neurons. Neurons are decision makers that decide from instant to instant whether to fire or not to fire and how often to fire based on information received through neurotransmitter electric charge. By firing they accomplish two goals. First, they pass information to other neurons which in turn make a decision to fire or not to fire. Second, their firing serves to express electrically (and chemically) the information received and modified by other previously learned information in memory. Typically, a neuron usually has a cell body, an axon and dendrites with synaptic vesicles through which neurotransmitter chemicals that carry electric charges pass from one neuron to another. By receiving charges and thus also the information they carry from many neurons, a neuron electrically synthesizes this variety of signals and decides to fire or not to fire depending on the threshold reached. How do these signals develop, how are they synthesized and can they be used to create meaning from sense data is one concern that needs the mathematics of complex variables because it is both electrical and quantitative.

In addition to the quote at the top of this chapter, Kuffler and Nicholls [2] observe that signal transmission in sensory neurons proceeds in a hierarchic fashion. Each set of neurons synapses into the next, often funneling information through synthesis from detailed to composite impressions. A fundamental principle of hierarchic synthesis is that a set of neurons specialized in the representation of a stimulus X must transmit that stimulus to the next level, perhaps with a different degree of detail. Here is another observation about the relative way with which we formulate our impressions that is analogous to synthesis in a hierarchy. S. Grossberg [2] writes: "One illustrative type of psychological data that Helmholtz studied concerns color perception... Helmholtz realized... that the light we perceive to be white tends to be the average color of a whole scene. Moreover, this averaging process must be nonlinear since it is more concerned with relative than absolute light intensities... we tend to see... the relative amounts of light of each wavelength that they [the objects] reflect, not the total amount of light reaching us from each point."

To derive a general expression for the response of a group of neurons to a stimulus coordinating their responses at the macro level, we have on occasion used the method of steepest descent. This method assumes that only those stimuli or inputs which maximize the overall response are selectively accumulated in the synthesis process which conforms with the observation that neurons fire in response to supra-threshold stimuli. In this chapter we continue with our generalization of the functional equations approach. In either case our conclusion is that we are dealing with a set of dense generalized functions, linear combinations of which are used to approximate to all the stimuli of which we are aware.

Neurons respond to several kinds of external stimuli:

(1) Energy propagated as light and sound vibrations, heat and pressure
(2) Energy in the form of electric charges,
(3) Fields such as gravity which generates the sensation of falling,
(4) Matter in the form of molecules creating actions and reactions according to the laws of chemistry
(5) Matter encountered physically in bulk, responding to it according to the laws of Physics.

In contrast with conscious discrete decision-making that we studied before in this book, the brain also makes judgments not only by thinking, but also by sensing and feeling. In addition, the nervous system (that includes the autonomic subsystem involving the regulation of many homeostatic mechanisms) makes subconscious decisions to run the body in response to chemical changes. Other kinds of subconscious responses are a result of repetition and training that we can then do without thinking and they become a habit or an automatic reflex such as developing skills for swimming, riding a bicycle, driving a car and playing the piano.

When we fall short in our physical habits relative to known standards, our mind analyzes the causes of such incompatibility in terms of actions needed and their priorities, and attempts to implement them to improve performance. Strengthening a habit (a sequence of actions) involves analysis, decision and implementation to close the gap and improve compatibility to meet standards. Unless a person has been trained to make decisions mentally as a habit, making a decision consciously without much thinking and fast as if it lies between habit and a continuous effort to constantly modify the habit that decision is likely to be subject to many errors. Making successive intelligent strokes in swimming or pedaling a bicycle are examples of decisions that involve uniformity (periodicity) of action and require one to be trained to make them without hesitation. They are spontaneous decisions in which reason, that may have initially served to establish behavior through conscious interaction, now acquires a more automatic and intuitive relationship and becomes a habit. Important rational decisions are intellectual requiring much reflection and thinking and changing one's mind, activities that are not characteristic of automatic decisions. We need rational decisions to satisfy our need to reason and think and look out to the environment for the favorable and the undesirable that it presents us with. These decisions do not belong to the subliminal category because they require reflection and connection of many different, often new kinds of stimuli, and require creativity in the process of making them. They involve such substantial diversity and variation that they cannot be made automatically. If they are worked out in advance for implementation they can be automated and made by a machine, but they are not precisely what interest's developers of decision-making theories today.

While "thinking" is generally carried out in the neo-cortex of the brain, feelings and partly emotions are associated with the autonomic (sympathetic and parasympathetic) nervous system that in part is known to operate independently of the thought processes of the brain. There is very little conscious control over many activities of the autonomic nervous system. It is as if there are two persons in each of us. One that looks out at the physical environment to give us information for survival, and another that looks inside to keep our biological system running.

Even when our understanding is holistic and intuitive, it is fragmentary and needs to be laid out in detail and made complete by connecting the related parts within a *structure*, using a conscious thought process that brings together analytical thinking and memories in the brain with the intuition and experience of the autonomic nervous system. The elements and connections may not be complete to create meaning and the individual will make them coherent by adding or deleting elements and connections to fill the gaps in his/her perception that may or may not be consistent with reality. Thus one's perceptions or mental models are essentially a combination of observations about reality and the assumptions that are built in the mind to make the data meaningful. In mental learning we have no other way but to use our thinking and modeling to understand complexity from the incomplete pieces that we share.

This chapter gives a broad view of how neurons work as a group to create images and different types of impressions. We synthesize the solutions derived for the response of individual neurons, to obtain the general form of response of many neurons. To describe how a diversity of stimuli may be grouped abstractly into visual, auditory, sensual, and other kinds of response, the outputs of such syntheses are interpreted as points of an inner direct sum of a space of functions of the form given in Chapter 15 as Dirac distributions or generalized functions that are impulsive and can be used to represent how the nervous system makes its firings. They are the same kind of entity in each term, but each entity says a different thing, or better represents a different meaning and these meanings combine to make us feel stable or satisfied or unstable and dissatisfied according to our basic strategic criteria to assess our satisfaction with the fulfillment of each of our physical, mental, behavioral and other needs and summing these intensities of satisfaction into an overall satisfaction whose level of sophistication and intensity we acquire through experience. In other words, different people have different standards of satisfaction, actual and perceived by comparing with others. It is much easier to be satisfied when comparison with others is absent.

There are two basic assumptions in our model: (1) only those stimuli or inputs which maximize the overall response are selectively accumulated in the synthesis process, and (2) the response of networks of neurons has the property of being dense in the space of all responses. This implies that the output of a finite (generally large) number of neurons is sufficient to approximate to all the stimuli we receive. This approximation would be our own perception of the stimuli. Finally, we put forth a mathematical theory of the synthesis of impulses in the brain.

Neural Firings, Their Mathematical Representations, Feelings, Senses, Thoughts and Memories

Why is the brain a natural subject for the mathematics of decision making? One reason is that neurons constantly make decisions to fire or not to fire by responding to stimuli. In addition their firing takes the form of Dirac delta functions. The theory of generalized functions was developed to accommodate the idea of a Dirac Delta function with the property that

$\delta(x) = 0$ for $x \neq 0$, $\int_a^b \delta(x) \, dx = 1$ for $a < 0 < b$. These functions are dense in

very general mathematical spaces known as Sobolev spaces (named after the Russian mathematician Sergei L. Sobolev, 1908-1989). As a result, linear combinations of them serve as approximations for representing all that we sense, perceive and think and all the properties that we experience.

The electric potential and the firing process and its frequency are quantitative activities that combine to represent the performance of the nervous system to carry us in the environment as a vehicle. The difference from a vehicle is that we go where it takes us and also where we program it and control it to take us chemically for body and nerve performance and electrically for perception, thought, decision making, action and reaction by evaluating the outcome. This way of thinking needs knowledge of complex variables and functions of complex variables, the behavior of such functions, Dirac distributions, the density of functions, representing functions of many variables in terms of a sum of functions of single variables and perhaps even future use of quaternions, octonions, sedonions and still higher forms of numbers and functions of them

In general, neural response involves both spontaneous activity which is firing without input stimuli, during a short period of time, and non-spontaneous activity. Firing always gives rise to generalized functions of the Dirac type that represent spikes. For spontaneous unstimulated firing we solve a homogeneous eigenvalue equation and obtain a family of Dirac type functions. Finite linear combinations of these functions are dense in Sobolev spaces. The solution of the inhomogenous equation representing non-spontaneous firing also belongs to these spaces. Non-spontaneous activity is characterized as a perturbation of the background activity taking place in the neural network. To derive the response function when neurons are stimulated from external sources, we consider an inhomogeneous equation to represent stimuli acting on the neuron in addition to existing spontaneous activity. For that purpose, we solve the inhomogeneous Fredholm equation of the second kind given by:

$$w(s) - \lambda_0 \int_0^b K(s,t)w(t)dt = f(s)$$

The left side of this equation is the already familiar Fredholm equation of the second kind that represents the internal reciprocal comparison judgment process, but the right side is the forcing function that represents an external stimulus to which the judgments must respond. This equation has a solution in $W_p^k(\Omega)$ Sobolev space of Dirac distributions (in the sense of Schwartz) in $L_p(W)$ (the space of Lebesgue integrable functions whose derivatives of order k also belong to the space $L_p(W)$, where W is an open subset of the vector space R^n which comes with a standard basis:

$$e_1 = (1,0,...,0), e_2 = (0,1,0,...,0),..., e_n = (0,0,...,1).$$

An arbitrary vector in $\mathbf{R}^n$ can then be written in the form $x = \sum_{i=1}^{n} x_i e_i$. Here the idea of representing a complex entity x as a linear combination of simpler entities is critical and also applies when instead of a standard basis one were to use members of a dense set of functions or of distributions. Sobolev spaces are sets of functions which all have a certain degree of smoothness. They are a fundamental tool in mathematics and in its applications in science and engineering.

Next we note that the forcing function $f(s)$ itself is a linear combination of such Dirac distributions and thus represents a synthesis of stimuli that cause a neuron to fire. This highlights the fact that stimuli themselves are impulses that arrive in the form of distributions and that the functions we ascribe to their description such as periodic, exponential and logarithmic are simply envelopes of such dense distributions yielding two dual ways to analyze the mathematical representation of stimuli such as light seen is the form of photons or of waves.

We show that the solution of the inhomogeneous equation can be expressed as a linear combination of the foregoing basic distribution functions that describe neural responses to stimuli represented by the forcing function. The need for a firing threshold, characteristic of the Dirac distribution, emerges as a necessary condition for the existence of a solution. Second, we study the synthesis of the response of several neurons in both hierarchic and feedback network arrangements. The analysis is then briefly generalized to examine response to several stimuli and represent it as a direct sum of topological spaces. One observation is that generalized functions are appropriate representations of neural firings. Another is that understanding the structure of this representation is facilitated by the inevitable use of a fundamental set of dense functions to deal with the huge diversity we experience in the physical world and in the nervous system itself.

While a function of a real variable depends on a single argument, a function of a complex variable depends on two independent variables—one real and one imaginary—and thus cannot be drawn in the plane. Further, complex valued functions cannot be drawn as one does ordinary functions of three real variables. They depend on a real and an imaginary variable. Nevertheless, one can make a plot of the modulus or absolute value of such a function. The basic assumption we make to represent the response to a sequence of individual stimuli is that all the layers in a network of neurons are identical, and each stimulus value is represented by the firing of a neuron in each layer to synthesize in stages specialized information from each receptor neuron into a more complex package that characterizes more closely what is perceived. This representation it is not invariant with respect to the order in which the stimuli are fed into the network. It is known in the case of vision that the eyes do not scan pictures symmetrically if they are not symmetric, and hence our representation must satisfy some order invariant principle. Taking into account this principle would allow us to represent images independently of the form in which stimuli are input into the network. For example, we recognize an image even if it is subjected to a rotation, or to some sort of deformation. Thus, the invariance principle must include affine and similarity transformations. This invariance would allow the network to recognize images even when they are not identical to the ones from which it recorded a given concept, e.g., a bird. The next step would be to use the network representation given here with additional conditions to uniquely represent patterns from images, sounds and perhaps other sources of stimuli such as smell. Our representation focuses on the real part of the magnitude rather than the phase of the Fourier transform. Tests have been made to see the effect of phase and of magnitude on the outcome of a representation of a complex valued function. There is much more blurring due to change in magnitude than there is to change in phase. Thus we focus on representing responses in terms of Dirac functions, sums of such functions, and on approximations to them without regard to the coefficients in the linear combination.

   The functions we derive are an outcome of modeling neural firing as a pairwise comparison process in time. It is assumed that a neuron compares neurotransmitter-generated charges in increments of time. This leads to the continuous counterpart of a reciprocal matrix known as a reciprocal kernel. A reciprocal kernel K is an integral operator that satisfies the condition, $K(s,t)K(t,s)=1$, for all s and t. A non-negative response function $w(s)$ of the neuron in spontaneous activity results from solving the homogeneous equation $(I-\lambda_0 K)w=0$, $w \in L_2[0,b]$. This solution exists when K is a compact integral operator defined on the space $L_2[0, b]$ of Lebesgue square integrable function and is continuously differentiable [4].

   We have already encountered the solution to our proportionality functional equation in the real domain. We need to use it to derive the general solution of the corresponding equation in the complex domain. Our solution in Chapter 15 took the form of the first case and now we need to study it in the form of the last case as a complex function of a complex variable and complex parameters of which the real variable and real parameters problem is a special case. We generalize our solution to the complex case by replacing s with a complex variable z with the assumption that a stimulus involves both amplitude and angle, a property of electric signals.

It is the practice that when one goes from a function of a real variable to its generalization to complex variables, one simply replaces the variables if the new expression makes sense, as in the case of rational functions. If not, for instance $\sin(x+iy)$, $\exp(x+iy)$, $\log(x+iy)$, a^{x+iy}, $(x+iy)^b$ where b is not an integer, then one generalizes some properties of the corresponding real functions, their power series expansion, and for $\log(x+iy)$, a^{x+iy}, $(x+iy)^b$ (b not an integer) one needs to make careful analysis of their connection to the exponential (and to Euler's formula $e^{it} = \cos t + i \sin t$). The same kind of observations about generalization, also apply when going from ordinary functions to distributions. However, one cannot obtain the solution of a functional equation for complex variables (and functions) simply by replacing x by $x+iy$ in the solution of the corresponding real equation. In some cases, like simple differential equations, or "algebraic" functional equations, as is the equation we are dealing with in this chapter, one can replace the real solution by the corresponding complex one, with the proviso that it be kept single-valued.

If a is a real constant, then $aG(z)$ just stretches $G(z)$ by a with no rotation. If $F(z)=aG(z)$ for two complex valued functions F and G, where $a = c$ $\exp(id)$ is a complex constant (c nonnegative, d real, both constants) then one gets every value $F(z)$ by "stretching" $G(z)$ by c ($|F(z)|=c|G(z)|$) and rotating $G(z)$ by d because arg $F(z)=d+$arg $G(z)$.

Adding the complex constant b to the complex function $F(z)$ means adding, in the vector addition sense, that is, the real part of b is added to the real part of $F(z)$ and the imaginary part of b is added to the imaginary part of $F(z)$. So $aG(z)+b=c\exp(id)G(z)+b$ means that $G(z)$ has been stretched c-fold, the result rotated by the angle d and what we thus get is shifted (translated in a parallel direction) by the vector $b=B+iC$.

We substitute the real solution using the complex variable z into the equation $w(az)-bw(z)=0$ to make some useful observations about the behavior of complex valued quantities because of mutivaluedness. For example az with $a>0$ is a *similarity transformation* that may not allow us to use the principal value Log z which is the complex logarithm and can be shown to satisfy Log $z = \log |z| + i\theta$, where θ is determined within an integral multiple of 2π. The values of θ denoted by θ_P with $0 \leq \theta_P < 2\pi$ are known as the principal values of the logarithm, and thus $\log z = \log |z| + i (\theta_P + 2n\pi)$, $n = 0, \pm 1 \pm 2, \ldots$. The reason is that our solution makes use of $\log(az) = \log a + \log z$, and even if $\log a = \text{Log } a$, this is exactly the equation which holds for the multivalued log but not for the principal value Log . We note for emphasis that $|b|$ stretches and arg b rotates $w(z)$ to get $w(az)$ and angles are preserved. That is:

$$\arg w(az) - \arg w(au) = \arg w(z) - \arg w(u)$$

We have $w(az)$ in the equation. If z is in any of the rings [3], then az will be in the next ring. This way we can (seamlessly) cover the whole complex plane starting with an arbitrary function in the first ring. This corresponds to what we did in the real case. We choose w arbitrarily on the left closed, right open interval $[1,a)$ and continue by using the equation $w(as) = bw(s)$ itself.

Remark. We note that our generalization of pairwise comparisons to the continuum need not hold for every point of a set on which our response functions are defined. In that case the notion of measure and of sets of measure zero for which proportionality does not hold can be useful. This may be of great value in considering chaotic phenomena that do not conform to the order imposed by the use of one or several ratio scales and the spaces defined by them. Measurable solutions of our fundamental equation could be the beginning of such investigation.

The General Multivalued Solution of $w(az) = bw(z)$

Let us denote our functional equation $w(az) = bw(z)$ by (E). The general solution of (E) with a, b, and z complex, is given by

$$w\left(z\right) = z^{\ln b / \ln a} P\left(\ln z / \ln a\right)$$

Here $P(u)$ with $u = \ln z / \ln a$, is an arbitrary multivalued periodic function in u of period 1. Even without the multivaluedness of P, the function $w(z)$ could be multivalued because $\ln b/\ln a$ is generally a complex number. If P is single-valued and $\ln b/\ln a$ turns out to be an integer or a rational number, then $w(z)$ is a single-valued or finitely multivalued function, respectively. This generally multivalued solution is obtained in a way analogous to the real case.

The Fourier Transform is a Linear Combination of Impulses

The **Fourier transform** describes which frequencies are present in the original function that is transformed. It decomposes a function into oscillatory functions. For our solution, we begin with

$$w(z)dz = b^{(\log z/\log a)} P(\frac{\log z}{\log a})dz = |J| \, b^u P(u)du, u = \frac{\log z}{\log a}, z = a^u, |J| = a^u \log a$$

$$w(z)dz = (ab)^u \log a \sum_n a_n' e^{2\pi nui} du = \log a \sum_n a_n' e^{[2\pi n + \theta(b)]iu} e^{(\log a + \log|b|)u} du$$

and the Fourier transform is given by

$$F(x) = \log a \sum_{n=-\infty}^{\infty} a_n' (1/(2\pi i)) \int_{-\infty}^{\infty} e^{[2\pi n + \theta(b)]ui} e^{(\log a + \log|b|)u} e^{-ixu} du$$

$$= (1/2\pi) \log a \sum_{n=-\infty}^{\infty} a_n' \frac{(2\pi n + \theta(b) - x)}{\log a |b| + (2\pi n + \theta(b) - x)} i\delta(2\pi n + \theta(b) - x)$$

where $\delta(2\pi n + \theta(b)-x)$ is the Dirac delta function.

In the real situation our Fourier series is finite as the number of synapses and spines on a dendrite are finite. Our Fourier transform can be written as

$$F(x) = (1/2\pi) \log a \sum_{n=-N}^{N} a_n' \frac{(2\pi n + \theta(b) - x)}{\log a |b| + (2\pi n + \theta(b) - x)} i\delta(2\pi n + \theta(b) - x)$$

Again with Dirac type of functions involved.

The Analytic Solution

Analytic function and holomorphic function are often used interchangeably. When we say a function is "holomorphic at a point a" we means not just that it is differentiable at a, but differentiable everywhere within some open disk centered at a in the complex plane. A holomorphic on the whole complex plane is called an entire function.

If f is an analytic function defined on an open subset U of the complex plane **C** and if U is contained in a larger open subset V of and if F is an analytic function defined on V with

$$F(z) = f(z) \text{ for all } z \text{ in } U,$$

then F is called an analytic continuation of f. In other words, the *restriction* of F to U is the function f we started with.

Analytic continuations are unique that is: if V is connected and F_1 and F_2 are two analytic continuations of f defined on V, then $F_1 = F_2$ everywhere because $F_1 - F_2$ is an analytic function which vanishes on the intersection of their domains, a non-empty open set, and an analytic function which vanishes on a non-empty open set must vanish everywhere on its domain and is thus identically zero. Analytic continuation is such an important concept for remembering. Our memory is gifted with a process of recall that is analytic continuation. Think of an instance of something and all its history quickly unfolds.

J. Aczél obtained solutions of (E) that are conformal, except possibly at borders between rings, by choosing an arbitrary analytic function with derivative different from 0 on the first ring and continuing by using the equation itself. If on the first ring one chooses the function to be the constant 1, then one gets only the $b^{[\log |z| / \log |a|]}$ part of the general solution. On all the rings, $w(z)$ will be analytic (with nonzero derivative) and thus is represented by conformal mappings. The analyticity can break down only on the boundaries of the rings. The latter are represented by the integer part sign [ ]. If one desires a multivalued solution, one starts on the original ring by a multivalued function or uses the arg (angle) construction. A single valued analytic complex solution exists everywhere except at zero, only if a is a root of unity, that is there exist integers k and q, $q < k$, for which $a^k = 1$ and $b = a^q$. When 0 is excluded, R. Ger (private communication) determined all solutions (in the form of their Taylor or, when 0 is excluded, Laurent series expansions) which contain only powers of z that are multiples of k, multiplied by z^q [3].

Here, one first solves the simpler and more basic case $g(az)=g(z)$ (the multiplicatively periodic function case where $b=1$). Then one substitutes

$$g(z) = \sum_{n=0}^{\infty} b_n z^n$$

where g is analytic everywhere. The summation goes from 0 to infinity (Taylor series) but from minus infinity to plus infinity if g is analytic everywhere except at 0 (Laurent series). Substitution into $g(az)=g(z)$ yields

$$b_n a^n z^n = b_n z^n$$

for all n. Thus for any n either $b_n=0$ or $a^n=1$. If $b_n=0$ for all n, then we have the trivial solution $g(z) = 0$ for all z. Otherwise a is a root of unity. Let k be the smallest positive integer for which $a^k = 1$. All other n for which $a^n=0$ must be (positive or negative) integer multiples of k. Thus, the general solution of $g(az)=g(z)$, analytic except perhaps at 0, is given by

$$g(z) = \sum_{k=0}^{\infty} b_{jk} a^{jk} z^k$$

We now return to our equation (E) in which we substitute

$$w(z) = \sum_{n=0}^{\infty} c_n z^n$$

and get $c_n a^n = b c_n$. Thus for all n either $c_n = 0$ or $a^n = b$. But $c_n = 0$ for all n again leads to the trivial solution $w(z) = 0$. If $a^n = b$ for one $n = q$, then all other c_n are 0 and (E) becomes $w(az) = b^q w(z)$ with $w(z) = cz^q$ as the only analytic solution. If $a^q = b$ then there exists k with $a^k = 1$ and $a^n = b$ for all $n = q + jk$; $j = 0, \pm 1, \dots$. Let k be the smallest positive integer for which $a^k = 1$, thus a is again a root of unity. All such exponents will be multiples of k and because $a^{n-q} = 1$, we have $n = q + jk$, $b = a^{q+jk} = a^q$. Let q be the smallest positive integer for which $a^q = b$ ($q < k$). Then (E) becomes $w(az) = a^q w(z)$, which is the only possible form of (E) *with nontrivial solutions*. If we now differentiate this equation q times and denote by g the kth derivative of w, then g would satisfy $g(az) = g(z)$, and thus has the solution form we derived above for g. If we integrate the latter solution q times (we can do this even with a Laurent series if it has no $1/z$ term; and our solution does not) we get, by renaming the coefficients, the following general analytic (except perhaps at 0) solution of (E), if it converges:

$$w(z) = \sum a_j^{"} z^{jk+q}, q < k$$

the sum taken from 0 to plus infinity if w is assumed to be analytic everywhere, but the sum is taken from minus infinity to plus infinity if w need not be analytic at 0.

The Taylor-Laurent formula developed above is not equivalent but much more special than the other solutions we have. It involves analyticity everywhere (except possibly at 0) and also excludes all nontrivial (nonconstant) solutions of those equations (E) where a is not a root of unity or b does not equal a power of a. The reason why analyticity is a very strong condition in the complex domain is that analyticity in a region (that is differentiability once in that region), implies differentiability any number of times and convergence of the Laurent series (if the region is simply connected then its Taylor series) to the function. Note that in the complex plane, analyticity at a point means differentiability in a neighborhood of that point (not just at the point itself). The analyticity of a real function requires that it be infinitely differentiable and that its Taylor series expansion converges to it.

The analytic solution given by a Taylor (or Laurent) series, convergent on a (possibly punctured) circular disk (some border points may be missing) is always single-valued. Multi- (and also single-) valued functions can be generated by a quaint procedure called analytic continuation: One takes a point close to the border of the circle of convergence, expands into power series around it, thus one may succeed to go outside the original circle of convergence. Continuing this procedure one may get to a circle covering a point already covered before. If the value now assigned is different from the original then one has a multivalued function.

Note that since $g(z)=\sum a''_j z^{j\,k}$ satisfies $g(az)=g(z)$ (because $a^k=1$) and $q=\log b/\log a$, the analytic solution fits nicely into the general solution $w(z)=g(z)z^{\{\log b/\log a\}}$ of $w(az)=b\,w(z)$ which is not a multivalued solution, because here, $\log b/\log a = q$ is an integer.

Angle Preservation

In the case of a real valued response function for a general solution we obtained the ratio property. We now show that in the complex case we have in addition, angle preservation and hence our solution is an *isogonal transformation*. Thus if in (E) b is a complex constant then $w(z)$ will be (stretched by $|b|$) and rotated by $arg\,b$ ($b=|b|\,exp(i\,arg\,b)$) to get $w(az)$. But $w(z)$ will be rotated for each z by the same (constant) angle. So the angle between $w(az_1)$ and $w(az_2)$ will be the same as between $w(z_1)$ and $w(z_2)$. This follows from:

$$\arg[w(az_1)]-\arg[w(az_2)] = \arg[w(az_1)/w(az_2)]$$
$$= \arg([bw(z_1)]/[bw(z_2)]) = \arg[w(z_1)]-\arg[w(z_2)].$$

Isogonality holds (for complex b and complex valued w) whether a and z are real or complex.

Our result is a special case of the (general) conformal mapping which permits different ratios of dilation (or contraction) at different points. Ours is the particular case where they are all equal. Still, it is after taking the Fourier transform that the two results would become comparable and ratios at different points are different.

The Fourier Transform of the Analytic Solution is Impulsive

We can interchange the sum and the integral in this case so that we have for the Fourier transform:

$$\int_{-\infty}^{\infty} e^{-ixz} w(z)dz = \sum_{j=0}^{\infty} a'_j \int_{-\infty}^{\infty} e^{-ixz} z^{jk+q}dz, q < k = 2\pi\sum_{j=0}^{\infty} (-i)^{-(jk+q)} a'_j \frac{d^{jk+q}\delta(x)}{dx^{jk+q}}$$

which once more involves Dirac type of functions. Note that the number of nonzero terms in this sum is finite.

The General Single-Valued Solution in The Complex Plane

Now we consider the solution of (E) in the complex domain. We assume that $a > 0$ and $z > 0$. We note that our concern would be to determine when our solution is single-valued and when it is multivalued, and under what conditions on the parameters a and b that is so. In fact we could conjecture from the emotional nature of humans, that their brains on occasion, present them with multivalued situations that lead to breakdown in their logical and analytical thinking. But that is not necessarily undesirable, because when emotions are filtered through logical analysis, they provide multiple choices and can lead to creative discovery, not perceived in the usual way of analysis.

The general solution can be obtained as follows. We choose the values of the function $w(z)$ arbitrarily in the ring between circles around 0 of radii 1 (incl), and $|a|$ (excl), and we designate it by $W(z)$. Thus $w(z)=W(z)$ for $1 \le |z| < |a|$. By the equation itself, $w(z)=w(z/a)b=W(z/a)b$ for $|a| \le |z| < |a|^2$, $w(z)=w(z/a)b=w(z/a^2)b^2=W(z/a^2)b^2$ for $|a|^2 \le |z| < |a|^3$, and so on (also $w(z)=w(az)/b=W(az)b^{-1}$ for $1/|a| \le |z| < 1$ etc). Note that we successively multiply the three terms of each inequality describing a ring by $|a|$ and then replace the values of w at az by its value at z using the equation itself. Thus the general complex solution of (E) is given by $w(z) = W(z/a^n) b^n$ for $|a|^n \le |z| < |a|^{n+1}$ where $W(z)$ is arbitrary for $1 \le |z| < |a|$. From, $|a|^n \le |z| < |a|^{n+1}$ we have, $n = [\log |z| / \log |a|]$ where as usual, $[x]$ is the integer closest to x from below. Here logarithms of real values are taken, so there are no multivalues to be concerned about. Our solution becomes

$$w(z) = b^{[\log |z| / \log |a|]} W(z/a^{[\log |z| / \log |a|]}),$$

with W arbitrary on the ring $1 \le |z| < |a|$ and need not be defined elsewhere. This is the *general complex solution* of our functional equation. To simplify this solution we introduce

$$g(z) = W(z/a^{[\log |z| / \log |a|]})$$

It satisfies the functional equation $g(az)=g(z)$. Every solution of this equation in $g(z)$ can be written in this form. Thus the general complex solution of our functional equation becomes:

$$w(z) = Cb^{[\log |z| / \log |a|]} g(z)$$

where, as in the real case, $C > 0$ and g is an arbitrary solution of $g(az)=g(z)$. To see that this solution satisfies the equation (E), it is sufficient to note that $[\log |az|/\log|a|] = [(\log|a|+\log|z|)/\log|a|] = [1 + \log |z|/\log|a|] = [\log |z|/\log$

$|a|]+1$. The construction itself proves that every solution must be of this form.

Relation to the Real Valued Solution

We now show that when $z = s$ is real and positive, the long formula (containing W) for the general complex solution transforms into our familiar general real solution formula (containing the periodic part P). In that case we have $|z|=z=s$. We write $u=\log s/\log a$, from which $s=a^u$. Note that any function of $u-[u]$ is periodic with period 1 and every periodic function P with period 1 can be written as $P(u)=r(u-[u])$. We see that conversely, every function of this form has period 1 as follows

$$P(u+1) = r(u+1-[u+1]) = r(u+1-([u]+1)) = r(u-[u])=P(u).$$

We transform the formula containing W for real $z=s=a^u$ (i.e., $u=\log s/\log a$) as follows:

$$w(s) = b^{[u]} W(s/a^{[u]})= b^{[u]} W(a^{(\log s/\log a)}/a^{[u]})= b^{(u-(u-[u]))} W(a^{(u-[u])}).$$

We introduce the function $P(u)=W(a^{(u-[u])})/b^{(u-[u])}$, which we have just shown to be periodic with period 1. We obtain $w(s)=b^u P(u)=exp(u \log b)P(u)$, ($u=\log s/\log a$) as before.

In the complex case there is a problem in defining $P(\log z/\log a)$ because the logarithm is multivalued. However, $g(z)=p(\log|z|/\log|a|)$ always satisfies $g(az)=g(z)$, (also for complex values), for all periodic functions p of period 1. To see that, we write:

$$g(az)=p\left(\frac{\log|az|}{\log|a|}\right)= p\left(\frac{\log|a|+\log|z^*|}{\log|a|}\right)= p\left(1+\frac{\log|z|}{\log|a|}\right)= p\left(\frac{\log|z|}{\log|a|}\right)= g(z)$$

The Fourier Transform

With the argument of our solution involving both z and $|z|$ and also involving the nearest integer approximation, there does not seem to be a nice closed analytic expression for the Fourier transform of this solution. However, as in all the cases above our solutions and their transforms for neural firing apply in finite ranges of the complex domain and the transform can be obtained computationally. We have sufficient knowledge from the earlier transforms of the complex valued solutions to assume that here also the transform would involve a sum of damped Dirac type distributions.

We note that the values of multivalued functions need not be so nicely arranged on Riemann surfaces as in the case of analytic functions, they can vary in unexpected and not very nice ways. The function we get is doubly periodic in one real variable (the first variable is an unchanged parameter) with two periods whose quotient is irrational, therefore, if continuous (or measurable) then constant. A not everywhere continuous real function which has two periods with irrational quotient is very "wild" (nowhere continuous, etc). For such irrational transcendental aberrations, we can use lay language to call it *irrational*, mathematically *unreasonable*, or in the vernacular, *emotional*!

One may conclude from the foregoing that in general, all our thoughts, perceptions and sensations are registered in the brain as linear combinations of Dirac type of delta functions.

The structures of seeing and hearing and of other sensations are part of the brain itself, but what happens within these structures is the result of neural activity. Let us look at the structures first and then at how the brain approximates to sensations and ideas in terms of single variables. How does the brain deal with many things at the same time? In science and mathematics such an event is represented by a function of several variables defined on a surface. The brain however is not a continuous n-dimensional surface, known as a manifold in mathematics, but consists of billions of linear strands of neurons connected with numerous synapses. Each neuron fires with a certain characteristic frequency of electric impulses. They must be mixed or synthesized into multilinear forms (analogous to the synthesis of priorities in AHP and ANP decision making) and it is this synthesis in a local field induced by the electricity that determines the shapes of images we see and sounds we hear and all the other sensations and in addition the intensity of their responses combined into a single feeling or response. In the brain, functions of several variables are compositions of functions of single variables. The priority, or better, the intensity of our feelings is again a synthesis that indicates the degree of satisfaction we get that eventually calms or quiets down the firing of the neurons.

The Hypermatrix of the Brain

How do we maintain an ongoing record of the signals transmitted in the brain that is updated, revised, and synthesized, to capture the transient information that is communicated through neural firings?

The approach we follow to represent interactions in the brain is a result of representing the network of neurons by a graph, whose nodes are the neurons themselves, and whose synaptic connections with other neurons are arcs or line segments that connect the nodes. Electric potentials are measured across the arcs. We assign the potentials direction so that they are read in a positive direction. In the opposite direction we assign them a zero value.

Thus we represent the neurons of the brain conceptually by listing them in a column on the left of the hypermatrix in Table 1 and listing them again in a row above the columns of the matrix. We assume that for convenience, we have arranged the neurons into components, which correspond to subcomponents or layers and these in turn according to the components or modules to which they belong. One can then enter a zero or a one in each column of the matrix to indicate whether a neuron in a row synapses with a neuron in a column. In fact, instead of the number one, a positive integer can be used to indicate the number of synapses that a neuron on the left has with a neuron at the top of the matrix. In that case each column of the matrix would represent the number of synapses of all neurons with a given neuron represented at the top of the matrix. That would be the most elementary way to represent the connections of the brain. It all hangs together in one piece, because every element is connected to some other element. Such a representation in a matrix can be modified by multiplying its nonnegative integer entries by the damped periodic oscillations of period one corresponding to the neuron with which the synapses are associated. In neural terminology, summing the elements in a column corresponds to spatial summation at an instant of time.

The different components of the hypermatrix are represented as block supermatrices. The control subsystems are connected to the supermatrices, which they control, and among themselves, and also to higher-level control components. We shall see in the next section that the outcome obtained from the hypermatrix is somewhat different from that of the supermatrix.

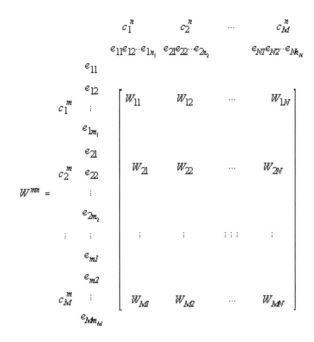

Table 1 The Hypermatrix

The i,j block of this matrix is a supermatrix.

Figures 1 and 2 below are hard-worked-on but rudimentary applications of the hypermatrix to modules and submodules of the brain to illustrate what we have in mind. We warn the reader that we are simply using some knowledge and imagination to brave the complexity. The size of the hypermatrix to describe the brain would be of the order of 100 billion by 100 billion (we have not consulted the Cray Research people about whether the development of their supercomputers comes close to satisfying the dicta of brain computing). It is far beyond our capability to handle the size of such a matrix, or know enough about the physical reality of the brain and its synapses to create the entries in the matrix. Figure 2 shows the supermatrix of vision as part of the hypermatrix.

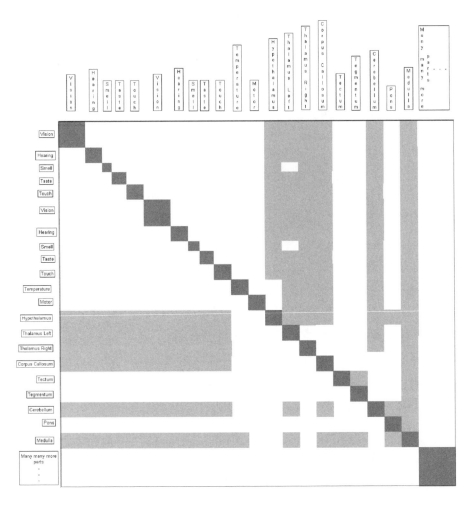

Figure 1 Hypermatrix of the Brain

Synthesis; With its Specialized Neurons and Use of Synapses, the Brain does not Synthesize as in the Discrete Case

We believe that the process of analytic continuation in the theory of functions of a complex variable provides insight into how neurons seem to know one another. Defining a function in complex analysis proceeds by first specifying that function in a small region, and then extending it from that region, often in pieces, by analytic continuation using series expansion. The uniqueness of analytic continuation is a powerful process. It says that knowing the value of a complex function in a finite complex domain uniquely determines the entire function at every other point. But neurons in the brain are only connected after they receive neurotransmitters from other neurons.

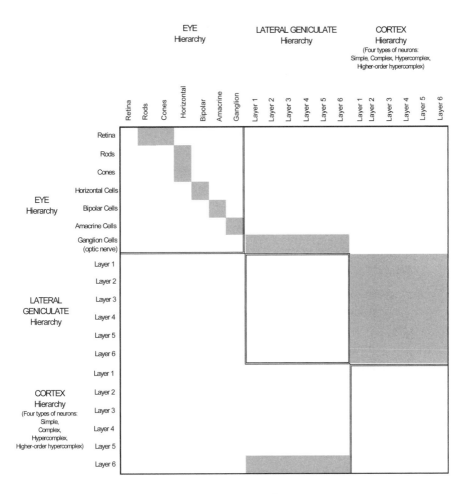

Figure 2 Supermatrix of Vision

Because neurons are specialized to fire in a given range, they do not accumulate different voltages and our framework of discrete analysis does not apply as one does in the supermatrix of a complex decision. One idea was that by raising the hypermatrix to powers one obtains transitive interactions. This means that a neuron influences another neuron through intermediate neurons. All such two-step interactions are obtained by squaring the matrix. Three step interactions are obtained by cubing the matrix and so on. By raising the matrix to sufficiently large powers, the influence of each neuron on all the neurons with which one can trace a connection, yields the transient influence of neurons in the original hypermatrix Multiplying the hypermatrix by itself allows for combining the functions that represent the influence from pre-to post- synaptic neurons to accumulate all the transitive influences from one neuron to another and allow for feedback. The Fourier transform that takes place as a result of firing and the density of the resulting firings give us the desired synthesis. Depending on what parts of the brain are operational and participating in the synthesis, different physical and behavioral attributes are observed to take place, including consciousness related to the Fourier transform of the single valued sensory functions.

Density and Approximation

The utility of artificial neural network models lies in the fact that they can be used to infer a function from observations. But the brain itself has its well established system to determine the functions it needs to capture its perceptions and thoughts.

Approximation theory is concerned with approximating functions by simpler and more easily calculated functions. The first question we ask in approximation theory concerns the possibility of approximation. Is the given family of functions that we use for approximation dense in the set of functions to be approximated? Although continuous functions contain many pathological examples and deficiencies, every such function can be approximated arbitrarily close by polynomials, considered the best kind of smooth function. Approximation is about how general functions can be decomposed into more simple building blocks: polynomials, splines, wavelets, and the like. One needs to guarantee specified rates of convergence when the smoothness of the kind of functions being approximated is specified, such as in Sobolev or Lipschitz spaces. A function $f(x)$ belongs to a Lipschitz class Lip[α] if there exists a constant $C > 0$ such that $|f(x) - f(y)| \leq C |x-y|^{\alpha}$.

The General Problem of Approximation: Let x be a metric space and k a subset of x. For a given point x ı X define $d(x,k) = \inf d(x,y)$ for y in k. The general problem of approximation is to find whether such a y exists for which the infimum is attained, and to determine whether it is unique or not.

An element $y_0 \in k$ for which the infimum is attained is called an element of best approximation to the element $x \in X$ (or simply, a best approximation). An alternative way of defining the problem is as follows: Let X be a normed linear space and Y a subspace of X. Given an element $x \in X$, we wish to determine $d(x,y) = \inf ||x\text{-}y||$ for y in Y and study the existence and uniqueness of the element(s) y_0, for which $||x\text{-} y_0|| = d(x,y)$. The Fundamental Theorem of Approximation Theory [5] states that if Y is a finite dimensional subspace of a normed linear space X, then there always exists an element $y_0 \in Y$ of best approximation for each $x \in X$. However, the element of best approximation may not be unique. Uniqueness can only be guaranteed if X is a strictly normalized space, i.e., $|x_1 + x_2| = || x_1 ||+ || ||$ $x_2 ||$ holds only for $x_2 = ax_1$, (a ^{3} 0).

The Weierstrass approximation theorem proved by Karl Weierstrass in 1885 says that a continuous function on a closed interval can be uniformly approximated as closely as desired by a polynomial function. The degree of the polynomial depends on the function being approximated and on the closeness of the approximation desired. Because polynomials are the simplest functions, and computers can directly evaluate polynomials, this theorem has both practical and theoretical relevance. Weierstrass also proved that trigonometric polynomials can also be used to approximate to a continuous function that has the same value at both end point of a closed interval. That is trigonometric polynomials are dense in this class of continuous functions. Each polynomial function can be uniformly approximated by one with rational coefficients; there are only countably many polynomials with rational coefficients.

For complex analysis S.N. Mergelyan proved in 1951 that: If *K* is a compact subset of the complex plane **C** such that **C***K* (the complement of *K* in C) is connected, then every continuous function *f*: *K*→ **C** whose restriction to the interior of *K* is holomorphic, can be approximated uniformly on *K* with polynomials. It has been noted that Mergelyan's theorem is the ultimate development and generalization of Weierstrass theorem and Runge's approximation theorem in complex analysis which says that: If *K* is a compact subset of **C** (the set of complex numbers), *A* is a set containing at least one complex number from every bounded connected component of **C***K*, and *f* is a holomorphic function on *K*, then there exists a sequence (r_n) of rational functions with poles in *A* such that the sequence (r_n) approaches the function *f* uniformly on *K*. It gives the complete solution of the classical problem of approximation by polynomials.

In the case that $C \backslash K$ is *not* connected, in the initial approximation problem the polynomials have to be replaced by rational functions. An important step of the solution of this further rational approximation problem was also suggested by S.N. Mergelyan in 1952.

Marshall H. Stone considerably generalized the theorem and later simplified the proof; his result is known as the Stone-Weierstrass theorem. Let K be a compact Hausdorff space and A is a subalgebra of $C(K,\mathbf{R})$ which contains a non-zero constant function. Then A is dense in $C(K,\mathbf{R})$ if and only if it separates points.

This implies Weierstrass' original statement since the polynomials on $[a,b]$ form a subalgebra of $C[a,b]$ which separates points.

But the problem of approximation is even simpler in conception. David Hilbert noticed that all basic algebraic operations are functions of one or two variables. So, he formulated the hypothesis that not only one cannot express the solution of higher order algebraic equations in terms of basic algebraic operations, but no matter what functions of one or two variables we add to these operations, we still would not be able to express the general solution. Hilbert included this hypothesis as the 13th of his list of 23 major problems that he formulated in 1900 as a challenge for the 20th century.

This problem remained a challenge until 1957, when Kolmogorov proved that an arbitrary continuous function $f(x_1,...,x_n)$ on an n-dimensional cube (of arbitrary dimension n) can be represented as a composition of addition of some functions of one variable. Kolmogorov's theorem shows that any continuous function of n dimensions can be completely characterized by a one dimensional continuous function. This is particularly useful in interpreting how the brain, which consists of separate neurons and deals with multiple dimensions by synthesizing information acquired through individual neurons that process single dimensions. Kolmogorov's theorem does not guarantee any approximation accuracy and his functions are very non-smooth and difficult to construct. In 1987, R. Hecht-Nielsen noticed that Kolmogorov's theorem actually shows that an arbitrary function f can be implemented by a 3-layer neural network with appropriate activation functions. The more accurately we implement these functions, the better approximation to f we get. Kolmogorov's proof can be transformed into a fast iterative algorithm that converges to the description of a network, but it does not *guarantee* the approximation accuracy by telling us after what iteration we get it.

The existence of a neural network that approximates any given function with a given precision was proven by K. Hornik, M. Stinchcombe,

H. White. The utility of artificial neural network models lies in the fact that they can be used to infer a function from observations. This is particularly useful in applications where the complexity of the data or task makes the design of such a function by hand impractical. Neural nets have been successfully used to solve many complex and diverse tasks, ranging from autonomously flying aircrafts to detecting credit card fraud.

In the artificial intelligence field, artificial neural networks have been applied successfully to speech recognition, image analysis and adaptive control, in order to construct software agents (in computer and video games) or autonomous robots. Most of the currently employed artificial neural networks for artificial intelligence are based on statistical estimation, optimization and control theory.

Neural networks, as used in artificial intelligence, have traditionally been viewed as simplified static models of neural processing in the brain, even though the relation between this model and brain biological architecture is very much debated. To answer this question, Marr has proposed various levels of analysis which provide us with a plausible answer for the role of neural networks in the understanding of human cognitive functioning.

The question of what is the degree of complexity and the properties that individual neural elements should have in order to reproduce.

Neural networks are made of units that are often assumed to be simple in the sense that their state can be described by single numbers, their "activation" values. Each unit generates an output signal based on its activation. Units are connected to each other very specifically, each connection having an individual "weight" (again described by a single number). Each unit sends its output value to all other units to which they have an outgoing connection. Through these connections, the output of one unit can influence the activations of other units. The unit receiving the connections calculates its activation by taking a weighted sum of the input signals (i.e. it multiplies each input signal with the weight that corresponds to that connection and adds these products). The output is determined by the activation function based on this activation (e.g. the unit generates output or "fires" if the activation is above a threshold value). Networks learn by changing the weights of the connections.

In modern software implementations of artificial neural networks the approach inspired by biology has more or less been abandoned for a more practical approach based on statistics and signal processing. In some of these systems neural networks, or parts of neural networks (such as artificial neurons) are used as components in larger systems.

An Alternative Way for Generating Impulsive Functions in the Real Domain

There is a useful link between forms which we perceive in nature and how these forms emanate energy as stimuli that enable us to sense and respond to them through the firings of neurons. Because Fourier analysis gives periodic function approximation to functions with compact support, it is possible to use the Fourier transform to represent a periodic function as a sequence of pulsations which is what we want for representing stimuli as energy packets. That is, stimuli are periodic functions over short time intervals so that they can be quantized as forcing functions, which is the only condition under which there is a solution to the Fredholm equation $\lambda \int K(s,t)w(t)dt - w(s) = f(s)$.

In general we recognize a stimulus only by the impact of its intensity $x(t)$ and frequency ω on our senses. We denote by $f(x(t),\omega)$ the forcing function associated with that stimulus. To recognize a stimulus, its intensity must remain constant over a short duration t, and $x(t) = a$. The response function during t is given by $W(x(t),\omega)$. It is a transformation of $f(x(t),\omega)$ given by:

$$W(x(t),\omega) = T[f(x(t),\omega)]$$

or $W(a,\omega) = T[f(a,\omega)]$. As an energy form, $f(a,\omega)$ may be written as a linear combination of pulsations as follows:

$$f(a,\omega) = \tau \sum_{k=-\infty}^{\infty} f(a,k\omega_0)\delta(\omega - k\omega_0)$$

As with ordinary functions one can define periodic distributions. A function $\phi(x)$ is a periodic testing function if it is periodic and infinitely differentiable (smooth). One can then define a space for all testing functions of period T. A periodic distribution $f(x)$ is defined in the same way a periodic function is defined. A distribution is periodic if there is a real positive number T such that $f(x - T) = f(x)$. The space of distributions of period T can also be defined. Each of its members is a continuous linear functional on the space of testing functions of period T. A "temperate distribution" is a continuous linear functional defined on the space of rapidly decreasing test functions. The Fourier transform of a distribution is the Fourier transform of the linear functional defining that distribution. The Fourier transform and its inverse are linear and continuous operations on the space of tempered distributions. There exists a Fourier series expansion for any periodic distribution.

By using the Fourier transform of f we can determine the amplitude and frequency at each of these points. The Fourier transform of $f(a,\omega)$ is given by:

$$F(t) = \int_{-\infty}^{\infty} g(a,\omega)e^{-iwt}\,d\omega = \omega_0 \sum_{k=-\infty}^{\infty} f(a,k\omega_0)e^{-ik\omega_0 t}$$

which can also be written as:

$$F(t) = \sum_{k=-\infty}^{\infty} F\left(t + \frac{2\pi k}{\omega_0}\right),$$

where $F(f) = F(a,t)$ is the Fourier transform of $f(a,t)$. Conversely, if $f(a,\omega)$ is a periodic function with period ω_0, then it can be written as:

$$f(a,\omega) = \sum_{k=-\infty}^{\infty} \alpha_k e^{ik\tau\omega},\ \tau = \frac{2\pi}{\omega_0}$$

where

$$\alpha_k = \omega_0^{-1} \int_{-\omega_0/2}^{\omega_0/2} f(a,\omega)e^{-jkt\omega}\,d\omega,$$

and its Fourier transform $F(f)$ is a sequence of equidistant pulses given by:

$$F(f) = 2\pi \sum_{k=-\infty}^{\infty} \alpha_k \delta(t - k\tau).$$

In the study of periodic motion in 2 dimensions where two periodic functions with different periods occur in the solution, whereby each variable is a trigonometric function of the angle, the question of commensurability of the periods arises. If the periods are commensurable, proportionality is involved and it is possible to reconcile them and conclude that the resulting motion is periodic. If they are not periodic, generally one does not have periodicity. The same idea also applies to the n-dimensional periodic motion.

Examples of Geometric Figures Using Dense Functions in the Real Case

Here are two examples that use the modulus of the complex representation with dense impulsive functions. The eye perceives distances and angles to draw pictures in the neuronal field. We use coordinate axes to show them, but their representation in the brain is not a two dimensional picture but a sequence of impulsive functions.

The basic assumption we made to represent the response to a sequence of individual stimuli is that all the layers in a network of neurons are identical, and each stimulus value is represented by the firing of a neuron in each layer. A shortcoming of this representation is that it is not invariant with respect to the order in which the stimuli are fed into the network. It is known in the case of vision that the eyes do not scan pictures symmetrically if they are not symmetric, and hence our representation must satisfy some order invariant principle. Taking into account this principle would allow us to represent images independently of the form in which stimuli are input into the network. For example, we recognize an image even if it is subjected to a rotation, or to some sort of deformation. Thus, the invariance principle must include affine and similarity transformations. This invariance would allow the network to recognize images even when they are not identical to the ones from which it recorded a given concept, e.g., a bird. The next step would be to use the network representation given here with additional conditions to uniquely represent patterns from images, sounds and perhaps other sources of stimuli such as smell. Our representation focuses on the real part of the magnitude rather than the phase of the Fourier transform. Tests have been made to see the effect of phase and of magnitude on the outcome of a representation of a complex valued function. There is much more blurring due to change in magnitude than there is to change in phase. Thus we focus on representing responses in terms of Dirac functions, sums of such functions, and on approximations to them without regard to the coefficients.

The functions result from modeling the neural firing as a pairwise comparison process in time. It is assumed that a neuron compares neurotransmitter-generated charges in increments of time. This leads to the continuous counterpart of a reciprocal matrix known as a reciprocal kernel. A reciprocal kernel K is an integral operator that satisfies the condition $K(s,t)K(t,s) = 1$, for all s and t. The response function $w(s)$ of the neuron in spontaneous activity results from solving our homogeneous Fredholm equation of the second kind.

Saaty and Vargas [4] gave a global view of how neurons work as a group to create images and impressions. We synthesized the solutions derived from the response of individual neurons to obtain the general form of the response of many neurons. To describe how a diversity of stimuli may be grouped abstractly into visual, auditory, sensual, and other kinds of response, the outputs of such syntheses are interpreted as points of an inner direct sum of a space of functions of the form $\{t^\alpha e^{-\beta t}, \alpha, \beta \geq 0\}$ or more generally as distributions (generalized functions in the sense of Schwartz) that can be used to represent images, sound and perhaps other sensations.

To use the functions $\{t^\alpha e^{-\beta t}, \alpha, \beta \geq 0\}$ to represent images and sounds, we created a 2-dimensional network of neurons consisting of layers. For illustrative purposes, we assume that there is one layer of neurons corresponding to each of the stimulus values. Thus, if the list of stimuli consists of n numerical values, we created n layers with a specific number of neurons in each layer. Under the assumption that each numerical stimulus is represented by the firing of one and only one neuron, each layer of the network must also consist of n neurons with thresholds varying between the largest and the smallest values of the list of stimuli. We also assumed that the firing threshold of each neuron had the same width. Thus, if the perceptual range of a stimulus varies between two values θ_1 and θ_2, and each layer of the network has n neurons, then a neuron in the ith position of the layer will fire if the stimulus value falls between $\theta_1 + (i-1)\dfrac{\theta_2 - \theta_1}{n-1}$ and $\theta_1 + i\dfrac{\theta_2 - \theta_1}{n-1}$. This task is computationally demanding even for such simple geometric figures as the bird and the flower shown in Figures 3 and 4. For example, for the bird picture, the stimuli list consists of 124 values, and we would need $124^2 = 15376$ neurons, arranged in 124 layers of 124 neurons each. To implement this network, we defined the **neuron** class in the object oriented programming language called LISP using CLOS (Common Lisp Object System). Each neuron is now an object and its characteristics are represented as class-slots (see Table 1). Finally, given this class, we defined instances of neurons. For example, the neuron in the ith position of a layer is obtained as follows: (setq **neuron-i** (make-instance '**neuron**:threshold-lower $\theta_1 + (i-1)\dfrac{\theta_2 - \theta_1}{n-1}$:threshold-upper $\theta_1 + i\dfrac{\theta_2 - \theta_1}{n-1}$)). Details of the experiment are given in Saaty, The Brain [3].

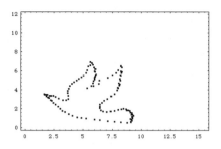

Figure 3 Bird

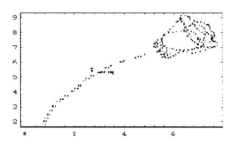

Figure 4 Rose

Sound Experiment

In the sound experiment we first recorded with the aid of Mathematica the first few seconds of Haydn's symphony no.102 in B-flat major and Mozart's symphony no. 40 in G minor. The result is a set of numerical amplitudes between -1 and 1. Each of these amplitudes was used to make neurons fire when the amplitude falls within a prescribed threshold range. Under the assumption that each neuron fires in response to one stimulus, we would need the same number of neurons as the sample size, i.e., 117,247 in Haydn's symphony and 144,532 in Mozart's symphony. Our objective was to approximate the amplitude using one neuron for each amplitude value, and then use the resulting values in Mathematica to play back the music. A small sample of the numerical data for Mozart's symphony is displayed in Figure 5.

How to use Dirac functions to represent all the sensations we receive and all the other things the brain does would require electronic and other instruments and knowledge of how to use them to substantiate our proof of the form of the general response functions and its Fourier transform.

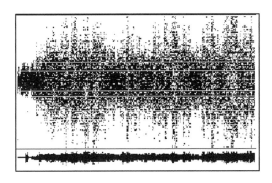

Figure 5 Mozart Symphony No. 40 in G Minor, KV. 550, in 1788

References

1. Kuffler, S.W. and J.G. Nicholls (1976), *From Neuron to Brain*. Sunderland, MA, USA: Sinauer Associates
2. Cohen, R. and M.M. Wartofsky eds. (1982), *Studies of Brain and Mind*, Dordrecht: Reidel, p. 3
3. Saaty, T.L. (2000), *The Brain, Unraveling the Mystery of How it Works: The Neural Network Process*, RWS Publications, Pittsburgh, PA
4. Saaty, T.L. and L.G. Vargas (1993), A Model of Neural Impulse Firing and Synthesis, *Journal of Mathematical Psychology* 37, pp. 200-219
5. Achieser, N.I. (1956), *Theory of Approximation*, Ungar Publishing Company, New York
6. Brinley, Jr., F.J. (1980), "Excitation and Conduction in Nerve Fibers." Chapter 2 in *Medical Physiology*, V.B. Mountcastle (ed.), 14th edition, The C.V. Mosby Co.
7. De Bruijn, N.G. (1958), *Asymptotic Methods in Analysis*, North Holland
8. Dollard, J.D. and C.N. Friedman (1979), *Product Integration with Applications to Differential Equations*, Addison-Wesley Pub. Co.
9. Hubel, D.H. and T.N. Wiesel (1963), Shape and Arrangement of Columns in Cat's Striate Cortex, *Journal of Physiology* 165, pp. 559-568
10. J. Kandel, E.R. and J.H. Schwartz (1985), *Principles of Neural Science*. Elsevier/North-Holland
11. Maz'ja, V.G. (1985), *Sobolev Spaces*, Springer Verlag
12. Saaty, T.L. (1988), *The Analytic Hierarchy Process*. RWS Publications, Pittsburgh, PA

13. Saaty, T.L. and L.G. Vargas (1987), Stimulus Response with Reciprocal Kernels: The Rise and Fall of Response, *Journal of Mathematical Psychology* 31, pp. 83-92

14. Shapshnicova, T.O., R.S. Andersen and S.G. Mikhlin (Eds.) (1975), *Integral Equations*, Leyden Noordhoff

Part VII

Our tradition in science and mathematics reduces our knowledge and understanding to the result of external impulses that bring us that knowledge and to chemical changes that work in our bodies requiring medical understanding and repair. These impulses and chemical changes make us think that our survival depends only on outside forces. Only recently we are being told that our feelings and emotions dominate our thinking and logic. As we have seen in the AHP with judgment we are able to reproduce valid results with our minds even as similar measurements are also obtained through scientific measurement. Thus we do not have to force ourselves to seem objective by sacrificing the variety of subjective experience and understanding that have. They too are the work of our mathematical brains processing external information obtained by using the scientific method. Our problem is to show that the mathematics of responding to stimuli goes beyond the measurements used in science today and include science as a way of learning the truth about the world. This has makes it infinitely more difficult to write this chapter so that the reader can be convinced that continuous sensation yields analytically valid eigenfunctions that tell us something precise about the phenomena outside the mind. Science is our broad way of understanding anything including decision making. Decision making mostly uses discrete judgments applied to make pairwise comparisons to derive order preserving priority eigenvectors within complex hierarchic and network discrete structures. In general, science needs continuous judgments applied to make continuous comparisons to derive order preserving eigenfunctions within, yet to be explored complex continuous structures. One major limitation of modern science is that it uses language and logic to make its deduction, but verbal logic does not admit dependence and feedback to deal with complexity. Generalization of the ANP would help us do that and perhaps remove much of the ambiguity and uncertainty in our conclusions and understanding of the world.

So it would seem that meaning is intimately linked to priority that indicates importance or significance. Judgment is our basic connection to the real world and how we feel about it both consciously and subconsciously. Judgment also controls action. Action is response to stimuli within and outside the brain. To think about how to act we need proportionality between what we think and how we act. This proportionality applies not simply to elementary stimuli but also to a combination or a cluster of stimuli even when they are infinite. The response as the solution of our equation can mathematically be a real valued function, a complex valued function, a function defined on quaternions (which as rotations in 3- space do not commute), octonions (which are non-associative) and even higher numbers. The term hypercomplex number has been used in mathematics for the elements of algebras that extend beyond complex number arithmetic. We need a more general solution of our functional equation that goes beyond the complex numbers, but so far it is unavailable.

The law that underlies all happening is that of stimulus-response. We need to examine it in its most general context, an operator form. Proportionality applies not only to stimuli but also to responses to stimuli so they can be combined in balanced controllable ways to obtain a harmonious overall response that gives us satisfaction.

Chapter 18

The Mathematical Nature of Response is Defined by the Operator Equation $W(\alpha x)=\beta W(x)$ for Proportionality
The Real Laws of Thought

*Give thy thought no tongue, nor any **unproportioned** thought his act.*
- Polonius advice to Laertes, act 1 scene 3, Hamlet, William Shakespeare

Introduction

The thought process is a higher level response activity to all the responses which themselves serve as second order stimuli for the thinking brain to analyze and respond proportionately. Every stimulus is the product of some other stimulus and must satisfy conditions imposed by that stimulus. There are two possibilities. Either all stimuli are interdependent and there is no first stimulus, or there is a first stimulus whose origins cannot be explained. There is neither a beginning nor an end to that stimulus. We who think about and practice the ANP believe that the former situation of interdependence is the more likely situation. It is also in agreement with what cosmologists tell us about the origins of the universe and about the Big Bang, although perhaps not with the way it has been interpreted due to limitations in our reasoning with linear logic about a process that is by its very nature cyclic.

Thus we can think of thoughts themselves as stimuli. First order stimuli related to nature lead to natural laws and second order stimuli lead to the laws of thought, because thought are themselves stimuli both for acting on nature and for stimulating other thought in response. We go from a stimulus representing a variable, to response to that stimulus in the form of a judgment which can be represented as a function and now move to higher order response (a thought) to a response function which can be represented as an operator on functions. An "operator" is a transformation that applies to a set of functions rather than to a set of points, a "function of functions". In this chapter we develop the theme of proportionality among responses to stimuli and then move deeper into proportionality among the responses themselves. As in group decisions, we need to combine responsès registered in memory into a single overall response by synthesizing them according to their importance. It is not difficult to see that we need that because we need to be rational, connected with non-reducible logic, to explain our diverse responses. Here again we have two ways to justify our approach. The first is to intuitively justify as we did in Chapter 15 the need to solve a general proportionality functional equation in operators and the second is to derive in this chapter this condition as a necessary condition for solving an operator equation that is a generalization of Fredholm's equation.

A variable is a quantity that can take on any value from a set of numbers. A function is a relation (a set of ordered pairs) that assigns to each element of a set called its domain one and only one element of the same or of another set called its range. It is called a multivalued function when it assigns more than one element to an element in its domain. Operators transform functions to other functions, they are functions of functions. They are one of the most useful concepts in modern mathematics. In this chapter they help us understand that how we think is a generalization of how we respond to stimuli. They also help us generalize the natural arithmetic operations we need to deal with proportionality by including non-commutativity and non-associativity for example which take us to numbers like quaternions and octonions. When working with operators it is useful to know what kinds of functions they transform whose result is a similar kind of functions. It is for this reason that we need the idea of a Banach space in mathematics. It is so important to maintain good understanding of what we do. A Banach space is a complete, normed vector space. Complete means that every infinite sequence (of a certain kind like, real numbers, complex numbers, continuous functions, differentiable functions) whose elements become *arbitrarily close to each other*, known as a Cauchy sequence, converges to a limit in the space itself. This makes it possible for us to talk about neural firing and synthesis in general terms to obtain answers that are both logical and relate closely to what we already know.

Among the important things the brain does is to synthesize information from different stimuli of varied intensities into an overall response. To sort and store its response to stimuli in a continuous formulation, the brain must treat the synthesis of different stimuli along discrete lines as one does with hierarchic composition, preserving their separate priorities rather than mixing them like different vegetables in a pot of soup. There are several controlling parts of the brain. Central is the thalamus which is thought to be the center of consciousness and a relay for sensory and motor signals. Through the thalamus all information to and from the cortex is processed. Sensory impulses that pass through the thalamus are integrated to form a composite sense. It also receives motor impulses from the cerebellum.

J. Edward Tether, M.D., writes in the Encyclopedia Americana, Brain, p. 424 that *"The thalamus receives crude impulses of touch, temperature, and pain from lower areas. It then fuses these sensations and modifies them so that they are felt as a more complex sensation....The thalamus is also considered to be a center of consciousness since even a slight manipulation of this area during brain surgery produces unconsciousness. Local anesthetics are used so the patient remains conscious."*

In synthesizing signals from different sorts of stimuli we associate a composite feeling of satisfaction or dissatisfaction that simultaneously branches into each of these signals or sensations. The mixing operations of the thalamus suggest that our operations of addition and multiplication of ordinary arithmetic need to be generalized so that parts such as different kinds of response (vision, sound, taste and the like) are taken together as a bundle of parts not mixed into a single outcome, that are remembered individually. In mathematics, this generalization corresponds to direct sums and direct products that yield linked bundles of different things. We need to move at least to this higher level of abstraction when we think about the workings of the brain. The concept of synergy resides in such mixing or bundling that gives rise to new entities that have properties not shared by the individual parts from which they are constituted. A car, an airplane and a television are each a collection of dissimilar components that work together to perform a function not served by any single component.

Every system has a structure, functions performed by flows within the structure and a purpose to fulfill. All structures have geometry associated with them, but the geometry of thought structures is uniquely hierarchical or network and it is this geometry that we use to explain the world and its objective geometry. It is the relations among the flows that are proportionate, not the geometric structure. The geometry of relations is not the geometry of the real world. It is the geometry of thought. We see the world with our senses. We interpret it with our brains.

There is no escaping our subjectivity. Our system of thinking is our own. Even when we measure we must interpret and that is inescapably subjective. How can we avoid the trap of being so closely tied to our earth experience and environment that our resulting concepts hamper us from recognizing exotic life forms in the universe even if we were to find them?

It may be that the solution of the stimulus-response equation expresses response by all forms of existence. Something like judgment with humans, leads one to the study of the invariance. Invariants are numbers or expressions related to some mathematical object or formula that remain unchanged under certain transformations of the object or the frame of reference in which the object is described. To establish such invariants, we need to maintain what is known in creativity as lateral thinking, rely on the most general and best established laws and mathematics to describe them and keep our speculations both free and disciplined. Our thinking process is also defined by a structure of language and connections that make logic flow with the function to follow rules of deduction with the purpose of understanding.

Our understanding of the universe is strongly influenced by our senses and the way we use them to perceive, measure and analyze. We are eye-hand-coordinated animals. The sensory and psychological apparatus for perceiving reality mentioned in Chapter 2 comprise the four modes: 1) Sensory 2) Clairvoyant; 3) Transpsychic and 4) Mythic. As information passes through our senses and is filtered through our nervous system we may become prejudiced in favor of some particular picture of the universe. The suspicion remains, however, that a different picture may be formed by intelligent beings that have a different form and different apparatus than we have. The objectivity of the world depends on how we are constituted, or does it?

Coordinate systems vs. relative systems: Our explanations with language and logic are linear, if-then type of reasoning. But it maybe that because of all the interdependencies and feedback we need the ANP to understand physics and cosmology. We need to represent interaction between the physical world and our own subjective thinking, between an "objective" world described through coordinate systems and a "subjective" world described by a network. That would combine mind with matter according to influence to make our explanations. Just like before electricity was accommodated in physics after Newton, who thought that gravity was the main force in nature, a mind field can account for the missing link that physicists have been calling for in saying that mind and matter are closely related.

Comparisons are essential for relative measurement. They enable us to measure intangibles. Using measurement on axes is artificial. The result of making judgments and paired comparisons has to do with the measurement of flow that in the end is nothing but influence of some kind.

All beings, in fact all things are subject to the law of stimulus response surmised by thoughtful beings that synthesize information through the use of judgment. As we have seen, judgment and comparisons lead us to formulate natural law. We metrize our spaces not as in topology by eventually using an arbitrary unit and then interpreting the outcome with "judgment objectified through experience", but by deriving from multiple pairwise comparison subjective judgments about dominance by experts "objectified by their multiplicity and group understanding", relative priorities that have norms that can be converted to metrics.

We live in a physical universe that is evolving and constantly changing. We are purpose-driven entities but we have no evidence that the material universe has any purpose. Measurements in the physical world are based on metric properties. Each type of measurement has a zero and an arbitrary unit. A metric satisfied the properties:

$$d(x, y) \geq 0 \qquad x \neq y$$
$$d(x, y) = d(y, x)$$
$$d(x, z) \leq d(x, y) + d(y, z)$$

As purposeful beings we have a sense of priority and order. Priorities are measured with a norm.

A norm defined on a vector space to the real numbers is a function that satisfies for all vectors
1. $\|ax\| = |a| \|x\|$ positive homogeneity or positive scalability
2. $\|x+y\| \leq \|x\| + \|y\|$ triangular inequality or subadditivity
3. $\|x\| = 0$ if and only if $x=0$ positive definite

A consequence of the first two axioms, positive homogeneity and the triangular inequality, is that $\|x\| \geq 0$.

A seminorm is a norm with the requirement of positive definiteness removed. Norms are a special kind of a metric. In other words every norm is a metric but not every metric is a norm.

Priorities can be assigned an arbitrary unit but they are not objective and differ from one person to another person. They fall on an n-dimensional tetrahedron. People have tried and still try to derive priorities by using metric properties involving measurements. But only a small set of things is measureable. Most factors or criteria are intangible and have no scales of measurement. They must be compared to derive their priorities. They also vary from one situation to another and cannot be fixed once and for all. Nor were physical measurements fixed once and for all a few billion years ago when everything was a swirling gas. They last longer than behavioral properties, but they were all forms of energy that is elusive to fixed measurement at one time and may also become that eventually. Thus objectivity in science is not absolute but transient over a long period of time. There's a narrow sense of the word "physical" in which minds, mental properties, and mental processes are clearly not physical phenomena: terms like "mind," "thinking," and "feeling" don't appear in the theories of fundamental physics.

There are exactly four normed division algebras: the real numbers (R), complex numbers (C), quaternions (H), and octonions (O). Beyond those four are the sedenions, but these algebras are perhaps less interesting because they are no longer division algebras—that is, $ab=0$ no longer implies that either $a=0$ or $b=0$. Quaternions are an alternative method of handling rotations, besides rotation matrices. The advantage of quaternions over other representations is that they allow interpolation between two rotations. Another way to say what's special about 2 dimensions is that rotation commutes, but not in 3 or more dimensions. Thus, there is advantage to the fact that quaternions do not commute. It was Hamilton who first noticed that multiplication of octonions is not associative, that is, $a \times (b \times c)$ does not equal to $(a \times b) \times c$.

With quaternions we lose the commutative law, with octonions we also lose the associative law. The main thing we are left with is the ability to divide in order to give meaning to proportionality. The solutions to our operator equation do not extend to quaternions and octonions when the parameters and the variables belong to these algebras. An exception is when they are real or complex, then it has solution in the algebra of quaternions. The derivations of different kinds of quantitative thinking learned from the types of responses we make used in scientific inquiry to understand the world is taken up next.

The General Functional Equation in Operators [1,2]

For a **continuum number of stimuli** let $K(\mathbf{X}, \mathbf{Y})$ be a compact consistent kernel i.e. $K(x,y)K(y,z)=K(x,z)$, for all $x \in \mathbf{X}$ and $y \in \mathbf{Y}$ and $z \in \mathbf{Z}$, where $\mathbf{X}$, $\mathbf{Y}$ and $\mathbf{Z}$ are compact subsets of the reals. We have the equation $w(\mathbf{X}) = \lambda \int_{\Omega} K(\mathbf{X}; \mathbf{Y}) w(\mathbf{Y})$. Solution of this equation involves not simply distributions, but also Lebesgue integrals of distributions. Stimuli or impulses are studied mathematically in more general spaces than continuous functions. These are the spaces of Schwartz distributions defined on Sobolev spaces that involve distributions with derivatives of order k in Lebesgue spaces of order p.

By analogy with theorem 3 in Chapter 15, we state without proof: A necessary condition for the operator $\mathbf{W(X)}$ to be a generalized solution of Fredholm's equation of the second kind in operator form $W(X) = \lambda \int_{\Omega} K(X;Y) W(Y)$ where $K(\mathbf{X};\mathbf{Y})$ is a consistent kernel that is homogeneous of order 1 is that it satisfies the functional equation in operator form $W(\alpha X) = \beta W(X)$.

The Functional Equation of Response W(αX)=βW(X) as an Operator Equation [3]

We have already dealt with solutions in the real and complex domains of the simple linear functional equation $W(\alpha X) = \beta W(X)$ that describes proportion between the stimulus and the response. We now examine that equation in the operator form $W(\alpha X) = \beta W(X)$, ($x \in E$), where W maps E to G, both normed linear spaces over K. K is either R (the real numbers) or C (the complex numbers), α and β are given scalars in K. The norm in E or G is denoted by $\| . \|$. Since the cases $\alpha = 0$, $\alpha = 1$, $\beta = 0$ are trivial, we shall suppose $\alpha \neq 0$, $\alpha \neq 1$, $\beta \neq 0$. Let us note first that $W(\alpha X) = \beta W(X)$, ($x \in E$) is equivalent to the functional equation $W(\frac{X}{\alpha}) = \frac{1}{\beta} W(X)$ ($x \in E$). Therefore, we may assume $\mid \alpha \mid \geq 1$. We have $W(\frac{X}{\alpha}) = \frac{1}{\beta} W(X)$ or

$$W(X) = \beta W(\frac{x}{\alpha}) = \beta^2 W(\frac{x}{\alpha^2}) = ... = \beta^p W(\frac{x}{\alpha^p}) = ... = \beta^{2p} W(\frac{x}{\alpha^{2p}}) = ... =$$

$$\beta^{(n-1)p} W(\frac{x}{\alpha^{(\alpha n-1)p}})$$

and α and β oppose each other depending on the values they take. Note also that if $\alpha^n = 1$ and $\beta^n = 1$, then a solution always exists. Without too much detail for deriving a solution, different types of solution are given in Table 1 below.

Actually, invariance under a continuous, one-to-one, order-preserving transformation must be admitted. Subjective time, in order to have an element taken out of it which has nothing to do with the world, must have its essential properties invariant under a group, of continuous transformations which can be considered as generalizations of translations and changes of scale.

Newton's law was given in terms of particles. But usually we deal with continuously distributed matter, not with particles. We then divide the body into small parts, adding the vector of forces or influences and passing to the limit. We must often consider influence on the different parts as their number increases indefinitely. Solutions below, to the functional equation, deal with this kind of consideration (see the interpretation given later).

Table 1 Different Solutions of $W(\alpha X)=\beta W(X)$, $(x\in E)$

	$W:E\rightarrow G$; E and G are normed linear spaces over the real or complex fields
	General Solution
α root of 1 of order n $\beta^n\neq 1$	1) $W\equiv 0$.
$\beta^n=1$	2) There exists a non-empty subset of $E \setminus \{0\}$ satisfying $$E = \bigcup_{p=0}^{n-1}\alpha^p B\cup\{0\} \text{ where } \alpha^i B\cap\alpha^j B = \varnothing \text{ for all } i, j=0,...,n\text{-}1.$$ $$W(X)\begin{cases} \beta^p W_0(\alpha^{-p}X), & \text{if } X\in\alpha^p B \text{ and } p\in\{0,...,n-1\}, \\ b, & \text{if } X = 0. \end{cases}$$ where b = $\begin{cases} 0, \text{if } \beta\neq 1, \\ \text{is an arbitrary element of } G, \text{ if } \beta = 1, \end{cases}$ B is subset of $E \setminus \{0\}$ and $W_0=W_{|B}$.
α not root of 1	Same as 2)
	Continuous Solutions
α root of 1 of order n $\beta^n=1$	Same as 2) with limit conditions $$\lim_{\substack{Y\circledast 0 \\ Y\bar{I} B}} W_0(Y) = b$$ $$\lim_{\substack{Y\to X \\ Y\in B}} W_0(Y) = \beta^p W_0(\alpha^{-p}X)$$

	if $X \in \overline{B} \cap \alpha^p B$ $p \in \{0, 1, .., n-1\}$ (where $\overline{B}$ denotes the closure of B)
α not root of 1, $|\alpha|=1$ $|\beta|\neq 1$	$W \equiv 0$
$|\beta|=1$	β root of 1 and not equal to one $W \equiv 0$
	β root of 1 and equal to one $W(X) = W_0 (\pi(X))$ where W_0 is an arbitrary continuous mapping and $\pi(X)$ is the continuous natural mapping
	β not root of 1 and $\beta=\alpha^p$ for all p If E = C, $W(X) = \begin{cases} \left(\dfrac{X}{|X|}\right)^p W_0(|X|), & \text{if } X \neq 0, \\ 0, \text{if } X = 0 \end{cases}$ where $W_0(0,+\infty) \to G$ is arbit. continuous
	and if E is a separable inner product space, by: $W(X) = \left(\dfrac{X_{i(x)}}{|X_{i(x)}|}\right)^p g_{i(x)}\left(|X_{i(x)}|, \dfrac{|X_{i(x)}|}{X_{i(x)}}\left(X - X_{i(x)}e_{i(x)}\right)\right) \quad (X \neq 0)$ and $W(0) = 0$, where the functions g_n are continuous and satisfy $\begin{cases} \bullet \ \forall n \in N, \forall q \in N \setminus \{0\}, \ \lambda^p g_n\left(t, \dfrac{Y}{\lambda}\right) \text{ converges to} \\ \left(\dfrac{X_{n+q}}{|X_{n+q}|}\right)^p g_{n+q}\left(|X_{n+q}|, \dfrac{|X_{n+q}|}{X_{n+q}}\left(X - X_{n+q}e_{n+q}\right)\right) \text{ as } (t,Y) \text{ goes to} \\ \qquad\qquad\qquad (0, X) \\ \text{uniformity with respect to } \lambda \in U, \\ \bullet \ \forall n \in N, \ \lim_{(t,X)\to(0,0)} g_n(t,X) = 0 \end{cases}$
$|\alpha|>1$ $|\beta|\leq 1$ $\beta \neq 1$	$W \equiv 0$
$\beta = 1$	Constant functions

$|\beta|>1$	Same as in 2) above with $\beta=1$ and $p = \left[\dfrac{\ln\|X\|}{\ln|\alpha|}\right]$ and W_0 arbitrary continuous function such that (for every real number y, $[y]$ = the integer part of y) and $W_0 : \Omega \to G$ is an arbitrary continuous function satisfying for all X in E such that $\|X\| = |\alpha|$: $$\lim_{\substack{Y\to X \\ Y\in\Omega}} W_0\left(Y\right) = \beta\, W_0\left(\frac{X}{\alpha}\right)$$

	Differentiable Solutions
α root of 1 of order n $\beta^n = 1$	In this case, there exists a unique p in $\{0, 1, \ldots, n-1\}$ such that $\beta = \alpha^p$ $$W(X_1,\ldots,X_q) = \sum_{(n_1,\ldots,n_q)\in J} a_{n_1\ldots n_q} X_1^{n_1}\ldots X_q^{n_q} \text{ where } J = \{(n_1, \ldots, n_q) \in N^q : n_1$$ $+ \ldots + n_q = p + j\,n \text{ for some } j \in N\}$ and $a_{n_1\ldots n_q}$ are arbitrary elements of G
α not root of 1, $|\alpha|=1$ $|\beta|\neq 1$	$W \equiv 0$
$|\beta|=1$	If β is root of 1 and $\beta \neq 1$ $W \equiv 0$
	If β is root of 1 and $\beta = 1$ the solution is the constant functions
	If β is not a root of 1 and $\beta\neq\alpha^p$ for all nonnegative integers p $W \equiv 0$
	If β is not a root of 1 and $\beta=\alpha^p$ for all nonnegative integers p, the homogeneous polynomials of degree p
$|\alpha|>1$ $|\beta|\leq 1$ $\beta \neq 1$	$W \equiv 0$
$\beta = 1$	Constant functions
$|\beta|> 1$	$\beta\neq\alpha^k$ for all positive integers k $W \equiv 0$
	$\beta=\alpha^k$ for some k $W(X) = L(X, \ldots, X)$ $(X \in C^q)$, where L is an arbitrary k-linear symmetric continuous mapping from $(C^q)^k$ into G.

	Analytic Solution
	$$W(z) = \sum_{j=-\infty}^{\infty} c_j z^{jk+q} \quad \alpha^k = 1, \alpha^q = \beta$$

What we would also like to have are stochastic solutions of our equation $f(\alpha x) = \beta f(x)$ because at the micro level things do not respond to laws in a deterministic way, but do it statistically, that is some do and some do not.

If α and β are real or complex and if w from K into K, where K is the field of quaternions, satisfies: $w(\alpha z) = \beta w(z)$, the results apply because K can be considered as a normed vector space of finite dimension over R or C. The answer is not known if α and β is in K.

What Kind of Functions are the Solutions

There are three kinds of solutions depending on the values of α and β: the general solution, the continuous and the differentiable solutions. It is worth noting by consulting the table that many of the solutions are zero for different values of α and β.

The general solution is based on decomposing the domain of definition E of the operator W. It shows that the response operator consists of pieces that are identical in their own domains, but it does not say much about the nature of the operators, except perhaps that there is periodicity in the decomposition of the response which indicates somehow different levels of the individual responses. This seems to imply that the response is the conglomerate (composition) of similar responses in different dimensions. This tells us that according to this equation the universe is fragmented into a myriad of parts each satisfying the same law.

The continuous solution when α and β are not a root of 1 and $\beta = \alpha^p$ is given by the solution of $W(\lambda X) = \lambda^p W(X)$, $X \in E$, $\lambda \in U$. For $E = C$, the solution is given by $\left(\dfrac{\mathbf{X}}{|\mathbf{X}|}\right)^p W_0(|\mathbf{X}|)$, which can be used to represent non-monotone responses in ordered spaces. This solution repeats for E separable into a finite number of domains obtained by an equivalence relation. Two functions f and g belong to the same equivalent class if they are homothetic. When the stimuli are proportional, the response is also proportional, but it does not have to be always monotone. The continuous solution for a separable stimulus (partitioned) is a conglomerate of the continuous solutions for the nonseparable case with a distinction for the boundary of the domains in which the stimulus takes place.

For $|\alpha| > 1$ and $|\beta| > 1$, the continuous solution is the same as the general solution with the additional condition that W_0 is a continuous operator.

The differentiable solutions are given by the sums of products of powers of the functions into which the stimuli are decomposed. For example, if α is a root of 1 of order n and $\beta^n=1$, we have

$$W(\mathbf{X}_1,...,\mathbf{X}_q) = \sum_{(n_1...n_q)\in J} a_{n_1...n_q} \mathbf{X}_1^{n_1}...\mathbf{X}_q^{n_q}$$

where $J = \{(n_1...n_q)\in \mathbf{N}^q : n_1 +...+ n_q = p + jn, j\in \mathbf{N}\}$. If α and β are not a root of 1, $|\alpha|=1$ and $\beta=\alpha^p$, the differentiable solution is any homogeneous polynomial (or algebraic form) of degree p. A homogeneous polynomial is a (multivariate) polynomial in more than one variable whose terms are monomials all having the same total degree; or are elements of the same dimension. For example, $x^3+xyz+y^2z+z^3$ is a homogeneous polynomial of degree three. An algebraic form, or simply form, is another term for homogeneous polynomial. These then generalize from quadratic forms to degrees 3 and more, and have in the past also been known as quantics. To specify a type of form, one has to give the degree of a form, and the number of variables n. A form is defied over some given field K, if it maps from K^n to K, where n is the number of variables of the form. In multilinear algebra, a multilinear form is a map of the type $f:V^n \to K$, where V is a vector space over the field K, that is separately linear in each of its N variables. As the word "form" usually denotes a mapping from a vector space into its underlying field, the more general term "multilinear map" is used, when talking about a general map that is linear in all its arguments. If $|\alpha|>1$ and $|\beta|>1$ and there exists a positive integer k such that $\beta=\alpha^k$, this correspond to the decomposition of the stimulus into k parts, the differentiable solution is given by a k-linear symmetric continuous mapping.

It was proved by Adolf Hurwitz in 1898 in Gottingen Nachrichten, page 309-316 that any finite-dimensional real division algebra must have dimension that is a power of 2; these powers were shown to be 1, 2, 4, or 8: the real numbers, the complex numbers, the quaternions and the octonions. He used in his proof the fact that the product of an element and its conjugate (as in the complex conjugate) should equal to the sum of the squares of the coefficients and this holds only for dimensions 1, 2, 4 and 8. It is known that every finite-dimensional real commutative division algebra is either 1 or 2 dimensional. Much work was done by many people in the 20th century on the characterization of division algebras. While there are infinitely many non-isomorphic real division algebras of dimensions 2, 4 and 8, one can say the following: any real finite-dimensional division algebra over the reals must be

- isomorphic to R or C if unitary and commutative (equivalently: associative and commutative)
- isomorphic to the quaternions if non-commutative but associative
- isomorphic to the octonions if non-associative but alternative.

In an alternative algebra multiplication need not be associative but only alternative. That is, one must have

- $x(xy) = (xx)y$
- $(yx)x = y(xx)$

for all x and y in the algebra. Every associative algebra is alternative, but so too are some strictly nonassociative algebras such as the octonions. However, the sedenions (16 dimensional numbers) are not alternative. The following is known about the dimension of a finite-dimensional division algebra A over a field K:

- $\dim A = 1$ if K is algebraically closed,
- $\dim A = 1, 2, 4$ or 8 if K is real closed, and

If K is neither algebraically nor real closed, then there are infinitely many dimensions in which there exist division algebras over K.

As the word "form" usually denotes a mapping from a vector space into its underlying field, the more general term "multilinear map" is used, when talking about a general map that is linear in all its arguments. A determinant is a multilinear mapping. We say that a function $f(x_1,...,x_k)$ is k-linear if it is linear in each variable, so that

$$f(x_1,...,x_{i-1},x_i + \lambda y, x_{i+1},...,x_k) = f(x_1,...,x_{i-1},x_i,x_{i+1},...,x_k)$$

$+\lambda f(x_1,...,x_{i-1},y,x_{i+1},...,x_k)$ for any choice of variables $x_1,...,x_k$, y, scalar λ and index $1 \le i \le k$. A linear combination of k-linear functions is itself k-linear.

A symmetric polynomial in n variables $x_1,...,x_n$ (also called a totally symmetric polynomial) is a function that is unchanged by any permutation of its variables. In other words, symmetric polynomials satisfy the relation $f(y_1,...,y_n) = f(x_1,...,x_n)$ where $y_i = x_{v(i)}$ and V being an arbitrary permutation of the indices $i = 1,...,n.$.

Symmetric polynomials are always homogeneous. Any symmetric polynomial can be written as a polynomial in the elementary symmetric polynomials $\sum \prod_{1 \le i \le n} x_i$ on those variables. For example we have: $\sum_{1 \le i \le n} x_i$,

$\sum_{1 \le i < j \le n} x_i x_j$, $\sum_{1 \le i < j < k \le n} x_i x_j x_k$ and so on.

It is interesting to note that response to stimuli can take these few forms. This also says that as we use mathematics and science to interpret occurrences our expressions must consist of sums of products of powers of functions which can be homogeneous polynomials or linear symmetric mappings. These solutions apply to the case when E and/or G are the field of quaternions or octonions. The solutions have been proved to exist for α and β real or complex, and hopefully the question will be settled for α and β in the field of quaternions and octonions where divisibility is meaningful.

One might wonder that if there is feedback for response W to stimulus X what the form of the resulting functional equation of proportionality would be and what is its solution. It turns out that one obtains the same operator equation. There are two possibilities: α and β are the same parameters for the feedback equation or they are different.

(a) Parameters the same

$$W(\alpha X) = \beta W(X) \text{ and } X(\beta W) = \alpha X(W)$$

(b) Parameters not the same

$$W(\alpha X) = \beta W(X) \text{ and } X(\delta W) = \gamma X(W)$$

We believe that science in its use of mathematics has to become more organized in the way it models the real world along the lines of functional equations in order to have a sufficient number of examples that illustrate above solutions underlie all of them.

Concluding Remarks

It may be useful to conclude this book with a few observations about some philosophical and technical differences between the way we do measurement in the AHP, which can handle both tangibles and intangibles, and the traditional way measurement is used in the physical sciences and engineering that can only handle tangibles. Some of the discussion from Chapter 16 is summarized along with new observations. It is clear that order and priority are an important aspect of all creative thinking and hence prioritization is a fundamental facet of creativity: brainstorming to determine the objectives and factors that have bearing on an issue, morphological analysis to structure the factors in a meaningful framework with respect to an overall goal, lateral thinking to access all important elements to add to the structure in an ongoing and continued effort, and prioritization to determine the relative importance or influence of the factors and to select the best way or ways to act to satisfy the objectives the best outcome and subject it to stability analysis. Creative thinking precedes all other incidental thinking and analysis. We need to compare and contrast this approach with what is done today in science quantitatively.

Physical Sciences versus AHP/ANP

- Both the AHP/ANP and physical science are concerned with the outcome or effect of various influences as causes. In science prior knowledge is important and is often assumed and goes unspoken in the study of most problems. In AHP/ANP the assumptions are represented by factors that are included in the structure and organized as to how they interact based on previous experience. This structure can be agreed upon collectively by a group of people but every factor proposed can in principle be included. The structure is trimmed and modified until everyone agrees that it represents the problem.

- In physical science the only way to study things objectively is to consider the most likely outcome of influence. In the AHP/ANP the alternative outcomes of the influences in the model can be evaluated in terms of the most likely outcome, as in predicting presidential election results by looking at the evidence as to how the voting will go, or as importance or preference among the alternative outcomes. The latter two are of course while the first is as objective as people can make it by looking at the data.

- Physical science purports that everything follows physical laws and that when the correct theory is found it will be able to explain everything. But physics is knowledge created to be understood by people living at a given time and is often closely tied to what went before. Isaac Newton (1643-1727) borrowed his coordinate axes and analytic geometry from the mathematician Rene Descartes (1596-1650) and Albert Einstein (1879-1955) borrowed the idea of curved space from the mathematician Bernhard Riemann (1826-1866), and more amazingly, time as a fourth dimension from H.G. Wells (1866-1946) (The Time Machine, 1895) which he proceeded to "prove" that it was the fourth dimension! In AHP/ANP each problem has the factors thought to be relevant at that time by the people involved. Creativity is needed to decide which factors to include and how to arrange them within a structure that will be used to determine influence according to priority.

- In science measurement is objective but interpretation in the end is subjective. In AHP/ANP the interpretation is in the beginning and it is subjective, but the conclusions are derived by following prescribed mathematical steps that objectively give the answer. This answer is then subjected to sensitivity analysis as to its stability under various changes in the judgments used in the initial interpretation.

Different ways to study the outcome of influence

- The physical sciences are concerned with energy and matter as the essence of influence and follow certain rules called the scientific method to study them. Through cosmology, physical science does not hypothesize fictional factors, something like the religion of Zen Buddhism does not hypothesize fictional characters, but attempts to explain the origins, the workings and the eventual destiny of the universe supported by observation and "common sense." It relies on language based on Aristotelian logic and mathematics which follows that logic. The propositional "if-then" logic of the physical sciences is linear and does not allow for inconsistency in the form of intransitivity. It is nearly impossible to use in situations where there is dependence and feedback or where one must go from conclusions to assumptions and back again in a circular pattern.

- Mathematics and the physical sciences rely on a system of Cartesian coordinates with to represent tangibles that are "physical" in nature: time, length, mass, temperature and a few others that are used to explain the origins and the workings of the universe for all time. These coordinate axes have arbitrary units of measurement. There is no way to deal with the measurement of an intangible and include it as a new axis in such coordinate systems unless of course one can come up with an arbitrary unit that can be applied uniformly everywhere to measure it. In this case it has been converted to a tangible. Incidentally all tangibles started out as intangibles and went through this process of specifying a measurement unit for them. That seems to work well for durable properties but not so well for properties whose importance changes according to the circumstances so that a unit cannot be applied uniformly to them in an acceptable way.

- One might say that science is limited in its explanations, not simply by choice, but because its coordinate system or many dimensions approach excludes important intangible factors. It does not know how to deal with new intangible factors mathematically so that in the end it is doubtful that all the factors have been considered that should have been. We should be able to include the factors we need to even if it is discovered later that they are unimportant. It would help remove much of the doubt that scientists themselves have often expressed about the completeness of their theory. People with knowledge and awareness often find it difficult to exclude intangibles on the ground of technical difficulty. The quantum physicist David Bohm wrote: "The question is whether matter is crude and mechanical or whether it gets more and more subtle and becomes indistinguishable from what people have called mind." Arthur Eddington writes, "To put the conclusion crudely - the stuff of the world is mind-stuff." As a result of using coordinate systems, the idea of many dimensions is central in mathematical thinking even though we live in a dimensionally limited physical universe of space with time added as a fourth variable for convenience of interpretation. Two kinds of time are recognized in science. Physical time which passes uniformly according to the rotation of the earth around the sun, and psychological time whose duration depends on how people feel. The fact that the number of people is very large and that such interpretation of time can be different is not accorded much thought by science except for the effect of change in coordinates on the interpretation of physical happenings as in the theory of relativity.

- In science the meaning of measurements with their arbitrary units can differ from culture to another and conversion of one ratio scale of measurements to another does not remove the arbitrariness of the unit and what the measurement readings mean. The meaning is obtained through explanation and rationalization by relating the measurements to other familiar measurements even though the numbers may be unimaginably large or small. Those who interpret the numbers are "authorities" who are expert in developing theories and have adopted a tradition of some kind to make such interpretation whose only meaning is obtained through comparing them with other more familiar numbers. But the size of the numbers can defy human understanding more when the numbers are beyond those dealt with in daily life. What the meaning of such numbers is remains inadequately justified in science to this very day. Science has no scientific way to admit that our beliefs about the physical world are the result of judgments of ordinary, otherwise fallible people. They may be experts in a narrow area but are not wise enough to rise above ordinary daily problems and frequently do not get along well in the world despite their scientific wisdom. Yet they feel confident to speak about universal truths in terms of only those factors they know how to measure.

The role of human beings and their minds

- In physical science the universe is assumed to be made of and driven by matter and energy. Man is not important in the general scheme of things. But many great physicists have often concluded that mind is also part of the story somehow and they don't know how to include it in their formulas. In AHP/ANP both physical and psychological influences are included and man with his intelligence and imagination is of the greatest importance for understanding the effects of all the influences and providing the judgments. Truth in physical science is eternal whereas in AHP/ANP truth is temporary and local and must explain each situation as it is conceptualized to determine the most likely outcome.

- Decision making must consider numerous intangible factors, thus the AHP/ANP finds its best applications in that area. It is similar to applied mathematics that uses measurements on ratio scales and has found its best applications in physics and engineering. Today's mathematics is not fully separate from the physical world. It has borrowed many of its concepts in geometry and topology from the physical world: points and lines and surfaces including spheres and polyhedra, deformation, reflection, translation and rotation and on and on. On the other hand, algebra and its abstractions are involved with numbers and operations on numbers and their generalizations. It is a more abstract science suited to dealing with intangibles in general. It turns out that the AHP/ANP is based on algebraic concepts and their abstractions.

How to make group decisions

- There is no way in science to combine the interpretation and understanding of different people "scientifically" into a single representative interpretation in a mathematical way. An agreement is reached through discussion and argument and the use of authority and debate, in the same not very scientific way that people use to settle arguments. It depends on many psychological factors in a loose way: whom one listens to, what their reputation is, what institution they work for, and what theory they developed that gives them the right to speak, and how long they can stay around to make the argument. In AHP/ANP individuals can combine their judgments or their separate final outcomes in a mathematical way that also includes their separate importance priorities. These priorities are derived by using a structure for a problem by, if desired, including everything any individual thinks is important.

Structure

- According to recent findings in astronomy about the Big Bang theory there is originally one form of energy from which space and time evolved and from that everything else is created. This is a physical science view used to explain things. To make the contrast, the AHP/ANP is generally applied in more local situations, where a model is constructed using the most general set of diverse influences to explain whatever outcomes one may desire. The world of the intangibles of the AHP/ANP does not have a simple uniform origin to explain how things happen. In physical science one can add a new element if it is compatible with what is already known. Lateral thinking is the phrase used for changing concepts and perceptions. It is inherent in AHP/ANP where the structure can be readily modified to change understanding of the problem or fit newly discovered data.

- As in engineering and other applied fields in the AHP/ANP each problem is analyzed individually with its important variables and one does not deal with universals. However, (and this is important) an attempt has been made to list a diversity of factors, including a very large number of intangibles, that have bearing on all human goals and purposes and on human needs. This list provides the groundwork for a universal framework from which the criteria to be considered in any decision can be drawn.

Creativity and synthesis

- To teach the mechanics of the AHP/ANP takes little time, but to structure a problem requires a little exposure, practice and good knowledge about the problem. Anyone, if qualified by knowing some of the issues of the problem, can participate in making the judgments in an AHP/ANP model. In general, it takes a much longer time to learn to practice science. There are those who think science cannot cope well with the idea of synergy or with systems thinking, because the whole approach is one of breaking things down to understand the world. Science does not have effective ways of synthesis. The AHP/ANP is a method of systems thinking and of synthesis.

Validation

- Both science and AHP/ANP are concerned with validation. Science uses few tangibles to seek permanent answers for the world for all time and for every situation. The AHP/ANP deals with problems one at a time using the principles: of structure, judgment, synthesis and sensitivity analysis. Both in the end rely on checking the accuracy of the findings against known data and occurrences in the world.

We have the suspicion from what we have learned through frequent practice with the AHP/ANP that mind developed as an instrument for responding to stimuli and itself became an influential stimulus for other things. If there is a field of mental processes that we have yet to discover, it could have been involved somehow in influencing at the quantum level the formation of the universe in a way that our physics has not been able to include mathematically as an influence. The use of hierarchies and networks that include purpose and also both the tangibles of physics and the intangibles of the mind and of behavior can. The AHP/ANP says that we are the result of response to stimuli. Our brain and natural laws are also results of this response to natural stimuli that brought us about.

References

1. Saaty, T.L. (2000), The Brain, Unraveling the Mystery of How it Works: The Neural Network Process, RWS Publications, Pittsburgh, PA
2. Saaty, T.L. and L.G. Vargas (1993), A Model of Neural Impulse Firing and Synthesis, Journal of Mathematical Psychology 37, pp. 200-219
3. Brillouët-Belluot, Nicole, (1999),On a Simple Linear Functional Equation on Normed Linear Spaces, Ecole Centrale de Nantes, Departement d'Informatique et de 3. Mathematique, 1, rue de la Noë, F-44 072 Nantes-cedex 03, France

INDEX